THE CERTIFIED QUALITY
INSPECTOR HANDBOOK

Also available from ASQ Quality Press:

The Probability Handbook
Mary McShane Vaughn

The Probability Workbook
Mary McShane Vaughn

The Certified Quality Technician Handbook, Third Edition
H. Fred Walker, Donald W. Benbow, Ahmad K. Elshennawy

The Certified Quality Engineer Handbook, Fourth Edition
Sarah E. Burke and Rachel T. Silvestrini

The Certified Reliability Engineer Handbook, Third Edition
Mark Allen Durivage

The ASQ CQE Study Guide
Connie M. Borror and Sarah E. Burke

The Certified Manager of Quality/Organizational Excellence Handbook, Fourth Edition
Russell T. Westcott, editor

The Certified Six Sigma Black Belt Handbook, Third Edition
T. M. Kubiak and Donald W. Benbow

The Certified Six Sigma Yellow Belt Handbook
Govindarajan Ramu

The Certified Six Sigma Green Belt Handbook, Second Edition
Roderick A. Munro, Govindarajan Ramu, and Daniel J. Zrymiak

Practical Attribute and Variable Measurement Systems Analysis (MSA): A Guide for Conducting Gage R&R Studies and Test Method Validations
Mark Allen Durivage

The Quality Toolbox, Second Edition
Nancy R. Tague

Root Cause Analysis: Simplified Tools and Techniques, Second Edition
Bjørn Andersen and Tom Fagerhaug

To request a complimentary catalog of ASQ Quality Press publications, call 800-248-1946, or visit our website at http://www.asq.org/quality-press.

THE CERTIFIED QUALITY INSPECTOR HANDBOOK

Third Edition

H. Fred Walker, Ahmad Elshennawy,
Bhisham C. Gupta, and Mary McShane Vaughn

ASQ Quality Press
Milwaukee, Wisconsin

American Society for Quality, Quality Press, Milwaukee 53203
© 2019 by ASQ
All rights reserved. Published 2019
Printed in the United States of America
25 24 23 22 21 LSC 8 7 6 5 4

Library of Congress Cataloging-in-Publication Data

Names: Walker, H. Fred, 1963– author. | Elshennawy, Ahmad K., author. |
 Gupta, Bhisham C., 1942– author. | McShane-Vaughn, Mary, 1963– author.
Title: The certified quality inspector handbook / H. Fred Walker, Ahmad K.
 Elshennawy, Bhisham C. Gupta, Mary McShane Vaughn.
Description: Third edition. | Milwaukee, Wisconsin : ASQ Quality Press,
 [2019] | Includes bibliographical references and index.
Identifiers: LCCN 2018058749 | ISBN 9780873899819 (hard cover : alk. paper)
Subjects: LCSH: Quality control—Handbooks, manuals, etc. | Quality control
 inspectors—Certification—United States.
Classification: LCC TS156 .W3139 2019 | DDC 658.5/62—dc23
LC record available at https://lccn.loc.gov/2018058749

ISBN: 978-0-87389-981-9

ASQ Mission: The American Society for Quality advances individual, organizational, and
community excellence worldwide through learning, quality improvement, and knowledge
exchange.

Attention Bookstores, Wholesalers, Schools, and Corporations: ASQ Quality Press books,
video, audio, and software are available at quantity discounts with bulk purchases for
business, educational, or instructional use. For information, please contact ASQ Quality Press
at 800-248-1946, or write to ASQ Quality Press, P.O. Box 3005, Milwaukee, WI 53201-3005.

To place orders or to request ASQ membership information, call 800-248-1946. To view our
online catalog, visit our website at http://www.asq.org/quality-press.

 Printed on acid-free paper

Quality Press
600 N. Plankinton Ave.
Milwaukee, WI 53203-2914
E-mail: authors@asq.org
ASQ The Global Voice of Quality®

In loving memory of my father, Carl Ellsworth Walker.
—Fred

In loving memory of my parents, Mohammed Elshennawy and Ikram Ismail.
—Ahmad

In loving memory of my parents, Roshan Lal and Sodhan Devi.
—Bhisham

In loving memory of my father, Charles H. McShane.
—Mary

Table of Contents

List of Figures and Tables . . . . *xix*
Preface . . . . *xxvii*
Acknowledgments . . . . *xxviii*
How to Use This Book . . . . *xxix*

Section I   Technical Mathematics **1**

Chapter 1   A. Basic Shop Math **3**
Properties of Real Numbers   3
Positive and Negative Numbers   3
    Adding and Subtracting with Positive and Negative Numbers   4
    Multiplying and Dividing with Positive and Negative Numbers   4
Fractions   4
    Equivalent Fractions   5
    Simplified Fractions   5
    Proper and Improper Fractions   5
    Adding and Subtracting Fractions with Like Denominators   5
    Adding and Subtracting Fractions with Unequal Denominators   6
    Adding or Subtracting Mixed Numbers   7
    Multiplying and Dividing Fractions   7
Decimals   8
    Decimal and Fraction Equivalents   8
    Converting Fractions to Decimals   8
    Rational and Irrational Numbers   8
    Converting Decimals to Percentages   9
    Adding and Subtracting Decimals   10
    Multiplying and Dividing Decimals   10
Squares and Square Roots   10
    Imaginary Numbers   10
    Exponents   10
Order of Operations   11
Factorials   11
Truncating, Rounding, and Significant Digits   11
    Adding and Subtracting Measurements   12
    Multiplying and Dividing Using Significant Digits   12
Bibliography   12

Chapter 2   B. Basic Algebra **13**
Solving Algebraic Equations 13
  Properties of Real Numbers....................................... 13
  Inverse Operations... 13
  Solving Equations Using One Inverse Operation 14
  Solving Equations Using Two or More Inverse Operations 15
  Solving Equations by Collecting Terms 15
  Solving Equations with Parentheses................................ 16
  Solving Inequalities... 17
  Solving Inequalities with Negatively Signed Values 18
Bibliography 18

Chapter 3   C. Basic Geometry **19**
Areas of Basic Geometric Shapes 19
  Examples of Area Calculations 19
Perimeter and Circumference of Basic Geometric Shapes 21
  Examples of Perimeter and Circumference Calculations 21
Volume of Basic Geometric Shapes................................. 23
  Examples of Volume Calculations.................................. 23
Surface Area of Basic Geometric Shapes 24
  Examples of Surface Area Calculations 24
Complementary and Supplementary Angles 26
Bibliography 26

Chapter 4   D. Basic Trigonometry **27**
The Right Triangle... 27
  Pythagorean Theorem.. 27
Trigonometric Functions... 28
  Values of Trigonometric Functions for Some Common Angles 28
  Trigonometric Identities 28
Solving for Unknown Sides and Angles of a Right Triangle 30
  Finding the Unknown Angle.. 30
  Finding the Unknown Sides.. 31
Inverse Trigonometric Functions................................... 32
Oblique Triangles.. 32
Solving Oblique Triangles 32
  Law of Sines 33
  Law of Cosines 34
  Three Sides Known 34
  Two Sides and an Angle between Them Known 35
  One Side and Two Angles Known 37
Bibliography 38

Chapter 5   E. Measurement Systems **39**
Measurement Systems.. 39
English System Measurements 39
SI/Metric System Measurements 43
English-to-SI/Metric Conversions................................... 45
Bibliography 50

Chapter 6   F. Numeric Conversions **51**
    Exponents 51
        Positive Exponents 51
        Negative Exponents 52
        Powers of 10 52
    Scientific Notation 52
        Procedure for Values Greater Than 1 or Less Than –1 53
        Procedure for Values between –1 and +1 53
        Converting Scientific Notation back to Original Form 54
    Decimals and Fractions 54
        Converting Fractions to Decimals 54
        Converting Decimals to Fractions 55
    Bibliography 55

Section II   Metrology **57**

Chapter 7   A. Common Gauges and Measurement Instruments **59**
    Introduction 59
    1. Variable Gauges 60
        Steel Rules 60
        Verniers 60
        Micrometers 63
        Vernier Scales 64
        Digital Micrometers 64
        Micrometer Calipers 64
        Gauge Blocks 65
        Dial Indicators 66
        Borescopes 67
        Thermometers and Temperature Probes 67
        Coordinate Measuring Machines 67
    2. Attribute Gauges 71
        Common Gauges 72
    3. Transfer Gauges 77
    4. Measurement Scales 77
    Reference 77
    Bibliography 77

Chapter 8   B. Special Gauges and Applications **79**
    1. Electronic Gauging Tools 79
        Advantages 80
        Oscilloscopes 81
        Multimeters 81
        Pyrometers 81
    2. Automatic Gauging Components 81
        Interferometry 82
        Machine Vision 84
        X-Ray Inspection 85
    3. Pneumatic Gauging Components 85

4. Force Gauging   87
5. Environmental Instrumentation   88
Summary of Gauge Uses and Applications.   88
References   90
Bibliography   90

Chapter 9   C. Gauge Selection, Handling, and Use **91**
1. The Rule of Ten (10:1 Rule)   91
2. Gauge Selection   92
3. Gauge Handling, Preservation, and Storage   92
4. Gauge Correlation   94
Reference   95
Bibliography   95

Chapter 10   D. Surface Plate Tools and Techniques **97**
1. Surface Plate Equipment.   97
    Surface Plate   97
    Dial Indicators   99
    Vernier Height Gauge   100
2. Angle Measurement Instruments   100
    Sine Bar   101
    Angle Blocks.   102
    Protractors.   102
Reference.   103
Bibliography   103

Chapter 11   E. Specialized Inspection Equipment **105**
1. Measuring Mass.   105
    Weights, Balances, and Scales   105
    Measuring Weight and Mass   106
    Balances and Scales   106
    Surface Metrology   107
2. Measuring Finish.   109
3. Measuring Shape and Profile.   111
    Comparators   111
    Measurement of Roundness.   111
4. Optical Equipment.   112
    Optical Tooling.   112
5. Software-Based Measurement Systems   116
    Machine Vision Systems   116
    Laser Trackers.   117
    Other Digital Inspection Systems   117
6. Measuring Inclination.   118
References   118
Bibliography   118

Chapter 12   F. Calibration **121**
1. Calibration Systems.   121
    Calibration Interval Prompt.   122
    Uncertainty   123

Tracking and Identification Methods 123
Calibration Documentation and History 124
Calibration Equipment 124
Calibration Procedures 124
2. Calibration Standards and Equipment Traceability 124
Equipment Traceability 126
3. Gauge Calibration Environment 126
4. Out-of-Calibration Effects 127
References 127
Bibliography 128

Chapter 13 G. Measurement System Analysis (MSA) **129**
1. Process Variability 130
Variability in the Measurement Process 130
2. Evaluating Measurement System Performance 131
3. The Range-Based Method 131
4. The ANOVA Method 137
Gauge R&R Study—ANOVA Method 137
Graphical Representation of Gauge R&R Study 140
5. Measurement Capability Indices 143
MCI as a Percentage of Process Variation (MCI_{pv}) 143
MCI as a Percentage of Process Specification (MCI_{ps}) 144
References 144

Section III Inspection and Test **145**

**Chapter 14 A. Blueprints, Drawings, Geometric Dimensioning &
Tolerancing (GD&T) and Model Based Definitions** **147**
Introduction 147
1. Blueprints and Engineering Drawings, and Model Based Definitions 148
Sections of Technical Drawings 149
Model Based Definition 153
2. Terminology and Symbols 153
3. Position and Bonus Tolerances 154
4. Part Alignment and Datum Structure 158
References 159

Chapter 15 B. Sampling **161**
Introduction 161
Advantages 162
Sampling Concepts 163
Random Sampling 163
The Operating Characteristic Curve 163
Acceptance Sampling by Attributes 164
Acceptance Quality Limit 164
Lot Tolerance Percent Defective 164
Producer's and Consumer's Risks 164
Average Outgoing Quality 165
Average Outgoing Quality Limit 165

Lot Size, Sample Size, and Acceptance Number   166
Types of Attribute Sampling Plans   166
   Single Sampling Plans   166
   Double Sampling Plans   166
   Multiple Sampling Plans   166
Sampling Standards and Plans   166
   ANSI/ASQ Z1.4-2008   166
   Levels of Inspection   167
   Types of Sampling   168
Variables Sampling Plans   169
   ANSI/ASQ Z1.9-2008   170
Sequential Sampling Plans   171
Continuous Sampling Plans   171
   MIL-STD-1235B   172
References   173
Bibliography   173

Chapter 16   C. Inspection Planning and Processes **175**
Introduction   175
Inspection Planning   176
1. Inspection Types   177
   Incoming Material Inspection   177
   First-Piece Inspection   179
   In-Process Inspection   179
   Final Inspection   179
2. Inspection Errors   180
   Inspector Qualifications and Training   182
   The Characteristics of a Quality Inspector   183
3. Product Traceability   184
   Factors to Consider   184
4. Identification of Nonconforming Material   186
   Principles of Identification   186
   Mechanics   186
5. Levels of Severity   187
Control of Nonconforming Materials   188
   Control of Nonconforming Product   188
   Corrective Action   189
   Preventive Action   190
6. Disposition of Nonconforming Material   191
   Material Segregation   191
   Material Review Board   191
References   192
Bibliography   193

Chapter 17   D. Testing Methods **195**
1. Nondestructive Testing   195
   Definition   195
   NDT Applications and Objectives   195
   Methods of NDT   196

2. Destructive Testing 201
    Definition 201
    Destructive Testing Applications and Objectives 202
    Methods of Destructive Testing 202
3. Functionality Testing 205
    Definition 205
    Functionality Testing Objectives 205
    Methods of Functionality Testing 206
4. Hardness Testing 207
    Brinell 207
    Rockwell 208
    Vickers 208
    Microhardness Test 210
References 210

Chapter 18   E. Software for Test Equipment **213**
Software Testing 213
Testing versus Inspection 214
Functional Testing in Software Development 214
Software Testing Terminology 215
    Automated Software Testing 215
    Automated Testing Tools 215
    Basis Path Testing 215
    Basis Test Set 215
    Bebugging 215
    Benchmark Testing 215
    Benchmark Testing Methods 216
    Compatibility Testing 216
    Debugging 217
    Desk Checking 217
    Design-Based Testing 217
    Dynamic Testing 217
    Functional Decomposition 217
    Functional Requirements 217
    Manual Testing 217
    Metric 218
    Modified Condition/Decision Coverage 218
    Modified Condition/Decision Testing 218
    Monkey Testing 219
    Negative Testing 219
    Portability Testing 219
    Positive Testing 219
    Recovery Testing 219
    Security Testing 219
    Traceability 220
    Validation Testing 220
References 220
Bibliography 220

Section IV   Quality Assurance 221

Chapter 19   A. Basic Statistics and Applications........................ 223
1. Graphical Methods 223
   Frequency Distribution Table................................... 224
   Qualitative Data... 224
   Quantitative Data.. 224
   Dot Plot 228
   Pie Chart 228
   Bar Chart.. 229
   Pareto Chart 230
   Scatter Plot 233
   Histograms... 234
   Stem-and-Leaf Diagram 240
2. Numerical Methods.. 242
   Measures of Centrality 242
   Measures of Dispersion 248
   Measures of Percentages.. 252
   Box-and-Whisker Plot 256
3. Normal Distribution 260
   Standard Normal Distribution Table 262
   References... 266

Chapter 20   B. Statistical Process Control (SPC)........................ 269
1. Basic Concepts of Quality and Its Benefits...................... 269
2. Flowchart 270
3. What Is a Process?.. 270
4. Check Sheet.. 272
5. Cause-and-Effect (Fishbone or Ishikawa) Diagram 272
6. Defect Concentration Diagram 274
7. Run Chart 275
8. Control Charts 276
   Preparation for Use of Control Charts 277
   Benefits of Control Charts 279
   Rational Subgroups for a Control Chart......................... 279
9. Average Run Length 279
10. Operating Characteristic Curve................................. 280
11. Common Causes versus Special Causes............................ 282
    Process Evaluation.. 282
    Action on Process... 282
    Action on Output.. 282
    Variation 283
    Common Causes, or Random Causes............................... 283
    Special Causes, or Assignable Causes 283
12. Control Limits versus Specification Limits 284
13. Control Charts for Variables.................................... 285
    Shewhart $\bar{X}$ and R Control Chart...................... 285
    Calculation of Sample Statistics.............................. 285
    Calculation of Control Limits................................. 285

Interpretation of Shewhart $\bar{X}$ and R Control Charts   288
Shewhart $\bar{X}$ and R Control Chart When Process Mean µ and
   Process Standard Deviation σ Are Known   291
Shewhart $\bar{X}$ and S Control Chart   292
Calculation of Control Limits.   293
14. Control Charts for Attributes   295
The p Chart: Control Chart for Fraction of Nonconforming Units   296
Control Limits for the p Chart   297
Interpreting the Control Chart for Fraction Nonconforming   299
The p Chart: Control Chart for Fraction Nonconforming
   with Variable Samples   302
The np Chart: Control Chart for Number of Nonconforming Units   304
Control Limits for np Control Chart   304
The c Chart (Nonconformities versus Nonconforming Units)   306
The u Chart.   309
15. Process Capability Analysis   310
Process Capability Index: C_p   315
Process Capability Index: C_{pk}   319
Process Capability Indices: P_p and P_{pk}   321
References   322

Chapter 21   C. Quality Improvement **325**
1. Terms and Concepts   325
Prevention versus Detection   325
The Importance of Customer Satisfaction   326
The Cost of Poor Quality   327
2. Products and Processes.   327
Product   327
Process.   327
The Interrelatedness of Products and Processes.   328
References   328
Bibliography   328

Chapter 22   D. Quality Audits. **329**
Terms and Definitions.   330
1. Types of Audits.   330
Roles and Responsibilities in Audits   331
2. Audit Process   332
3. Audit Tools   333
Checklists   333
Log Sheets.   333
Sampling Plans.   334
4. Communication Tools and Techniques   334
5. Corrective Action Requests (CARs)   334
Audit Outcomes.   334
Audit Reporting and Follow-Up   335
References   336
Bibliography   336

Chapter 23   E. Quality Tools and Techniques **337**
   Seven Basic Quality Control Tools 337
   Bibliography 338

Chapter 24   F. Problem-Solving Tools and Continuous Improvement
Techniques **339**
   1. Plan–Do–Check–Act (PDCA) or Plan–Do–Study–Act (PDSA) Cycles..... 339
      Plan 340
      Do... 340
      Check.. 341
      Act 341
   2. Lean Tools for Eliminating Waste.................................. 342
      5S 342
      Error-Proofing 343
      Value Stream Mapping 344
      Lean Concepts 345
   3. Six Sigma Phases 346
      The Scientific Method 346
      Six Sigma.. 346
      Root Cause Analysis 347
   4. Failure Mode and Effects Analysis (FMEA) 348
      Selecting a Standard for FMEA.................................... 348
      Planning for an FMEA 348
      Establishing a Single Point of Responsibility 349
      FMEA Team Members 349
      Inputs to an FMEA 350
      FMEA and Other Quality Tools..................................... 350
      Outputs from an FMEA 351
      Basic Steps in an FMEA 351
      Quantifying the Risk Associated with Each Potential Failure...... 352
      FMEAs Encountered by Quality Professionals....................... 354
      Design and Process FMEA.. 355
      Heading Information and Documentation 355
      Analysis Content and Documentation 358
      A Final Word on Taking Corrective Action......................... 362
      Assessing Criticality 363
      A Caution about Using FMEA....................................... 364
      Design and Process FMEA Examples................................. 364
      FMEA Summary 364
   5. 8D Methodology.. 364
   6. 5 Whys... 367
   7. Fault Tree Analysis (FTA) 368
   References.. 369
   Bibliography 370

Chapter 25   G. Resources **371**
   1. Environmental and Safety Support................................. 372
   2. Reference Documents 374
   3. Employees as Resources 375

Empowering Employees. 375
Employee Involvement 375
Team Roles and Responsibilities. 376
Stages of Team Development. 377
Conflict Resolution 378
Consensus. 378
Brainstorming. 378
Meeting Management. 379
4. Quality Documentation 379
ISO 9001. 380
First Article Inspection Report (FAI) 381
Initial Sample Inspection Report (ISIR) 382
Production Part Approval Process (PPAP). 389
Basic Quality Documentation 390
References. 391
Bibliography. 391

Section V Appendices **393**

**Appendix A American Society for Quality Certified Quality
Inspector (CQI) Body of Knowledge 2018** 395

Appendix B Computer Resources to Support the CQI Handbook 403

Appendix C General Tables of Units of Measurement 431

Appendix D Standard Normal Distribution . . . .

**Appendix E Factors Helpful in Constructing Control Charts
for Variables**. . . . .

**Appendix F Values of K_1 for Computing Repeatability Using the
Range Method**. . . . .

**Appendix G Values of K_2 for Computing Reproducibility Using the
Range Method** . . . .

**Appendix H Sample Tables of ANSI/ASQ Z1.4-2008 and
ANSI/ASQ Z1.9-2008 Standards** . . . .

Glossary . . . .
Index . . . .

List of Figures and Tables

Section I

Table 1.1	Properties of real numbers.	3
Figure 1.1	Example prime factorization tree.	6
Table 1.2	Place values for ABCDEFG.HIJKLM.	9
Table 1.3	Decimal and fraction equivalents.	9
Table 2.1	Additional properties of real numbers.	14
Table 2.2	Inverse operations.	14
Table 3.1	Calculation of area for basic geometric shapes.	20
Table 3.2	Calculation of perimeter and circumference of basic geometric shapes.	22
Table 3.3	Calculation of volume of basic geometric shapes.	24
Table 3.4	Calculation of surface area for basic geometric shapes.	25
Figure 4.1	The right triangle.	27
Table 4.1	Calculation of trigonometric functions.	29
Table 4.2	Values of trigonometric functions for common angles.	30
Figure 4.2	Finding angles in a right triangle.	31
Table 4.3	Oblique triangles.	33
Figure 4.3	Oblique triangle.	33
Figure 4.4	Three sides known.	35
Figure 4.5	Two sides and angle between known.	35
Figure 4.6	Two sides and opposite angle known.	36
Figure 4.7	One side and two angles known.	37
Table 5.1	Converting measures of length.	40
Table 5.2	Converting measures of area.	41
Table 5.3	Converting measures of volume.	41
Table 5.4	Converting measures of weight.	42
Table 5.5	Converting measures of liquid.	42
Table 5.6	Converting measures of pressure.	43
Table 5.7	Converting measures of length—metric units.	44
Table 5.8	Converting measures of area—metric units.	44
Table 5.9	Converting measures of volume—metric units.	45
Table 5.10	Converting measures of mass—metric units.	45
Table 5.11	Converting liquid measures—metric units.	46

Table 5.12   Converting measures of length—English and metric units.   46

Table 5.13   Converting measures of area—English and metric units.   47

Table 5.14   Converting measures of volume—English and metric units.   47

Table 5.15   Converting measures of weight and mass.   48

Table 5.16   Converting measures of liquid—English and metric units.   48

Table 5.17   Converting temperatures—Celsius to Fahrenheit.   49

Table 5.18   Converting temperatures—Fahrenheit to Celsius.   49

Table 5.19   Converting temperatures—English and metric units.   49

Table 6.1   Powers of 10.   52

Table 6.2   Common fractions and their decimal equivalents.   54

Figure 7.1   Fine-adjustment style vernier caliper.   61

Figure 7.2   LCD digital-reading caliper with 0–152 mm (0–6 in.) range.   62

Figure 7.3   Digital-reading, single-axis height gauge for two-dimensional
measurements.   62

Figure 7.4   A 0–25 mm micrometer caliper.   63

Figure 7.5   Micrometer reading of 10.66 mm   64

Figure 7.6   Scales of a vernier micrometer showing a reading of 10.666 mm.   65

Figure 7.7   A digital micrometer.   65

Figure 7.8   An indicating micrometer.   66

Figure 7.9   A schematic showing the process of wringing gauge blocks.   66

Figure 7.10   CMM classifications.   69

Figure 7.11   Examples of typical gauges.   73

Figure 8.1   Elements of electronic gauges.   80

Figure 8.2   (a) Light-wave interference with an optical flat, (b) application of an
optical flat, (c) diagram of an interferometer.   83

Figure 8.3   Diagram of air gauge principles.   86

Table 8.1   Summary of commonly used gauges and their applications.   88

Figure 10.1   Granite surface plate for checking the flatness of a part, with dial
indicator and leveling screws.   98

Figure 10.2   Simple dial indicator mechanism.   99

Figure 10.3   An application of dial indicators for inspecting flatness by placing
the workpiece on gauge blocks and checking full indicator
movement (FIM).   100

Figure 10.4   Application of a sine bar.   101

Figure 10.5   Addition and subtraction of angle blocks.   102

Figure 11.1   (a) Typical surface highly magnified, (b) profile of surface roughness,
(c) surface quality specifications.   108

Figure 11.2   (a) Skid-type or average surface finish measuring gauge, (b) skidless
or profiling gauge.   110

Figure 11.3   Optical tooling.   113

Figure 11.4   Optical comparator system.   114

Figure 11.5   Horizontal optical comparator with a 356 mm (14 in.) viewing screen,
digital readout, and edge-sensing device.   115

Figure 12.1   The calibration system.   122

Figure 12.2   Calibration standards hierarchy.   125

Figure 13.1   Components of total variation.   130

Figure 13.2   (a) Accurate and precise, (b) accurate but not precise, (c) not accurate
but precise, (d) neither accurate nor precise.   132

Figure 13.3   Diagram showing the linear relationship between the actual and the
observed values.   133

Table 13.1   Data on an experiment involving three operators, 10 bolts, and three
measurements (in mm) on each bolt by each operator.   135

Figure 13.4   Two-way ANOVA table with interaction (Minitab printout).   137

Figure 13.5   Two-way ANOVA table without interaction (Minitab printout).   138

Figure 13.6   Gauge R&R (Minitab printout).   139

Figure 13.7   An example: percent tolerance contribution by the various components
of the measurement system.   139

Figure 13.8   Percent contribution of variance components for the data in
Example 13.1.   141

Figure 13.9 $\bar{X}$ and R chart for the data in Example 13.1.   141

Figure 13.10   Interaction between operators and parts for the data in Example 13.1.   142

Figure 13.11   Scatter plot for measurements versus operators.   142

Figure 13.12   Scatter plot for measurements versus parts (bolts).   143

Figure 14.1   Blueprint for a house floor plan.   148

Figure 14.2   Placement of the title block and notes on engineering drawings.   149

Figure 14.3   Example of title and notes blocks on an engineering drawing.   150

Figure 14.4   Example of a revision block.   151

Figure 14.5   Example of a technical engineering drawing with an indication of
geometric tolerances.   151

Figure 14.6   Visual representation of the control frame of a hole.   152

Figure 14.7   Features that can be specified by geometric tolerancing.   152

Figure 14.8   Simple 2-D example of position tolerance.   153

Figure 14.9   Top, front, and right side views of an item.   154

Figure 14.10   Engineering drawing line types and styles.   155

Table 14.1   Other feature control symbols.   157

Figure 14.11   Example of symbols on an engineering drawing.   157

Figure 14.12   Form tolerance example.   158

Figure 15.1   An OC curve.   163

Figure 15.2   AOQ curve for $N = \infty$, $n = 50$, $c = 3$.   165

Figure 15.3   Switching rules for normal, tightened, and reduced inspection.   168

Figure 15.4   Structure and organization of ANSI/ASQ Z1.9-2008.   170

Figure 15.5   Decision areas for a sequential sampling plan.   171

Figure 16.1   Inspection decisions.   176

Figure 16.2   An example of a flowchart of a repair job.   178

Figure 16.3   Factors affecting the measuring process.   182

Table 16.1   Standards pertaining to MRB operations.   192

Figure 17.1   Visual inspection ensures consistency.   197

Figure 17.2   Inspection using X-ray.   197

Figure 17.3   Example of an inspection using X-ray.   198

Figure 17.4   Eddy current method.   199

Figure 17.5   The general inspection principle for ultrasonic testing.   199

Figure 17.6   Magnetic particle inspection.   201

Figure 17.7   Liquid penetrant testing steps.   202

Figure 17.8   Tensile test for a furnace.   203

Figure 17.9   Free-bend test.   204

Figure 17.10 Crash testing.   205

Figure 17.11 Tension test machine.   206

Figure 17.12 Torque can be calculated by multiplying the force applied to a lever by
              its distance from the lever's fulcrum.   207

Figure 17.13 Compression test.   207

Figure 17.14 Brinell hardness test method.   208

Figure 17.15 Rockwell hardness test method.   209

Figure 17.16 The Vickers hardness test.   210

Table 19.1   Classification of annual revenues of 110 small to midsize companies
              located in the Midwestern region of the United States.   225

Table 19.2   Complete frequency distribution table for the 110 small to midsize
              companies.   225

Table 19.3   Complete frequency distribution table for the data in Example 19.2.   226

Table 19.4   Frequency table for the data on rod lengths.   227

Figure 19.1   Dot plot for the data on defective motors received in 20 different
              shipments.   228

Table 19.5   Understanding defect rates as a function of various process steps.   229

Figure 19.2   Pie chart for defects associated with manufacturing process steps.   230

Figure 19.3   Bar chart for annual revenues of a company over a five-year period.   231

Table 19.6   Frequency distribution table for the data in Example 19.7.   232

Figure 19.4   Bar graph for the data in Example 19.7.   232

Figure 19.5   Pareto chart for the data in Example 19.7.   233

Table 19.7   Frequencies and weighted frequencies when different types of defects
              are not equally important.   234

Figure 19.6   Pareto chart when weighted frequencies are used.   234

Table 19.8   Cholesterol levels and systolic blood pressures of 30 randomly
              selected US males.   235

Figure 19.7   Scatter plot of the data in Table 19.8.   236

Table 19.9   Frequency distribution table for the survival time of parts.   237

Figure 19.8   Frequency histogram for survival time of parts under extreme
              operating conditions.   238

Figure 19.9   Relative frequency histogram for survival time of parts under
              extreme operating conditions.   238

Figure 19.10   Frequency polygon for the data in Example 19.9.   239

Figure 19.11   Relative frequency polygon for the data in Example 19.9.   239

Figure 19.12   A typical frequency distribution curve.   240

Figure 19.13   Three types of frequency distribution curves.   240

Figure 19.14   Ordinary and ordered stem-and-leaf diagram for the data on survival
time for parts under certain conditions.   241

Figure 19.15   Frequency distributions showing the shape and location of measures
of central tendency.   247

Figure 19.16   Two frequency distribution curves with equal mean, median, and
mode values.   248

Figure 19.17   Application of the empirical rule.   251

Figure 19.18   Amount of soft drink contained in a bottle.   252

Figure 19.19   Dollar value of units of bad production.   253

Figure 19.20   Percentile of salary data.   254

Figure 19.21   Quartiles and percentiles.   255

Figure 19.22   Box-and-whisker plot.   256

Figure 19.23   Box plot for the data in Example 19.25.   257

Figure 19.24   Box plot for the data shown in Example 19.26.   259

Figure 19.25   The normal probability function curve with mean μ and standard
deviation σ   261

Figure 19.26   Curves representing the normal density function with different
means, but with the same standard deviation.   261

Figure 19.27   Curves representing the normal density function with different
standard deviations, but with the same mean.   261

Figure 19.28   The standard normal density function curve.   262

Figure 19.29   Probability ($a \leq Z \leq b$) under the standard normal curve.   262

Table 19.10   A portion of the standard normal distribution table from Appendix D. . . .   263

Figure 19.30   Shaded area equal to $P(1.0 \leq Z \leq 2.0)$.   264

Figure 19.31   Two shaded areas in Figure 19.31 showing $P(-1.5 \leq Z \leq 0) =$
$P(0 \leq Z \leq 1.5)$.   264

Figure 19.32   Two shaded areas showing $P(-2.2 \leq Z \leq -1.0) = P(1.0 \leq Z \leq 2.2)$.   264

Figure 19.33   Shaded area showing $P(-1.5 \leq Z \leq 0.8) = P(-1.5 \leq Z \leq 0) + P(0 \leq Z \leq 0.8)$. . . .   265

Figure 19.34   Shaded area showing $P(Z \leq 0.7)$.   265

Figure 19.35   Shaded area showing $P(Z \geq -1.0)$.   265

Figure 19.36   Shaded area showing $P(Z \geq 2.15)$.   266

Figure 19.37   Shaded area showing $P(Z \leq -2.15)$.   266

Figure 19.38   Converting normal $N(6,4)$ to standard normal $N(0,1)$.   267

Figure 19.39   Shaded area showing $P(0.5 \leq Z \leq 2.0)$.   267

Figure 19.40   Shaded area showing $P(-1.0 \leq Z \leq 1.0)$.   268

Figure 19.41   Shaded area showing $P(-1.5 \leq Z \leq -0.5)$.   268

Figure 20.1   Flowchart of a process.   271

Table 20.1   Check sheet summarizing the data of a study over a period of
four weeks.   272

Figure 20.2   Initial form of a cause-and-effect diagram. 273

Figure 20.3   A completed cause-and-effect diagram. 274

Figure 20.4   A damaged item shaped as a rectangular prism. 275

Table 20.2   Percentage of nonconforming units in 30 different shifts. 276

Figure 20.5   Run chart. 276

Figure 20.6   A pictorial representation of the components of a control chart. 277

Figure 20.7   OC curves for the $\bar{X}$ chart with 3-sigma limits, for different sample
                sizes n. 281

Table 20.3   Diameter measurements (mm) of ball bearings used in the wheels of
                heavy construction equipment. 289

Figure 20.8 $\bar{X}$ and R control chart for the ball bearing data in Table 20.3. 290

Figure 20.9 $\bar{X}$ and S control chart for the ball bearing data in Table 20.3. 295

Table 20.4   Control charts for attributes. 297

Table 20.5   Number of nonconforming computer chips out of 1000 inspected
                each day during the study period of 30 days. 300

Figure 20.10 p chart for nonconforming computer chips, using trial control limits
                for the data in Table 20.5. 301

Table 20.6   Number of nonconforming computer chips with different size
                samples inspected each day during the study period of 30 days. 303

Figure 20.11 p chart for nonconforming chips with variable sample sizes, using
                trial control limits for the data in Table 20.6. 304

Figure 20.12 np chart for nonconforming computer chips, using trial control limits
                for the data in Table 20.5. 305

Table 20.7   Total number of nonconformities in samples of five rolls of paper. 307

Figure 20.13 c control chart of nonconformities for the data in Table 20.7. 308

Table 20.8   Number of nonconformities on printed boards for laptops per sample;
                each sample consists of five inspection units. 311

Figure 20.14 u chart of nonconformities for the data in Table 20.8, constructed
                using Minitab. 311

Table 20.9   Number of nonconformities on printed boards for laptops per sample,
                with varying sample size. 312

Figure 20.15 u chart of nonconformities for the data in Table 20.9, constructed using
                Minitab. 313

Table 20.10   Data showing the lengths of tie rods for cars. 317

Table 20.11   Different processes with the same value of C_{pk}. 321

Table 20.12   Parts per million of nonconforming units for different values of C_{pk}. 321

Figure 24.1   The plan–do–check–act cycle. 341

Figure 24.2   Blank design FMEA form. 356

Figure 24.3   Blank process FMEA form. 357

Table 24.1   Design FMEA severity criteria. 359

Table 24.2   Process FMEA severity criteria. 360

Table 24.3   Design FMEA occurrence criteria. 361

Table 24.4   Process FMEA occurrence criteria. 361

Table 24.5   Design FMEA detection criteria.   362

Table 24.6   Process FMEA detection criteria.   363

Figure 24.4   Design FMEA example.   365

Figure 24.5   Process FMEA example.   366

Figure 24.6   List of the eight disciplines (8D).   367

Figure 24.7   Fault tree depicting the root causes of hazard to patients during
                surgery.   369

Figure 25.1a   First article inspection process—First Article Inspection Report
                Approval Form.   383

Figure 25.1b   First article inspection process—First Article Inspection Report
                Content/Check Sheet.   384

Figure 25.1c   First article inspection process—Form 1: Part Number Accountability. . . .   385

Figure 25.1d   First article inspection process—Form 2: Product Accountability—Raw
                Material, Specifications and Special Process(es), Functional Testing.   386

Figure 25.1e   First article inspection process—Form 3: Characteristic
                Accountability, Verification and Compatibility Evaluation.   387

Figure 25.1f   First article inspection process—Form 3: Characteristic
                Accountability, Verification and Compatibility Evaluation.   388

Figure B.1   The screen that appears first in the Minitab environment.   404

Figure B.2   Minitab window showing the menu command options.   405

Figure B.3   Minitab window showing input and output for *Column Statistics*.   407

Figure B.4   Minitab window showing various options available under the
                Stat menu.   408

Figure B.5   Minitab display of the histogram for the data given in Example B.3.   409

Figure B.6   Minitab window showing *Edit Bars* dialog box.   410

Figure B.7   Minitab display of a histogram with five classes for the data in
                Example B.3.   411

Figure B.8   Minitab dot plot output for the data in Example B.4.   412

Figure B.9   Minitab scatter plot output for the data given in Example B.5.   413

Figure B.10   Minitab display of box plot for the data in Example B.6.   414

Figure B.11   Minitab display of graphical summary for the data in Example B.7.   415

Figure B.12   Minitab display of the bar chart for the data in Example B.8.   417

Figure B.13   Minitab display of the pie chart for the data in Example B.9.   418

Figure B.14   Minitab window showing the *Xbar-R Chart* dialog box.   421

Figure B.15   Minitab window showing the *Xbar-R Chart—Options* dialog box.   421

Figure B.16   Minitab window showing the *Xbar-S Chart* dialog box.   423

Table B.1   Data for 25 samples each of size five from a given process.   424

Figure B.17   Minitab window showing the *Capability Analysis (Normal Distribution)*
                dialog box.   425

Figure B.18   Minitab windows showing the Minitab process capability analysis.   425

Figure B.19   Minitab window showing the *P Chart* dialog box.   426

Figure B.20   Minitab window showing the *C Chart* dialog box.   428

Figure B.21   Minitab window showing the *U Chart* dialog box.   429

Figure H.1   ANSI/ASQ Z1.4-2008 Table VIII: Limit numbers for reduced inspection. . .

Figure H.2   ANSI/ASQ Z1.4-2008 Table I: Sample size code letters. . . . .

Figure H.3   ANSI/ASQ Z1.4-2008 Table II-A: Single sampling plans for normal
distribution. . . . .

Figure H.4   ANSI/ASQ Z1.4-2008 Table III-A: Double sampling plans for normal
inspection. . . . .

Figure H.5   ANSI/ASQ Z1.9-2008 Table IV-A: Multiple sampling plans for
normal inspection. . . . .

Figure H.6   ANSI/ASQ Z1.9-2008 Table A-2*: Sample size code letters.** . . . .

Figure H.7   ANSI/ASQ Z1.9-2008 Table C-1: Master table for normal and tightened
inspection for plans based on variability unknown (single specification
limit—Form 1). . . . .

Figure H.8   ANSI/ASQ Z1.9-2008 Table B-5: Table for estimating the lot percent
nonconforming using standard deviation method. Values tabulated
are read as percentages. . . . .

Figure H.9   ANSI/ASQ Z1.9-2008 Table B-3: Master table for normal and tightened
inspection for plans based on variability unknown (double specification
limit and Form 2—single specification limit). . . . .

Preface

The quality inspector is the person perhaps most closely involved with day-to-day activities intended to ensure that products and services meet customer expectations. The quality inspector is required to understand and apply a variety of tools and techniques as codified in the American Society for Quality (ASQ) Certified Quality Inspector (CQI) Body of Knowledge (BoK). The tools and techniques identified in the ASQ CQI BoK include technical math, metrology, inspection and test techniques, and quality assurance. Quality inspectors frequently work with the quality function of organizations in the various measurement and inspection laboratories, as well as on the shop floor supporting and interacting with quality engineers and production/service delivery personnel. This book, *The Certified Quality Inspector Handbook* (CQIH), was commissioned by ASQ Quality Press to support individuals preparing to perform, or those already performing, this type of work.

The CQIH is intended to serve as a ready reference for quality inspectors and quality inspectors in training, as well as a comprehensive reference for those individuals preparing to take the ASQ CQI examination. Examples and problems used throughout the handbook are thoroughly explained, are algebra-based, and are drawn from real-world situations encountered in the quality profession.

Acknowledgments

The authors would like to thank their families.

Fred would like to acknowledge the patience and support of his wife, Julie, and sons, Carl and George, as he worked on this book.

Ahmad would like to acknowledge the patience and support provided by his wife, Hanan, sons, Mohammed and Omar, and daughter, Leemar. Without their love, devotion, and encouragement, work on this book would not have been possible or meaningful.

Bhisham is indebted to his wife, Swarn, daughters, Anita and Anjali, son, Shiva, sons-in-law, Prajay and Mark, daughter-in-law, Aditi, and granddaughters, Priya and Kaviya, for their deep love and devotion. Without the encouragement of both our families, this project would not have been possible or meaningful.

Mary thanks her husband, Jim, and their six children for their support and understanding while she was working on this project.

We are grateful to the several anonymous reviewers whose constructive suggestions greatly improved this book. We also want to thank Matt Meinholz and Paul O'Mara of ASQ Quality Press for their patience and cooperation throughout this project.

H. Fred Walker
Ahmad K. Elshennawy
Bhisham C. Gupta
Mary McShane Vaughn

How to Use This Book

To assist readers in using this book as a ready reference or as a study aid, the book has been organized so as to conform explicitly to the ASQ CQI BoK. Each chapter title, all major topical divisions within the chapters, and every main point has been titled and then numbered exactly as they appear in the CQI BoK.

To gain the most benefit from reading this book, it is intended that readers initially read the material in the order in which it is presented. Having read the material sequentially from beginning to end, readers are encouraged to then reread material unfamiliar or unclear to them to gain additional insights and mastery.

It should be noted that many references were used to support development of the ASQ CQI BoK, and by the authors to write this book. Individuals learning about quality inspection should expect to begin building a library of their own support materials—materials that have been identified in this book as well as identified and recommended on ASQ's website.

Section I
Technical Mathematics

Chapter 1   A. Basic Shop Math

Chapter 2   B. Basic Algebra

Chapter 3   C. Basic Geometry

Chapter 4   D. Basic Trigonometry

Chapter 5   E. Measurement Systems

Chapter 6   F. Numeric Conversions

Chapter 1

A. Basic Shop Math

Basic Shop Math

Solve basic shop math problems using addition, subtraction, multiplication, division of fractions and decimals, squares and square roots. Use methods such as truncating and rounding to obtain significant digits for positive and negative numbers. (Apply)

Body of Knowledge I.A.

PROPERTIES OF REAL NUMBERS

When performing arithmetic operations on numbers, keep in mind the fundamental properties as shown in Table 1.1.

Let a, b, and c represent real numbers.

POSITIVE AND NEGATIVE NUMBERS

A positive number is one that is greater than zero; a negative number is less than zero. For example, the number 6 is a positive number, while –2 is a negative number.

Table 1.1 Properties of real numbers.

Property	Example
Commutative property for addition	$a + b = b + a$
Commutative property for multiplication	$a \times b = b \times a$
Associative property for addition	$(a + b) + c = a + (b + c)$
Associative property for multiplication	$(a \times b) \times c = a \times (b \times c)$
Distributive property	$a(b + c) = ab + ac$

3

Adding and Subtracting with Positive and Negative Numbers

We can add and subtract positive and negative numbers, as the examples show:

$$4 + 3 = 7$$
$$4 + -3 = 1$$
$$-4 + 3 = -1$$
$$-4 + -3 = -7$$
$$8 - 2 = 6$$
$$8 - (-2) = 10$$
$$-8 - 2 = -10$$
$$-8 - (-2) = -6$$

Multiplying and Dividing with Positive and Negative Numbers

We can also multiply and divide positive and negative numbers, as the examples show:

$$4 \times 3 = 12$$
$$4 \times -3 = -12$$
$$-4 \times 3 = -12$$
$$-4 \times -3 = 12$$
$$8 \div 2 = 4$$
$$8 \div (-2) = -4$$
$$-8 \div 2 = -4$$
$$-8 \div (-4) = 2$$

FRACTIONS

A fraction relates a number of parts to the whole, and is usually written in the form

$$\frac{a}{b}$$

The number a is the *numerator* and the number b is the *denominator*. For example, the fraction

$$\frac{3}{8}$$

refers to 3 parts from a total of 8 parts. Here, 3 is the numerator and 8 is the denominator.

Equivalent Fractions

Equivalent fractions are those that express the same proportion of parts to the whole. For example, the fractions

$$\frac{1}{2}, \frac{2}{4}, \frac{40}{80}$$

are equivalent.

Simplified Fractions

A simplified fraction refers to a fraction in which the numerator and the denominator do not share any factors in common. A simplified fraction is found by dividing both numerator and denominator by the *greatest common factor* (GCF). We can find the GCF by factoring both numerator and denominator and choosing the largest factor in common.

For example, given the fraction

$$\frac{27}{45}$$

we can factor the numerator and the denominator

$$\frac{3 \times 9}{5 \times 9}$$

and determine that the GCF is 9. Dividing the numerator and the denominator each by 9 yields the simplified fraction

$$\frac{3}{5}$$

Proper and Improper Fractions

A *proper fraction* is one in which the numerator is less than the denominator. The fractions

$$\frac{2}{3}, \frac{14}{17}, \frac{75}{100}$$

are all examples of proper fractions. An *improper fraction* is one in which the numerator is larger than the denominator. Improper fractions can be converted into a *mixed number*, or a whole number and a proper fraction, by dividing the denominator into the numerator. For example:

$$\frac{10}{7} = 10 \div 7 = 1\frac{3}{7}$$

Adding and Subtracting Fractions with Like Denominators

To add or subtract fractions with equal denominators:

1. Add or subtract the numerators and leave the denominator the same

2. Simplify the resulting fraction if necessary

$$\frac{3}{8} + \frac{4}{8} - \frac{1}{8} = \frac{6}{8} = \frac{3}{4}$$

Adding and Subtracting Fractions with Unequal Denominators

Many times, the denominators of the fractions we wish to add or subtract are not equal. In this case:

1. Find the *least common denominator* (LCD) using prime factorization

2. Find the equivalent fractions using the LCD

3. Perform the addition or subtraction

4. Simplify the resulting fraction if necessary

Prime Factorization. A *prime number* is an integer greater than one that is a multiple of only itself and the number 1. For example, the number 7 is a prime number since it can only be divided evenly by the numbers 1 and 7, which are called the *factors* of 7. Conversely, 8 is not a prime number since its factors are 1, 2, 4, and 8. A list of the first few prime numbers follows: 1, 2, 3, 5, 7, 11, 13, 17, 19, 23, 29.

A *prime factorization* expresses a number in terms of prime number factors. For example, the prime factorization of the number 12 is (2 × 2 × 3). To find the prime factorization of a given number, we can draw a number tree in which we successively break down the factors until we find the prime components. For example, the prime factorization of the number 100 is (2 × 2 × 5 × 5) and can be found using the tree in Figure 1.1.

Least Common Denominator. To find the LCD, express each denominator in terms of its prime factors. For example, if asked to solve

$$\frac{1}{6} + \frac{12}{18} - \frac{1}{4} = ?$$

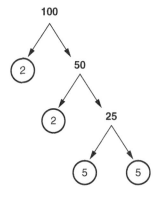

Figure 1.1   Example prime factorization tree.

we begin with expressing the denominators in terms of their prime factors:

$$6 = (2 \times 3)$$

$$18 = (2 \times 3 \times 3)$$

$$4 = (2 \times 2)$$

Record the maximum number of times each factor is used in any one expression. This will indicate how many times each factor must be multiplied to find the LCD. The factor 2 appears at most two times in the expressions, and the factor 3 appears at most two times. Therefore the LCD is calculated as:

$$LCD = (2 \times 2) \times (3 \times 3) = 36$$

Next, find the equivalent fractions using the LCD. The numerators can be found by cross multiplying:

$$\frac{\text{Old numerator}}{\text{Old denominator}} = \frac{\text{New numerator}}{\text{LCD}}$$

$$\frac{\text{Old numerator} \times \text{LCD}}{\text{Old denominator}} = \text{New numerator}$$

$$\frac{1 \times 36}{6} = 6$$

$$\frac{12 \times 36}{18} = 24$$

$$\frac{1 \times 36}{4} = 9$$

Now add the equivalent fractions, and simplify the result if needed:

$$\left(\frac{1}{6} + \frac{12}{18} - \frac{1}{4} \right) = \frac{6 + 24 - 9}{36} = \frac{21}{36} = \frac{7}{12}$$

Adding or Subtracting Mixed Numbers

To add or subtract mixed numbers, we can convert the mixed numbers back into improper fractions and then proceed, or we can first add and subtract the whole number parts and then add and subtract the fractions. For example:

$$\left(1\frac{1}{2} + 2\frac{3}{4} \right) = \left(\frac{3}{2} + \frac{11}{4} \right) = \left(\frac{6 + 11}{4} \right) = \frac{17}{4} = 4\frac{1}{4}$$

$$\left(1\frac{1}{2} + 2\frac{3}{4} \right) = 3 + \left(\frac{1}{2} + \frac{3}{4} \right) = 3 + \left(\frac{2 + 3}{4} \right) = \left(3 + \frac{5}{4} \right) = 4\frac{1}{4}$$

Multiplying and Dividing Fractions

To multiply fractions:

1. Multiply the numerators to obtain the numerator of the result

2. Multiply the denominators to obtain the resulting denominator

3. Simplify the resulting fraction if necessary

For example:

$$\frac{3}{8} \times \frac{4}{5} \times \frac{1}{2} = \frac{12}{80} = \frac{3}{20}$$

To divide fractions, we convert the problem into a multiplication problem:

1. Switch the numerator and the denominator of the second fraction

2. Multiply the numerators to obtain the numerator of the result

3. Multiply the denominators to obtain the resulting denominator

4. Simplify the resulting fraction if necessary

For example:

$$\frac{2}{9} \div \frac{4}{6} = \frac{2}{9} \times \frac{6}{4} = \frac{12}{36} = \frac{1}{3}$$

DECIMALS

Given a number of the form:

ABCDEFG.HIJKLM

we can define the place values for each letter-position as shown in Table 1.2.

Decimal and Fraction Equivalents

Decimal and fraction equivalents are shown in Table 1.3.

Converting Fractions to Decimals

Fractions can be converted to decimals by dividing the denominator into the numerator. For example:

$$\frac{3}{8} = 3 \div 8 = 0.375$$

We read this decimal as *375 thousandths.*

Rational and Irrational Numbers

A *rational number* can be represented in fractional form. It has either a finite number of decimal places or an infinite (never-ending) number of repeating decimal places. For example, the numbers 0.37, 0.6894, 1.33562, $4.\overline{3}$, $8.\overline{519}$ are all examples of rational numbers.

Table 1.2   Place values for ABCDEFG.HIJKLM.

Position	Value
A	Million
B	Hundred thousand
C	Ten thousand
D	Thousand
E	Hundred
F	Ten
G	One
H	Tenth
I	Hundreth
J	Thousandth
K	Ten-thousandth
L	Hundred-thousandth
M	Millionth

Table 1.3   Decimal and fraction equivalents.

Number	Decimal	Fraction
One tenth	0.1	$\dfrac{1}{10}$
One hundredth	0.01	$\dfrac{1}{100}$
One thousandth	0.001	$\dfrac{1}{1000}$
On ten-thousandth	0.0001	$\dfrac{1}{10000}$
One hundred-thousandth	0.00001	$\dfrac{1}{100000}$

An *irrational number* is a number that has an infinite number of decimal places that do not repeat. An example of an irrational number is $\pi = 3.14159\ldots$, since its digits are nonrepeating and infinite.

Converting Decimals to Percentages

To convert a decimal into a percentage, multiply by 100, as shown:

$$0.375 \times 100 = 37.5\%$$

Adding and Subtracting Decimals

To add or subtract decimals, line up the numbers at their decimal places. For example, the numbers 3.475, 11.55, and 2.2 can be added as shown:

$$
\begin{array}{r}
3.475 \\
11.55 \\
+ 2.2 \\
\hline
17.225
\end{array}
$$

Multiplying and Dividing Decimals

To multiply or divide decimals, count the total number of decimal places in the problem. The final answer will have that number of decimal places.

$$
\begin{array}{rl}
3.75 & \text{2 decimal places} \\
\times\ 2.3 & \text{1 decimal place} \\
\hline
8.625 & \text{3 decimal places}
\end{array}
$$

SQUARES AND SQUARE ROOTS

The *square* of a number is simply that number multiplied by itself. The square of a number can also be written as that number to the second power. For example, the square of 7 is calculated as

$$7 \times 7 = 7^2 = 49$$

A square root is denoted as follows:

$$\sqrt{25} = 25^{\frac{1}{2}} = 5, \text{ since } 25 = (5 \times 5) = 5^2$$

Every positive number has a square root. For example, using a calculator, we can determine that

$$\sqrt{54.3} = 7.369$$

Imaginary Numbers

The square root of a negative number does not exist on the real number line. Rather, the *imaginary number i* is defined as the square root of negative one. The result is written in terms of *i*. For example,

$$\sqrt{-25} = \sqrt{-1 \times 25} = \sqrt{-1} \times \sqrt{25} = 5i$$

Exponents

A whole number exponent indicates how many times a number is multiplied by itself. For example:

$$7 \times 7 = 7^2$$

$$7 \times 7 \times 7 = 7^3$$

ORDER OF OPERATIONS

The order of operations can be remembered by using the mnemonic device of *PEMDAS*, or *Please Excuse My Dear Aunt Sally*, which stands for *parentheses, exponents, multiplication, division, addition,* and *subtraction*. As an illustration, the expression

$$6 \times 4 + (9 - 1) \div 2 - 5^2$$

is correctly evaluated as follows:

$$
\begin{aligned}
6 \times 4 + (9 - 1) \div 2 - 5^2 &= 6 \times 4 + \mathbf{8} \div 2 - 5^2 \quad &\text{P} \\
&= 6 \times 4 + 8 \div 2 - \mathbf{25} \quad &\text{E} \\
&= \mathbf{24} + 8 \div 2 - 25 \quad &\text{M} \\
&= 24 + \mathbf{4} - 25 \quad &\text{D} \\
&= \mathbf{28} - 25 \quad &\text{A} \\
&= \mathbf{3} \quad &\text{S}
\end{aligned}
$$

FACTORIALS

A *factorial* is a mathematical operation denoted by an exclamation point (!), and is evaluated in the following manner:

$$5! = 5 \times 4 \times 3 \times 2 \times 1$$

By definition, 0! = 1.

Factorials are used when calculating probabilities from the binomial, hypergeometric, and Poisson distributions, among others.

TRUNCATING, ROUNDING, AND SIGNIFICANT DIGITS

To display a result with a certain number of decimal places, we can choose to *truncate* the number. For example, we can truncate the number 3.527 to two decimal places by writing 3.52.

We can *round* a result to a certain number of digits by looking at the value of the digit to the right of the decimal place of interest. For example, if we want to round the number 3.527 to the hundredths place, we will look at the third decimal place (in this case 7) as our decision point. The rule for rounding is this: If the decision number is less than 5, do not round up. If it is 5 or greater, round up. Therefore, 3.527 would be rounded up to 3.53. However, if we rounded to the tenths place, 3.527 would be displayed as 3.5, since 2 would be our decision number.

When dealing with the precision of a measurement, we must consider *significant digits*. For example, instrument measurements have a certain inherent precision, which can be expressed in terms of a certain number of significant digits. We must take care to express instrument measurements using the proper number of significant digits.

Adding and Subtracting Measurements

When adding or subtracting measurements, the final answer will only be as precise as the *least* precise reading. Therefore, the number of decimal places of the answer should match that of the least precise reading. In the following example, the reading of 5.2 is the least precise, and the final answer is rounded to the tenths place:

$$
\begin{array}{r}
4.573 \\
3.77 \\
5.2 \\
+\ 6.1299 \\
\hline
19.6729 \cong 19.7
\end{array}
$$

Multiplying and Dividing Using Significant Digits

When multiplying measurements, display the final result with the same number of significant digits as the *least* accurate reading. For example, the following result will be rounded to three significant digits since the value 3.21 has three significant digits and 20.45 has four:

$$
\begin{array}{r}
20.45 \\
\times\ 3.21 \\
\hline
65.6445 \cong 65.6
\end{array}
$$

BIBLIOGRAPHY

Achatz, T. 2006. *Technical Shop Mathematics*. 3rd ed. New York: Industrial Press.
Griffith, G. 1986. *Quality Technician's Handbook*. Englewood Cliffs, NJ: Prentice Hall.
Horton, H. L. 1999. *Mathematics at Work*. 4th ed. New York: Industrial Press.

Chapter 2

B. Basic Algebra

SOLVING ALGEBRAIC EQUATIONS

When we solve an algebraic equation, we are finding the value of the unknown variable, which is denoted by a letter. To illustrate, the following equations are all examples of algebraic expressions:

$$x + 3 = 5$$

$$6a - 2 = 24$$

$$4s + 4 = 6s - 9$$

$$\frac{7}{8}y + 30 \geq 51$$

In each, the goal is to solve for the value or values of the variable that make the expression true. We accomplish this by collecting terms and then *isolating* the unknown variable on one side of the equation by performing inverse operations.

Properties of Real Numbers

In addition to the commutative, associative, and distributive properties of real numbers (see Table 1.1), fundamental properties for real numbers also exist, as shown in Table 2.1. Let a, b, and c be real numbers.

Inverse Operations

To isolate the variable on one side of the equation, we perform a series of inverse operations on both sides of the equation. A list of inverse operations is shown in Table 2.2.

13

Table 2.1   Additional properties of real numbers.

Property	Example
Reflexive property	$a = a$
Symmetric property	If $a = b$, then $b = a$
Transitive property	If $a = b$ and $b = c$, then $a = c$
Additive identity	$a + 0 = a$
Multiplicative identity	$a \times 1 = a$

Table 2.2   Inverse operations.

Operation	Inverse operation	Example
Addition	Subtraction	$a + (-a) = 0$
Subtraction	Addition	$-a + a = 0$
Multiplication	Division	$a \times \dfrac{1}{a} = 1$
Division	Multiplication (×)	$\dfrac{1}{a} \times a = 1$
Exponent r	rth root	$\sqrt[r]{a^r} = a$, for $a \geq 0$
rth root	Exponent r	$\left(\sqrt[r]{a}\right)^r = a$, for $a \geq 0$
Power of 10	Log base 10	$\log_{10}\left(10^a\right) = a$
Log base 10	Power of 10	$10^{\log_{10}(a)} = a$

Solving Equations Using One Inverse Operation

In order to isolate x, we perform the appropriate inverse operation on *both* sides of the equation. In the following example, note that the inverse of adding 3 is subtracting 3:

$$x + 3 = 5$$

$$x + 3 - 3 = 5 - 3$$

$$x = 2$$

Always perform a *check of your work* by putting the value of the variable into the original equation.

$$x + 3 = 5$$

$$2 + 3 = 5$$

Solving Equations Using Two or More Inverse Operations

To solve a problem such as $ax + b = c$, we must do a series of inverse operations on both sides of the equation in order to isolate the variable a. In the following example, addition and division inverse operations are employed in succession to find the solution:

$$6a - 2 = 22$$

$$6a - 2 + 2 = 22 + 2$$

$$6a = 24$$

$$6a \div 6 = 24 \div 6$$

$$a = 4$$

Next, check the solution:

$$6a - 2 = 22$$

$$6 \times 4 - 2 = 22$$

$$24 - 2 = 22$$

$$22 = 22$$

Solving Equations by Collecting Terms

To solve a problem where the variable and/or constants appear in more than two terms, we must first collect terms and then perform the inverse operations. For example, to solve the equation $8z + 5 + 4z + -1 = 16$, we must collect the variable and the constant terms before proceeding with the solution:

$$8z + 5 + 4z - 1 = 16$$

$$12z + 4 = 16$$

$$12z + 4 - 4 = 16 - 4$$

$$12z = 12$$

$$12z \div 12 = 12 \div 12$$

$$z = 1$$

Check the solution:

$$8z + 5 + 4z - 1 = 16$$

$$(8 \times 1) + 5 + (4 \times 1) - 1 = 16$$

$$8 + 5 + 4 - 1 = 16$$

$$16 = 16$$

To solve a problem such as $4s + 4 = 6s - 9$, we must collect terms that appear on both sides of the equation:

$$4s + 4 = 6s - 9$$

$$4s + 4 - 4s = 6s - 4s - 9$$

$$4 = 2s - 9$$

$$4 + 9 = 2s - 9 + 9$$

$$13 = 2s$$

$$13 \div 2 = 2s \div 2$$

$$\frac{13}{2} = s$$

$$6\frac{1}{2} = s$$

Check the solution:

$$4s + 4 = 6s - 9$$

$$4 \times 6\frac{1}{2} + 4 = 6 \times 6\frac{1}{2} - 9$$

$$(24 + 2) + 4 = (36 + 3) - 9$$

$$30 = 30$$

Solving Equations with Parentheses

To solve equations with parentheses, follow the order of operations rule PEMDAS, in which parentheses, exponents, multiplication, division, addition, and subtraction operations are performed left to right, in that order. Using the rule, operations included in parentheses are evaluated first. For example:

$$2(10x - 2x) + 50 = 14$$

$$2 \times 8x + 50 = 14$$

$$16x + 50 - 50 = 14 - 50$$

$$16x = -36$$

$$16x \div 16 = -36 \div 16$$

$$x = -2\frac{1}{4}$$

Converting

$$-2\frac{1}{4} \text{ to } -\frac{9}{4}$$

we can check the solution:

$$2\left(10\times\left(-\frac{9}{4}\right)-2\left(-\frac{9}{4}\right)\right)+50=14$$

$$2\times\frac{-36}{2}+50=14$$

$$-36+50=14$$

$$14=14$$

Solving Inequalities

To solve an inequality, remember that the solution will be a *range* of values. In the following example, the equation is true for any value of y equal to or greater than 24.

$$\frac{7}{8}y+30\geq51$$

$$\frac{7}{8}y+30-30\geq51-30$$

$$\frac{7}{8}y\geq21$$

$$\frac{8}{7}\times\frac{7}{8}y\geq21\times\frac{8}{7}$$

$$y\geq21\times\frac{8}{7}$$

$$y\geq24$$

To check your work, you must first check to see if the equality holds true. Then choose a number that is in the range of solutions to make sure the inequality is also correct, as shown in the following example. Check for the equality condition:

$$\frac{7}{8}y+30\geq51$$

$$\frac{7}{8}\times24+30=51$$

$$21+30=51$$

$$51=51$$

To check for the inequality condition, use a number in the solution range. Recall that the solution to the example was $y\geq24$. Here, we arbitrarily choose 40 to perform the check:

$$\frac{7}{8}y + 30 \geq 51$$

$$\frac{7}{8} \times 40 + 30 \geq 51$$

$$35 + 30 \geq 51$$

$$65 \geq 51$$

Solving Inequalities with Negatively Signed Values

When solving an inequality, be careful when multiplying or dividing both sides by a negative number—the inequality sign reverses! Checking your work after solving an inequality is very important to make sure that the sign of your answer is correct. For example:

$$-7x + 4 \leq 25$$

$$-7x + 4 - 4 \leq 25 - 4$$

$$-7x \leq 21$$

$$-7x \div -7 \geq 21 \div -7$$

$$x \geq -3$$

Check for the equality condition:

$$-7x + 4 \leq 25$$

$$(-7x - 3) + 4 = 25$$

$$21 + 4 = 25$$

$$25 = 25$$

Check for the inequality condition. Here, the number 2 is chosen for the check:

$$-7x + 4 \leq 25$$

$$(-7 \times 2) + 4 \leq 25$$

$$-14 + 4 \leq 25$$

$$-10 \leq 25$$

BIBLIOGRAPHY

Achatz, T. 2006. *Technical Shop Mathematics*. 3rd ed. New York: Industrial Press.

Barnett, R., and P. Schmidt. 2004. *Schaum's Outline of Elementary Algebra*. 3rd ed. New York: McGraw-Hill.

Moyer, R., and M. R. Spiegel. 2005. *Schaum's Outline of College Algebra*. 3rd ed. New York: McGraw-Hill.

Chapter 3

C. Basic Geometry

AREAS OF BASIC GEOMETRIC SHAPES

The area of a shape is expressed in terms of squared units, such as cm^2 or ft^2. The calculations for finding the area of basic geometric shapes are shown in Table 3.1.

Examples of Area Calculations

A rectangle has a length of 6 cm and a width of 4 cm. Its area is 6 cm × 4 cm = 24 cm^2.

A square has sides 10 inches in length. Its area is 10 in. × 10 in. = 100 $in.^2$.

A parallelogram has a height equal to 32 mm and a base of 40 mm. Its area is 32 mm × 40 mm = 1280 mm^2.

A trapezoid has a length of 12 inches at the top and 24 inches at the base. Its height is 15 inches. Its area is (12 in. + 24 in.) × 15 in./2 = 270 $in.^2$.

A regular hexagon (meaning one with all sides the same length) has sides 8.0 cm in length. Its area is 2.597 × $(8 \text{ cm})^2$ = 2.597 × 64 cm^2 = 166.208 cm^2.

A regular hexagon has a radius of 3.5 inches. Its area is 3.464 × $(3.5 \text{ in.})^2$ = 3.464 × 12.25 $in.^2$ = 42.434 $in.^2$.

A right triangle (meaning that the triangle has a 90° angle) has a base of 65 mm and a height of 120 mm. Its area is (1/2) × 65 mm × 120 mm = 3900 mm^2.

A triangle has a base of 34 cm and a height of 20 cm. Its area is (1/2) × 34 cm × 20 cm = 340 cm^2.

Table 3.1   Calculation of area for basic geometric shapes.

Shape	Example	Formula(e)
Rectangle		$A = l \times w$
Square		$A = s^2$
Parallelogram		$A = b \times h$ where b is base and h is height
Trapezoid		$A = \dfrac{(a+b)h}{2}$
Regular hexagon		$A = 2.597s^2$ $A = 3.464r^2$
Right triangle		$A = \dfrac{1}{2}b \times h$
Triangle		$A = \dfrac{1}{2}b \times h$

Continued

Table 3.1 *Continued.*

Shape	Example	Formula
Circle		$A = \pi r^2$ where r is radius and $\pi = pi = 3.14159...$
Circular ring		$A = \pi\left(r_2^2 - r_1^2\right)$

A circle has a radius of 25 inches. Its area is $\pi \times (25 \text{ in.})^2 = 1963.495 \text{ in.}^2$. Note: When possible, use a calculator to find areas that use the number π (pi) in order to avoid round-off errors.

A circular ring has an outer radius of 10.5 cm and an inner radius of 3.5 cm. Its area is $\pi \times [(10.5 \text{ cm})^2 - (3.5 \text{ cm})^2] = \pi \times (110.25 \text{ cm}^2 - 12.25 \text{ cm}^2) = 307.8761 \text{ cm}^2$.

PERIMETER AND CIRCUMFERENCE OF BASIC GEOMETRIC SHAPES

Perimeter and circumference are expressed in terms of linear units, such as cm or ft. The term "perimeter" is used for the linear distance around a shape that has angles; the term "circumference" is reserved for the linear distance around a circle. Formulas for perimeter and circumference are shown in Table 3.2.

Examples of Perimeter and Circumference Calculations

A rectangle has a length of 6 cm and a width of 4 cm. Its perimeter is $(2 \times 6 \text{ cm}) + (2 \times 4 \text{ cm}) = 20 \text{ cm}$.

A square has sides 10 inches in length. Its perimeter is $4 \times 10 \text{ in.} = 40 \text{ in.}$

A parallelogram has two sides equal to 26 mm and a top and base each equal to 40 mm. Its perimeter is $(2 \times 26 \text{ mm}) + (2 \times 40 \text{ mm}) = 132 \text{ mm}$.

A trapezoid has sides with lengths of 12 cm, 15 cm, 24 cm, and 27 cm. Its perimeter is $(12 \text{ cm} + 15 \text{ cm} + 24 \text{ cm} + 27 \text{ cm}) = 78 \text{ cm}$.

A regular hexagon (meaning one with all sides the same length) has sides 8.0 cm in length. Its perimeter is $6 \times 8.0 \text{ cm} = 48.0 \text{ cm}$.

Table 3.2   Calculation of perimeter and circumference of basic geometric shapes.

Shape	Example	Formula
Rectangle		$P = 2l + 2w$
Square		$P = 4s$
Parallelogram		$P = 2a + 2b$
Trapezoid		$P = a + b + c + d$
Regular hexagon (all sides equal length)		$P = 6s$
Right triangle		$P = a + b + c$ Note: $a^2 + b^2 = c^2$ (Pythagorean theorem)
Triangle		$P = a + b + c$

Continued

Table 3.2 *Continued.*

Shape	Example	Formula
Circle		Circumference = $2\pi r = \pi D$ where r is radius and D is diameter

A right triangle (meaning that the triangle has a 90° angle) has a base of 65 mm, a height of 120 mm, and a hypotenuse of 136.47 mm. Its perimeter is (65 mm + 120 mm + 136.47 mm) = 321.47 mm.

A triangle has sides with lengths of 20 cm, 34 cm, and 40 cm. Its perimeter is (20 cm + 34 cm + 40 cm) = 94 cm.

A circle has a radius of 25 inches and, hence, a diameter of 50 inches. Its circumference is (2 × π × 25 in.) = (π × 50 in.) = 157.08 in. Note: since the formula involves pi, use a calculator when possible to find circumference in order to avoid round-off errors.

VOLUME OF BASIC GEOMETRIC SHAPES

Volume is expressed in terms of cubic units, such as cm^3 or ft^3. Formulas for calculating volume are shown in Table 3.3.

Examples of Volume Calculations

A square prism has a length, width, and height equal to 23 cm, 12 cm, and 30 cm, respectively. Its volume is (23 cm × 12 cm × 30 cm) = 8280 cm^3.

A cube has sides with lengths of 13 inches. Its volume is $(13 \text{ in.})^3$ = (13 in. × 13 in. × 13 in.) = 2197 $in.^3$.

A cylinder has a radius of 120 mm and a height of 250 mm. Its volume is π × $(120 \text{ mm})^2$ × (250 mm) = 11,309,734 mm^3. Note: Since the formula involves pi, use a calculator when possible to find the volume of a cylinder in order to avoid round-off errors.

A cone has a radius of 3.5 inches and a height of 12 inches. Its volume is (1/3) × π × $(3.5 \text{ in.})^2$ × 12 in. = 153.938 $in.^3$. Note: Since the formula involves pi, use a calculator when possible to find the volume of a cone in order to avoid round-off errors.

A sphere has a radius equal to 2.05 cm. Its volume is (4/3) × π × $(2.05 \text{ cm})^3$ = 36.087 cm^3. Note: Since the formula involves pi, use a calculator when possible to find the volume of a sphere in order to avoid round-off errors.

Table 3.3 Calculation of volume of basic geometric shapes.

Shape	Example	Formula
Square prism		$V = abc$
Cube (all sides equal length)		$V = s^3$
Cylinder		$V = \pi r^2 h$
Cone		$V = \dfrac{1}{3}\pi r^3 h$
Sphere		$V = \dfrac{4}{3}\pi r^3$

SURFACE AREA OF BASIC GEOMETRIC SHAPES

Surface area is expressed in terms of squared units, such as cm² or ft². It is the area of the outside of a shape. Calculations for surface area are shown in Table 3.4.

Examples of Surface Area Calculations

A square prism has a length, width, and height equal to 23 cm, 12 cm, and 30 cm, respectively. Its surface area is 2 × [(23 cm × 12 cm) + (12 cm × 30 cm) + (23 cm × 30 cm)] = 2 × (276 cm² + 360 cm² + 690 cm²) = 2652 cm².

Table 3.4   Calculation of surface area for basic geometric shapes.

Shape	Example	Formula
Square prism		$SA = 2(ab + bc + ac)$
Cube (all sides equal length)		$SA = 6s^2$
Cylinder		$SA = 2\pi r^2 + 2\pi rh$
Cone (includes the area of the base)		$SA = \pi r^2 + \pi r\sqrt{r^2 + h^2}$
Sphere		$SA = 4\pi r^2$

A cube has sides with lengths of 13 inches. Its surface area is $6 \times (13$ in.$)^2$ = $(6 \times 13$ in. $\times 13$ in.$) = 1014$ in.^{2}.

A cylinder has a radius of 120 mm and a height of 250 mm. Its surface area is $2 \times \pi \times (120$ mm$)^2 + (2 \times \pi \times 120$ mm $\times 250$ mm$) = 278973.4$ mm^2. Note: Since the formula involves pi, use a calculator when possible to find the surface area of a cylinder in order to avoid round-off errors.

A cone has a radius of 3.5 inches and a height of 12 inches. Its surface area is $\pi \times (3.5$ in.$)^2 + \pi \times (3.5$ in.$) \times$ sqrt $((3.5$ in.$)^2 + (12$ in.$)^2) = 175.93$ in.^{2}.

Note: Since the formula involves pi, use a calculator when possible to find the surface area of a cone in order to avoid round-off errors.

A sphere has a radius equal to 2.05 cm. Its surface area is $4 \times \pi \times (2.05 \text{ cm})^2$ = 52.81 cm^2. Note: Since the formula involves pi, use a calculator when possible to find the surface area of a sphere in order to avoid round-off errors.

COMPLEMENTARY AND SUPPLEMENTARY ANGLES

Two angles that add to 90°, or a right angle, are called *complementary angles*. For example, the angles 30° and 60° are complementary angles.

Two angles that add to 180°, which is a straight line, are called *supplementary angles*. For example, the angles 45° and 135° are supplementary angles.

BIBLIOGRAPHY

Achatz, T. 2006. *Technical Shop Mathematics*. 3rd ed. New York: Industrial Press.
Griffith, G. 1986. *Quality Technician's Handbook*. Englewood Cliffs, NJ: Prentice Hall.
Horton, H. L. 1999. *Mathematics at Work*. 4th ed. New York: Industrial Press.

Chapter 4

D. Basic Trigonometry

THE RIGHT TRIANGLE

As shown in Figure 4.1, a right triangle has sides a (the height), b (the base), and c (the hypotenuse). There is one 90°, or right, angle. Since the angles of a triangle add to 180°, the sum of the remaining two angles will equal 90°, making them *complementary* angles. Here, $\angle A$ and $\angle B$ will sum to 90°. Because each of these angles is less than 90°, they are also classified as *acute* angles. Angles that are greater than 90° are called *obtuse* angles. Note that there are no obtuse angles in a right triangle.

Pythagorean Theorem

The sides of a right triangle are related according to the *Pythagorean theorem*, which states that the sum of the squared sides of a right triangle equals the hypotenuse squared:

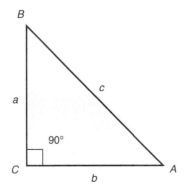

Figure 4.1   The right triangle.

27

$$a^2 + b^2 = c^2$$

The relationship can also be written as

$$\sqrt{a^2 + b^2} = c$$

Using the theorem, the length of a third side can be found if two sides are known. For example, if side $a = 3$ cm and $b = 4$ cm, the length of hypotenuse c can be found:

$$\sqrt{3^2 + 4^2} = c$$

$$\sqrt{25} = c$$

$$5 = c$$

TRIGONOMETRIC FUNCTIONS

There are six main trigonometric functions, which are ratios of the sides of a right triangle: sine (sin), cosine (cos), tangent (tan), cotangent (cot), secant (sec), cosecant (csc). These functions and their calculations are illustrated in Table 4.1.

Values of Trigonometric Functions for Some Common Angles

Note that angles can be expressed in terms of degrees or radians. For example, a circle has a total of 360 degrees, a straight line has 180 degrees, and a right angle is 90 degrees. The same circle has 2π radians, a straight line has π radians, and a right angle is $1/2\ \pi$ radians. To convert an angle A expressed in degrees to radians, multiply by the factor

$$\frac{\pi}{180}$$

To convert an angle in radians to degrees, multiply radians by the factor

$$\frac{180}{\pi}$$

Values of the trigonometric functions for common angles are shown in Table 4.2.

Trigonometric Identities

Some useful trigonometric identities include the following:

$$\sin^2(A) + \cos^2(A) = 1$$

$$1 + \tan^2(A) = \sec^2(A)$$

$$1 + \cot^2(A) = \csc^2(A)$$

To find the cosine of an angle A when the sine of the angle is known, we can use the first identity as follows:

Table 4.1   Calculation of trigonometric functions.

Function	Example	Formula
Sine		$\sin(A) = \dfrac{\text{Opposite side}}{\text{Hypotenuse}} = \dfrac{a}{c}$
Cosine		$\cos(A) = \dfrac{\text{Adjacent side}}{\text{Hypotenuse}} = \dfrac{b}{c}$
Tangent		$\tan(A) = \dfrac{\text{Opposite side}}{\text{Adjacent side}} = \dfrac{a}{b}$ $= \dfrac{\sin(A)}{\cos(A)}$
Cotangent		$\cot(A) = \dfrac{\text{Adjacent side}}{\text{Opposite side}} = \dfrac{b}{a}$ $= \dfrac{1}{\tan(A)} = \dfrac{\cos(A)}{\sin(A)}$
Secant		$\sec(A) = \dfrac{\text{Hypotenuse}}{\text{Adjacent side}} = \dfrac{c}{b}$ $= \dfrac{1}{\cos(A)}$
Cosecant		$\csc(A) = \dfrac{\text{Hypotenuse}}{\text{Opposite side}} = \dfrac{c}{a}$ $= \dfrac{1}{\sin(A)}$

Table 4.2   Values of trigonometric functions for common angles.

Angle in degrees	Angle in radians	Sine	Cosine	Tangent	Cotangent	Secant	Cosecant
0	0	0	1.000	0	Undefined	1.000	Undefined
30	$1/6\,\pi$	0.5000	0.8660	0.5774	1.7321	1.1547	2.000
45	$1/4\,\pi$	0.7071	0.7071	1.000	1.000	1.4142	1.4142
60	$1/3\,\pi$	0.8660	0.5000	1.7321	0.5774	2.000	1.1547
90	$1/2\,\pi$	1.000	0	Undefined	0	Undefined	1.000

$$\sin^2(A) + \cos^2(A) = 1$$

$$\cos^2(A) = 1 - \sin^2(A)$$

$$\sqrt{\cos^2(A)} = \sqrt{1 - \sin^2(A)}$$

$$\cos(A) = \sqrt{1 - \sin^2(A)}$$

For example, for the angle $A = 30°$, and $\sin(30)$ known to be 0.5:

$$\sin^2(A) + \cos^2(A) = 1$$

$$\cos^2(A) = 1 - 0.5^2$$

$$\sqrt{\cos^2(A)} = \sqrt{1 - 0.5^2}$$

$$\cos(A) = 0.866$$

SOLVING FOR UNKNOWN SIDES AND ANGLES OF A RIGHT TRIANGLE

Using the six basic trigonometric functions and the Pythagorean theorem, we can find the length of the unknown sides of a triangle, given the values of one side and one angle. For example, given angle A is 36° and side a has a length of 6, angle B can be found, as well as the lengths of sides b and c as shown in Figure 4.2.

Finding the Unknown Angle

Since the angles of a triangle sum to 180°, we can find the unknown angle via subtraction. For example, given the triangle in Figure 4.2, we can find the unknown angle B.

$$\angle A + \angle B + \angle C = 180°$$

$$49° + \angle B + 90° = 180°$$

$$139° + \angle B = 180°$$

$$\angle B + 139° - 139° = 180° - 139°$$

$$\angle B = 41°$$

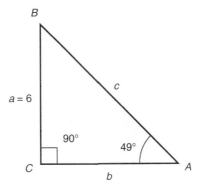

Figure 4.2   Finding angles in a right triangle.

Alternatively, we can also use the fact that the two acute angles of a right triangle are complementary, meaning that they sum to 90°:

$$\angle A + \angle B = 90°$$

$$49° + \angle B = 90°$$

$$\angle B + 49° - 49° = 90° - 49°$$

$$\angle B = 41°$$

After finding all the angles, we can find the lengths of the unknown sides b and c.

Finding the Unknown Sides

We can find the lengths of the unknown sides using the trigonometric functions and a calculator:

$$\sin(A) = \sin(49°) = 0.7547$$

$$\frac{\text{Opposite side}}{\text{Hypotenuse}} = 0.7547$$

$$\frac{6}{c} = 0.7547$$

$$\frac{6}{c} \times c = 0.7547 \times c$$

$$6 = 0.7547c$$

$$6 \div 0.7547 = 0.7547c \div 0.7547$$

$$7.950 = c$$

Now that we know the length of c, we can find the length of side b using the Pythagorean theorem:

$$a^2 + b^2 = c^2$$

$$6^2 + b^2 = (7.950)^2$$

$$6^2 + b^2 - 6^2 = (7.950)^2 - 6^2$$

$$b^2 = 27.2025$$

$$\sqrt{b^2} = \sqrt{27.2025}$$

$$b = 5.216$$

Alternatively, we can use a trigonometric function to find the length of side b:

$$\cot(A) = \cot(49°) = 0.8693$$

$$\frac{\text{Adjacent side}}{\text{Opposite side}} = 0.8693$$

$$\frac{b}{a} = 0.8693$$

$$\frac{b}{6} \times 6 = 0.8693 \times 6$$

$$b = 5.216$$

INVERSE TRIGONOMETRIC FUNCTIONS

In some cases, we know the value of a trigonometric function for a particular angle but do not know the degree measure of the angle. We can use an *inverse trigonometric function* to solve for the angle. These inverse functions are of the form:

$$\sin^{-1}(x), \cos^{-1}(x), \tan^{-1}(x), \sec^{-1}(x), \csc^{-1}(x)$$

where x is the value of the trigonometric function. Each inverse function returns the angle measure associated with the value x. For example, given that $\sin(A) = 0.4580$, we can find the angle A in degrees using a scientific calculator:

$$\angle A = \sin^{-1}(0.4580) = 27.26°$$

OBLIQUE TRIANGLES

An *oblique triangle* has no 90° angles. Some special types of oblique triangles include the *equilateral triangle, isosceles triangle*, and the *scalene triangle*, shown in Table 4.3.

SOLVING OBLIQUE TRIANGLES

Each triangle has three sides and three angles. To solve for an unknown side or angle in an oblique triangle, three pieces of information must be known. We will use the *laws of sines and cosines* to solve these problems.

Table 4.3   Oblique triangles.

Triangle type	Example
Equilaterial triangle Three equal sides, three 60° angles	
Isosceles triangle Two equal sides, two equal angles	
Scalene triangle All sides, all angles unique	

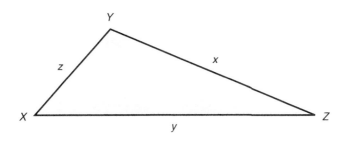

Figure 4.3   Oblique triangle.

Law of Sines

Given an oblique triangle such as the one in Figure 4.3, the law of sines states

$$\frac{\sin(X)}{x} = \frac{\sin(Y)}{y} = \frac{\sin(Z)}{z}$$

This law can also be written in terms of its reciprocal:

$$\frac{x}{\sin(X)} = \frac{y}{\sin(Y)} = \frac{z}{\sin(Z)}$$

Law of Cosines

Given an oblique triangle as in Figure 4.3, the law of cosines states

$$x^2 = y^2 + z^2 - 2yz\cos(X)$$
$$y^2 = x^2 + z^2 - 2xz\cos(Y)$$
$$z^2 = x^2 + y^2 - 2xy\cos(Z)$$

Three Sides Known

Given three sides, we can find the values of the three angles using the law of cosines. For example, given the triangle in Figure 4.4 we can find the values of the three angles:

$$x^2 = y^2 + z^2 - 2yz\cos(X)$$
$$8^2 = 10^2 + 5^2 - 2(10)(5)\cos(X)$$
$$64 = 125 - 100\cos(X)$$
$$64 - 125 = 125 - 100\cos(X) - 125$$
$$-61 = -100\cos(X)$$
$$-61 \div -100 = -100\cos(X) \div -100$$
$$0.61 = \cos(X)$$

$$\cos^{-1}(0.61) = \angle X$$

$$\angle X = 52.41°$$

Angle Y can also be found using the law of cosines, and angle Z can be found using the fact that the angles of a triangle sum to 180°. Note that the law of sines should not be used to find angle Y since it is not known whether it is obtuse or acute.

$$y^2 = x^2 + z^2 - 2xz\cos(Y)$$
$$10^2 = 8^2 + 5^2 - 2(8)(5)\cos(Y)$$
$$100 = 89 - 80\cos(Y)$$
$$100 - 89 = 89 - 80\cos(Y) - 89$$
$$11 = -80\cos(Y)$$
$$11 \div -80 = -80\cos(Y) \div -80$$
$$-0.1375 = \cos(Y)$$

$$\cos^{-1}(-0.1375) = \angle Y$$

$$\angle Y = 97.90°$$

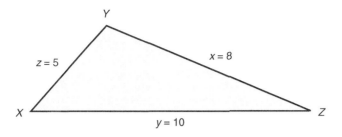

Figure 4.4   Three sides known.

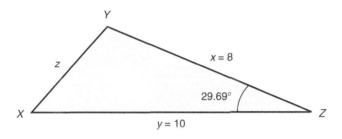

Figure 4.5   Two sides and angle between known.

Angle Z can now be found via subtraction:

$$\angle Z = 180° - \angle X + \angle Y$$

$$\angle Z = 180° - 52.41° + 97.90°$$

$$\angle Z = 29.69°$$

Two Sides and an Angle between Them Known

Given two sides and the angle between them, we can find the value of the remaining side and the other two angles. For example, given the triangle shown in Figure 4.5, we see that sides x and y are 8 and 10 units, respectively, and angle Z is 29.69 degrees. We can find the length of side z using the law of cosines:

$$z^2 = x^2 + y^2 - 2xy\cos(Z)$$

$$z^2 = 8^2 + 10^2 - 2(8)(10)\cos(29.69)$$

$$z^2 = 164 - 160\cos(29.69)$$

$$z^2 = 164 - 160(0.8687)$$

$$z^2 = 25$$

$$\sqrt{z^2} = \sqrt{25}$$

$$z = 5$$

We can then apply the law of cosines to find angle X:

$$x^2 = y^2 + z^2 - 2yz\cos(X)$$

$$8^2 = 10^2 + 5^2 - 2(10)(5)\cos(X)$$

$$64 = 125 - 100\cos(X)$$

$$64 - 125 = 125 - 100\cos(X) - 125$$

$$-61 = -100\cos(X)$$

$$-61 \div -100 = -100\cos(X) \div -100$$

$$0.61 = \cos(X)$$

$$\cos^{-1}(0.61) = \angle X$$

$$\angle X = 52.41$$

Angle Y can be found through subtraction:

$$\angle Y = 180° - \angle X - \angle Z$$

$$\angle Y = 180° - 29.69° - 52.41°$$

$$\angle Y = 97.90°$$

Given two sides and the angle opposite one of the known sides, we can find the value of the remaining side and the other two angles.

Note that the case in which two sides and an opposite angle are known does not result in a unique solution. Refer to the two triangles in Figure 4.6. Here, sides a and b as

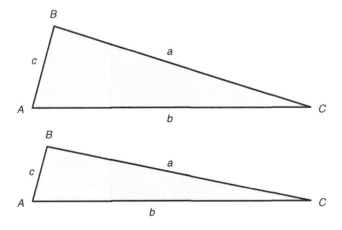

Figure 4.6   Two sides and opposite angle known.

well as the opposite angle A are identical for both triangles. However, the length of the third side c is not the same, demonstrating that the solution given two sides and an opposite angle is not unique.

One Side and Two Angles Known

Given one side and two angles, we can find the other two sides and the third angle. Here, side x is known, and angles Y and Z are known. An example is shown in Figure 4.7.

Angle X can be calculated via subtraction

$$\angle X = 180° - \angle Y - \angle Z$$

$$\angle X = 180° - 97.90° - 29.69°$$

$$\angle X = 52.41°$$

With all angles now known, the lengths of the sides y and z can be found using the law of sines:

$$\frac{x}{\sin(X)} = \frac{y}{\sin(Y)} = \frac{z}{\sin(Z)}$$

$$\frac{8}{\sin(52.41)} = \frac{y}{\sin(97.90)}$$

$$\frac{8}{0.7924} = \frac{y}{0.9905}$$

$$10.10 = \frac{y}{0.9905}$$

$$10.10 \times 0.9905 = \frac{y}{0.9905} \times 0.9905$$

$$10 = y$$

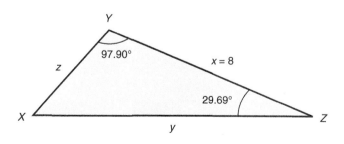

Figure 4.7   One side and two angles known.

$$\frac{8}{\sin(52.41)} = \frac{z}{\sin(29.69)}$$

$$\frac{8}{0.7924} = \frac{z}{0.4953}$$

$$10.10 = \frac{z}{0.4953}$$

$$10.10 \times 0.4953 = \frac{z}{0.4953} \times 0.4953$$

$$5 = z$$

BIBLIOGRAPHY

Achatz, T. 2006. *Technical Shop Mathematics*. 3rd ed. New York: Industrial Press.
Griffith, G. 1986. *Quality Technician's Handbook*. Englewood Cliffs, NJ: Prentice Hall.
Horton, H. L. 1999. *Mathematics at Work*. 4th ed. New York: Industrial Press.

Chapter 5

E. Measurement Systems

> **Measurement Systems**
>
> Convert units within and between English and metric measurement systems (SI) such as inch to micro-inch, liter to quart, meter to millimeter, etc. (Apply)
>
> Body of Knowledge I.E

MEASUREMENT SYSTEMS

There are three measurement systems that are commonly used in industry: the International System of Units (SI), the metric system, and the English system. The units of SI are internationally accepted standards and are generally the same as the units used in the metric system, with a few exceptions. Conversion of units within each of the SI and metric systems is relatively straightforward since the systems are based on units that vary by factors of 10. For example:

$$1 \text{ liter} = 10 \text{ deciliters} = 100 \text{ centiliters} = 1000 \text{ milliliters}$$

In contrast, the English measurement system, still used by many companies in the United States, has many conversion factors. As a result, changing units within the English system can be quite cumbersome. For example:

$$1 \text{ quart} = 2 \text{ pints} = 4 \text{ cups} = 32 \text{ fluid ounces}$$

Quality inspectors should feel comfortable converting units within systems as well as between the English, SI, and metric systems. What follows is a listing of common measures and conversion factors for the three systems. A more comprehensive listing of measurement conversion factors can be found in Appendix C.

ENGLISH SYSTEM MEASUREMENTS

To convert units within the English system, use the relationships found in Tables 5.1–5.6.

Table 5.1   Converting measures of length.

From	To	Multiply by	Divide by
Inch	Micro-inch	1,000,000	
Micro-inch	Inch		1,000,000
Feet	Inches	12	
Inches	Feet		12
Yards	Feet	3	
Feet	Yards		3
Miles	Feet	5280	
Feet	Miles		5280
Miles	Yards	1760	
Yards	Miles		1760

To convert length units within the English system, use the relationships given in Table 5.1. For example, to convert miles into feet, multiply the number of miles by a factor of 5280. Thus, to convert 2 miles into feet,

$$2 \text{ miles} = 2 \times 5280 = 10{,}560 \text{ feet}$$

Similarly, to convert feet into miles, use the reverse operation; that is, divide the feet by a factor of 5280. Thus,

$$10{,}560 \text{ feet} = 10{,}560 \div 5280 = 2 \text{ miles}$$

To convert area units within the English system, use the relationships given in Table 5.2. For example, to convert square feet into square inches, multiply the number of square feet by a factor of 144. Thus, to convert 2 square feet into square inches,

$$2 \text{ square feet} = 288 \times 144 = 2 \text{ square feet}$$

Similarly, to convert square inches into square feet, use the reverse operation; that is, divide the square inches by a factor of 144. Thus,

$$288 \text{ square inches} = 288 \div 144 = 2 \text{ square feet}$$

To convert volume units within the English system, use the relationships given in Table 5.3. For example, to convert cubic yards into cubic feet, multiply the number of cubic yards by a factor of 27. Thus, to convert 2 cubic yards into cubic feet,

$$2 \text{ cubic yards} = 2 \times 27 = 54 \text{ cubic feet}$$

Similarly, to convert cubic feet into cubic yards, use the reverse operation; that is, divide the cubic feet by a factor of 27. Thus,

$$54 \text{ cubic feet} = 54 \div 27 = 2 \text{ cubic yards}$$

Table 5.2 Converting measures of area.

From	To	Multiply by	Divide by
Square inches	Square feet		144
Square feet	Square inches	144	
Square feet	Square yards		9
Square yards	Square feet	9	
Square yards	Square inches	1296	
Square inches	Square yards		1296
Acres	Square yards	4840	
Square yards	Acres		4840
Acres	Square feet	43,560	
Square feet	Acres		43,560
Square miles	Acres	640	
Acres	Square miles		640

Table 5.3 Converting measures of volume.

From	To	Multiply by	Divide by
Cubic feet	Cubic inches	1728	
Cubic inches	Cubic feet		1728
Cubic yards	Cubic feet	27	
Cubic feet	Cubic yards		27
Cubic yards	Cubic inches	46,656	
Cubic inches	Cubic yards		46,656

To convert weight units within the English system, use the relationships given in Table 5.4. For example, to convert pounds into ounces, multiply the number of pounds by a factor of 16. Thus, to convert 2 pounds into ounces,

$$2 \text{ pounds} = 2 \times 16 = 32 \text{ ounces}$$

Similarly, to convert ounces into pounds, use the reverse operation; that is, divide the ounces by a factor of 16. Thus,

$$32 \text{ ounces} = 32 \div 16 = 2 \text{ pounds}$$

To convert units of liquid measure within the English system, use the relationships given in Table 5.5. For example, to convert cups into tablespoons, multiply the number of cups by a factor of 16. Thus, to convert 2 cups into tablespoons,

$$2 \text{ cups} = 2 \times 16 = 32 \text{ tablespoons}$$

Table 5.4   Converting measures of weight.

From	To	Multiply by	Divide by
Pounds	Ounces	16	
Ounces	Pounds		16
Tons	Pounds	2000	
Pounds	Tons		2000
Long tons	Pounds	2240	
Pounds	Long tons		2240

Table 5.5   Converting measures of liquid.

From	To	Multiply by	Divide by
Tablespoons	Teaspoons	3	
Teaspoons	Tablespoons		3
Tablespoons	Fluid ounces	0.5	
Fluid ounces	Tablespoons		2
Cups	Tablespoons	16	
Tablespoons	Cups		16
Cups	Fluid ounces	8	
Fluid ounces	Cups		8
Pints	Cups	2	
Cups	Pints		2
Pints	Fluid ounces	16	
Fluid ounces	Pints		16
Quarts	Pints	2	
Pints	Quarts		2
Quarts	Cups	4	
Cups	Quarts		4
Quarts	Fluid ounces	32	
Fluid ounces	Quarts		32
Gallons	Quarts	4	
Quarts	Gallons		4
Gallons	Pints	8	
Pints	Gallons		8
Gallons	Cups	16	
Cups	Gallons		16
Gallons	Fluid ounces	128	
Fluid ounces	Gallons		128

Table 5.6 Converting measures of pressure.

From	To	Multiply by	Divide by
Pounds per square inch	Pounds per square foot		144
Pounds per square foot	Pounds per square inch	144	
Pounds per square inch	Atmospheres		14.7
Atmospheres	Pounds per square inch	14.7	
Pounds per square foot	Atmospheres		2116.3
Atmospheres	Pounds per square foot	2116.3	

Similarly, to convert tablespoons into cups, use the reverse operation; that is, divide the tablespoons by a factor of 16. Thus,

$$32 \text{ tablespoons} = 32 \div 16 = 2 \text{ cups}$$

To convert pressure units within the English system, use the relationships given in Table 5.6. For example, to convert pounds per square foot into pounds per square inch (psi), multiply the number of pounds per square foot by a factor of 144. Thus, to convert 2 pounds per square foot into pounds per square inch,

$$2 \text{ pounds per square foot} = 2 \times 144 = 288 \text{ pounds per square inch}$$

Similarly, to convert pounds per square inch into pounds per square foot, use the reverse operation; that is, divide the pounds per square inch by a factor of 144. Thus,

$$288 \text{ pounds per square inch} = 288 \div 144 = 2 \text{ pounds per square foot}$$

SI/METRIC SYSTEM MEASUREMENTS

To convert length units within the metric or SI system, use the relationships given in Table 5.7. For example, to convert centimeters into millimeters, multiply the number of centimeters by a factor of 10. Thus, to convert 2 centimeters into millimeters,

$$2 \text{ centimeters} = 2 \times 10 = 20 \text{ millimeters}$$

Similarly, to convert millimeters into centimeters, use the reverse operation; that is, divide the millimeters by a factor of 10. Thus,

$$20 \text{ millimeters} = 20 \div 10 = 2 \text{ centimeters}$$

To convert area units within the metric or SI system, use the relationships given in Table 5.8. For example, to convert square centimeters into square millimeters, multiply the number of square centimeters by a factor of 100. Thus, to convert 2 square centimeters into square millimeters,

$$2 \text{ square centimeters} = 2 \times 100 = 200 \text{ square millimeters}$$

Similarly, to convert square millimeters into square centimeters, use the reverse operation; that is, divide the square millimeters by a factor of 100. Thus,

$$200 \text{ square millimeters} = 200 \div 100 = 2 \text{ square centimeters}$$

Table 5.7   Converting measures of length—metric units.

From	To	Multiply by	Divide by
Microns	Millimeters		1000
Millimeters	Microns	1000	
Millimeters	Centimeters		10
Centimeters	Millimeters	10	
Centimeters	Meters		100
Meters	Centimeters	100	
Millimeters	Meters		1000
Meters	Millimeters	1000	
Meters	Kilometers		1000
Kilometers	Meters	1000	

Table 5.8   Converting measures of area—metric units.

From	To	Multiply by	Divide by
Square millimeters	Square centimeters		100
Square centimeters	Square millimeters	100	
Square centimeters	Square meters		10,000
Square meters	Square centimeters	10,000	
Square meters	Square kilometers		1,000,000
Square kilometers	Square meters	1,000,000	
Square meters	Ares		100
Acres	Square meters	100	

To convert volume units within the metric or SI system, use the relationships given in Table 5.9. For example, to convert cubic centimeters into cubic millimeters, multiply the number of cubic centimeters by a factor of 1000. Thus, to convert 2 cubic centimeters into cubic millimeters,

$$2 \text{ cubic centimeters} = 2 \times 1000 = 200 \text{ cubic millimeters}$$

Similarly, to convert cubic millimeters into cubic centimeters, use the reverse operation; that is, divide the cubic millimeters by a factor of 1000. Thus,

$$2000 \text{ cubic millimeters} = 2000 \div 1000 = 2 \text{ cubic centimeters}$$

To convert mass units within the metric or SI system, use the relationships given in Table 5.10. For example, to convert centigrams into milligrams, multiply the number of centigrams by a factor of 10. Thus, to convert 2 centigrams into milligrams,

$$2 \text{ centigrams} = 2 \times 10 = 20 \text{ milligrams}$$

Table 5.9   Converting measures of volume—metric units.

From	To	Multiply by	Divide by
Cubic millimeters	Cubic centimeters		1000
Cubic centimeters	Cubic millimeters	1000	
Cubic centimeters	Cubic meters		1,000,000
Cubic meters	Cubic centimeters	1,000,000	

Table 5.10   Converting measures of mass—metric units.

From	To	Multiply by	Divide by
Micrograms	Milligrams		1000
Milligrams	Micrograms	1000	
Milligrams	Centigrams		10
Centigrams	Milligrams	10	
Centigrams	Grams		100
Grams	Centigrams	100	
Grams	Kilograms		1000
Kilograms	Grams	1000	

Similarly, to convert milligrams into centigrams, use the reverse operation; that is, divide the milligrams by a factor of 10. Thus,

$$20 \text{ milligrams} = 20 \div 10 = 2 \text{ centigrams}$$

To convert units of liquid measure within the metric or SI system, use the relationships given in Table 5.11. For example, to convert liters into centiliters, multiply the number of liters by a factor of 100. Thus, to convert 2 liters into centiliters,

$$2 \text{ liters} = 2 \times 100 = 200 \text{ centiliters}$$

Similarly, to convert centiliters into liters, use the reverse operation; that is, divide the centiliters by a factor of 100. Thus,

$$200 \text{ centiliters} = 200 \div 100 = 2 \text{ liters}$$

ENGLISH-TO-SI/METRIC CONVERSIONS

Use these relationships to convert from the English system to the SI/metric system, or from the SI/metric system to the English system.

To convert length units between the English and metric or SI systems, use the relationships given in Table 5.12. For example, to convert feet into centimeters, multiply the number of feet by a factor of 30.48. Thus, to convert 2 feet into centimeters,

$$2 \text{ feet} = 2 \times 30.48 = 60.96 \text{ centimeters}$$

Table 5.11   Converting liquid measures—metric units.

From	To	Multiply by	Divide by
Milliliters	Centiliters		10
Centiliters	Milliliters	10	
Centiliters	Liters		100
Liters	Centiliters	100	
Liters	Kiloliters		1000
Kiloliters	Liters	1000	

Table 5.12   Converting measures of length—English and metric units.

From	To	Multiply by	Divide by
Inches	Centimeters	2.54	
Centimeters	Inches		2.54
Feet	Centimeters	30.48	
Centimeters	Feet		30.48
Feet	Millimeters	304.8	
Millimeters	Feet		304.8
Yards	Meters	0.9144	
Meters	Yards		0.9144
Yards	Centimeters	91.44	
Centimeters	Yards		91.44
Miles	Kilometers	1.609	
Kilometers	Miles		1.609
Miles	Meters	1609	
Meters	Miles		1609

Similarly, to convert centimeters into feet, use the reverse operation; that is, divide the centimeters by a factor of 30.48. Thus,

$$60.96 \text{ centimeters} = 60.96 \div 30.48 = 2 \text{ feet}$$

To convert area units between the English and metric or SI systems, use the relationships given in Table 5.13. For example, to convert square inches into square millimeters, multiply the number of square inches by a factor of 645.2. Thus, to convert 2 square inches into square millimeters,

$$2 \text{ square inches} = 2 \times 645.2 = 1290.4 \text{ sqare millimeters}$$

Similarly, to convert square millimeters into square inches, use the reverse operation; that is, divide the square millimeters by a factor of 645.2. Thus,

1290.4 square millimeters = 1290.4 ÷ 645.2 = 2 square inches

To convert volume units between the English and metric or SI systems, use the relationships given in Table 5.14. For example, to convert cubic inches into cubic centimeters, multiply the number of cubic inches by a factor of 16.38716. Thus, to convert 2 cubic inches into cubic centimeters,

2 cubic inches = 2 × 16.38716 = 32.77432 cubic centimeters

Table 5.13 Converting measures of area—English and metric units.

From	To	Multiply by	Divide by
Square inches	Square centimeters	6.452	
Square centimeters	Square inches		6.452
Square inches	Square millimeters	645.2	
Square millimeters	Square inches		645.2
Square feet	Square meters	0.0929	
Square meters	Square feet		0.0929
Square feet	Square centimeters	929	
Square centimeters	Square feet		929
Square yards	Square meters	0.836	
Square meters	Square yards		0.836
Acres	Ares	40.47	
Ares	Acres		40.47
Square miles	Square kilometers	2.5899	
Square kilometers	Square miles		2.5899

Table 5.14 Converting measures of volume—English and metric units.

From	To	Multiply by	Divide by
Cubic inches	Cubic centimeters	16.38716	
Cubic centimeters	Cubic inches		16.38716
Cubic feet	Cubic meters	0.02832	
Cubic meters	Cubic feet		0.02832
Cubic yards	Cubic meters	0.7645	
Cubic meters	Cubic yards		0.7645

Similarly, to convert cubic centimeters into cubic inches, use the reverse operation; that is, divide the cubic inches by a factor of 16.38716. Thus,

$$32.77432 \text{ cubic centimeters} = 32.77432 \div 16.38716 = 2 \text{ cubic inches}$$

To convert weight and mass units between the English and metric or SI systems, use the relationships given in Table 5.15. For example, to convert pounds into grams, multiply the number of pounds by a factor of 453.6. Thus, to convert 2 pounds into grams,

$$2 \text{ pounds} = 2 \times 453.6 = 907.2 \text{ grams}$$

Similarly, to convert grams into pounds, use the reverse operation; that is, divide the grams by a factor of 453.6. Thus,

$$907.2 \text{ grams} = 907.2 \div 453.6 = 2 \text{ pounds}$$

To convert units of liquid measure between the English and metric or SI systems, use the relationships given in Table 5.16. For example, to convert quarts into liters, multiply the number of quarts by a factor of 0.946. Thus, to convert 2 quarts into liters,

$$2 \text{ quarts} = 2 \times 0.946 = 1.892 \text{ liters}$$

Similarly, to convert liters into quarts, use the reverse operation; that is, divide the liters by a factor of 0.946. Thus,

$$1.892 \text{ liters} = 1.892 \div 0.946 = 2 \text{ quarts}$$

Table 5.15   Converting measures of weight and mass.

From	To	Multiply by	Divide by
Pounds	Grams	453.6	
Grams	Pounds		453.6
Pounds	Kilograms	0.4536	
Kilograms	Pounds		0.4536
Tons	Kilograms	907.2	
Kilograms	Tons		907.2

Table 5.16   Converting measures of liquid—English and metric units.

From	To	Multiply by	Divide by
Quarts	Liters	0.946	
Liters	Quarts		0.946
Gallons	Liters	3.785	
Liters	Gallons		3.785

To convert temperature units from Celsius to Fahrenheit, use the relationship given in Table 5.17. To convert degrees Celsius to degrees Fahrenheit, multiply degrees Celsius by 9/5 and then add 32. Thus, to convert 20 degrees Celsius to degrees Fahrenheit,

$$20 \times \frac{9}{5} + 32 = 68 \text{ degrees Fahrenheit}$$

Recall that 0 degrees Celsius converts to 32 degrees Fahrenheit, and that the boiling point of water is 100 degrees Celsius or 212 degrees Fahrenheit.

To convert temperature units from Fahrenheit to Celsius, use the relationship given in Table 5.18. To convert degrees Fahrenheit to degrees Celsius, subtract 32 from degrees Celsius and then divide by 9/5. Thus, to convert 68 degrees Fahrenheit to degrees Celsius,

$$(68 - 32) \div \frac{9}{5} = 20 \text{ degrees Celsius}$$

Recall that 32 degrees Fahrenheit converts to 0 degrees Celsius, and that the boiling point of water is 212 degrees Fahrenheit or 100 degrees Celsius.

To convert temperature units from Celsius to Kelvin, or Fahrenheit to Rankin, use the relationships given in Table 5.19. For example, to convert degrees Celsius to degrees Kelvin, add 273.15 to degrees Celsius. Thus, to convert 20 degrees Celsius to degrees Kelvin,

20 degrees Celsius = 20 + 273.15 = 293.15 degrees Kelvin

Table 5.17   Converting temperatures—Celsius to Fahrenheit.

From	To	Multiply by	Add
Degrees Celsius	Degrees Fahrenheit	9/5	32

Table 5.18   Converting temperatures—Fahrenheit to Celsius.

From	To	Subtract	Divide by
Degrees Fahrenheit	Degrees Celsius	32	9/5

Table 5.19   Converting temperatures—English and metric units.

From	To	Subtract	Add
Degrees Rankin	Degrees Fahrenheit	459.67	
Degrees Fahrenheit	Degrees Rankin		459.67
Degrees Kelvin	Degrees Celsius	273.15	
Degrees Celsius	Degrees Kelvin		273.15

Similarly, to convert degrees Kelvin into degrees Celsius, use the reverse operation; that is, subtract 273.15 from degrees Kelvin. Thus,

$$293.15 \text{ degrees Kelvin} = 293.15 - 273.15 = 20 \text{ degrees Celsius}$$

More conversion factors are given in Appendix C.

BIBLIOGRAPHY

Achatz, T. 2006. *Technical Shop Mathematics*. 3rd ed. New York: Industrial Press.
Griffith, G. 1986. *Quality Technician's Handbook*. Englewood Cliffs, NJ: Prentice Hall.
Horton, H. L. 1999. *Mathematics at Work*. 4th ed. New York: Industrial Press.

Chapter 6

F. Numeric Conversions

Numeric Conversions

Use various numbering methods such as scientific notation, decimals, and fractions, and convert values between these systems. (Apply)

Body of Knowledge I.F

EXPONENTS

Positive Exponents

Using positive exponents is a shorthand way to represent a number that is multiplied by itself. For example, given

$$2 \times 2 \times 2 = 8$$

we can represent the multiplication statement in exponent form: 2^3. The first number, 2, represents the number being multiplied by itself. The superscript, 3, is the *exponent*, and it tells us how many times the number 2 is multiplied by itself.

Conversely, an exponent can be converted into a multiplication statement. For example, 4^5 represents

$$4 \times 4 \times 4 \times 4 \times 4 = 1024$$

A special case occurs when the exponent equals zero. Any nonzero number with an exponent equal to 0 will equal 1. For example, $5^0 = 1$. This is read as "five to the zero power equals one."

For any number x with an exponent equal to 1, we say "x to the first power." For example, 5^1 is read "five to the first power."

For any number x with an exponent equal to 2, we say "x squared." For example, 5^2 is read as "five squared."

For any number x with an exponent equal to 3, we say "x cubed." For example, 5^3 is read as "five cubed."

If we have 5^4, we say "five to the fourth power." The number 5^5 is read "five to the fifth power," and so on.

Negative Exponents

We can also use exponents to represent multiplication statements such as

$$\frac{1}{2} \times \frac{1}{2} \times \frac{1}{2} = \frac{1}{8}$$

This statement is written as 2^{-3}. In this case we use a negative exponent to show that the number 2 is in the denominator. Note that 2^{-3} can also be written as

$$\frac{1}{2^3}$$

meaning that 2^{-3} and 2^3 are reciprocals. We read 2^{-3} as "2 to the negative three power."

Powers of 10

Table 6.1 shows the powers of 10 and the numbers they represent. These powers of 10 are used in scientific notation.

SCIENTIFIC NOTATION

For very large or very small values, it is often more convenient to represent a number in terms of scientific notation. Scientific notation uses powers of 10. For example, the number 100 can be written as 1×10^2. The decimal 0.01 can be shown as 1×10^{-2}.

Table 6.1   Powers of 10.

Exponent form	Number
10^{-6}	0.000001
10^{-5}	0.00001
10^{-4}	0.0001
10^{-3}	0.001
10^{-2}	0.01
10^{-1}	0.1
10^{0}	1
10^{1}	10
10^{2}	100
10^{3}	1,000
10^{4}	10,000
10^{5}	100,000
10^{6}	1,000,000

Procedure for Values Greater Than 1 or Less Than –1

To display a number greater than 1 or less than –1 in scientific notation, perform these three steps:

1. Move the decimal point to the left so that the original number is now displayed with a nonzero digit in the ones place.

   For example, the number 234 would be displayed as 2.34 when we move the decimal point to the left two times. The number –5567.8 would be displayed as –5.5678 when we move the decimal point three times to the left.

2. Next, display the number of places the decimal moved to the left as a positive power of 10.

   For example, the decimal was moved two times to the left to convert 234 to 2.34. We will denote this 10^2.

   The decimal was moved three times to the left to convert –5567.8 to –5.5678. This is denoted as 10^3.

3. Put the two pieces together, linked by a multiplication sign.

   For example, the value 234 is displayed as 2.34×10^2 in scientific notation. The value –5567.8 is displayed as -5.5678×10^3 in scientific notation.

Procedure for Values between –1 and +1

To display a number between 0 and 1 or between –1 and 0 in scientific notation, perform these three steps:

1. Move the decimal point to the right so that the original number is now displayed with a nonzero digit in the ones place.

   For example, the number 0.234 would be displayed as 2.34 when we move the decimal point to the right one time. The number –0.00556 would be displayed as –5.56 when we move the decimal point three times to the right.

2. Next, display the number of places the decimal moved to the right as a negative power of 10.

   For example, the decimal was moved one time to the right to convert 0.234 to 2.34. We will denote this 10^{-1}.

   The decimal was moved three times to the right to convert –0.00556 to –5.56. This is denoted as 10^{-3}.

3. Put the two pieces together, linked by a multiplication sign.

   For example, the value 0.234 is displayed as 2.34×10^{-1} in scientific notation. The value –0.00556 is displayed as -5.56×10^{-3} in scientific notation.

Converting Scientific Notation back to Original Form

To convert a number displayed in scientific notation back to its original form, take the first number in the scientific notation statement and move the decimal point to the right or left as indicated by the power of 10. For negative powers of 10, move the decimal to the left. For positive powers of 10, move the decimal to the right.

For example, to convert 2.34×10^{-1} back to original form, we take 2.34 and move the decimal one place to the *left*—since the power of 10 is negative—to get 0.234.

To convert 2.34×10^2 back to original form, we take 2.34 and move the decimal two places to the *right*—since the power of 10 is positive—to get 234.

DECIMALS AND FRACTIONS

Converting Fractions to Decimals

Fractions can be converted to decimals by dividing the denominator into the numerator. For example:

$$\frac{3}{8} = 3 \div 8 = 0.375$$

We read this decimal as "375 thousandths."

Some common fractions and their decimal equivalents are listed in Table 6.2.

Table 6.2   Common fractions and their decimal equivalents.

Fraction	Decimal
1/16	0.0625
1/10	0.1
1/8	0.125
1/5	0.2
1/4	0.25
3/8	0.375
2/5	0.4
1/2	0.5
3/5	0.6
5/8	0.625
3/4	0.75
4/5	0.8
7/8	0.875
15/16	0.9375

Note that the decimal equivalents of the fractions 1/3, 1/6, 1/7, and 1/9 are infinitely repeating decimals, as shown here. A line drawn above a number or a sequence of numbers indicates that the number or sequence repeats infinitely.

$$\frac{1}{3} = 0.33\overline{3}$$

$$\frac{1}{6} = 0.166\overline{6}$$

$$\frac{1}{7} = 0.\overline{142857}$$

$$\frac{1}{9} = 0.11\overline{1}$$

Converting Decimals to Fractions

To convert a decimal to a fraction, divide the decimal by 1. Then move the decimal point to the right in the numerator to make a whole number. Move the decimal place in the denominator the same number of times. For example, to convert the decimal 0.234 to a fraction, the decimal point in both the numerator and the denominator is moved four places to the right:

$$\frac{0.0234}{1} = \frac{234}{10,000}$$

The resulting fraction can then be simplified if desired.

BIBLIOGRAPHY

Achatz, T. 2006. *Technical Shop Mathematics*. 3rd ed. New York: Industrial Press.
Griffith, G. 1986. *Quality Technician's Handbook*. Englewood Cliffs, NJ: Prentice Hall.
Horton, H. L. 1999. *Mathematics at Work*. 4th ed. New York: Industrial Press.

Section II
Metrology

Chapter 7	A. Common Gauges and Measurement Instruments
Chapter 8	B. Special Gauges and Applications
Chapter 9	C. Gauge Selection, Handling, and Use
Chapter 10	D. Surface Plate Tools and Techniques
Chapter 11	E. Specialized Inspection Equipment
Chapter 12	F. Calibration
Chapter 13	G. Measurement System Analysis (MSA)

Metrology is defined as the science of precision measurements. It has many applications in science and industry and employs a wide range of measuring instruments. In the competitive manufacture of precision-engineered products, where a high degree of quality is required, it is particularly important that the proper measuring instruments be employed to provide accurate, reliable, and cost-effective inspection results. Thus, the selection of appropriate measuring and gauging instruments is becoming even more critical in the ever-increasing requirement to stay competitive and to meet customer demand for higher-quality products.

Chapter 7

A. Common Gauges and Measurement Instruments

1. *Variable gauges.* Identify and use variable gauges, including micrometers, calipers, dial indicators, and Coordinate Measuring Machines (CMM). Understand linear scales, such as steel rule, and gage blocks. Use borescopes, thermometers, and temperature probes. (Apply)

2. *Attribute gauges.* Identify and use attribute gauges, including thread plugs, progressive rings, flush pins, pin gauges, and radius gauges. (Apply)

3. *Transfer gauges.* Identify and use transfer gauges, including small-hole gauges, telescoping gauges, and spring calipers. (Apply)

4. *Measurement scales.* Describe and distinguish between dial, digital, and vernier scales. (Remember)

Body of Knowledge II.A

INTRODUCTION

Dimensional metrology is concerned with the measurement or gauging of a variety of workpiece characteristics, including length, diameter, thickness, angle, taper, roughness, concentricity, and profile. Different sensing technologies may be employed to measure or gauge those characteristics, depending on the requirements for accuracy and other considerations. There are basically five different technologies that may be used individually or in combination to perform these inspection functions:

1. *Mechanical.* Small displacements are amplified by a mechanical system.

2. *Electronic.* Utilize an electric or electronic phenomenon such as electrical resistance.

3. *Air or pneumatic.* Small variations made in the dimension are measured with respect to a reference dimension and are shown by a variation in air pressure or the velocity of airflow.

4. *Light waves.* Utilizing the phenomenon of the interference of light waves to provide a standard. Such a standard is the wavelength of a monochromatic light, expressed in terms of the meter.

5. *Electron beam.* Stabilized lasers are used as working standards for dimensional measurements, providing a precise and stable frequency for the standard.

In general, the mechanical and electronic types of measuring and gauging instruments have sensing devices or probes that come into contact with the workpiece, and are referred to as *contact instruments.* Air instruments, while employing contacting elements, rely on air pressure difference to effect measurement. Thus, they are basically *noncontact instruments.* Although different technologies are involved in the light-wave and electron-beam instruments, they both utilize a variety of optical systems. Thus, they are often grouped together as *optical noncontact instruments.*

1. VARIABLE GAUGES

Most of the basic or general-purpose linear measuring instruments are typified by the steel rule, the vernier caliper, or the micrometer caliper.

Steel Rules

Steel rules are used effectively as line measuring devices, which means that the ends of a dimension being measured are aligned with the graduations of the scale, from which the length is read directly. A depth rule for measuring the depth of slots, holes, and so on, is a type of steel rule. Steel rules are also incorporated into vernier calipers, where they are adapted to end-measuring operations. These are often more accurate and easier to apply than in-line measuring devices.

Verniers

The *vernier caliper* shown in Figure 7.1 typifies the type of instrument using the vernier principle of measurement. The main or beam scale on a typical metric vernier caliper is numbered in increments of 10 mm, with the smallest scale division equivalent to 1 mm. The vernier scale slides along the edge of the main scale and is separated into 50 divisions, and these 50 divisions are the same in total length as the 49 divisions on the main scale. Each division on the vernier scale is equal to 1/50 of (49 × 1), or 0.98 mm, which is 0.02 mm less than each division on the main scale.

Aligning the zero lines on both scales would cause the first lines on each scale to be 0.02 mm apart, the second lines 0.04 mm apart, and so on. A measurement on a vernier is designated by the positions of its zero line and the line that coincides with a line on the main scale. For example, the metric scale in Figure 7.1a shows a reading of 12.42 mm. The zero index of the vernier is located just beyond the line at 12 mm on the main scale, and line 21 (after 0) coincides with a line on the main scale, indicating the zero index is 0.42 mm beyond the line at 12 mm. Thus, 12.00 + 0.42 = 12.42 mm.

The vernier caliper illustrated in Figure 7.1 also has an inch scale so that it can be used interchangeably for either inch or millimeter measurements. The smallest division on the main scale represents 0.25 in. and the vernier is divided into

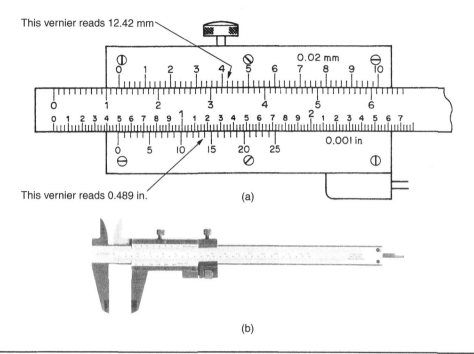

This vernier reads 12.42 mm

0.02 mm

This vernier reads 0.489 in.   (a)

0.001 in

(b)

Figure 7.1   Fine-adjustment style vernier caliper.
Courtesy Fred V. Fowler Company.

0.001 in. increments. Thus, the measurement illustrated is 0.475 in. away from the main scale plus 0.014 in. from the vernier scale, for a total of 0.489 in.

The vernier caliper shown in Figure 7.1b consists of a steel rule with a pair of fixed jaws at one end and a pair of sliding jaws affixed to a vernier. Outside dimensions are measured between the lower jaws, and inside dimensions are measured over the tips of the upper jaws.

The *digital reading caliper* shown in Figure 7.2 provides LCD readouts in either millimeters or inches and operates on a microprocessor-based system. The caliper has a measuring range of 0–152 mm (0–6 in.) with readings in increments of 0.013 mm (0.0005 in.). The unit is capable of retaining a reading in the display when the tool is used in an area where visibility is restricted.

The *vernier height gauge* is similar to a vernier caliper except the fixed jaw has been replaced by a fixed base, and the sliding jaw may have a scriber attached to it for layout work, or a dial indicator for measuring or comparing operations. A more sophisticated version of the vernier height gauge is shown in Figure 7.3. This instrument can easily measure in two dimensions, in either angular or polar coordinates. It can measure external, internal, and distance dimensions, as well as perpendicularity, flatness, straightness, centers, and diameters.

Vertical measurements are made on the gauge shown in Figure 7.3 in either metric or inch units to a resolution of 0.0005 mm (0.00002 in.) by an optoelectronic sensor moving over a high-accuracy glass scale. The gauge head moves on a cushion of air generated by a completely self-contained pneumatic system. Dedicated

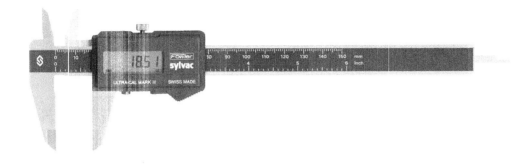

Figure 7.2 LCD digital-reading caliper with 0–152 mm (0–6 in.) range.
Courtesy Fred V. Fowler Company.

Figure 7.3 Digital-reading, single-axis height gauge for two-dimensional measurements.
Courtesy Brown and Sharpe Manufacturing Company.

function programs, along with a keypad and interactive LCD display, are designed to guide operators smoothly and efficiently through a variety of measurement operations. The gauge can be used for direct data transfer to other data collection devices.

Micrometers

The *micrometer caliper* illustrated in Figure 7.4 is representative of the type of instrument using a precision screw as a basis for measuring. The measuring elements consist of a fixed anvil and a spindle that moves lengthwise as it is turned.

The thread on the spindle of a typical metric micrometer has a lead of 1/2 or 0.5 mm, so one complete revolution of the thimble produces a spindle movement of this amount. The graduated scale on the sleeve of the instrument has major divisions of 1.0 mm and minor divisions of 0.5 mm. Thus, one revolution of the spindle causes the beveled edge of the thimble to move through one small division on the sleeve scale. The periphery of the beveled edge of the thimble is graduated into 50 equal divisions, each space representing 1/50 of a complete rotation of the thimble, or a 0.01 mm movement of the spindle. Micrometers with scales in inch units operate in a similar fashion. Typically, the spindle thread has a lead of 0.025 in., and the smallest division on the sleeve represents 0.025 in. The periphery of the beveled edge of the thimble is graduated into 25 equal divisions, each space representing 1/25 of a complete rotation of the thimble or a spindle movement of 0.001 in.

A reading on a micrometer is made by adding the thimble division that is aligned with the longitudinal sleeve line to the largest reading exposed on the sleeve scale. For example, in Figure 7.5 the thimble has exposed the number 10, representing 10.00 mm, and one small division worth 0.50 mm. The thimble division 16 is aligned with the longitudinal sleeve line, indicating that the thimble has

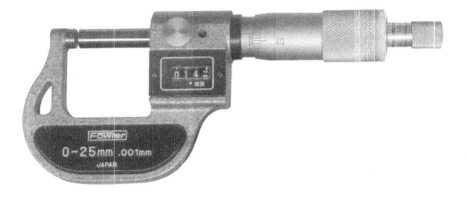

Figure 7.4   A 0–25 mm micrometer caliper.
Courtesy Fred V. Fowler Company.

Reading to 0.01 mm

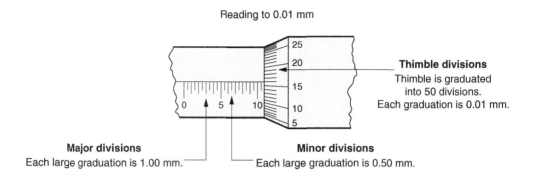

Thimble divisions
Thimble is graduated
into 50 divisions.
Each graduation is 0.01 mm.

Major divisions
Each large graduation is 1.00 mm.

Minor divisions
Each large graduation is 0.50 mm.

Figure 7.5   Micrometer reading of 10.66 mm.

Reprinted with permission of the Society of Manufacturing Engineers, *Manufacturing Processes and Materials*, 4th edition, copyright 2000.

moved 0.16 mm beyond the last small division on the sleeve. Thus, the final reading is obtained by summing the three components: 10.00 + 0.50 + 0.16 = 10.66 mm.

Vernier Scales

A *vernier micrometer caliper*, such as that represented by the scales shown in Figure 7.6, has a vernier scale on the sleeve, permitting measurement to 0.001 mm. The vernier scale shown has 10 divisions over a length equivalent to 19 divisions around the periphery of the thimble. Thus, the difference in length of a division on the vernier scale and two divisions on the thimble is $0.02 - (1/10)(19 \times 0.01) = 0.001$ mm. Thus, the reading illustrated in Figure 7.6 is 10.00 + 0.50 + 0.16 + 0.006 = 10.666 mm.

Digital Micrometers

Micrometers with digital readouts make readings faster and easier for inspection personnel regardless of their degree of experience. The digital micrometer shown in Figure 7.4 represents one instrument of this type for use in measuring to a resolution of 0.001 mm. The instrument shown in Figure 7.7 has a digital readout with a resolution to 0.0001 in. When equipped with vernier scales, the resolution may be increased to 0.001 mm (commonly 0.0001 in. in the case of an inch-reading device).

Micrometer Calipers

The *micrometer caliper*, or *mike* as it is often called, is an end-measuring instrument for use in measuring outside dimensions. Although the mike is fairly easy to apply, its accuracy depends on the application of the proper amount of torque to the thimble. Too much torque is likely to spring the frame and cause error. Thus, it is important that personnel using these instruments be trained in their use and be required to periodically check their measurements against a standard to

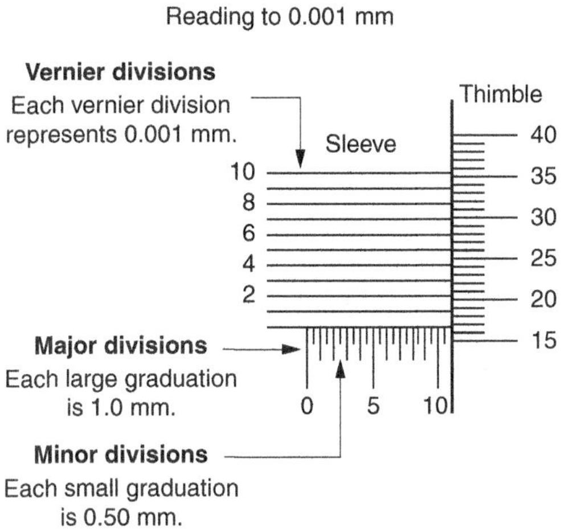

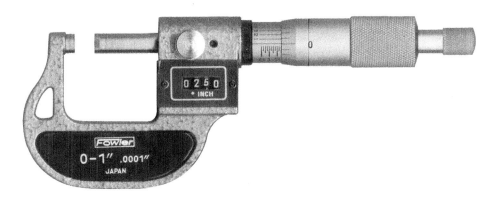

Reading to 0.001 mm
Vernier divisions
Each vernier division represents 0.001 mm.
Sleeve
Thimble
40
35
30
25
20
15
10
8
6
4
2
Major divisions
Each large graduation is 1.0 mm.
0
5
10
Minor divisions
Each small graduation is 0.50 mm.

Figure 7.6 Scales of a vernier micrometer showing a reading of 10.666 mm.

Reprinted with permission of the Society of Manufacturing Engineers, *Manufacturing Processes and Materials,* 4th edition, copyright 2000.

0250
INCH
Fowler
0-1″ .0001″
JAPAN

Figure 7.7 A digital micrometer.

Courtesy Fred V. Fowler Company.

minimize errors. The indicating micrometer (Figure 7.8) has a built-in dial indicator to provide a positive indication of the measuring pressure applied. The instrument can be used like an indicating snap gauge.

Gauge Blocks

Gauge blocks are dimensional measurement standards that are used to calibrate other measuring devices. They come in sets of different grades depending on the desired measurement accuracy required. Each set has many blocks of incremental lengths. These blocks are stacked together (wringed) to build a desired length.

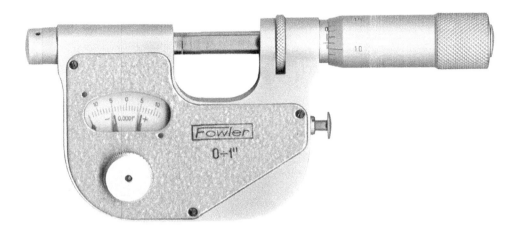

Figure 7.8   An indicating micrometer.
Courtesy Fred V. Fowler Company.

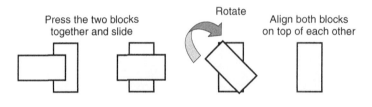

Figure 7.9   A schematic showing the process of wringing gauge blocks.

The process of building a desired length of a stack of gauge blocks is *wringing*. After the reference block is built, the blocks are said to be "wrung" together. This process, shown in the schematic in Figure 7.9, is as follows:

- The blocks should be clean.

- Lubricate the surfaces of the two blocks lightly and then clean them, creating a thin film of oil that allows one block to slide over the other and allows the blocks to be separated after the measurement.

- Slide the surfaces of the blocks together as shown. Apply pressure while sliding the blocks. The blocks should strongly adhere to each other after being rotated into place.

Dial Indicators

Dial indicators are used for many kinds of measuring and gauging operations. They also serve to check machines and tools, alignments, and cutter runout. Dial indicators are often incorporated into special gauges in measuring instruments.

Borescopes

A borescope is an optical device (such as a prism or optical flat) used to inspect an inaccessible space (such as an engine cylinder) (*Merriam-Webster's Dictionary*). Borescopes are used for the inspection of parts' locations and dimensions that are very difficult to access and determine or very costly to gain access to inspect.

Thermometers and Temperature Probes

A *thermometer* is an instrument for measuring temperature, either digital or analog and produced in many shapes to accommodate different industrial, metrological, medical, or other applications. *Temperature probes* are metallic or plastic sensors that are conveniently used to measure temperatures when running experiments in metals, meat, and other substances. Applications vary in biology, chemistry, material science, and other medical fields.

Coordinate Measuring Machines

The *coordinate measuring machine* (CMM) is a flexible measuring device capable of providing highly accurate dimensional position information along three mutually perpendicular axes. This instrument is widely used in manufacturing industries for the post-process inspection of a large variety of products and their components. It is also very effectively used to check dimensions on a variety of process tooling, including mold cavities, die assemblies, assembly fixtures, and other work-holding or tool-positioning devices.

Over the last decade coordinate measuring machines have become a primary means of dimensional quality control for manufactured parts of complex form where the volume of production does not warrant the development of functional gauging. The advent of increasingly inexpensive computing power and more fully integrated manufacturing systems will continue to expand the use of these machines into an even larger role in the overall quality assurance of manufactured parts.

Coordinate measuring machines (CMMs) can most easily be defined as physical representations of a three-dimensional rectilinear coordinate system. Coordinate measuring machines now represent a significant fraction of the measuring equipment used for defining the geometry of different-shaped workpieces. Most dimensional characteristics of many parts can be measured within minutes with these machines. Similar measurements would take hours using older measuring equipment and procedures. Besides flexibility and speed, coordinate measuring machines have several additional advantages:

1. Different features of a part can be measured in one setup. This eliminates errors introduced due to setup changes.

2. All CMM measurements are taken from one geometrically fixed measuring system, eliminating the accumulation of errors resulting from using functional gauging and transfer techniques.

3. The use of digital readouts eliminates the necessity for the interpretation of readings, such as with the dial or vernier-type measuring scales.

4. Most CMMs have automatic data recording, which minimizes operator influence.

5. Part alignment and setup procedures are greatly simplified by using software supplied with computer-assisted CMMs. This minimizes the setup time for measurement.

6. Data can be automatically saved for further analysis.

Coordinate Measuring Machine Classification. Although coordinate measuring machines can be thought of as representations of a simple rectilinear coordinate system for measuring the dimensions of different-shaped workpieces, they naturally are constructed in many different configurations, all of which offer different advantages. CMMs provide a means for locating and recording the coordinate location of points in their measuring volumes. Traditional coordinate measuring machines are classified according to their configurations, as follows (ASME 1985):

1. *Cantilever configuration,* in which the probe is attached to a vertical machine ram (z-axis) moving on a mutually perpendicular overhang beam (y-axis) that moves along a mutually perpendicular rail (x-axis). Cantilever configuration is limited to small- and medium-sized machines. It provides for easy operator access and the possibility of measuring parts longer than the machine table.

2. *Bridge-type configuration,* in which a horizontal beam moves along the x-axis, carrying the carriage that provides the y motion. In other configurations, the horizontal beam (bridge structure) is rigidly attached to the machine base, and the machine table moves along the x-axis. This is called *fixed bridge* configuration. A bridge-type coordinate measuring machine provides more-rigid construction, which in turn provides better accuracy. The presence of the bridge on the machine table makes it a little more difficult to load large parts.

3. *Column-type configuration,* in which a moving table and saddle arrangement provides the x and y motions and the machine ram (z-axis) moves vertically relative to the machine table.

4. *Horizontal-arm configuration* features a horizontal probe ram (z-axis) moving horizontally relative to a column (y-axis), which moves in a mutually perpendicular motion (x-axis) along the machine base. This configuration provides the possibility for measuring large parts. Other arrangements of the horizontal-arm configuration feature a fixed horizontal-arm configuration in which the probe is attached and moving vertically (y-axis) relative to a column that slides along the machine base in the x direction. The machine table moves in a mutually perpendicular motion (z-axis) relative to the column.

5. *Gantry-type configuration* comprises a vertical ram (z-axis) moving vertically relative to a horizontal beam (x-axis), which in turn moves

along two rails (*y*-axis) mounted on the floor. This configuration provides easy access and allows the measurement of large components.

6. *L-shaped bridge configuration* comprises a ram (*z*-axis) moving vertically relative to a carriage (*x*-axis), which moves horizontally relative to an L-shaped bridge moving in the *y* direction.

Figure 7.10 shows CMM types according to this classification.

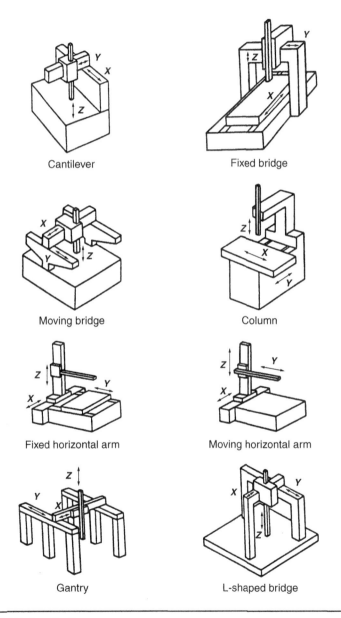

Cantilever   Fixed bridge

Moving bridge   Column

Fixed horizontal arm   Moving horizontal arm

Gantry   L-shaped bridge

Figure 7.10   CMM classifications.

In addition to classifying CMMs according to their physical configuration, they can also be classified according to their mode of operation: manually oriented, computer-assisted, or direct computer-controlled. In manual machines, the operator moves the probe along the machine's axes to establish and manually record the measurement values provided by digital readouts (DROs). In some machines, digital printout devices are used.

Computer-assisted CMMs can be either manually positioned (free-floating mode) by moving the probe to measurement locations, or manually driven by providing power-operated motions under the control of the operator. In either case, a computer accomplishes the data processing. Some computer-assisted CMMs can perform some or all of the following functions: inch to metric conversion, automatic compensation for misalignment, storing of premeasured parameters and measurement sequences, data recording, means for disengagement of the power drive to allow manual adjustments and manipulations of the machine motions, and geometric and analytical evaluations.

Direct computer-controlled CMMs use a computer to control all machine motions and measuring routines and to perform most of the routinely required data processing.

These machines are operated in much the same way as CNC machine tools. Both control and measuring cycles are under program control. Off-line programming capability is also available.

The effective use of computers for CMM applications is a principal feature differentiating available CMM systems. The value of a measurement system depends a great deal on the sophistication and ease of use of the associated software and its functional capabilities. The functional capabilities of a CMM software package depend on the number and types of application programs available. The following is a list of the many different types of system software available for CMMs:

1. Printout instructions, measurement sequence, zero reference, and so on.

2. Automatic compensation for misalignment of the workpiece with the machine axes.

3. Coordinate conversion between Cartesian and polar coordinates.

4. Tolerance calculations providing out-of-tolerance conditions.

5. Defining geometric elements such as points, lines, circles, planes, cylinders, spheres, cones, and their intersections.

6. Automatic redefinition of coordinate systems or machine axes, and printout of origin and inspection planes.

7. Inspection of special shapes or contours, such as gears and cams.

8. Multiple-point hole checking using least squares techniques for determining best fit center, mean diameter, roundness, and concentricity.

9. Evaluating geometric tolerance conditions by defining type of form and positional relationship, such as roundness, flatness, straightness, parallelism, or squareness.

10. Hold diameter and location checking considering maximum and minimum material conditions as defined in ANSI Y14.5.

11. Friendly operator interfaces for self-teaching or part programs.

12. Other software for statistical analysis includes graphic data display, histograms, integration of areas under a curve, contour plotting, automatic part or lot acceptance or rejection based on statistical evaluation, and so on.

2. ATTRIBUTE GAUGES

In some operations it is uneconomical to attempt to obtain absolute sizes during each inspection operation. In many cases it is only necessary to determine whether one or more dimensions of a mass-produced part are within specified limits. For this purpose, a variety of inspection instruments referred to as *gauges* are employed. However, the distinction between gauging devices and measuring devices is not always clear, as there are some instruments referred to as gauges that do not give definite measurements.

To promote consistency in manufacturing and inspection, gauges may be classified as working, inspection, or reference or master gauges.

Working gauges are used by the machine operator or shop inspector to check the dimensions of parts as they are being produced. They usually have limits based on the piece being inspected.

Inspection gauges are used by personnel to inspect purchased parts when received or manufactured parts when finished. These gauges are designed and made so as not to reject any product previously accepted by a properly designed and functioning working gauge.

Reference, or *master*, *gauges* are used only for checking the size or condition of other gauges, and they represent as exactly as possible the physical dimensions of the product.

A gauge may have a single size and be referred to as a *nonlimit gauge*, or it may have two sizes and be referred to as a *limit gauge*. A limit gauge, often called a *go/no-go gauge*, establishes the high and low limits prescribed by the tolerance on a dimension. A limit gauge may be either double-end or progressive. A *double-end gauge* has the "go" member at one end and the "no-go" member at the other. Each end of the gauge is applied to the workpiece to determine its acceptability. The go member must pass into or over an acceptable piece, but the no-go member should not. A *progressive gauge* has both the go and the no-go members at the same end so that a part may be gauged with one movement.

Some gauges are fixed in size, while others are adjustable over certain size ranges. *Fixed gauges* are usually less expensive initially, but they have the disadvantage of not permitting adjustment to compensate for wear.

Most gauges are subjected to considerable abrasion during their application and therefore must be made of materials resistant to wear. High-carbon and alloy steels have been used as gauge materials for many years because of their relatively high hardenability and abrasion resistance. Further increased surface hardness and abrasion resistance may be obtained through the use of chrome plating or cemented carbides as surface material on gauges. Some gauges are made entirely of cemented carbides, or they have cemented carbide inserts at certain wear points. Chrome plating is also used as a means of rebuilding and salvaging worn gauges.

Common Gauges

Typical common functional gauges can be classified on the basis of whether they are used to check outside dimensions, inside dimensions, or special features. Some examples of typical gauges are shown in Figure 7.11. They include:

- *Ring* and *snap gauges* for checking outside dimensions

- *Plug gauges* for checking inside dimensions

- Other gauges for checking other geometrical shapes, such as tapers, threads, and splines

Typical *plug gauges*, such as the ones shown in the top view of Figure 7.11a, consist of a hardened and accurately ground steel pin with two gauge members: the go gauge member and the no-go gauge member. *Progressive plug gauges* (bottom view of Figure 7.11a) combine both go and no-go members into one. The design of the gauge member and the method used to attach it to the handle depend on its size, as shown in Figure 7.11b. The gauge members are usually held in the handle by a threaded collet and bushing (view 1); a taper lock, where gauge members have a taper shank on one end that fits into the end of the handle (view 2); or a trilock, where the gauge members have a hole drilled through the center and are counterbored on both ends to receive a standard socket-head screw (view 3). One way of checking a hole for out-of-roundness is to have flats ground on the side of the gauge member, as shown in Figure 7.11c.

Ring Gauges. Ring gauges, such as those shown in Figure 7.11d, are used for checking the limit sizes of a round shaft. They are generally used in pairs: the go gauge for checking the upper limit of the part tolerance and the no-go gauge for checking the lower limit. The no-go ring has a groove in the outside diameter of the gauge to distinguish it from the go ring. It is possible that a shaft's ends are larger than the middle, or it could suffer an out-of-roundness condition. This situation cannot be detected with a standard cylindrical ring gauge. Such an out-of-roundness condition can be checked by a ring gauge that has the inside diameter relaxed, such as the one shown in Figure 7.11e.

Snap Gauges. A *snap gauge* is another fixed gauge with the gauging members specially arranged for measuring diameters, thickness, and lengths. A typical (may also be called *adjustable*) *external measuring snap gauge* is shown in Figure 7.11f. It consists of a C-frame with gauging members in the jaw of the frame. Figure 7.11g shows other types of snap gauges. Threads can be checked with thread plug gauges, thread ring gauges, thread snap gauges, or a screw thread micrometer. *Thread snap gauges* have two pairs of gauging elements combined in one gauge. With appropriate gauging elements, these gauges may be used to check the maximum and minimum material limits of external screw threads in one pass.

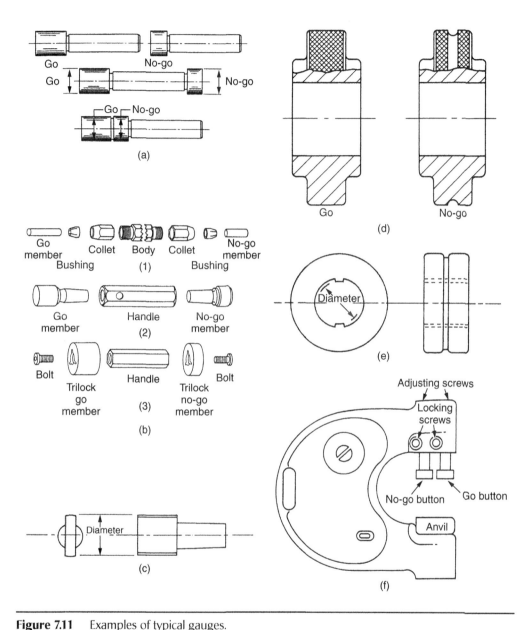

Figure 7.11   Examples of typical gauges.
Reprinted with permission of the Society of Manufacturing Engineers, *Manufacturing Processes and Materials,* 4th edition, copyright 2000.

An example of a thread snap gauge is shown in Figure 7.11h. In some cases special snap gauges may be desired. The example in Figure 7.11i illustrates the use of a special double-end snap gauge for inspecting the outside diameter of a narrow groove.

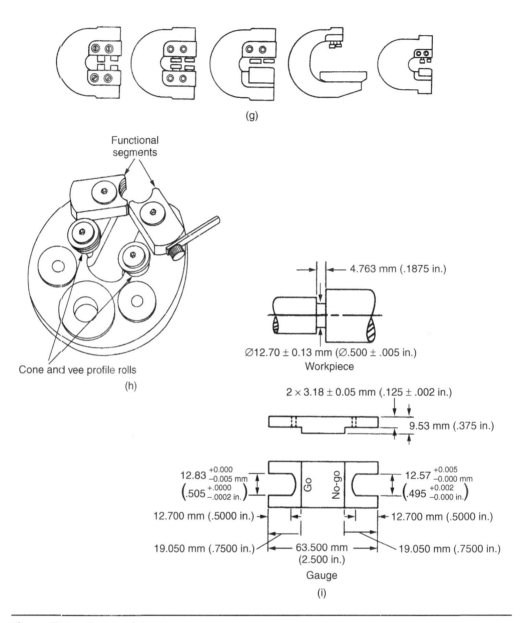

(g)

Functional
segments

Cone and vee profile rolls

(h)

— 4.763 mm (.1875 in.)

⌀12.70 ± 0.13 mm (⌀.500 ± .005 in.)
Workpiece

2 × 3.18 ± 0.05 mm (.125 ± .002 in.)

9.53 mm (.375 in.)

$12.83\,^{+0.000}_{-0.005}$ mm
$\left(.505\,^{+.0000}_{-.0002}\text{ in.}\right)$

Go

No-go

$12.57\,^{+0.005}_{-0.000}$ mm
$\left(.495\,^{+0.002}_{-0.000}\text{ in.}\right)$

12.700 mm (.5000 in.)

12.700 mm (.5000 in.)

19.050 mm (.7500 in.) ←— 63.500 mm —→ 19.050 mm (.7500 in.)
(2.500 in.)

Gauge

(i)

Figure 7.11   *Continued.*

Spline Gauges. A *spline gauge* is often used to inspect splined workpieces prior to assembly. External splines are checked with internal-toothed rings, whereas internal splines are checked with external-toothed plugs. Figure 7.11j shows the two basic types of fixed-limit spline gauges: composite and sector gauges. *Composite gauges* have the same number of teeth as that of the part. *Sector gauges* have only two sectors of teeth 180° apart. These gauges are further subdivided into go and no-go gauges. View 1 of Figure 7.11j shows a go composite ring gauge, and a no-go sector ring gauge is illustrated in view 2.

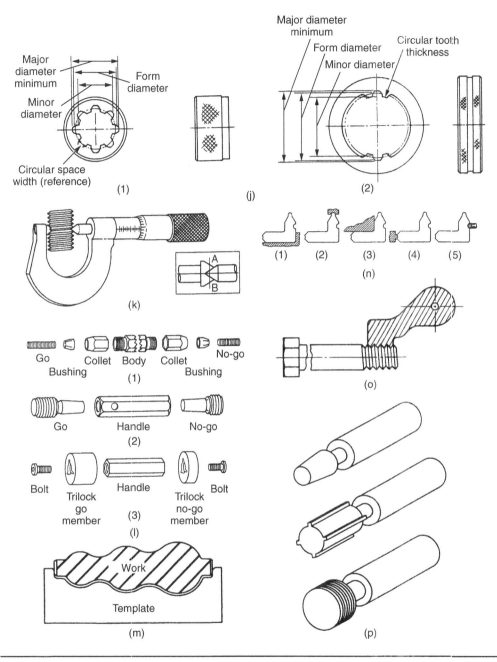

Figure 7.11   *Continued.*

Screw Thread Micrometer. A *screw thread micrometer,* such as the one shown in Figure 7.11k, has a specially designed spindle and anvil so that externally threaded parts can be measured. Screw thread micrometers are generally designed to measure threads within a narrow range of pitches. *Thread plug gauges* are similar in

Ring gauge accepting part that is out-of-round

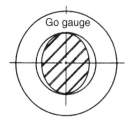

Step 1: Go gauge slips over shaft   Step 2: No-go gauge will not slip over shaft

Snap gauge rejecting part that is out-of-round

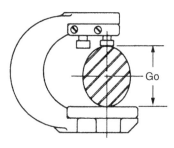
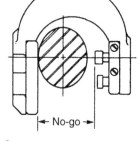

Step 1: Part enters go gauge   Step 2: Same part when inspected 90° from
and does not enter no-go   first position will enter no-go gauge

(q)

Figure 7.11   *Continued.*

design to cylindrical plug gauges except that they are threaded. They are designed to check internal threads. Typical thread plug gauges, such as those shown in Figure 7.11l, consist of a handle and one or two thread gauge members. Depending on the size of the gauging member, the member can be held in the handle using a threaded collet and bushing design (view 1), a taper lock design (view 2), or a trilock design (view 3).

Templates. To check a specified profile, *templates* may be used. They may also be used to control or gauge special shapes or contours in manufactured parts. These templates are normally made from thin, easy-to-machine materials. An example of a contour template for inspecting a turned part is shown in Figure 7.11m. To visually inspect or gauge radii or fillets, special templates, such as those shown in Figure 7.11n, may be used. The five basic uses of such templates are (1) inspection of an inside radius tangent of two perpendicular planes, (2) inspection of a groove, (3) inspection of an outside radius tangent to two perpendicular planes, (4) inspection of a ridge segment, and (5) inspection of roundness and diameter of a shaft.

Screw Pitch Gauges. The pitch of a screw may be checked with a *screw pitch gauge.* To determine the pitch, the gauge is placed on the threaded part as shown in

Figure 7.11o. A drawback of using screw pitch gauges is their inability to give an adequate check on thread form for precision parts.

Special Gauges. It is sometimes necessary to design special gauges for checking special part features such as square, hexagonal, or octagonal holes. Figure 7.11p shows some special plug gauges for checking the profile or taper of holes. As an inspection tool, a snap gauge is sometimes a better choice than a ring gauge. Figure 7.11q illustrates how a ring gauge may accept an out-of-roundness condition that would otherwise be rejected by a snap gauge. *Flush pin gauges* check the limits of dimensions between surfaces in a specified position.

3. TRANSFER GAUGES

Transfer-type linear measuring devices are typified by the spring caliper, spring divider, firm joint caliper, telescoping gauge, and small-hole gauge.

The outside caliper is used as an end measure to measure or compare outside dimensions, while the inside caliper is used for inside diameters, slot and groove widths, and other internal dimensions. They are quite versatile but, due to their construction and method of application, their accuracy is somewhat limited.

Telescope gauges are T-shaped instruments. They consist of a pair of telescoping tubes connected to a handle. The tubes are called *legs* or *plungers*. They are closed at their outer ends and spring-loaded to push them apart. The knob on the end of the handle provides careful adjustment of a locking action. The spacing of the outer end duplicates the distance between the reference and measured points of the part features. Telescope gauges are made in sizes to measure holes from one-half to six inches.

4. MEASUREMENT SCALES

Measuring instruments may use analog or digital displays. Some instruments use both. The micrometer shown in Figure 7.4 has an analog display, where measurement can be defined on a continuous display of values. The micrometer shown in Figure 7.8, however, uses a digital display, which makes the reading much easier.

Depending on the application, measurement scales can be either graduated or nongraduated. Examples of graduated scales are those used on rules, vernier calipers, micrometers, dial indicators, and so on. Some tools, such as surface plates, the sine bar, calipers, straightedges, and so on, use nongraduated scales.

REFERENCE

ASME (American Society of Mechanical Engineers). 1985. *ANSI/ASME B89.1.12M-1985 Methods for Performance Evaluation of Coordinate Measuring Machines.* New York: ASME.

BIBLIOGRAPHY

Bosch, J. A. 1984. *66 Centuries of Measurement.* Dayton, OH: Sheffield Measurement Division.
Bucher, J. 2004. *The Metrology Handbook.* Milwaukee: ASQ Quality Press.

Busch, T., R. Harlow, and R. Thompson. 1998. *Fundamentals of Dimensional Metrology*. 3rd ed. Albany, NY: Delmar.

Curtis, M. 2010. *Handbook of Dimensional Measurement*. 4th ed. New York: Industrial Press.

De Silva, G. M. S. 2002. *Basic Metrology for ISO 9000 Certification*. Woburn, MA: Butterworth-Heinemann.

Dotson, C. L. 2006. *Fundamentals of Dimensional Metrology*. 5th ed. New York: Delmar Cengage Learning.

Farago, F. T., and M. Curtis. 1994. *Handbook of Dimensional Measurement*. 3rd ed. New York: Industrial Press.

Gaylor, J. F. W., and C. R. Shotbolt. 1964. *Metrology for Engineers*. London: Cassell & Company.

ISO (International Organization for Standardization). 2007. *ISO Guide 99: International Vocabulary of Metrology—Basic and General Concepts and Associated Terms (VIM)*. Geneva: ISO.

Kimothi, S. K. 2002. *The Uncertainty of Measurements: Physical and Chemical Metrology and Analysis*. Milwaukee: ASQ Quality Press.

NASA (National Aeronautics and Space Administration). 2010. *Measurement Uncertainty Analysis: Principles and Methods, NASA Measurement Quality Assurance Handbook*. Washington, DC: NASA.

———. 2010. *Measuring and Test Equipment Specifications, NASA Measurement Quality Assurance Handbook*. Washington, DC: NASA.

Pennella, R. 2004. *Managing the Metrology System*. Milwaukee: ASQ Quality Press.

Rashed, A. F., and A. M. Hamouda. 1974. *Technology for Real Quality*. Alexandria, Egypt: Egyptian University House.

Schrader, G. F., and A. K. Elshennawy. 2000. *Manufacturing Processes and Materials*. 4th ed. Dearborn, MI: Society of Manufacturing Engineers.

Simpson, J. A. 1981. "Foundations of Metrology." *Journal of Research of the National Bureau of Standards* 86 (3): 36–42.

Wunchell, W. 1996. *Inspection and Measurement in Manufacturing*. Dearborn, MI: Society of Manufacturing Engineers.

Chapter 8

B. Special Gauges and Applications

1. ELECTRONIC GAUGING TOOLS

Certain gauges are called *electric limit gauges* because they have the added feature of a rack stem that actuates precision switches. The switches connect lights or buzzers to show limits and also may energize sorting and corrective devices.

An *electronic gauge* gives a reading in proportion to the amount a stylus is displaced. It may also actuate switches electronically to control various functions. Figure 8.1 shows an example of an electronic gauge and diagrams of the most common kinds of gauge heads. The *variable inductance* or *inductance-bridge transducer* has an alternating current fed into two coils connected to a bridge circuit. The reactance of each coil changes as the position of the magnetic core is changed. This changes the output of the bridge circuit. The *variable transformer* or *linear variable displacement transformer* (LVDT) transducer has two opposed coils into which currents are induced from a primary coil.

The net output depends on the displacement of the magnetic core. The deflection of a strain gauge transducer is sensed by the changes in length and the resistance of strain gauges on its surface. This is also a means for measuring forces. Displacement of a variable capacitance head changes the air gap between plates of a condenser connected in a bridge circuit. In every case, an alternating current is fed into the gauge as depicted in Figure 8.1e. The output of the gauge head

79

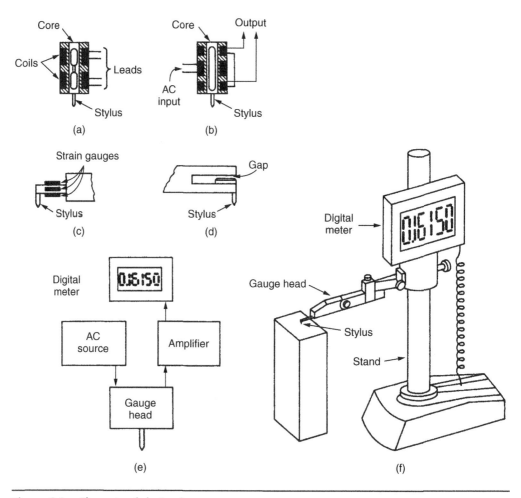

Figure 8.1   Elements of electronic gauges.

circuit is amplified electronically and displayed on a dial or digital readout. In some cases the information from the gauge may be recorded on tape or stored in a computer.

Advantages

Electronic gauges have several advantages:

1. They are very sensitive (they commonly read to a few micrometers).

2. Output can be amplified as much as desired; a high-quality gauge is quite stable.

3. They can be used as an absolute measuring device for thin pieces up to the range of the instrument.

The amount of amplification can easily be switched, and three or four ranges are common for one instrument. Two or more heads may be connected to one amplifier to obtain sums or differences of dimensions, as for checking thickness, parallelism, and so on.

Other types of electronic test equipment commonly used in practice are oscilloscopes, multimeters, and pyrometers. Brief descriptions of such instruments follow. For additional information, see Hickman (2001), Mazur (2009), and Burgess (2006).

Oscilloscopes

The basic principle of oscillography is the representation, by graphical means, of a voltage that is varying (Hickman 2001).

A typical oscilloscope is box shaped with a visual screen, attached connectors, and control knobs and buttons on the front panel. A grid is normally drawn on the screen. Each square in the grid is known as a *division*. One of the most common uses of the oscilloscope is to troubleshoot the failure of electronic equipment by graphically showing signals that indicate failure or malfunctioning.

Multimeters

A *multimeter* is an electronic gauge that combines more than one function in a single unit. Multimeters use either analog or digital displays. A multimeter is commonly used for fault discovery, in fieldwork of electronic or telecommunications technicians, or as a basic workshop instrument. Standard measurements of a multimeter include voltage, current, and resistance (see Mazur 2009).

Pyrometers

A *pyrometer* is a noncontact measuring instrument that is often used to measure the temperature of an object by measuring its self-emission and emissivity.

Pyrometers are widely used in medical monitoring of the human body temperature, sheet-metal manufacturing, and other semiconductor manufacturing. For more information, see Burgess (2006).

2. AUTOMATIC GAUGING COMPONENTS

As industrial processes become automated, gauging must keep pace. Automated gauging is performed in two general ways. The first is in-process or on-the-machine control by continuous gauging of the work. The second is post-process or after-the-machine gauging control. Here, the parts coming off the machine are passed through an automatic gauge. A control unit responds to the gauge to sort pieces by size, and adjusts or stops the machine if parts are found out of limits.

Interferometry

Light waves of any kind are of invariable length and are the standard for ultimate measures of distance. Basically, all interferometers divide a light beam and send it along two or more paths. Then the beams are recombined and always show interference in some proportion to the differences between the lengths of the paths. One of the simplest illustrations of this phenomenon is the optical flat and a monochromatic light source of known wavelength.

The optical flat is a plane lens, usually a clear fused quartz disk, that is about 51–254 mm (2–10 in.) in diameter and 13–25 mm (0.5–1 in.) thick. The faces of a flat are accurately polished to nearly true planes; some have surfaces within 25 nm (0.000001 in.) of true flatness.

Helium is commonly used in industry as a source of monochromatic or single wavelength light because of its convenience. Although helium radiates a number of wavelengths of light, the portion that is emitted with a wavelength of 587 nm (0.00002313 in.) is so much stronger than the rest that the other wavelengths are practically unnoticeable.

Principle of Operation. The principle of light wave interference and the operation of the optical flat are illustrated in Figure 8.2a, wherein an optical flat is shown resting at a slight angle on a workpiece surface. Energy, in the form of light waves, is transmitted from a monochromatic light source to the optical flat. When a ray of light reaches the bottom surface of the flat, it is divided into two rays. One ray is reflected from the bottom of the flat toward the eye of the observer, while the other continues downward and is reflected, and loses one-half wavelength upon striking the top of the workpiece. If the rays are in phase when they re-form, their energies reinforce each other and they appear bright. If they are out of phase, their energies cancel each other and they are dark. This phenomenon produces a series of light and dark fringes or bands along the workpiece surface and the bottom of the flat, as illustrated in Figure 8.2b.

The distance between the workpiece and the bottom surface of the optical flat at any point determines which effect takes place. If the distance is equivalent to some whole number of half wavelengths of the same monochromatic light, the reflected rays will be out of phase, thus producing dark bands. This condition exists at positions x and z of Figure 8.2a. If the distance is equivalent to some odd number of quarter wavelengths of the light, the reflected rays will be in phase with each other and produce light bands. The light bands would be centered between the dark bands. Thus, a light band would appear at position y in Figure 8.2a.

Since each dark band indicates a change of one-half wavelength in distance separating the work surface and flat, measurements are made by simply counting the number of these bands and multiplying that number by one-half the wavelength of the light source.

This procedure may be illustrated by the use of Figure 8.2b as follows:

- The diameter of a steel ball is compared with a gauge block of known height

- Assume a monochromatic light source with a wavelength of 0.5875 µm (23.13 µin.)

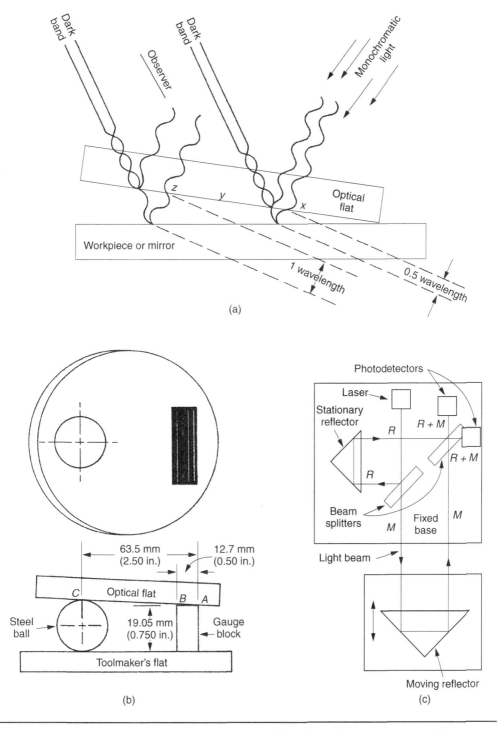

Figure 8.2   (a) Light wave interference with an optical flat, (b) application of an optical flat, (c) diagram of an interferometer.

Reprinted with permission of the Society of Manufacturing Engineers, *Manufacturing Processes and Materials*, 4th edition, copyright 2000.

- From the block, it is obvious that the difference in elevation of positions *A* and *B* on the flat is (4 × 0.5875)/2 = 1.175 μm ([4 × 23.13]/2 or 46.26 μin.)

- By simple proportion, the difference in elevation between points *A* and *C* is equal to (1.175 × 63.5)/12.7 = 5.875 μm ([46.26 × 2.5]/0.5 = 231.3 μin.)

- Thus, the diameter of the ball is 19.05 + 0.005875 = 19.055875 mm (0.750 + 0.0002313 = 0.7502313 in.)

Optical Flats. Optical flats are often used to test the flatness of surfaces. The presence of interference bands between the flat and the surface being tested is an indication that the surface is not parallel with the surface of the flat.

The way dimensions are measured by interferometry can be explained by moving the optical flat of Figure 8.2a in a direction perpendicular to the face of the workpiece or mirror. It is assumed that the mirror is rigidly attached to a base and that the optical flat is firmly held on a true slide. As the optical flat moves, the distance between the flat and the mirror changes along the line of traverse, and the fringes appear to glide across the face of the flat or mirror. The amount of movement is measured by counting the number of fringes and fraction of a fringe that pass a mark. It is difficult to precisely superimpose a real optical flat on a mirror or the end of a piece to establish the end points of a dimension to be measured. This difficulty is overcome in sophisticated instruments by placing the flat elsewhere and by optical means reflecting its image in the position relative to the mirror in Figure 8.2a. This creates interference bands that appear to lie on the face of and move with the workpiece or mirror. The image of the optical flat can be merged into the planes of the workpiece surfaces to establish beginning and end points of dimensions.

Machine Tool Application. A simple interferometer for measuring movements of a machine tool slide to nanometers (millionths of an inch) is depicted in Figure 8.2c. A strong light beam from a laser is split by a half mirror. One component becomes the reference *R* and is reflected solely over the fixed machine base. The other part *M* travels to a reflector on the machine side and is directed back to merge with ray *R* at the second beam splitter. Their resultant is split and directed to two photodetectors. The rays pass in and out of phase as the slide moves. The undulations are converted to pulses by an electronic circuit; each pulse stands for a slide movement equal to one-half the wavelength of the laser light. The signal at one photodetector leads the other according to the direction of movement.

When measurements are made to nanometers (millionths of an inch) by an interferometer, they are meaningful only if all causes of error, such as temperature, humidity, air pressure, oil films, impurities, and gravity, are closely controlled. Consequently, a real interferometer is necessarily a highly refined and complex instrument; only its basic elements have been described here.

Machine Vision

One of the most common applications of machine vision is in the inspection of manufactured products such as semiconductor components. Machine vision is also used in the automotive industry and has medical applications as well.

There are numerous applications of machine vision (see, for example, Davies [2005] and Myler [1999]). Examples of such applications include:

- Coordinate measurements of large components

- Safety and hazard applications

- Security applications

- Coordinate measuring machines

- Automated guided vehicles

- Automated manufacturing

- Medical imaging processing

- Complex surgical procedures

- Robotics

- Product failure identification

X-Ray Inspection

The quality control role played by X-ray systems in the nondestructive testing and inspection of electronic assemblies—especially today's printed circuit boards, densely packed with area array components—is well understood. X-ray imaging is especially valuable in rapid prototyping and reverse-engineering applications in electronics, avionics, advanced materials research, and casting and other manufacturing industries. Unlike machine vision and optical inspection equipment, which can image only the surface of samples, X-ray systems penetrate substrate materials to expose hidden features. They are ideal for detecting and evaluating features in complex micro-electro-mechanical systems (MEMS) and micro-opto-electro-mechanical systems (MOEMS) devices, and for revealing cracks, voids, delamination, and other crucial component anomalies in prototype electronic assemblies, medical devices, and castings during preproduction (Rademaker 2005).

Once a need for X-ray inspection has been determined, the user must decide whether two-dimensional or three-dimensional imaging is best for the particular task at hand. While 2-D X-ray imaging is sufficient in many cases, 3-D X-ray images can reveal complex inner structures in an intuitive format so that anomalies can be viewed in their 3-D positions (Rademaker 2005).

3. PNEUMATIC GAUGING COMPONENTS

A *pneumatic gauge* is a means of measuring, comparing, or checking dimensions by sensing the flow of air through the space between a gauge head and workpiece surface. The gauge head is applied to each workpiece in the same way, and the clearance between the two varies with the size of the piece. The amount the airflow is restricted depends on the clearance. Four basic types of air gauge sensors are shown in Figure 8.3. All have a controlled constant-pressure air supply.

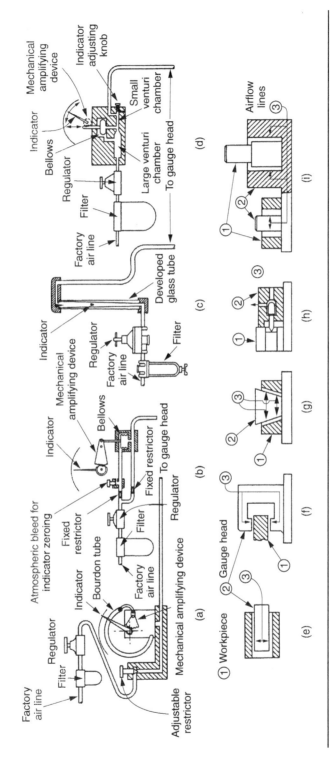

Figure 8.3   Diagram of air gauge principles.
Reprinted with permission of the Society of Manufacturing Engineers, *Manufacturing Processes and Materials*, 4th edition, copyright 2000.

The *back-pressure gauge* responds to the increase in pressure when the airflow is reduced. It can magnify from 1000:1 to over 5000:1, depending on the range, but is somewhat slow because of the reaction of air to changing pressure.

The *differential gauge* is more sensitive. Air passes through this gauge in one line to the gauge head and in a parallel line to the atmosphere through a setting valve. The pressure between the two lines is measured.

There is no time lag in the *flow gauge*, where the rate of airflow raises an indicator in a tapered tube. The dimension is read from the position of the indicating float. This gauge is simple, does not have a mechanism to wear, is free from hysteresis, and can amplify to over 500,000:1 without accessories.

The *venturi gauge* measures the drop in pressure of the air flowing through a venturi tube. It combines the elements of the back-pressure and flow gauges and is fast, but sacrifices simplicity.

A few of the many kinds of gauge heads and applications are also shown in Figure 8.3. An air gauge is basically a comparator and must be an asset to a master for dimension or to two masters for limits. The common single gauge head is the plug. Practically all inside and outside linear and geometric dimensions can be checked by air gauging.

Air match gauging, depicted in Figure 8.3i, measures the clearance between two mating parts. This provides a means of controlling an operation to machine one part to a specified fit with the other. A *multidimension gauge* has a set of cartridge or contact gauge heads (Figure 8.3h) to check several dimensions on a part at the same time. The basic gauge sensor can be used for a large variety of jobs, but a different gauge head and setting master are needed for almost every job and size.

A major advantage of a pneumatic gauge is that the gauge head does not have to tightly fit the part. A clearance of up to 0.08 mm (0.003 in.), and even more in some cases, between the gauge head and workpiece is permissible. Thus, no pressure is needed between the two, which causes wear, and the gauge head may have a large allowance for any wear that does occur. The flowing air helps keep surfaces clean.

The lack of contact makes air gauging particularly suitable for checking against highly finished and soft surfaces. Because of its loose fit, a pneumatic gauge is easy and quick to use. An inexperienced inspector can measure the diameter of a hole to 25 nm (0.000001 in.) in a few seconds with a pneumatic gauge. The same measurement (to 25 µm [0.001 in.]) with a vernier caliper by a skilled inspector may take up to one minute. The faster types of pneumatic gauges are adequate for high-rate automatic gauging in production.

4. FORCE GAUGING

Torque is the force applied on an object from a distance. A torque wrench is a simple tool that is used in applications such as a nut or a bolt needing tightening, or adjustment to a desired value. The application of force in this case may be manual or motorized depending on the type of application and nut or bolt size.

5. ENVIRONMENTAL INSTRUMENTATION

Some quality assurance applications for monitoring environmental conditions include hygrometers, data loggers, and chart recorders.

A *hygrometer* is an instrument for measuring the relative humidity in the atmosphere. Sometimes, such measurements are needed in a metrology laboratory to make sure experimental factors studies are not affected by humidity, temperature, pressure, or other environmental factors.

SUMMARY OF GAUGE USES AND APPLICATIONS

Table 8.1 provides a useful summary of the uses and applications of the gauges presented in Chapters 7 and 8.

Table 8.1   Summary of commonly used gauges and their applications.

Gauge	Uses and applications
Steel rule	Used effectively as a line measuring device, which means that the ends of a dimension being measured are aligned with the graduations of the scale, from which the length is read directly.
Depth rule	Used for measuring the depth of slots, holes, and so on.
Vernier caliper	Typifies instruments using the vernier principle of measurement. Outside dimensions are measured between the lower jaws, inside dimensions over the tips of the upper jaws.
Digital-reading caliper	Provides LCD readouts in either millimeters or inches and operates by a microprocessor-based system. Capable of retaining a reading in the display when the tool is used in an area where visibility is restricted.
Vernier height gauge	Similar to a vernier caliper except that the fixed jaw has been replaced by a fixed base, and the sliding jaw may have a scriber attached to it for layout work, or a dial indicator for measuring or comparing operations.
Digital micrometer	Used in measuring diameters, thicknesses, inside dimensions, heights, and outside dimensions.
Dial indicator	Used for applications such as measuring heights, flatness, diameters, and so on.
Optical comparator	Used for measuring complicated or difficult shapes and other configurations.
Gauge block	Dimensional measurement standards that are used to calibrate other measuring devices. They come in sets of different grades depending on the desired measurement accuracy required. Each set has many blocks of incremental lengths. These blocks are stacked together (wringed) to build a desired length.

Continued

Table 8.1 *Continued.*

Working gauge	Used by the machine operator or shop inspector to check the dimensions of parts as they are being produced. They usually have limits based on the piece being inspected.
Inspection gauge	Used by personnel to inspect purchased parts when received, or manufactured parts when finished. These gauges are designed and manufactured so as not to reject any product previously accepted by a properly designed and functioning working gauge.
Reference or master gauge	Used for checking the size or condition of other gauges, and representing as exactly as possible the physical dimensions of the product.
Limit gauge	Often called a go/no-go gauge, establishes the high and low limits prescribed by the tolerance on a dimension. A limit gauge may be either double-end or progressive.
Ring gauge	Used for checking outside dimensions, such as the limit sizes of a round shaft.
Plug gauge	Used for checking inside dimensions.
Snap gauge	A fixed gauge with the gauging members specially arranged for measuring diameters, thickness, and lengths.
Spline gauge	An instrument for inspecting splined workpieces prior to assembly.
Screw-thread micrometers	Designed to measure threads within a narrow range of pitches.
Template	Used to control or gauge special shapes or contours in manufactured parts, or to check a specified profile.
Screw-pitch gauge	Used to check the pitch of a screw.
Oscilloscope	Used for troubleshooting electronic equipment failure by graphically showing signals that indicate failure or malfunction.
Multimeter	An electronic gauge that combines more than one function in a single unit. Multimeters use either analog or digital displays. Common uses include fault discovery, fieldwork of electronic or telecommunications technicians, or as a basic workshop instrument. Standard measurements taken using a multimeter include voltage, current, and resistance.
Pyrometer	A noncontact instrument for measuring an object's temperature by measuring its self-emission and emissivity.
Pneumatic gauge	Used for measuring, comparing, or checking dimensions by sensing the flow of air through the space between a gauge head and workpiece surface.
Optical flats	Often used to test the flatness of surfaces. The presence of interference bands between the flat and the surface being tested is an indication that the surface is not parallel with the surface of the flat.
Machine vision	Used for inspection of manufactured products such as semiconductor components and automotive parts, and also used in medical applications.
X-ray systems	Used in nondestructive testing and inspection of electronic assemblies, especially printed circuit boards.

REFERENCES

Burgess, G. K. 2006. *Pyrometers: The Measurement of High Temperatures*. Palm Springs, CA: Wexford College Press.

Davies, E. R. 2005. *Machine Vision: Theory, Algorithms, Practicalities*. 3rd ed. San Francisco: Morgan Kaufmann/Elsevier.

Hickman, I. 2001. *Oscilloscopes*. 5th ed. Burlington, MA: Newnes/Elsevier.

Mazur, G. 2009. *Digital Millimeter Principles*. 4th ed. Orland Park, IL: American Technical Publishers.

Myler, H. 1999. *Fundamentals of Machine Vision*. Bellingham, WA: Society of Photo-Optical Instrumentation Engineers.

Rademaker, G. 2005. "X-Ray Inspection." *Quality Digest*, April. Accessed November 27, 2018. Available at http://www.qualitydigest.com/april05/articles/01_article.shtml.

BIBLIOGRAPHY

Bosch, J. A. 1984. *66 Centuries of Measurement*. Dayton, OH: Sheffield Measurement Division.

Bucher, J. 2004. *The Metrology Handbook*. Milwaukee: ASQ Quality Press.

Busch, T., R. Harlow, and R. Thompson. 1998. *Fundamentals of Dimensional Metrology*. 3rd ed. Albany, NY: Delmar.

Curtis, M. 2010. *Handbook of Dimensional Measurement*. 4th ed. New York: Industrial Press.

Dotson, C. L. 2006. *Fundamentals of Dimensional Metrology*. 5th ed. New York: Delmar Cengage Learning.

Farago, F. T., and M. Curtis. 1994. *Handbook of Dimensional Measurement*. 3rd. ed. New York: Industrial Press.

Gaylor, J. F. W., and C. R. Shotbolt. 1964. *Metrology for Engineers*. London: Cassell & Company.

Kimothi, S. K. 2002. *The Uncertainty of Measurements: Physical and Chemical Metrology and Analysis*. Milwaukee: ASQ Quality Press.

NASA (National Aeronautics and Space Administration). 2010. *Measuring and Test Equipment Specifications, NASA Measurement Quality Assurance Handbook*. Washington, DC: NASA.

Pennella, R. 2004. *Managing the Metrology System*. Milwaukee: ASQ Quality Press.

Rashed, A. F., and A. M. Hamouda. 1974. *Technology for Real Quality*. Alexandria, Egypt: Egyptian University House.

Schrader, G. F., and A. K. Elshennawy. 2000. *Manufacturing Processes and Materials*. 4th ed. Dearborn, MI: Society of Manufacturing Engineers.

Simpson, J. A. 1981. "Foundations of Metrology." *Journal of Research of the National Bureau of Standards* 86 (3): 36–42.

Wunchell, W. 1996. *Inspection and Measurement in Manufacturing*. Dearborn, MI: Society of Manufacturing Engineers.

Chapter 9

C. Gauge Selection, Handling, and Use

1. THE RULE OF TEN (10:1 RULE)

The *rule of ten*—sometimes referred to as the *10:1 rule* or the *gauge maker's rule*—serves as a baseline or beginning for the gauge selection process. It states that inspection measurements should be better than the tolerance of a dimension by a factor of 10, and that calibration standards should be better than inspection measurements by a factor of 10.

As an example, if the tolerance on a shaft diameter is ±0.025 mm (±0.0010 in.), then the increment of measurement on the inspection instrument should be as small as 0.025/10 = 0.0025 mm (0.00010 in.).

Similarly, the increment of measurement of the calibration standard for that inspection instrument should be as small as 0.025/10 = 0.0025 mm (0.00010 in.).

2. GAUGE SELECTION

Once the smallest increment of measurement for an instrument has been determined, candidate instruments need to be evaluated in terms of the degree of satisfaction they offer relative to the following performance criteria:

1. *Accuracy.* The ability to measure the true magnitude of a dimension

2. *Linearity.* The accuracy of the measurements of an instrument throughout its operating range

3. *Magnification.* The amplification of the output reading on an instrument over the actual input dimension

4. *Repeatability.* The ability of the instrument to achieve the same degree of accuracy on repeated applications (often referred to as *precision*)

5. *Resolution.* The smallest increment of measurement that can be read on an instrument

6. *Sensitivity.* The smallest increment of difference in dimension that can be detected by an instrument

7. *Stability or drift.* The ability of an instrument to maintain its calibration over a period of time

In addition to the above, other selection criteria may include factors such as the shape and size of the measured part or workpiece, workpiece material, capabilities of the metrology laboratory, and environment (such as the temperature, atmospheric pressure, humidity, and other conditions of the metrology laboratory).

Consideration of these factors, along with cost and operation convenience, should help in selecting an appropriate measuring or gauging device for a particular inspection operation. For operating convenience, most instruments are or can be equipped with discrete digital readout devices. Most of these can be connected to microprocessors or computers for data recording and analysis.

3. GAUGE HANDLING, PRESERVATION, AND STORAGE

The following guidelines for the control of measuring and monitoring devices are taken from section 7.6 of ISO 9000:2000:

- Determine the monitoring and measurement to be undertaken and the monitoring and measuring devices needed to provide evidence of conformity of product to determined requirements (7.2.1).

- Establish processes to ensure that monitoring and measurement can and will be carried out in a manner that is consistent with the monitoring and measurement requirements.

- Where necessary to ensure valid results, the measuring equipment shall:

  – Be calibrated or verified at specified intervals or prior to use against traceable standards.

- Where no standards exist, the basis for calibration or verification shall be recorded

- Be adjusted or readjusted as necessary

- Be identified to enable calibration status to be determined

- Be safeguarded from adjustments

- Be protected from damage and deterioration during handling, maintenance, and storage

- Assess and record the validity of previous measuring results when equipment is found to be nonconforming to requirements.

- Take appropriate action on any product affected.

- Record results of calibration and verification.

- Software—confirm ability prior to initial use and reconfirm as necessary, when used in monitoring and measurement of specified requirements.

- Define and implement effective and efficient measuring and monitoring processes, including verification of products and processes to ensure satisfaction of interested parties. This includes:

  - Surveys

  - Simulations

  - Other measurement and monitoring activities

- Measuring and monitoring processes should include confirmation that the devices are fit for use and are maintained to suitable accuracy and accepted standards, and be able to identify the status of the devices.

- Consider means to eliminate potential errors from processes.

In addition, section 8.2.4 discusses the monitoring and measurement of products. The following are points that management should consider:

- Monitor and measure the characteristics of the product to verify that requirements have been met.

- Perform monitoring and measurement at appropriate stages in the realization process in accordance with planned arrangements (7.1).

- Maintain evidence of conformity to acceptance criteria.

- Records shall indicate the person(s) authorizing release of product (4.2.4).

- Can't release and deliver product until all planned arrangements (7.1) have been completed (relevant authority and/or customer waiver).

- Establish and specify measurement requirements for products (including acceptance criteria). It should be planned and performed in order to verify that the requirements of interested parties have been achieved and used to improve the realization process.

- When selecting measurement methods, consider:
  - Types of product characteristics
  - Equipment, software, and tools required
  - Location of suitable measurement points in the realization process sequence
  - Qualification of people, materials, products, processes, and the quality management system (QMS)
  - Final inspection
  - Recording the results

4. GAUGE CORRELATION

Gauge correlation is about making sure the data collected from different gauges are credible. With so much focus these days on collecting and analyzing data, and on implementing Six Sigma and other initiatives to ensure that design goals are met, it's possible that critical details such as the level of accuracy of the data have gone unnoticed (Jenkins 2003).

ISO/IEC 17025 sets the guidelines of gauge correlation and measurement techniques. There are several factors that contribute to gauge correlation, such as measurement uncertainty, validation of data collection systems, interlaboratory assessment, and part features and characteristics, as well as equipment and operator variability. A gauge repeatability and reproducibility (gauge R&R) study is an effective way to isolate the different types of variation that exist in a measurement. The gauge R&R study is presented in detail in Chapter 13.

Although ISO/IEC 17025 doesn't—and indeed can't—mandate perfect measurements, it does provide some assurance that laboratory measurement quality is evaluated, defined, and controlled. The following concepts address several issues to consider when evaluating a testing or calibration supplier, given the current state of accreditation (Jenkins 2003):

- *Estimated measurement uncertainty.* These values are needed when determining calibration or test adequacy and subsequent conclusions. These values are also needed when performing actual measurements on certain parts or assemblies. If a part or an assembly is close to being out of specification, the estimated uncertainty may be the deciding factor in the acceptance/rejection decision.

- *Calibration and/or test data.* Prior to submitting a device or object for testing or calibration, a list of the measurements that will be taken and a sample data report should be available.

- *Ensuring quality of calibration and testing results.* ISO/IEC 17025 lists many methods that labs can use to ensure the quality of their calibration and testing results. One of these, proficiency testing, has since become a requirement by many accreditation bodies.

REFERENCE

Jenkins, J. D. 2003. "The Uncertain World of Measurement Credibility." *Quality Digest,* October. Accessed November 28, 2018. Available at http://www.qualitydigest.com/oct03/articles/03_article.shtml.

BIBLIOGRAPHY

Bosch, J. A. 1984. *66 Centuries of Measurement.* Dayton, OH: Sheffield Measurement Division.

Bucher, J. 2004. *The Metrology Handbook.* Milwaukee: ASQ Quality Press.

Busch, T., R. Harlow, and R. Thompson. 1998. *Fundamentals of Dimensional Metrology.* 3rd ed. Albany, NY: Delmar.

Curtis, M. 2010. *Handbook of Dimensional Measurement.* 4th ed. New York: Industrial Press.

De Silva, G. M. S. 2002. *Basic Metrology for ISO 9000 Certification.* Woburn, MA: Butterworth-Heinemann.

Dotson, C. L. 2006. *Fundamentals of Dimensional Metrology.* 5th ed. New York: Delmar Cengage Learning.

Farago, F. T., and M. Curtis. 1994. *Handbook of Dimensional Measurement.* 3rd ed. New York: Industrial Press.

Gaylor, J. F. W., and C. R. Shotbolt. 1964. *Metrology for Engineers.* London: Cassell & Company.

ISO (International Organization for Standardization). 2007. *ISO Guide 99: International Vocabulary of Metrology—Basic and General Concepts and Associated Terms* (VIM). Geneva: ISO.

Kimothi, S. K. 2002. *The Uncertainty of Measurements: Physical and Chemical Metrology and Analysis.* Milwaukee: ASQ Quality Press.

NASA (National Aeronautics and Space Administration). 2010. *Measurement Uncertainty Analysis: Principles and Methods, NASA Measurement Quality Assurance Handbook.* Washington, DC: NASA.

Pennella, R. 2004. *Managing the Metrology System.* Milwaukee: ASQ Quality Press.

Rashed, A. F., and A. M. Hamouda. 1974. *Technology for Real Quality.* Alexandria, Egypt: Egyptian University House.

Schrader, G. F., and A. K. Elshennawy. 2000. *Manufacturing Processes and Materials.* 4th ed. Dearborn, MI: Society of Manufacturing Engineers.

Simpson, J. A. 1981. "Foundations of Metrology." *Journal of Research of the National Bureau of Standards* 86 (3): 36–42.

Wunchell, W. 1996. *Inspection and Measurement in Manufacturing.* Dearborn, MI: Society of Manufacturing Engineers.

Chapter 10

D. Surface Plate Tools and Techniques

> 1. *Surface plate equipment.* Select and use height gauges, V-blocks, and other indicators, to measure various types of features. Understand the care, cleaning, calibration, and lapping of a surface plate. (Apply)
>
> 2. *Angle measurement instruments.* Identify and use protractors, sine bars, and angle blocks. (Apply)
>
> Body of Knowledge II.D

1. SURFACE PLATE EQUIPMENT

Surface Plate

A *surface plate* provides a true reference plane from which measurement can be made. A cast-iron surface plate is a heavy-ribbed, boxlike casting that stands on three points (establishing a plane) and has a thick and well-supported flat top plate. New plates generally have an average of 18 bearing spots on an area of 6.5 cm² ($\approx$ 1 in.²) that do not vary from a true plane by more than 0.005 mm (0.0002 in.). The use of natural stones for surface plates is becoming increasingly popular because of their hardness, resistance to corrosion, minimum response to temperature change, and nonmagnetic qualities. Figure 10.1 shows a granite surface plate used in inspection work.

Care and Maintenance of Granite Surface Plates. Quality magazine published useful guidelines for the care and maintenance of granite surface plates in its May 2003 issue. The following is a summary of these guidelines.

1. Be sure the granite surface plate is supported on the support system that comes furnished with the plate. The support system is normally a hard rubber pad that is attached to the bottom of the plate that forms a non-distortable three-point support system. The pads are installed during manufacturing, and the plate rests on them throughout lapping, inspection, and shipping. The pads are a critical factor in surface plate accuracy and must not be removed.

97

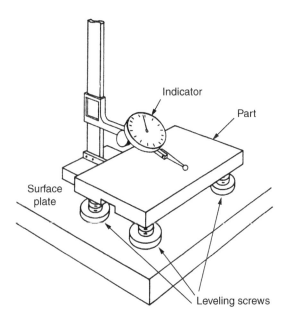

Figure 10.1   Granite surface plate for checking the flatness of a part, with dial indicator and leveling screws.

Reprinted with permission of the Society of Manufacturing Engineers, *Manufacturing Processes and Materials*, 4th edition, copyright 2000.

2. Do not move or lift a granite surface plate with a forklift by placing the metal forks against the granite. Always have protective padding between the metal forks and the granite. Preferably, use nylon slings to move it.

3. After setup, granite surface plates require little care and maintenance. Keep the surface clean and free from excess buildup of dust, dirt, grease, grime, or other foreign particles. Using a dirty surface plate will cause inaccuracies in tool readings and also cause the plate to wear faster. Environment and usage have a lot to do with the frequency of cleaning; however, as a rule, if a plate is used daily, it should be cleaned daily.

4. When using a granite surface plate, carefully set the workpiece to be measured on the plate. A sudden jolt or blow to the plate with a heavy metal object can damage the surface. Also, when inspecting workpieces, especially small parts, try to use different areas of the surface plate. Inspecting in the same spot on the surface plate month after month, year after year, will wear the plate in that spot.

5. Surface plates should be checked on a regular basis for wear. The plates can be checked with a reading gauge that is designed for this purpose.

Other important issues include:

- Calibration of overall flatness traceable to NIST can be performed periodically using an autocollimator.

- When inspection indicates that the overall accuracy of a surface plate is out of tolerance, the plate should be relapped.

- When using threaded inserts in a granite surface plate, use the minimum torque required on hold-down bolts, but do not exceed limits. A caution label is attached to all granite surface plates that are furnished with threaded inserts.

Dial Indicators

Indicating gauges and comparators magnify the amount a dimension deviates above or below a standard to which the gauge is set. Most indicate in terms of actual units of measurement, but some show only whether a tolerance is within a given range. The ability to measure to 25 nm (0.00001 in.) depends on the magnification, resolution, and accuracy of the setting gauges and staging of the workpiece and instrument.

Dial indicators are simple mechanical indicating gauges. An example of a dial indicator is depicted in Figure 10.2. Movement of stem *A* is transmitted from the

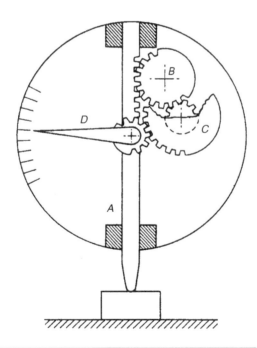

Figure 10.2   Simple dial indicator mechanism.

Reprinted with permission of the Society of Manufacturing Engineers, *Manufacturing Processes and Materials*, 4th edition, copyright 2000.

rack to compound gear trains *B* and *C* to pointer *D*, which moves around a dial face. Springs exert a constant force on the mechanism and return the pointer to its original position after the object being measured is removed.

Dial indicators are used for many kinds of measuring and gauging operations. One example is that of inspecting a workpiece, as illustrated in Figure 10.3. They also serve to check machines and tools, alignments, and cutter runout. Dial indicators are often incorporated in special gauges in measuring instruments, as exemplified by the indicating micrometer of Figure 7.8 in Chapter 7.

Vernier Height Gauge

The *vernier height gauge* is similar to a vernier caliper except the fixed jaw has been replaced by a fixed base, and the sliding jaw may have a scriber attached to it for layout work, or a dial indicator for measuring or comparing operations. See Chapter 7 for more information on vernier height gauges.

2. ANGLE MEASUREMENT INSTRUMENTS

The unit standard of angular measurement is the degree. The measurement and inspection of angular dimensions are somewhat more difficult than linear

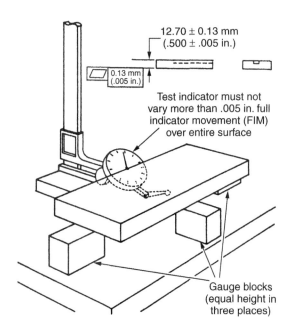

Figure 10.3   An application of dial indicators for inspecting flatness by placing the workpiece on gauge blocks and checking full indicator movement (FIM).

measures and may require instruments of some complexity if a great deal of angular precision is required.

Sine Bar

The *sine bar* is a hardened, precision-ground, and lapped tool for measuring angles in different settings. It is a relatively simple device for precision measuring and checking of angles. It consists of an accurately ground, flat-steel straightedge with precisely affixed round buttons that are a definite distance apart and of identical diameters.

Sine Bar Application. Figure 10.4 illustrates one method of applying a sine bar in the determination of the angle α on the conical surface of the part located on the surface plate.

For precise results, a sine bar must be used on true surfaces. In Figure 10.4:

- The center-to-center distance of the sine bar buttons = 127 mm (5 in.)

- The distances A and B are determined by means of gauge blocks or a vernier height gauge:

$$A = 25.400 \text{ mm } (1.0000 \text{ in.})$$

$$B = 89.794 \text{ mm } (3.5352 \text{ in.})$$

Thus,

$$\text{sine } \alpha = \frac{(89.794 - 25.400)}{127.00}$$

$$= 0.50704$$

From trigonometric tables, the angle α is 30° 28′.

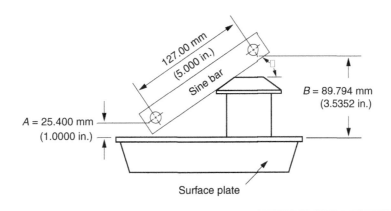

A = 25.400 mm (1.0000 in.)

127.00 mm (5.000 in.)

Sine bar

B = 89.794 mm (3.5352 in.)

Surface plate

Figure 10.4   Application of a sine bar.

Sine Tables. *Sine tables* are a further development of the sine bar. The sine table has a larger working surface and is much more robust than the sine bar. It is more suitable for larger, heavier parts.

Angle Blocks

Angle blocks are simply hardened blocks that are further lapped to precise angles and can be wrung together like gauge blocks. Unlike gauge blocks, angle blocks can be added or subtracted, as shown in Figure 10.5.

Protractors

Protractors are used to measure angles. A *simple protractor* consists of a graduated head (in degrees) along a semicircle. A blade is connected on the center pin. By rotating the blade on the pin, any angle from 0° to 180° can be measured.

Combination Sets. Combination protractor and depth gauges combine a movable graduated depth gauge with a protractor head.

The *combination set* consists of a center head, protractor, and square with a 45° surface, all of which are used individually in conjunction with a steel rule. The heads are mounted on the rule and clamped in any position along its length by means of a lock screw. The center head is used to scribe bisecting diameters of the end of a cylindrical piece to locate the center of the piece. The protractor reads directly in degrees. Both the square head and the protractor may contain a small spirit level.

A *bevel protractor* utilizes a vernier scale to show angles as small as 5 minutes. The universal bevel protractor is widely used for angle measurement in many applications. The word "universal" refers to the capacity of the instrument to be adaptable to a great variety of work configurations and angular interrelations (Farago and Curtis 1994).

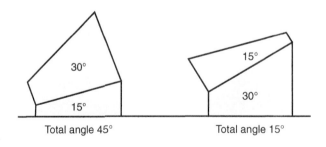

Figure 10.5   Addition and subtraction of angle blocks.

REFERENCE

Farago, F. T., and M. Curtis. 1994. *Handbook of Dimensional Measurement*. 3rd ed. New York: Industrial Press.

BIBLIOGRAPHY

Bosch, J. A. 1984. *66 Centuries of Measurement*. Dayton, OH: Sheffield Measurement Division.

Bucher, J. 2004. *The Metrology Handbook*. Milwaukee: ASQ Quality Press.

Busch, T. 1966. *Fundamentals of Dimensional Metrology*. Albany, NY: Delmar.

Busch, T., R. Harlow, and R. Thompson. 1998. *Fundamentals of Dimensional Metrology*. 3rd ed. Albany, NY: Delmar.

Curtis, M. 2010. *Handbook of Dimensional Measurement*. 4th ed. New York: Industrial Press.

Dotson, C. L. 2006. *Fundamentals of Dimensional Metrology*. 5th ed. New York: Delmar Cengage Learning.

Elshennawy, A. K., and Weheba, G. S. 2000. *Manufacturing Processes and Materials*. 5th ed. Dearborn, MI: Society of Manufacturing Engineers.

Farago, F. T. 1968. *Handbook of Dimensional Measurement*. New York: Industrial Press.

Gaylor, J. F. W., and C. R. Shotbolt. 1964. *Metrology for Engineers*. London: Cassell & Company.

Leach, R., ed. 2011. *Optical Measurement of Surface Topography*. Berlin/Heidelberg: Springer-Verlag.

Martin, C. 2005. *The Surface Texture Book*. London: Thomas and Hudson.

NASA (National Aeronautics and Space Administration). 2010. *Measuring and Test Equipment Specifications, NASA Measurement Quality Assurance Handbook*. Washington, DC: NASA.

Schrader, G. F., and A. K. Elshennawy. 2000. *Manufacturing Processes and Materials*. 4th ed. Dearborn, MI: Society of Manufacturing Engineers.

Simpson, J. A. 1981. "Foundations of Metrology." *Journal of Research of the National Bureau of Standards* 86 (3): 36–42.

Wunchell, W. 1996. *Inspection and Measurement in Manufacturing*. Dearborn, MI: Society of Manufacturing Engineers.

Chapter 11

E. Specialized Inspection Equipment

---

1. *Measuring mass.* Describe and apply weights, balances, and scales. (Apply)

2. *Measuring finish.* Describe and apply profilometers, and fingernail comparators. (Apply)

3. *Measuring shape and profile.* Describe and apply mechanical comparators, roundness testers, precision spindles, and profile tracers. (Apply)

4. *Optical equipment.* Describe and apply optical comparators, optical flats, and microscopes. (Apply)

5. *Software-based measurement systems.* Define and describe the use of digital cameras, in-line optical sensors, vision inspection systems (white light/blue light), articulating arms, laser trackers, contracers, and other digital systems for product inspection. Recognize software limitations with regard to locating functional datums, target points and areas, hole positions and the basic operation of the x, y, and z axes. (Understand)

6. *Measuring inclination.* Define and describe the measurement of the slope or slant of various equipment (mechanical/laser). (Understand)

Body of Knowledge II.E

1. MEASURING MASS

Weights, Balances, and Scales

Weight is a force, resulting from the action of gravity, that measures how hard an object presses down on a scale. Weight and mass are two fundamentally different quantities, though the weight of an object can provide an indication of the quantity that we are actually measuring—mass.

Measuring Weight and Mass

SI units (International System of Units) are used to measure physical quantities. The SI unit of mass is the kilogram, which is also used in the everyday language of measuring weights. The SI unit of weight is kg m/sec^2 (note that the weight is the mass times the gravitational acceleration [m/sec^2]). In the United States, the pound can be either a unit of weight (force) or a unit of mass.

In the international standard ISO 80000-4:2006, describing the basic physical quantities and units in mechanics as part of the international standard ISO/IEC 80000, the definition of *weight* is given as (F = m.g). We can convert between weight and mass. F (or W) is the force due to gravity (weight), *m* is the mass of the object, and *g* is the local acceleration of free fall (which equals approximately 9.8 m/s^2 or 32.2 ft/s^2).

Balances and Scales

Numerous types of balances and scales are used to cover a wide range of weight for different applications, such as laboratory, industrial, and research. They offer different capacities, resolutions, requirements, and configurations. Examples include:

- Lab balances
- Analytical balances
- Precision balances
- Industrial scales
- Bench scales
- Counting scales
- Mechanical balances
- Spring scales
- Jewelry scales

There are several national and international organizations that establish standards for weights and measures:

- The National Institute for Standards and Technology (NIST) is the nation's standards-defining authority. NIST Handbook 44 (*Specifications, Tolerances, and Other Technical Requirements for Weighing and Measuring Devices*) sets forth the minimum requirements for standards used primarily to test commercial or legal-for-trade weighing devices for compliance. NIST Special Publication 881 (*Guide for the Use of the International System of Units (SI)*) is also a good source.

- The American Society for Testing and Materials (ASTM) establishes test standards for materials, products, systems, and services for a wide range of industries. ASTM developed E617-97, *Standard Specification for*

Laboratory Weights and Precision Mass Standards to cover various classes of weights and mass standards used in laboratories.

- The International Organization of Legal Metrology (OIML) is an intergovernmental treaty organization. OIML has two grades of membership: member states (countries that actively participate in technical activities) and corresponding members (countries that join the OIML as observers). It was established in 1955 in order to promote the global harmonization of legal metrology procedures. OIML has since developed a worldwide technical structure, providing metrological guidelines for the elaboration of national and regional requirements concerning the manufacture and use of measuring instruments for legal metrology applications.

- The International Organization for Standardization (ISO) is the world's largest developer and publisher of international standards. ISO is a network of the national standards institutes of 164 countries, with one member per country, and a central secretariat in Geneva, Switzerland, that coordinates the system.

Surface Metrology

The measurement of the difference between what a surface actually is and what it is intended to be is the definition of *surface metrology*. *Surface measurement*, however, is involved with the relationship of a surface on the workpiece to a reference that is not actually on the workpiece. The most common aspect of surface metrology is the measurement of surface roughness as an average deviation from a mean centerline (Bosch 1984).

The quality of surface finish is commonly specified along with linear and geometric dimensions. This is becoming more common as product demands increase, because surface quality often determines how well a part performs. Heat-exchanger tubes transfer heat better when their surfaces are slightly rough rather than highly finished. Brake drums and clutch plates also work better with some degree of surface roughness. On the other hand, bearing surfaces for high-speed engines wear-in excessively and fail sooner if not highly finished, but still need certain surface textures to hold lubricants. Thus, there is a need to control all surface features, not just roughness alone.

Surface Characteristics. The American National Standards Institute (ANSI) has provided a set of standard terms and symbols to define such basic surface characteristics as profile, roughness, waviness, flaws, and lay. A *profile* is defined as the contour of any section through a surface. *Roughness* refers to relatively finely spaced surface irregularities such as might be produced by the action of a cutting tool or grinding wheel during a machining operation. *Waviness* consists of those surface irregularities that are of greater spacing than roughness. Waviness may be caused by vibrations, machine or work deflections, warping, and so on. *Flaws* are surface irregularities or imperfections that occur at infrequent intervals and at random locations. Such imperfections as scratches, ridges, holes, cracks,

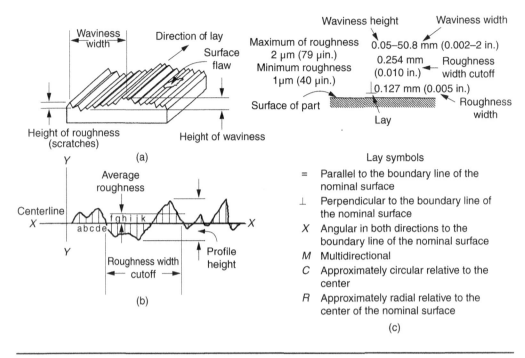

Lay symbols

=	Parallel to the boundary line of the nominal surface
⊥	Perpendicular to the boundary line of the nominal surface
X	Angular in both directions to the boundary line of the nominal surface
M	Multidirectional
C	Approximately circular relative to the center
R	Approximately radial relative to the center of the nominal surface

(c)

Figure 11.1   (a) Typical surface highly magnified, (b) profile of surface roughness, (c) surface quality specifications.

Reprinted with permission of the Society of Manufacturing Engineers, *Manufacturing Processes and Materials*, 4th edition, copyright 2000.

pits, checks, and so on, are included in this category. *Lay* is defined as the direction of the predominant surface pattern. These characteristics are illustrated in Figure 11.1.

Surface Quality Specifications. Standard symbols to specify surface quality are included in Figure 11.1c. Roughness is most commonly specified and is expressed in units of micrometers (μm), nanometers (nm), or microinches (μin.). According to ANSI/ASME B46.1-1985, the standard measure of surface roughness adopted by the United States and approximately 25 countries around the world is the arithmetic average roughness R_a (formerly AA or CLA). R_a represents the arithmetic average deviation of the ordinates of profile height increments of the surface from the centerline of that surface. An approximation of the average roughness may be obtained by:

$$R_{a+} = \frac{y_a + y_b + y_c + \ldots + y_n}{n}$$

where

R_{a+} = Approximation of the average roughness

$y_a \ldots y_n$ = Absolute values of the surface profile coordinates

n = Number of sample measurements

The longest length along the centerline over which the measurements are made is the roughness-width cutoff or sampling length. In many cases, the maximum peak-to-valley height on a surface (R_y) is about four to five times greater than the average surface roughness as measured by R_a. This may present a problem for precision parts having small dimensional tolerances. For example, a flat surface on a part with an R_a of 0.4 µm (16 µin.) might very well have a peak-to-valley height (R_y) of 1.6 µm (64 µin.) or greater. If the tolerance on that dimension is 0.0025 mm (0.0001 in.), then the 0.4 µm (16 µin.) surface finish represents nearly two-thirds of the permissible tolerance. The root-mean-square (rms) is used to designate surface roughness. If measurements are made (plus or minus) from the centerline like the ones in Figure 11.1b, the rms average is:

$$\left[\left(\sum y_i^2\right)/n\right]^{\frac{1}{2}}$$

where

y_i = Sum of measurements taken from the centerline

n = Number of measurements

RMS values are about 11% larger than R_a figures. Some surface roughness measuring instruments have a scale with numbers labeled "rms" and a scale calibrated in R_a values. On such instruments, the number called "rms" is a root-mean-square value only when the profile is sinusoidal. Waviness height alone may be specified, or it may be accompanied by a width specification. Thus, in Figure 11.1c, the specification 0.05–50.8 mm (0.002–2 in.) means that no waves over 0.05 mm (0.002 in.) high are allowed in any 50.8 mm (2 in.) of length. If no width specification is given, it is usually implied that the waviness height specified must be held over the full length of the work. Other specifications in Figure 11.1c are less common.

2. MEASURING FINISH

Waviness and roughness are measured separately. Waviness may be measured by sensitive dial indicators. A method of detecting gross waviness is to coat a surface with a high-gloss film, such as mineral oil, and then reflect it in a regular pattern, such as a wire grid. Waviness is revealed by irregularities or discontinuities in the reflected lines.

Many optical methods have been developed to evaluate surface roughness. Some are based on interferometry. One method of interference contrast makes different levels stand out from each other by lighting the surface with two out-of-phase rays. Another method projects a thin ribbon of light at 45° onto a surface. This appears in a microscope as a wavy line depicting the surface irregularities. For a method of replication, a plastic film is pressed against a surface to take its imprint. The film may then be plated with a thin silver deposit for microscopic examination, or it may be sectioned and magnified. These are laboratory methods and are economical in manufacturing only where other means are not feasible, such as on a surface inaccessible to a probe.

Except for extremely fine surface finishes that require laboratory measurement, most manufacturers measure surface texture at or near the workplace. A

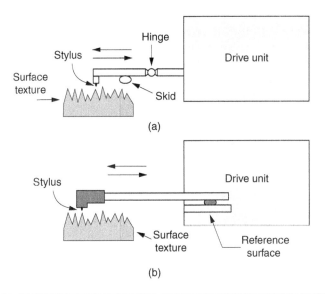

Figure 11.2 (a) Skid-type or average surface finish measuring gauge, (b) skidless or profiling gauge.

Reprinted with permission of the Society of Manufacturing Engineers, *Manufacturing Processes and Materials*, 4th edition, copyright 2000.

variety of instruments, called *surface finish gauges*, are commercially available as either handheld or table-mounted devices. These require only moderate skill, and roughness measurements are displayed on a dial, digital readout, chart, or a digital output for statistical process control (SPC) depending on the type of instrument used. Most of these instruments employ a diamond-tipped stylus that is moved across the surface of the part to sense the point-to-point roughness of that surface. As illustrated in Figure 11.2, there are two basic types of gauges: *skid* or *skidless*. The skid type shown in Figure 11.2a has a hinged probe that rides the work surface in proximity to a fairly large skid that also contacts the work surface. The skid-type instruments usually have inductive transducers and are used predominantly for averaging measurements of surface roughness, but not waviness. The skid filters out waviness. Most portable or handheld instruments are the skid type, and they are reasonably accurate for roughness measurements in the range of 0.30–0.51 µm (12–20 µin.) R_a.

The skidless type of instrument illustrated in Figure 11.2b has a built-in reference surface that permits the probe to sense both long- and short-wavelength variations in surface conditions. Thus, these can be used to measure both waviness and roughness, as well as surface inclination (straightness). These instruments are often referred to as *profiling gauges*, and they usually generate a profile chart on paper or on a computer screen. The international standard for the assessment of surface texture, ISO/R 468 (ISO Recommendations on Roughness Measurements, ISO/R 468, 1878, 1880, TC 57), defines three parameters: R_a (CLA), R_z, and R_{Max}, all measured relative to a straight mean line:

1. R_a (centerline average) value is the arithmetic mean of the departures of a profile from the mean line. It is normally determined as the mean result of several consecutive sample lengths L.

2. R_z (10-point height) is the average distance between the five height peaks and the five deepest valleys within the sampling length, and is measured perpendicular to it.

3. R_{Max} is the maximum peak-to-valley height within the sampling length.

Other parameters of surface measurement are defined as follows:

1. R_{tm} is the average value of R_{Max}'s for five consecutive sampling lengths.

2. R_p is the maximum profile height from the mean line within the sampling length. R_{pm} is the mean value of R_p's determined over five sampling lengths.

3. PC (peak count) is the number of peak/valley pairs per inch projecting through a band of width b centered about the mean line.

3. MEASURING SHAPE AND PROFILE

Most of the recent applications of shape and profile measurements employ comparators and other devices for measuring roundness.

Comparators

Comparators normally employ dial indicators for their operation and come in different varieties: mechanical, optical, electronic, and pneumatic. *Optical projectors*, also known as *optical comparators*, employ a system in which light rays are directed against the object and then reflected back through a projection lens onto a screen. The projections are large enough to accurately measure small configurations of objects. Optical comparators are explained in more detail in a later section.

Measurement of Roundness

Geometrically, a part can be said to be round in a given cross section if there exists within the section a point from which all points on the periphery are equidistant. In practice, however, the radius of nominally round parts tends to vary from point to point. Thus, the problem found by the metrologist is one of displaying and assessing these variations, and correctly interpreting the results.

Although many methods have been used for roundness measurement, only those that provide valid radial-deviation data lend themselves to standardization and consistent, accurate measurement of all out-of-roundness conditions. For this reason, current industry, national, and international standards primarily cover measurements taken with precision spindle-type instruments with the data recorded on a polar chart. Precision spindle instruments are those in which the spindle supports and rotates the part, with the gauge tip remaining stationary, and those in which the spindle rotates the gauge tip about the part, which remains stationary (Drews 1978).

4. OPTICAL EQUIPMENT

Optical inspection instruments fall into four basic categories: optical comparators, video systems, microscopes, and laser systems (Klepp 1998).

Optical comparators use traditional optics to magnify and project an object's image onto a glass screen. This type of optical inspection instrument is by far the most widely used and is also the least expensive method of optical noncontact inspection. It also offers the greatest versatility because lightweight parts, as well as ones weighing hundreds of pounds, can be inspected on many available instruments. The optical edge finder, developed later, eliminates the operator's subjectivity from the measurement and allows the system to be fully automated.

Optical comparators are available in numerous styles and configurations from domestic as well as international manufacturers. Typical options include projection screen sizes from 10" to 80", horizontal or vertical light path configurations, profile and surface illumination systems, various stage travel options, magnifications from 5× to 200×, and digital readout options such as a basic two-axis display and automatic computer numeric-controlled systems. Accuracy and repeatability of instruments currently available can vary depending on the feature being inspected but usually fall within ±0.00010" under certain conditions.

Inspection microscopes use traditional optics to magnify a desired detail. Many inspection microscopes today are coupled with a video system and offer manual optical inspection as well as automated video inspection. These microscopes generally work best when inspecting lightweight and/or flat parts.

Laser inspection instruments, the latest development in optical inspection, offer the greatest accuracy of any optical inspection instrument. Accuracy and repeatability within ±0.0000010" can be expected under certain conditions. This type of instrument utilizes a reflected laser beam to accurately determine distances by using time-delay calculations. Extremely specialized, laser inspection instruments require fixturing to locate the laser device as well as substantial setup time to align the instrument. This measurement method is best suited for specialized production inspection or calibration applications.

Optical Tooling

Telescopes and accessories to establish precisely straight, parallel, perpendicular, or angled lines are called *optical tooling*. Two of many applications are shown in Figure 11.3a and b. One is to check the straightness and truth of ways of a machine tool bed at various places along the length. The other is to establish reference lanes for measurements on a major aircraft or missile component. Such methods are especially necessary for large structures. Accuracy of 1 part in 200,000 is regularly realized; this means that a point at a distance of 2.5 m (100 in.) can be located within 13 μm (0.0005 in.). Common optical tooling procedures are autocollimation, autoreflection, planizing, leveling, and plumbing.

Autocollimation is done with a telescope having an internal light that projects a beam through the crosshairs to a target mirror, as indicated in Figure 11.3a. If the mirror face is truly perpendicular to the line of sight, the crosshair image will be reflected back on itself. The amount the reflected image deviates from the actual reticle image is an indication of the tilt in the target. A target may have a cross-line pattern for alignment with the line of sight. An autocollimated image is not clear

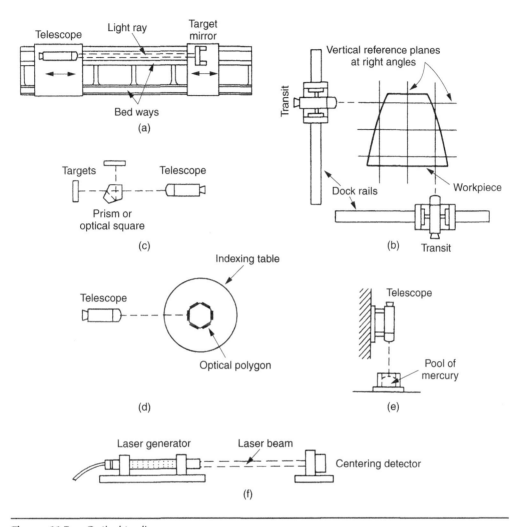

Figure 11.3   Optical tooling.
Reprinted with permission of the Society of Manufacturing Engineers, *Manufacturing Processes and Materials*, 4th edition, copyright 2000.

for distances over 15.2 m (50 ft), and thus a somewhat less accurate method must be used. This is *autoreflection*, with an optical flat containing a cross-line pattern mounted on the end of the illuminated telescope and focused to twice the distance of the target mirror. If the mirror is perpendicular to the line of sight, the pattern of the flat is reflected in coincidence with the crosshairs in the telescope.

Planizing involves fixing planes at 90° to other planes or with a line of sight. This may be done from accurately placed rails on which transits are mounted in a tooling dock, as indicated in Figure 11.3b. A *transit* is a telescope mounted to swing in a plane perpendicular to a horizontal axis. Square lines also may be established with an optical square or planizing prism mounted on or in front of a telescope, as depicted in Figure 11.3c. Angles may be precisely set by autocollimating on the precisely located faces of an optical polygon, as in Figure 11.3d.

Leveling establishes a horizontal line of sight or plane. This may be done with a telescope fitted with a precision spirit level to fix a horizontal line of sight. A transit or sight level set in this manner may be swiveled around a vertical axis to generate a horizontal plane. *Plumbing*, shown in Figure 11.3e, consists of autocollimating a telescope from the surface of a pool of mercury to establish a vertical axis.

An advanced step in optical tooling is the use of the intense light beam of a laser. A centering detector, shown in Figure 11.3f, has four photocells equally spaced (top and bottom and on each side) around a point. Their output is measured and becomes equalized within the device, and is centered with the beam. This provides a means to obtain alignment with a straight line. Squareness may be established by passing a laser beam through an optical square.

Optical Comparators. Many industrial products and component parts are so small and of such complex configuration that they require magnification for accurate discernment. For this purpose, a number of measuring and gauging instruments using various optical systems (such as the toolmakers' microscope, the binocular microscope, and the optical projecting comparator) find wide application for the inspection of small parts and tools.

The *optical projecting comparator* projects a magnified image of the object being measured onto a screen. A workpiece is staged on a table to cast a shadow in a beam of light in *diascopic projection*, as shown in Figure 11.4. The outline of the part is magnified and displayed on a screen. In *episcopic projection*, the light rays are directed against the side of the object and then reflected back through the projection lens.

Optical projection provides a means to check complex parts quickly to small tolerances. Commonly, a translucent drawing is placed over the screen with lines drawn to scale for the contour of the part, the limits of the outline, or critical features such as angles. For instance, the outline of a part can be compared with

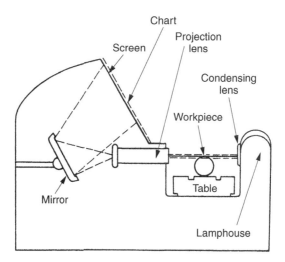

Figure 11.4   Optical comparator system.

Reprinted with permission of the Society of Manufacturing Engineers, *Manufacturing Processes and Materials*, 4th edition, copyright 2000.

a drawing on the screen, allowing deviations in the whole contour to be quickly seen. A fixture or stage may be supplied for a part to mount all pieces in the same way in rapid succession. The table can be adjusted in coordinate directions by micrometer screws or servomotors to 2 µm (0.0001 in.). Table positions can be determined from the micrometer readings or from digital readout devices. Thus, a part can be displaced to measure precisely how far a line is from a specified position. In addition, the screen can be rotated to a vernier scale to measure angular deviations in minutes or small fractions of a degree. Magnifications for commercial comparators range from 5× to as much as 500×. For example, at 250× magnification, 0.0020 mm (0.0008 in.) on a part becomes 0.500 mm (0.0197 in.) on the screen, which is readily discernible. The horizontal optical comparator shown in Figure 11.5 is table mounted and has a 356 mm (14 in.) diameter viewing screen.

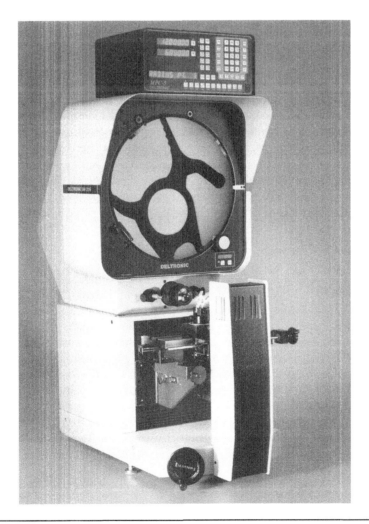

Figure 11.5   Horizontal optical comparator with a 356 mm (14 in.) viewing screen, digital readout, and edge-sensing device.

Courtesy Deltronic Corporation.

The designation "horizontal" means that the lens system is mounted horizontally, as illustrated in Figure 11.4. Comparators are also commercially available with a vertical lens configuration to facilitate the staging of thin parts.

One of the features of the comparator shown in Figure 11.5 is a computerized digital readout (DRO) located on top of the machine. The DRO has a two-axis digital display for establishing measurements in the x–y plane. In addition, a 12-character alphanumeric readout displays help messages, setup options, and the results of calculations. A fiber-optic edge-sensing device is also shown extending down the upper left portion of the screen. This device permits the DRO to precisely indicate the edges of a part. A 16-key external keypad mounted on the lower base provides the option of using the dedicated keys as they are identified or redefining any or all of those keys to execute any of 20 different programs containing up to 100 keystrokes each. The keypad includes a joystick capable of x-, y-, and z-axis control.

Another feature of the comparator shown in Figure 11.5 is an electric screen protractor that reads angles directly to either a minute or 0.01°. The angular setting of the protractor is displayed on an LED readout at the bottom right of the screen. The machine has built-in provisions for either diascopic projection (contour illumination) or episcopic projection (surface illumination) via a high-intensity tungsten-halogen light source. Lens changing is facilitated by the use of quick-change bayonet-type lens holders. Seven different lens magnifications are available, ranging from 5× to 100×, all with an optical focusing range of 76 mm (3 in.). This comparator includes the edge-sensing device, the computerized DRO, and one lens.

More discussion on optical flats and optical tooling can be found in Chapter 8.

5. SOFTWARE-BASED MEASUREMENT SYSTEMS

Machine Vision Systems

Typically, a machine vision system can be used to automate go/no-go inspection decisions, assembly verification, part location and machine guidance, gauging/dimensional measurements, feedback control loops, and a host of other tasks. It is a common misperception that machine vision systems provide generic optical detection and processing capabilities. While every system includes essential functions, most customers require some level of customization in development and should be cautious of vendors claiming to have one-size-fits-all solutions. Systems perform best in their own tightly controlled, highly specialized environment (Fabel 1997).

Application requirements vary drastically by industry, but a number of components are common to every machine vision system. Technology is rapidly evolving in all these areas, creating new opportunities on the manufacturing floor. (Fabel 1997):

Machine vision systems are used in a variety of applications, including (Heil and Daigle 2004):

- Pharmaceutical packaging inspection. The machine vision systems are typically 21 CFR Part 11 compliant.

- Automotive lightbulb inspection that meets Six Sigma standards.

- Inspection of fill levels of opaque bottles using smart cameras in concert with X-ray technology.

- Inspection to ensure Teflon coating is properly applied to medical inhalant canisters.

Machine vision systems range from small, integrated units, or *smart cameras*, to PC-controlled units with frame-grabbers, to high-speed multiprocessor systems. At the high end, recent improvements include enhanced communications capabilities, permitting use with Ethernet, PC, robots, and Fieldbus systems with transfer of data and images to an enterprise file server or display for operator use. Dramatic changes also have been made in small integrated units, also called smart cameras, that include the basic camera with lens and camera functions to control speed and exposure, a microprocessor, and software (Axelrod 2010).

Laser Trackers

A laser tracker is a portable coordinate measurement machine that uses a laser beam to accurately measure and inspect the features of an object in 3-D space. It excels in terms of accuracy, reliability, and durability for large-scale metrology applications (Martin 2015).

Handheld scanning, probing, and machine control products have increased the laser tracker's flexibility, and the number of possible applications has grown exponentially.

As laser tracker technology has become more economically accessible, the laser trackers themselves have also become smaller, lighter, faster, and increasingly user-friendly. Options such as battery operation and IP54 (ingress protection) have allowed today's laser trackers to go where people never thought possible. As demand for this technology continues to expand, its availability has expanded to even the smallest job shops. Laser trackers are demanding a second look from a larger audience.

Other Digital Inspection Systems

There are several triggering events that can justify making the investment in a new vision system. One is a desire to increase the throughput of an inspection system, which is set by the camera frame rate. A new requirement for color vision can also prompt movement to a new camera system. The need to replace failing components or ones that have become obsolete can be another triggering event. Virtually all of the new development in vision is based on digital camera systems, so a replacement for an obsolete analog camera that offers equivalent or better performance may be difficult to find. A digital camera quickly becomes the obvious choice.

Another benefit of digital inspection is the ability gained to augment camera operation with customized preprocessing. This preprocessing can represent unique value-added elements to the vision system's capabilities, or free the host PC from some imaging tasks to manage additional work. Digital cameras afford developers an opportunity to either lower the requirements for (and the cost of) the host PC's performance or increase system capabilities without requiring a new PC.

With all of the options and flexibility available, digital inspection makes sense. With the right camera, machine vision systems can increase productivity, simplify maintenance, and lower their total cost of ownership (Ahearn 2015).

6. MEASURING INCLINATION

Various companies have instruments that are designed for measuring slopes or inclination. Among these is the MSEM Inclinometer. An *inclinometer*, or *tilt sensor*, is an instrument used for measuring slope, tilt, or inclination by using gravity. An inclinometer creates an artificial plane defined at zero degrees, and measures the change in angle with respect to this plane. These devices go by many names, including tilt sensor, level sensor, bubble level, angle indicator, clinometer, protractor, slope meter, tilt meter, tilt/slope alarm, pitch/roll indicator, or level gauge. All refer to the same device (2GIG Engineering Undated).

REFERENCES

Ahearn, G. 2015. "Digital Inspection: A Camera Perspective." *Quality Magazine*, May 1. Accessed November 27, 2018. Available at https://www.qualitymag.com/articles/ 92585-digital-inspection-a-camera-perspective.

Axelrod, N. 2010. "Machine Vision Adds Value." *Quality Magazine*, February 25.

Bosch, J. A. 1984. *66 Centuries of Measurement*. Dayton, OH: Sheffield Measurement Division.

Drews, W. E. 1978. "How to Measure Roundness." *Tooling and Production*, June, 156–60.

Fabel, G. 1997. "Machine Vision Systems Looking Better All the Time." *Quality Digest*, October. Accessed November 27, 2018. Available at http://www.qualitydigest.com/ oct97/html/machvis.html.

Heil, P., and R. Daigle. 2004. "Vision Systems Look to the Future." *Quality Digest*, March. Accessed November 27, 2018. Available at https://www.qualitydigest.com/mar04/ articles/01_article.shtml.

ISO (International Organization for Standardization). 2006. ISO 80000-4:2006 *Quantities and units—Part 4: Mechanics*. Geneva: ISO.

Klepp, P. 1998. "The Future of Optical Gaging Equipment." *Quality Digest*, July. Accessed November 27, 2018. Available at http://www.qualitydigest.com/july98/html/ optgage.html.

Martin, J. 2015. "Tracking Progress: Re-evaluating Laser Tracker Technology." *Quality Magazine*, January 1. Accessed November 27, 2018. Available at https://www.quality mag.com/articles/92339-tracking-progress-re-evaluating-laser-tracker-technology.

2GIG Engineering. Undated. "MEMS Inclinometer." Accessed July 26, 2018. Available at https://www.2gig-eng.com/mems-inclinometer.

BIBLIOGRAPHY

American Society of Mechanical Engineers (ASME). 1985. *ANSI/ASME B89.1.12M-1985 Methods for Performance Evaluation of Coordinate Measuring Machines*. New York: ASME.

————. 1986. ANSI/ASME B46.1-1095 *Surface Texture—Surface Roughness, Waviness, and Lay*. New York: ASME.

Bucher, J. 2004. *The Metrology Handbook*. Milwaukee: ASQ Quality Press.

Curtis, M. 2010. *Handbook of Dimensional Measurement*. 4th ed. New York: Industrial Press.

Dotson, C. L. 2006. *Fundamentals of Dimensional Metrology*. 5th ed. New York: Delmar Cengage Learning.

Elshennawy, A. K., I. Ham, and P. H. Cohen. 1988. "Evaluating the Performance of Coordinate Measuring Machines." *ASQC Quality Progress*, January, 59–65.

Farago, F. T., and M. Curtis. 1994. *Handbook of Dimensional Measurement*. 3rd ed. New York: Industrial Press.

ISO (International Organization for Standardization). 2007. *ISO/IEC Guide 99: International vocabulary of metrology—Basic and general concepts and associated terms (VIM)*. Geneva: ISO.

NASA (National Aeronautics and Space Administration). 2010. *Measurement Uncertainty Analysis: Principles and Methods, NASA Measurement Quality Assurance Handbook*. Washington, DC: NASA.

————. 2010. *Measuring and Test Equipment Specifications, NASA Measurement Quality Assurance Handbook*. Washington, DC: NASA.

National Institute of Standards and Technology (NIST). 2003. *Specifications, Tolerances, and Other Technical Requirements for Weighing and Measuring Devices*. NIST Handbook 44. Gaithersburg, MD: NIST.

Reason, R. E. 1960. *The Measurement of Surface Texture*. London: CleaverHume Press.

Schrader, G. F., and A. K. Elshennawy. 2000. *Manufacturing Processes and Materials*. 4th ed. Dearborn, MI: Society of Manufacturing Engineers.

Simpson, J. A. 1981. "Foundations of Metrology." *Journal of Research of the National Bureau of Standards* 86 (3): 36–42.

Taylor, B. N. 1995. *Guide for the Use of the International System of Units (SI)*. NIST Special Publication 881. Gaithersburg, MD: NIST.

Wunchell, W. 1996. *Inspection and Measurement in Manufacturing*. Dearborn, MI: Society of Manufacturing Engineers.

Zipin, R. B. 1971. "Dimensional Measurements and Standards in Manufacturing." *Bendix Technical Journal* 1 (4): 15–19.

Chapter 12

F. Calibration

1. *Calibration systems.* Describe the principles and purpose of a calibration system, including the importance of establishing calibration intervals and uncertainty. Identify and use basic tracking and identification methods such as logs, stickers, radio frequency identifications (RFID), barcodes, and other identification codes to control calibration equipment. (Apply)

2. *Calibration standards and equipment traceability.* Describe the hierarchy of standards, from working standards through international standards and the documentation process of a measurement device traceable to the international standards. (Remember)

3. *Gauge calibration environment.* Describe the effects that environmental conditions have on the calibration process, such as temperature, humidity, vibration, and cleanliness of the gauge. (Apply)

4. *Out-of-calibration effects.* Describe the effects that out-of-calibration instruments can have on product acceptance and the actions to take in response to this situation. (Apply)

Body of Knowledge II.F

1. CALIBRATION SYSTEMS

The purpose of *calibration* is to ensure that various types of measurement and process equipment accurately and consistently perform as designed and intended. Further, it is also to ensure that equipment accuracy and consistency remain correlated with known quantities or values that are commonly referred to as *standards*. The basic principle of calibration, then, refers to the process of aligning measurement and process equipment performance with known quantities or values as specified in standards.

A calibration system, like any type of system, is composed of inputs, processes, outputs, and feedback (see Figure 12.1).

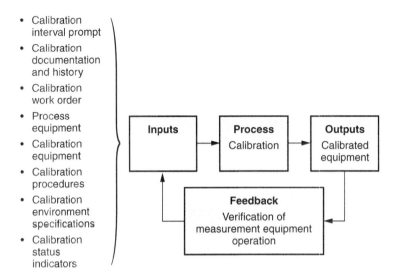

- Calibration interval prompt
- Calibration documentation and history
- Calibration work order
- Process equipment
- Calibration equipment
- Calibration procedures
- Calibration environment specifications
- Calibration status indicators

| Inputs | Process
Calibration | Outputs
Calibrated equipment |

Feedback
Verification of measurement equipment operation

Figure 12.1   The calibration system.

Calibration Interval Prompt

The calibration process is initiated in one of two ways: (1) a piece of malfunctioning equipment is submitted for repair and calibration, or (2) a piece of equipment is identified as being in need of calibration in accordance with an established interval.

A calibration interval is an interval based on time, such as weekly, monthly, quarterly, semiannually, annually, or biannually. A calibration interval may also be an interval based on cycles of operation, such as every 1000 uses. A calibration interval is established for equipment identified as being influenced by, or characteristic of, any of the following (Vogt 1980):

1. Regulatory or oversight control

2. Importance in process operation

3. Manufacturer guidelines or requirements

4. Historical performance accuracy and consistency

The duration of a calibration interval may be shortened at the discretion of an equipment owner, calibration laboratory manager, or other authorized individual within an organization. There are a number of techniques in use to establish calibration intervals initially and to adjust the intervals thereafter. These methods include setting the same interval for all equipment in the user's inventory, the same interval for families of instruments (for example, oscilloscopes, digital voltmeters [DVMs], and gauge blocks), and the same interval for a given manufacturer and model number. These initial intervals are then adjusted for the entire inventory, for individual families, or for manufacturer and model numbers, respectively, based on analyses or history. A study conducted for the National Institute of Standards and Technology (NIST) in connection with a review of government laboratory practices identifies these and other methods (Vogt 1980). It is generally not possible or advisable to lengthen the duration of a calibration interval without a detailed analysis of equipment performance and, in the case of regulatory control, authorization by an agent of the cognizant department or agency.

The actual prompt initiating the calibration process may be in either electronic or hard copy form. Electronic information systems supporting modern industrial operations most commonly track equipment on established calibration intervals and prompt the appropriate individuals when calibration is required. Paper-based information systems supporting industrial operations for calibration require the establishment of a "tickler" file system. A *tickler file* is most commonly some form of card index wherein each piece of equipment with a calibration interval has its own card, and cards are sorted such that equipment in need of calibration moves toward the front of the index, and the appropriate individuals physically pull the cards as the calibration interval requires.

Uncertainty

In gauge calibration work it is not uncommon to encounter situations where the typical uncertainty for a measurement is 50% of the tolerance for a given element when the gauge was new. Typical of this situation are pitch diameter measurements where the tolerances were generated long before measurement uncertainty became well known in the gauge making industry. When NIST's uncertainty falls in this range, you are not going to do better elsewhere, so you'll have to review your acceptance criteria to balance them against reality (Cox 2010).

Tracking and Identification Methods

The objective of identification and tracking systems has expanded in terms of their usage and overall function, thus, the use of the captured data becomes the real differentiating factor. The time of Big Data has arrived, and the way you capture and identify information has become all the more important. Using the right technology to identify your products in production and shipping can really help (Anderson 2015).

Object-specific information can be saved, updated, and called up at any time on the transponder without having to be connected to a central system. This means that objects equipped with RFID transponders can be tracked along the entire logistics or production chain. For example, load carriers, which often circulate in large numbers, can be located and tracked, and are therefore guaranteed to find the way back to their own inventory (Anderson 2015).

The use of RFID is also beneficial when there are harsh ambient conditions, extreme temperatures, or heavy mechanical loads on the objects to be identified. Optical technologies always require a line of sight in order to detect the code, and are therefore more sensitive to wear or contamination, so oftentimes there is less maintenance with an RFID-based system (Anderson 2015).

So, whether you are using the information to help keep the food supply safe, reduce the proliferation of counterfeit medication, or just make sure your shipment gets to Grandma's house, the technology used can play a big role in making sure the data are accurate (Anderson 2015).

Calibration Documentation and History

Each piece of equipment with a calibration interval generally has repair, maintenance, and calibration documentation. Such documentation forms a critically important component in the traceability and history of the equipment. The information contained in the calibration documentation and history includes, but is not limited to, the calibration interval, identification of calibration procedures, a summary of actions taken during calibration, a summary of failures/discrepancies, a summary of parts replaced, identification of calibration technicians who have worked on the equipment, and perhaps any special comments or warnings, such as any particular equipment function that may not have been calibrated, or functions that are inoperable.

Calibration Equipment

Calibration equipment refers to equipment used during, or in support of, the calibration process. Calibration equipment may be assemblies or subassemblies needed to evaluate the performance of any given piece of equipment. Calibration equipment usually encompasses, but is certainly not limited to, things such as oscilloscopes, electrical meters, flow meters, temperature gauges, special jigs and fixtures, and associated clips, leads, and wires.

It is important to note that any or all of the equipment needed to support calibration processes may have its own calibration interval and, in fact, may be one of the many pieces of equipment with its own calibration requirements.

Calibration Procedures

Calibration procedures are the step-by-step instructions that describe the calibration process for a given piece of equipment. Such procedures are not normally stored with the equipment while the equipment is installed for normal process use, and so these procedures are kept in the calibration laboratory.

Calibration procedures identify all process equipment models or configurations to which the procedures apply. The procedures also provide important safety warnings, as well as identify any specifications for the calibration environment.

It is important to note that the calibration procedures are step-by-step instructions, not guidelines. Therefore, calibration technicians are not at liberty to deviate from the instructions for any reason unless there is a documented cause for process improvement and/or equipment traceability.

2. CALIBRATION STANDARDS AND EQUIPMENT TRACEABILITY

Calibration standards are known, highly accurate, and verifiable quantities used as the basis of comparison in calibration processes. Virtually all industrialized nations maintain a set of calibration standards for the measurement of various quantities and phenomena.

NIST is the custodian of measurement standards in the United States. NIST was established by an act of Congress in 1901, although the need for such a body had been noted by the founders of the Constitution. NIST has two main facilities and laboratories in Gaithersburg, Maryland, and Boulder, Colorado, where research into the phenomenon of measurement, the properties of materials, and calibration of reference standards is carried out.

There are several levels of calibration standards arranged in a hierarchy. At the highest level are international standards, which serve as the basis of trade between nations. At the lowest level are transfer standards, which serve as the basis of trade between organizations. Calibration standards at the lowest levels in the hierarchy are used to support day-to-day operations by technicians and shop floor operators. Calibration standards in the middle of the hierarchy are generally used by personnel working in calibration laboratories who are dedicated to calibration processes. Calibration standards at the highest levels in the hierarchy are generally used by calibration specialists and government officials.

Figure 12.2 presents a hierarchy of calibration standards.

- *International standards*. A standard recognized by international agreement to serve internationally as the basis for fixing the value of all other standards of the quantity concerned.

- *National standards*. A standard recognized by an official national decision to serve in a country as a basis for fixing the value of all other standards of the quantity concerned. Generally, a national standard in a country is also a primary standard to which other standards are traceable.

- *Primary standards*. A standard that is designed or widely acknowledged as having the highest metrological quality and whose value is accepted without reference to other standards of the same quantity. National standards are generally primary standards.

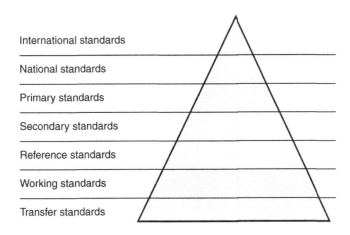

Figure 12.2   Calibration standards hierarchy.

Source: Used with permission of Bucher (2004, 2006).

- *Secondary standards.* A standard whose value is based on comparisons with some primary standard. Note that a secondary standard, once its value is established, can become a primary standard for some other user.

- *Reference standard.* A standard having the highest metrological quality available at a given location from which the measurements made at that location are derived.

- *Working standard.* A measurement standard not specifically reserved as a reference standard that is intended to verify measurement equipment of lower accuracy.

- *Transfer standard.* A standard that is the same as a reference standard except that it is used to transfer a measurement parameter from one organization to another for traceability purposes.

To maintain accuracy, standards in industrialized nations must be traceable to a single source, usually the country's national standards. Since the national laboratories of industrialized nations maintain close connections with the International Bureau of Weights and Measures, there is assurance that items produced from calibration standards in one country will be consistent with items produced from calibration standards in other countries.

Equipment Traceability

Traceability is a process intended to quantify a laboratory's measurement uncertainty in relationship to the national standards. Traceability is based on analyses of error contributions present in each of the measurement transfers: the calibration of the laboratory's reference standards by the NIST, the measurements made in the calibration transfers within the laboratory, and the measurements made on a product. Evidence of traceability is normally required. Such traceability may be as simple as retention of certificates and reports of calibration or as complex as reproduction of the analyses demonstrating the uncertainties claimed for the measurements (Rice 1976).

A laboratory that maintains its own reference standards (that is, it relies on no laboratory other than the NIST for calibration of its standards) must continually monitor its own performance. Measurements on check standards, intercomparisons of standards, and participation in measurement assurance programs sponsored by the NIST are means to quantify laboratory error sources as well as to provide indications of the causes (Rice 1976).

3. GAUGE CALIBRATION ENVIRONMENT

Conditions within the calibration laboratory or calibration environment (such as for equipment on the shop floor that cannot be easily removed and taken to a calibration laboratory) directly impact the calibration. And while it is not possible to control all the factors that may potentially influence a calibration, several factors are controlled for nearly all calibrations, such as cleanliness, temperature, humidity, and vibration. Any additional factor that is known or believed to impact a calibration (for example, pressure or flow rates in certain types of sensors) may require additional controls.

4. OUT-OF-CALIBRATION EFFECTS

The effects of using out-of-calibration equipment are the same as the type I and type II errors (also known as producer's and consumer's risks) discussed in Chapters 15 and 18 of this book. In essence, the effects of out-of-calibration equipment cause stakeholders to believe that (1) the equipment is calibrated and functioning properly when it is not, or (2) the equipment appears to fail calibration when it is, in fact, functioning correctly.

Using out-of-calibration equipment in production or service delivery operations can cause a number of difficulties for manufacturers and service providers. In a best-case scenario, once discovered, out-of-calibration equipment functions correctly and exceptions reporting must document the out-of-calibration incident, a *corrective action* plan must be developed/initiated, and product or service quality must be systematically verified—all of which is wasteful, potentially compromises customer confidence and goodwill, and costs the company time and money. In a worst-case scenario, once discovered, out-of-calibration equipment does not function correctly and containment of product or service delivery must be initiated, *material control* and segregation procedures must be employed, a comprehensive evaluation of product/service performance must be conducted, material review board action is required, a root cause analysis is required, warranty or recall may become necessary, and a company is exposed to legal/regulatory action.

At a minimum, procedures for dealing with an out-of-calibration event or discovery include the following:

1. Identification of the out-of-calibration condition (as described earlier in terms of type I or type II errors).

2. Determination of the magnitude of the condition (that is, how far out of calibration was the equipment?).

3. Assessment of when the out-of-calibration condition occurred.

4. Quantification of the amount of product/service delivery produced/ delivered during the out-of-calibration condition.

5. Evaluation of product or service delivery status (that is, was any product produced or any service provided to customers during the out-of-calibration condition?).

6. Identification of who is authorized to manage the containment efforts.

REFERENCES

Anderson, J. 2015. "Select the Best Identification Technology." *Quality Magazine*, March 3. Accessed November 27, 2018. Available at https://www.qualitymag.com/articles/92479-select-the-best-identification-technology.

Bucher, J. 2004. *The Metrology Handbook*. Milwaukee: ASQ Quality Press.

———. 2006. *The Quality Calibration Handbook: Developing and Managing a Calibration Program*. Milwaukee: ASQ Quality Press.

Cox, H. 2010. "Other Dimensions: Working with Measurement Uncertainty." *Quality Magazine*, January 28.

Rice, G. 1976. "Measurement Systems and the Standards Laboratory." Conference on the Management of Laboratory Instruments, Cairo, Egypt.

Vogt, T. 1980. *Optimizing Calibration Recall Intervals and Algorithms*. NBS-GCR-80-283. Washington, DC: NIST Press.

BIBLIOGRAPHY

American National Standards Institute (ANSI). 2002. ANSI Z540-1-1994 (Revised 2002). *American National Standard for Calibration: Calibration Laboratories and Measuring and Test Equipment (General Requirements)*. Boulder, CO: ANSI.

ISO (International Organization for Standardization). 2005. ISO/IEC 17025:2005 *General requirements for the competence of testing and calibration laboratories*. Geneva: ISO.

———. 2007. ISO/IEC Guide 99 *International vocabulary of metrology—Basic and general concepts and associated terms (VIM)*. Geneva: ISO.

National Conference of Standards Laboratories (NCSL). 1996. NCSL-RP-1 *Establishment and Adjustment of Calibration Intervals*. Boulder, CO: NCSL.

Pennella, R. 2004. *Managing the Metrology System*. Milwaukee: ASQ Quality Press.

Chapter 13

G. Measurement System Analysis (MSA)

Measurement System Analysis (MSA)

Define and describe the following elements of MSA. (Remember)

1. Bias

2. Stability

3. Precision

4. Accuracy

5. Linearity

6. Repeatability and reproducibility (R&R) studies

Body of Knowledge II.G

Measurement system analysis (MSA) is used to understand and quantify the variability associated with measurements and measurement systems. It should be noted that a discussion of MSA should come *after* mastery of the statistical content provided in Chapter 19, "Basic Statistics and Applications." However, MSA is being presented prior to the discussion of basic statistics and applications in this book to preserve the order of topics as presented in the Certified Quality Inspector Body of Knowledge.

The third edition of *Measurement Systems Analysis Reference Manual*, from the Automotive Industry Action Group (AIAG), defines *measurement* as "the assignment of numbers [or values] to material things to represent the relations among them with respect to particular properties" (AIAG 2002). Similarly, the manual defines a *measurement system* as "the collection of instruments or gauges, standards, operations, methods, fixtures, software, personnel, environment, and assumptions used to quantify a unit of measure or fix assessment to the feature characteristic being measured; the complete process used to obtain measurements" (AIAG 2002).

These definitions will serve as the basis of our discussion. However, before we begin that discussion we must first provide a clarification. The term "MSA" is commonly used interchangeably with the term "gauge repeatability and reproducibility" (gauge R&R). MSA is a more comprehensive analysis quantifying variability components from gauge stability, gauge bias, gauge linearity, gauge repeatability, and reproducibility (that is, variability from operator measurements). Gauge R&R is, in fact, a subset or component of MSA. The reason underlying the mistaken interchange of the terms "MSA" and "gauge R&R" is that many, if not most, problems with measurement systems are detected and corrected with the gauge R&R procedure without having to continue the more comprehensive analysis of MSA. For a detailed discussion of analysis techniques for gauge stability, gauge bias, and gauge linearity, readers are referred to the third edition of the AIAG *Measurement Systems Analysis Reference Manual*.

1. PROCESS VARIABILITY

All processes, no matter how well they are designed and executed, possess the component of variability. It is only the degree of variability that varies from process to process. The fact that variability exists in virtually any and all processes cannot be overemphasized. The total variability of a process consists of two components: parts variability and gauge variability. Further, note that variability in a process can be quantified by a probability distribution and can be expressed as

$$\sigma^2_{Total} = \sigma^2_{Parts} + \sigma^2_{Gauge} \qquad (13.1)$$

Variability in the Measurement Process

Extending our conversation from the previous section, it is critically important that we understand that the methods, procedures, tools, and equipment we use to make measurements constitute an independent process that creates, and is susceptible to, its own variation. This means there are two sources or components of variation present in each measurement we take, as is illustrated by equation 13.1 and in Figure 13.1.

It is important to ensure that the component of variability associated with the measurement system does not consume an excessive amount of variability as is allowed in the process specification, and so quantifying measurement system variability is the purpose of MSA. Note that the standard deviation of measurement error, α_{Gauge}, can be estimated by

$$\hat{\sigma}_{Gauge} = \frac{\bar{R}}{d_2}$$

where the values of d_2 for various sample sizes are given in Appendix E.

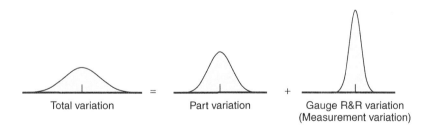

| Total variation | = | Part variation | + | Gauge R&R variation (Measurement variation) |

Figure 13.1   Components of total variation.

2. EVALUATING MEASUREMENT SYSTEM PERFORMANCE

As mentioned in Section I, the total process variation can be divided into two major categories: variation due to parts and variation due to the gauge or measurement system. Part-to-part variation may be due to the environment, methods, materials, machines, or some combination thereof, and other factors.

The variation due to the measurement system mainly consists of two major components: the instrument being used for taking measurements and the operators who use the instrument.

In the industrial world, these components are usually referred to as *repeatability* and *reproducibility*, respectively. Repeatability and reproducibility may be considered as the major indicators of measurement system performance. We will discuss repeatability and reproducibility in more detail later.

Since *repeatability* refers to the variation generated by the instrument (that is, measurement equipment or gauge), it is referred to as *equipment variation* (EV). *Reproducibility* refers to variation generated by operators using measurement instruments, and it is referred to as *operator* (that is, *appraiser*) *variation* (AV). The study of gauge R&R is usually referred to as a *gauge R&R study*.

The *Measurement Systems Analysis Reference Manual* (AIAG 2002) gives several methods for conducting gauge R&R. In this book we will study two methods: the range-based method and the analysis of variance (ANOVA) method. Since ANOVA is an advanced statistical technique that is not covered in this book, we will not go into much detail. We will focus our attention on explaining and interpreting the results of our example that we will work out using computer software.

3. THE RANGE-BASED METHOD

The range-based method has been presented by various authors including IBM (1986) and Barrentine (2003). Before we discuss the details of this method we will define certain terms, namely, measurement capability index, K_1-factor, and K_2-factor. In addition, we will define other terms that are useful in understanding MSA.

MSA is a technique for collecting and analyzing data in order to evaluate the effectiveness of the gauge. To collect data, we randomly select some parts and a certain number of operators (usually three or more, but as a general rule, the more the better). Each operator takes multiple measurements (at least two) on each part, and all the parts are measured in random order. These measurements are also known as *trials*. Using the terminology of control charts, the measurements on each part or the number of trials constitutes a rational subgroup, and the number of parts times the number of operators constitutes the number of subgroups or samples. Then $\bar{R}$ is defined as the average of the ranges of trials within the same operator, and $\bar{\bar{R}}$ is defined as the average of the $\bar{R}$s among the operators.

The *measurement capability index* (MCI) is a measurement that quantifies our belief that the gauge is reliable enough to support the decisions we make under the existing circumstances. The MCI relates to the following characteristics, which are key to any measurement system:

- Bias

- Precision

- Accuracy

- Stability

- Linearity

- Repeatability and reproducibility (R&R)

A measurement system is *biased* if it gives a measurement value that consistently overstates or understates the true value of the measurement. *Precision* refers to how close to each other any two or more measurements of a part are. Note that precision is independent of accuracy. A measurement may be very precise but may not be very accurate (see Figure 13.2). The characteristic *precision* is further subdivided into two categories: repeatability and reproducibility. *Repeatability* measures the preciseness of observations taken under the same conditions, which is achieved by computing the variance of such observations. For example, we say a gauge possesses the characteristic of repeatability if an operator obtains similar observations when measuring the same part again and again. *Reproducibility* measures the preciseness of the observations taken by different operators when measuring the same part. For example, we say a gauge possesses the characteristic of reproducibility if various operators obtain similar observations when measuring the same part again and again.

Accuracy of a measurement system is the closeness of the average of measurements taken to the true value. The distinction between precision and accuracy is very well explained in Figure 13.2.

Stability is defined by the total variation in measurements obtained with a measurement system on the same master or same parts when measuring a single characteristic over an extended period of time. The smaller the total variation, the more stable the measurement system.

Linearity is an indicator of the consistency of *measurements* over the entire range of *measurements*. Linearity is best explained by the diagram in Figure 13.3.

In any manufacturing process the total variability consists of two components: variability among the parts and variability in the measurement system. The

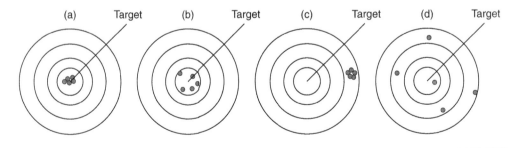

Figure 13.2   (a) Accurate and precise, (b) accurate but not precise, (c) not accurate but precise, (d) neither accurate nor precise.

MCI of a measurement system, which is directly related to the variability due to the measurement system (gauge), is a very pertinent factor in improving any process. The total variability due to the measurement system itself consists of three components, that is, variability due to operators, the instrument, and the interaction between the operators and the instrument. Statistically, these relationships can be expressed as follows:

$$\sigma^2_{Total} = \sigma^2_{Parts} + \sigma^2_{Gauge} \tag{13.2}$$

$$\sigma^2_{Gauge} = \sigma^2_{Inst.} + \sigma^2_{Operator} + \sigma^2_{Part. \times Operator} \tag{13.3}$$

The total variability due to the measurement system (σ^2_{Mean} or σ^2_{Gauge}) is also known as the *total gauge R&R variability*. The instrument variability is represented by the variability in the repeated measurements by the same operator, and for this reason it is also known as *repeatability*. In the ANOVA method, the repeatability variance component is the error variance (that is, $\sigma^2_{Inst.} = \sigma^2_{EV} = \sigma^2$). The remainder of the variability in the measurement system comes from various operators who use the instrument and the interaction between the instruments and the operators. Note that the interaction appears when any operator can measure one type of part better than another type of part. This total variability from the operators and the interaction between the operators and the instruments is also known as *reproducibility*. Equation 13.3 can also be expressed as

$$\sigma^2_{Gauge} = \sigma^2_{Repeatability} + \sigma^2_{Reproducibility} \tag{13.4}$$

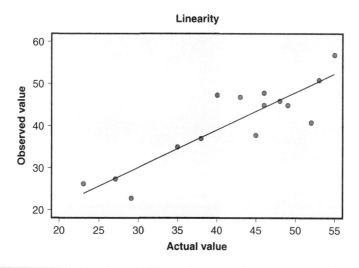

Figure 13.3   Diagram showing the linear relationship between the actual and the observed values.

Using Barrentine's (2003) approach, repeatability is defined as

$$\text{Repeatability} = \text{EV} = 5.15 \hat{\sigma}_{\text{Repeatability}} = 5.15 \frac{\overline{\overline{R}}}{d_2} = K_1 \overline{\overline{R}} \text{ where } K_1 = \frac{5.15}{d_2} \quad (13.5)$$

and where the factor 5.15 represents the 99% range of the standard normal distribution, which follows from the fact that

$$P(-2.575 \le Z \le 2.575) = 0.99 \quad (13.6)$$

Note that the AIAG recommends using the factor 6 instead of 5.15 since it covers almost 100%—or to be exact, 99.74%—of the range. Values of K_1 for various sample sizes (that is, the number of trials or the number of measurements taken on the same part by the same operator) are given in Appendix F. As noted by Barrentine, Duncan (1986) points out that this estimation procedure should be slightly modified if $n = r \times m = (\text{\# operators}) \times (\text{\# parts})$ is less than 16. Thus, if n is less than 16, then K_1 is defined as

$$K_1 = \frac{5.15}{d_2^*} \quad (13.7)$$

The values of d_2^* are listed in Duncan (1986), Table D_3. The values of K_1 listed in Appendix F are determined according to the value of n.

Again, using Barrentine's notation (2003, 57), Reproducibility = AV, ignoring the interaction term, is defined as

$$\text{Reproducibility} = \text{AV} = \sqrt{\left(K_2 R_{\overline{x}}\right)^2 - \frac{(\text{EV})^2}{(r \times n)}} \quad (13.8)$$

where r is the number of trials, n the number of parts, EV is as given in equation 13.5, $R_{\overline{x}}$ is the range of the operator's means, and the factor K_2 is defined as

$$K_2 = \frac{5.15}{d_2^*} \quad (13.9)$$

The value of d_2^* can be found from Duncan's Table D_3 by selecting $g = 1$ and number of operators = o. For example, if we have 5 operators, then from Duncan's Table D_3 for $g = 1$, $o = 5$, we have (Duncan's table uses $o = m$)

$$K_2 = \frac{5.15}{2.48} = 2.077$$

We now illustrate the range-based and ANOVA methods with the following example.

EXAMPLE 13.1

A manufacturer of bolts used in automotive applications has installed a new measuring gauge. In order to perform the MSA on the new gauge, the quality manager randomly selected three operators from Quality Control, who decided to take a random sample of 10 bolts. Each operator took three measurements on each bolt, which were randomly selected. The data obtained are shown in Table 13.1.

Continued

Table 13.1   Data on an experiment involving three operators, 10 bolts, and three measurements (in mm) on each bolt by each operator.

Bolt (part) number	Operator 1			Operator 2			Operator 3		
	Trial 1	Trial 2	Trial 3	Trial 1	Trial 2	Trial 3	Trial 1	Trial 2	Trial 3
1	26	22	26	21	23	21	24	22	26
2	28	26	28	24	29	26	24	25	24
3	28	31	28	28	27	28	32	30	27
4	35	33	31	35	31	30	34	35	31
5	37	35	38	36	38	35	35	34	35
6	40	38	40	40	38	40	36	37	38
7	39	42	41	40	39	43	43	41	43
8	42	43	46	42	46	42	43	44	45
9	50	52	50	53	52	53	49	53	49
10	28	31	28	28	27	28	32	30	27
	$\bar{R}_1 = 3.0$ $\bar{x}_1 = 35.40$			$\bar{R}_2 = 2.8$ $\bar{x}_2 = 34.77$			$\bar{R}_3 = 3.0$ $\bar{x}_3 = 34.93$		

Solution

We first discuss gauge R&R using the range-based method, the approach used by IBM (1986), Barrentine (2003), and others.

Step 1: Verify that gauge calibration is current.

Step 2: Identify operators. Three operators are typically used in gauge studies; however, the more operators the better.

Step 3: Select a random sample of parts and have each operator measure all parts. One operator measures all parts, taking several measurements on each part, then the second operator takes measurements, then the third operator takes measurements, and so on. All parts are measured in random order.

Step 4: Calculate the sample mean, intertrial range for each sample, and average range for each operator. The sample means and average ranges are provided in Table 13.1.

Step 5: Calculate the range of sample means ($R_{\bar{x}}$), that is

$$R_{\bar{x}} = Max(\bar{x}_i) - Min(\bar{x}_i)$$
$$= 35.40 - 34.77 = 0.63$$

Step 6:   Calculate the average range ($\bar{\bar{R}}$) for operators

$$\bar{\bar{R}} = \frac{\bar{R}_1 + \bar{R}_2 + \bar{R}_3}{3}$$
$$= \frac{3.00 + 2.80 + 3.00}{3} = 2.93$$

Continued

Step 7: Calculate repeatability (this value is also referred to as *equipment variation* [EV]) and the estimate of the standard deviation of repeatability ($\sigma_{Repeatability}$)

$$\text{Repeatability (EV)} = \bar{\bar{R}} \times K_1 = 2.93 \times 3.05 = 8.94$$

where from Appendix F with number of trials $r = 3$ and $n = $ # of parts $\times$ # of operators $= 30$, we have $K_1 = 3.05$.

$$\hat{\sigma}_{Repeatability} = \frac{EV}{5.15} = \frac{8.94}{5.15} = 1.74$$

Step 8: Calculate reproducibility (this value is also referred to as *appraiser variation* [AV] or *operator variation*) and the estimate of the standard deviation of reproducibility ($\sigma_{Reproducibility}$)

$$\text{Reproducibility (AV)} = \sqrt{\left(R_{\bar{x}} \times K_2\right)^2 - \left[\left(EV\right)^2 / m \times r\right]}$$

where from Appendix G for three operators, we have $K_2 = 2.70$, # of parts = $m = 10$, and # of trials $r = 3$. Thus, we have

$$\text{Reproducibility (AV)} = \sqrt{\left(0.63 \times 2.70\right)^2 - \left[\left(8.94\right)^2 / 10 \times 3\right]}$$

$$= 0.48$$

Note that if the number under the radical is negative, then AV is zero.

The estimate of the standard deviation of reproducibility ($\sigma_{Reproducibility}$) is

$$\hat{\sigma}_{Reproducibility} = \frac{0.48}{5.15} = 0.09$$

With this method, since reproducibility is calculated by ignoring the interaction term, the standard deviation of reproducibility may merely be looked upon as the operator standard deviation.

Step 9: Calculate gauge R&R (that is, repeatability and reproducibility) and the estimate of gauge R&R standard deviation.

$$\text{Gauge R\&R} = \sqrt{\left(\text{Repeatability}\right)^2 + \left(\text{Reproducibility}\right)^2}$$

$$= \sqrt{\left(8.94\right)^2 + \left(.48\right)^2}$$

$$= 8.95$$

The estimate of gauge R&R standard deviation is given by

$$\hat{\sigma}_{Gauge} = \frac{8.95}{5.15} = 1.74$$

$$\sigma_{Total}^2 = \sigma_{Parts}^2 + \sigma_{Gauge}^2$$

Where σ_{Total}^2, σ_{Parts}^2, and σ_{Gauge}^2 are the variance of total variability, parts variability, and gauge variability, respectively.

4. THE ANOVA METHOD

MSA using the ANOVA method is done by using two types of experimental designs: (1) *crossed* and (2) *nested*, or *hierarchical*, designs. Crossed designs are used when each operator measures the same parts, whereas nested or hierarchical designs are used when each operator measures different parts, in which case we say that the parts are nested within operators. In this chapter we discuss the case when each operator measures the same parts and thus uses crossed designs only.

Gauge R&R Study—ANOVA Method

Interpretation of Two-Way ANOVA Table with Interaction. In the ANOVA table in Figure 13.4, we test three hypotheses:

- H_0: All parts are similar versus H_1: All parts are not similar

- H_0: All operators are equally good versus H_1: All operators are not equally good

- H_0: Interactions between parts and operators are negligible versus H_1: Interactions between parts and operators are not negligible

The decision whether to reject any of these hypotheses depends on the p-value (shown in the last column) and the corresponding value of the level of significance. If the p-value is less than or equal to the level of significance (alpha), we reject the null hypothesis. Otherwise, we do not reject the null hypothesis. For example, the p-value for parts is 0, which means we reject the null hypothesis that the parts are similar at any level of significance. In other words, the measurement system is capable of distinguishing the different parts. The p-value for operators is 0.337. Therefore, at a given level of significance, which is less than 0.337, we do not reject the null hypothesis that the operators are equally good (in most applications, an acceptable value of the level of significance is 0.05). Finally, the interactions are not negligible at a significance level greater than 0.188. Since the chosen value of alpha is 0.25, the interaction term is not removed from the ANOVA.

Interpretation of Two-Way ANOVA Table without Interaction. Since in this case the value of $\alpha = 0.1$ is less than 0.188 (see Figure 13.5), the interaction term is removed from the ANOVA table and the sum of squares (SS) and degrees of

```
Source                    DF        SS        MS        F         P
Part Numbers               9   6185.79   687.310    235.20     0.000
Operators                  2      6.47     3.233      1.11     0.337
Part Numbers*Operators    18     71.31     3.962      1.36     0.188
Repeatability             60    175.33     2.922
Total                     89   6438.90

Alpha to remove interaction term = 0.25
```

Figure 13.4   Two-way ANOVA table with interaction (Minitab printout).

```
Source                  DF          SS          MS          F           P
Part Numbers             9     6185.79     687.310      217.36       0.000
Operators                2        6.47       3.233        1.02       0.364
Repeatability           78      246.64       3.162
Total                   89     6438.90

Alpha to remove interaction term = 0.1
```

Figure 13.5   Two-way ANOVA table without interaction (Minitab printout).

freedom (DF) are merged with corresponding terms of repeatability, which act as an error due to uncontrollable factors. The interpretation for parts and operators is the same as in the two-way ANOVA table with interaction. However, it is important to note that the p-values can change from one ANOVA table to another. For example, the *p*-values for operators are different in the two tables. The *p*-value for operators changed since the error due to uncontrolled factors has changed.

Note that variance components are derived as follows:

$$\sigma^2 = \text{MSE} = \sigma^2_{\text{Repeatability}}$$

$$\sigma^2_{p \times o} = \frac{\text{MS}_{p \times o} - \text{MS}_E}{r}$$

$$\sigma^2_o = \frac{\text{MS}_o - \text{MS}_{p \times o}}{mr}$$

$$\sigma^2_p = \frac{\text{MS}_p - \text{MS}_{p \times o}}{or}$$

where *o*, *m*, and *r* are, respectively, the number of operators, parts, and trials.

The first column in the printout in Figure 13.6 provides the breakdown of the variance components (estimates of variances). The second column provides the percent contribution of the variance components, which becomes the basis of gauge R&R study using the ANOVA method. For instance, the total variation due to gauge is 4.126%, of which 3.689% of the variation is contributed by the repeatability and the remaining 0.437% is contributed by the reproducibility. The variation due to parts is 95.873% of the total variation. This implies that the measurement system is very capable. Note that the values of repeatability and reproducibility and their standard deviations obtained by using the range method and the ANOVA method may be slightly different. Also note that the percent contributions are calculated simply by dividing the variance components by the total variation and then multiplying by 100. Thus, the percent contribution due to repeatability, for example, is given by

$$\frac{3.268}{79.201} \times 100 = 4.126\%$$

The part of the Minitab printout shown in Figure 13.7 provides various percent contributions using estimates of standard deviations, which are obtained by taking the square root of the variance components. The comparison with standard deviation makes more sense because the standard deviation uses the same units

```
                                              %Contribution
Source                         Var. Comp      (of Var. Comp)
Total Gauge R&R                   3.268            4.126
  Repeatability                   2.922            3.689
  Reproducibility                 0.346            0.437
    Operators                     0.000            0.00
    Operators*Part Numbers        0.346            0.437
Part-To-Part                     75.932           95.873
Total Variation                  79.201          100.00

Process tolerance = 60
```

Figure 13.6   Gauge R&R (Minitab printout).

```
                                   Study Var   %Study Var   %Tolerance
Source                 StdDev (SD)  (SV=6*SD)      (%SV)    (SV/Toler)

Total Gauge R&R            1.808     10.848        20.31       18.08
  Repeatability            1.710     10.260        19.21       17.10
  Reproducibility          0.589      3.534         4.23        5.89
    Operators              0.000      0.000         0.00        0.00
    Operators*Part Numbers 0.589      3.534         4.23        5.89
Part-To-Part               8.713     52.278        97.91       87.13
Total Variation            8.899     53.394       100.00       88.99

Number of Distinct Categories = 6
```

Figure 13.7   An example: percent tolerance contribution by the various components of the measurement system.

as those of the measurements. The study variation (that is, measurement system variation, which is equivalent to the process variation in the study of process control) is obtained by multiplying the standard deviation by 6. The percent study variations are calculated by dividing the standard deviation by the total variation and then multiplying by 100. The percent contribution due to part-to-part variation, for example, is given by

$$\frac{8.713}{8.899} \times 100 = 97.91\%$$

The percent tolerance is obtained by dividing (6 × SD) by the process tolerance and then multiplying by 100. The process tolerance of total gauge R&R, for example, is given by

$$\frac{10.848}{60} \times 100 = 18.08\%$$

Note that the total percent tolerances in this example do not add to 100. Rather, the total sum is 88.99, which means the total variation is using 88.99% of the specification band.

The last entry in the Minitab printout is the number of distinct categories, which in this case is 6. The number of distinct categories can be determined as shown in the following equation.

$$\text{Number of distinct categories} = \text{Integral part of} \left(\frac{\text{Part-to-part SD}}{\text{Total gauge R\&R SD}} \times 1.4142 \right)$$

$$= \text{Integral part of} \left(\frac{8.713}{1.88} \times 1.4142 \right) = 6$$

Under AIAG's recommendations, a measurement system is capable if the number of categories is greater than or equal to five, and the measurement system's capability is considered inadequate if the number of categories is less than two. In this example the measurement system is capable of separating the parts into the different categories that they belong to. This quantity is equivalent to the one defined in AIAG (2002) and Montgomery (2005), and is referred to as signal-to-noise ratio (SNR), that is,

$$\text{SNR} = \sqrt{\frac{2\rho_p}{1-\rho_p}} \tag{13.10}$$

where

$$\rho_p = \frac{\sigma_p^2}{\sigma_{\text{Total}}^2} \tag{13.11}$$

Graphical Representation of Gauge R&R Study

Figure 13.8 shows the various percent contributions of gauge R&R, repeatability, reproducibility, and part-to-part variation.

In Figure 13.9 we first interpret the R chart. All the data points are within the control limits, which indicates that the operators are measuring consistently. However, the $\bar{X}$ chart shows many points beyond the control limits. But this does not mean the measurement system is out of control. Rather, this indicates narrower control limits, that is, the span between the control limits has become smaller because the variation due to repeatability is small and the measurement system is capable of distinguishing the different parts.

Figure 13.10 plots the average of each part measured by any single operator. We have three line graphs since we have three operators. These line graphs intersect one another but are also very close to one another. This implies that there is some interaction between the operators and the parts, which is significant only at 0.188 or greater level of significance.

In Figure 13.11 the clear circles represent the measurements by each operator, and the black circles represent the means. The spread of measurements for each operator is almost the same. The means fall on a horizontal line, which indicates that the average measurement for each operator is also the same. So, the operators are measuring the parts consistently. In other words, the variation due to reproducibility is low.

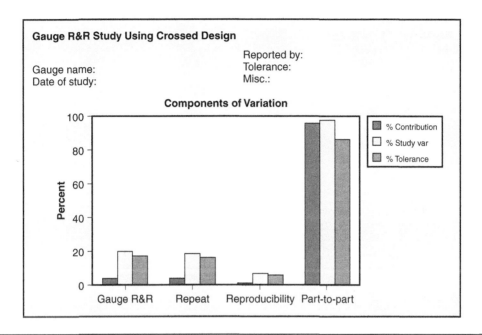

Figure 13.8   Percent contribution of variance components for the data in Example 13.1.

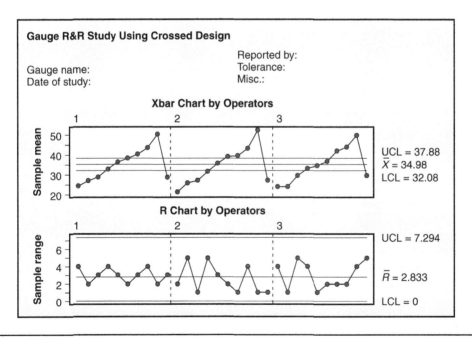

Figure 13.9 $\bar{X}$ and R chart for the data in Example 13.1.

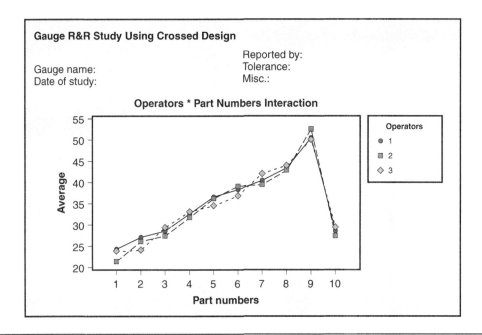

Figure 13.10   Interaction between operators and parts for the data in Example 13.1.

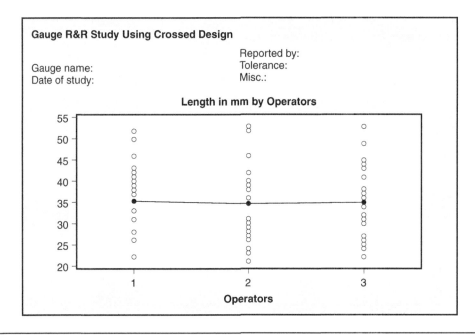

Figure 13.11   Scatter plot for measurements versus operators.

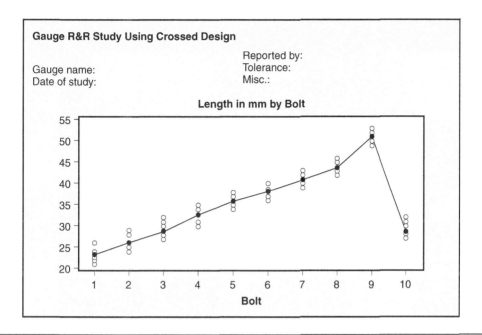

Figure 13.12   Scatter plot for measurements versus parts (bolts).

In Figure 13.12 the clear circles represent the measurements on each part, while the black circles represent the mean for each part. In this case the spread of measurements for each part is not almost the same but is nevertheless very small. This means that each part is being measured with the same precision and accuracy. Greater variability among the black circles indicates that the measurement system is quite capable of distinguishing the parts belonging to different categories. Thus, combining the outcomes of Figures 13.11 and 13.12, we can say that, overall, the gauge R&R variability is not very significant.

5. MEASUREMENT CAPABILITY INDICES

As the *process capability index* (PCI) quantifies the ability of a process to produce products of desired quality, the *measurement capability index* (MCI) quantifies the ability of a measurement system to provide accurate measurements. In other words, MCI evaluates the adequacy of the measurement system. There are various MCIs in use, such as the one defined earlier in equation 13.10. We discuss here the other two most commonly used MCIs: percent of process variation and process specification. The MCI should always be used in conjunction with the PCI (Barrentine 2003).

MCI as a Percentage of Process Variation (MCI$_{pv}$)

$$\text{MCI}_{pv} = 100 \times \frac{\hat{\sigma}_{\text{Gauge R\&R}}}{\hat{\sigma}_{\text{Total}}} \tag{13.12}$$

The criteria for assessment of this index (Barrentine 2003) are usually as follows:

1. $\leq 20\%$ implies the measurement system is good

2. $> 20\%, \leq 30\%$ implies the measurement system is marginal

3. $> 30\%$ implies the measurement system is unacceptable

Using the ANOVA table for the data in Example 13.1 (see Figure 13.7), we have

$$\text{MCI}_{pv} = 100 \times \frac{1.79780}{8.86139} = 20\%$$

Thus, this MCI indicates that the measurement system is good.

MCI as a Percentage of Process Specification (MCI$_{ps}$)

$$\text{MCI}_{ps} = \frac{6 \times \hat{\sigma}_{\text{Gauge R\&R}}}{\text{USL} - \text{LSL}} \tag{13.13}$$

The criteria for assessment of MCIps are similar to MCIpv (Barrentine 2003), that is,

1. $\leq 20\%$ implies the measurement system is good

2. $> 20\%, \leq 30\%$ implies the measurement system is marginal

3. $> 30\%$ implies the measurement system is unacceptable

Again, using the ANOVA table for the data in Example 13.1 (see Figure 13.7) and with process tolerance 60, we have

$$\text{MCI}_{ps} = 100 \times \frac{6 \times 1.79780}{60} = 18\%$$

Thus, this MCI indicates the measurement system is good.

REFERENCES

AIAG (Automotive Industry Action Group), Measurement Systems Analysis (MSA) Work Group. 2002. *Measurement Systems Analysis Reference Manual*. 3rd ed. Dearborn, MI: AIAG Press.

Barrentine, L. 2003. *Concepts for R&R Studies*. 2nd ed. Milwaukee: ASQ Quality Press.

Duncan, A. J. 1986. *Quality Control and Industrial Statistics*. 5th ed. Homewood, IL: Irwin.

IBM (International Business Machines Corporation). 1986. *Process Control, Capability and Improvement*. Thornwood, NY: The Quality Institute.

Montgomery, D. C. 2005. *Introduction to Statistical Quality Control*. 5th ed. New York: John Wiley & Sons.

Section III
Inspection and Test

Chapter 14   A. Blueprints, Drawings, Geometric Dimensioning, Tolerancing (GD&T) and Model Based Definitions

Chapter 15   B. Sampling

Chapter 16   C. Inspection Planning and Processes

Chapter 17   D. Testing Methods

Chapter 18   E. Software for Test Equipment

Chapter 14

A. Blueprints, Drawings, Geometric Dimensioning & Tolerancing (GD&T) and Model Based Definitions

1. *Blueprints, engineering drawings and model based definitions.* Define and interpret various sections of technical drawings: title blocks, tolerances, change or revision blocks, including notes, scale, and size details. (Apply)

2. *Terminology and symbols.* Define and interpret drawing views and details for product specifications or other controlling documents. Define and use various terms and symbols from the ASME Y14.5M standard. (Analyze)

3. *Position and bonus tolerances.* Calculate position and bonus tolerances from various drawings. (Analyze)

4. *Part alignment and datum structure.* Determine part alignment and setup using the datum structure. (Analyze)

Body of Knowledge III.A

INTRODUCTION

Geometric dimensioning and tolerancing (GD&T) is defined as the language of symbols used in mechanical drawing to efficiently and accurately communicate geometry requirements for features on parts and assemblies (ASME 1994). GD&T is used in a wide variety of manufacturing industries on the national and international levels. GD&T is used to ensure successful and accurate communication between the design department and the production department. GD&T is the language that enables design engineers to express what they mean on a drawing, thus improving product designs and lowering costs. Process engineers and manufacturing use the language to interpret the design intent and to determine the best manufacturing approach. Quality control and inspection use the GD&T language to determine proper setup and part verification (ASME 1994).

Understanding how to implement and translate GD&T drawings will aid in improving product design and effectively communicate design requirements for suppliers and manufacturing (Effective Training 2012).

1. BLUEPRINTS AND ENGINEERING DRAWINGS, AND MODEL BASED DEFINITIONS

An *engineering drawing* is a type of drawing that is technical in nature, used to fully and clearly define requirements for engineered items. The purpose of engineering drawings is to accurately and clearly capture all the geometric features of a product or a component that will convey the required information for the production team.

Engineering drawings are often referred to as *blueprints*, a name that reflects the way those prints were once made using chemical material to print blue lines on white paper. Although design engineers now use computers and other modern production processes that use different colors, they still call engineering drawings "blueprints" (Ware 1999).

Figure 14.1 depicts an example of a blueprint that was done using today's technology. Engineering drawings can be used in manufacturing, construction, operation, installation, and maintenance, and in other applications. They are made in a way that should be understandable for all users. When these drawings are used between two or more countries, it is essential that the drawing prepared in one country be easily and correctly interpreted in the other country or countries. These countries don't have to speak the same language or use the same units of measure. The drawing can be understood and translated based on the international standards provided by ISO/TC 10 technical drawing standards (ISO 2002).

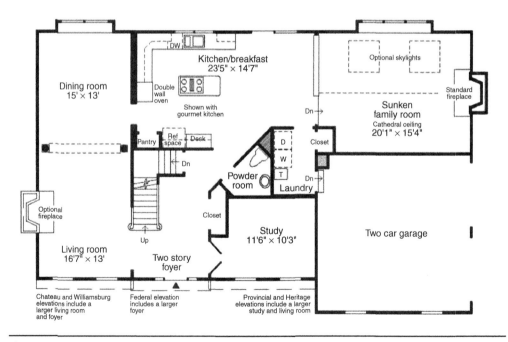

Figure 14.1   Blueprint for a house floor plan.

Sections of Technical Drawings

In technical drawings the following sections can be identified (Dirks 1995–2000):

- Title block
- Notes
- Scale
- Revision block
- Tolerance

Title Block. The title block includes the border and the various sections for providing quality, administrative, and technical information. The title block includes all the information that enables the drawing to be interpreted, identified, and archived. The title block is usually located in the lower right corner, as shown in Figure 14.2. This block must contain the title of the project or drawing, a description of the drawing, the scale, the name of the designer and/or draftsman, and the date. It might also contain information about the company, registration or ID number, and previous revisions. The title block should also include boxes for the legal signatures of the originator and other persons involved in production of the drawing to the required quality. The drawing sheet size should be in accordance with BS EN ISO 5457 TD *Sizes and layout of drawing sheets* (Dirks 1995–2000).

Notes. Notes are placed on drawings to give additional information to clarify an object on the blueprint. The notes area is not part of the title block. Figure 14.2 shows the placement of notes on engineering drawings. Notes might include legends and symbols or specially marked places on the blueprint (Dirks 1995–2000).

Scale. The scale block in the title block of the blueprint shows the size of the drawing compared with the actual size of the item. The scale may be shown as an enlargement or a reduction of the actual size. For example, a scale of 1/100 means that 1 unit on the drawing is equal to 100 units in real (actual) size (see Figure 14.3).

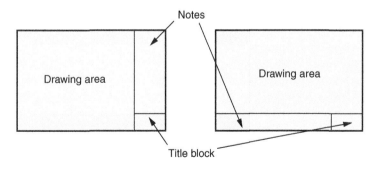

Figure 14.2   Placement of the title block and notes on engineering drawings.
Source: Fox (2012).

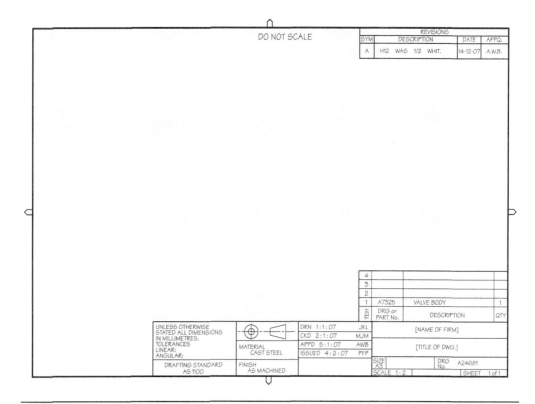

Figure 14.3   Example of title and notes blocks on an engineering drawing.
Source: Digital Design (2012).

Revision Block. The revision block is located in the upper-right corner of the blueprint or technical drawing. All modifications to the drawing are documented in this block. The most important modifications needed in the revision block are the revision date, revision number, revision symbol, change description, change authorization, and change code (MTAG 2001) (see Figure 14.4).

Tolerance. ASME Y14.5 (1994) defines *tolerance* as "the total amount by which a specific dimension may vary." Tolerance is the range of allowed values, which is normally specified by a certain standard. Tolerance is one of the main sections that appear in the engineering drawing and shows the variation of each dimension (Pyzdek and Berger 2003; ASTM 1996). The drawing includes the allowed boundaries of a generic shape in terms of its geometry and of the allowed dimensional values that can be accepted for a variation over the exact or nominal value expressed by the designer (Cañas and Novak 2006). Figure 14.5 shows an example of a technical engineering drawing with an indication of geometric tolerance.

Tolerance deals with the uncertainty of the dimensions of a real manufactured object compared with its ideal design. By default, parts have to deviate from the ideal design, which creates the need for tolerancing practices. In the drawing world, tolerances are noted on the drawing per standard notations such as those in ASME Y14.5 or ISO 1101.

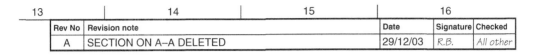

13	14	15	16

Rev No	Revision note	Date	Signature	Checked
A	SECTION ON A–A DELETED	29/12/03	R.B.	All other

Figure 14.4 Example of a revision block.
Source: Roymech, UK (2007).

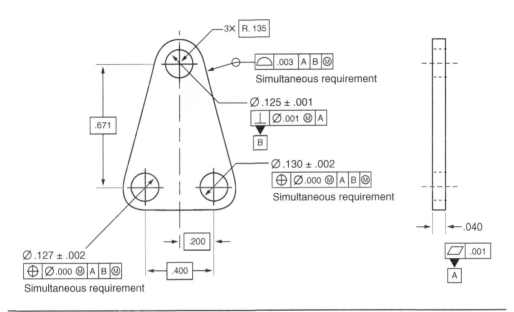

Figure 14.5   Example of a technical engineering drawing with an indication of geometric tolerances.
Source: Cañas and Novak (2006).

There are two main classes of tolerances: dimensional and geometric. Geometric tolerances are the more complex of these two types. Geometric tolerances provide more flexible means for controlling shape than do dimensional tolerances. They achieve this by enabling tolerances to be defined independently of explicit dimensions. This enables tolerances to be specified that are more closely related to the functional requirements of the design, such as strength and fit, by specifying item features and characteristics (Lamit and Kitto 1994).

From the previous discussion we can understand that a geometric tolerance describes a constraint on the acceptable deviation of a manufactured object from the ideal design. Tolerances are applied to the geometric features of a part, such as faces and holes.

There are several subtypes of the geometric tolerance entity that are not mutually exclusive. For example, tolerances that reference datums are of type *geometric tolerance with datum reference*. Tolerances that include a modifier such as maximum material condition are of type *modified geometric tolerance*. Many typical engineering tolerances combine these two types (Briggs and Hendrix 2003).

Consider an example of a location tolerance on a hole whose visual representation as a control frame is shown in Figure 14.6. Reading the control frame left to right, the location tolerance is a position tolerance, locating a cylindrical feature, with a tolerance value of 0.1, with a modifier condition of maximum material condition, referencing datums A, B, and C, in that order (Briggs and Hendrix 2003). Figure 14.7 provides the features that can be represented by geometric tolerancing.

Figure 14.8 provides a simple 2-D example wherein a position tolerance ⊕ is imposed on hole H. The exact ("true") position of H is defined in Figure 14.8a by two basic (boxed, signifying "exact") dimensions that are anchored to part

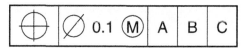

Figure 14.6   Visual representation of the control frame of a hole.

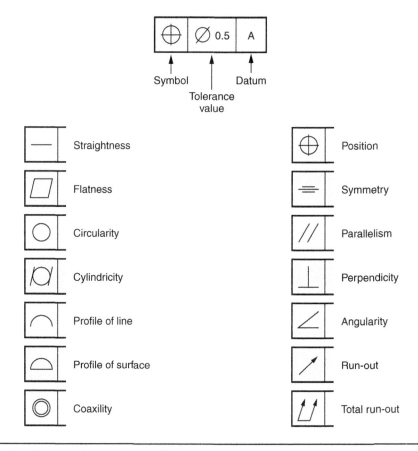

Figure 14.7   Features that can be specified by geometric tolerancing.
Source: Roymech, UK (2007).

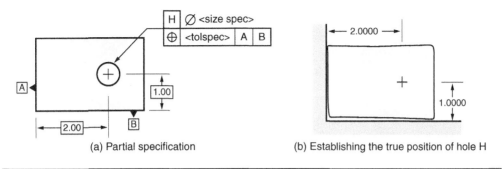

(a) Partial specification   (b) Establishing the true position of hole H

Figure 14.8   Simple 2-D example of position tolerance.

features A and B; the labels on these features designate them as datums. The left-to-right ordering of A and B in the ⊕ "callout block" sets the datum precedence: A is primary and B is secondary. The position tolerance ("<tolspec>" in Figure 14.8a) is a small disk-shaped zone defining the allowable variability of H's position (Briggs and Hendrix 2003).

MODEL BASED DEFINITION

Model based definition (MBD) is not a new concept in the aerospace manufacturing industry. While it has been applied to product definition and manufacturing for years, its use as a fully implemented process for quality control has been realized only recently. Many companies are modernizing quality assurance processes to embrace MBD because aerospace's prime manufacturers are demanding it. Advancements in both software and hardware technologies are making it easier to put all the key elements in place, giving aerospace manufacturers the last piece of the puzzle for an enterprise-wide system of digital product definition. With model based definition, an organization eliminates ambiguities, and creates many opportunities for cost reductions and improvements in lean principles (Knoche 2006).

2. TERMINOLOGY AND SYMBOLS

The Y14.3-2003 *Multiview and Sectional View Drawings* standard published by ASME establishes the requirements for creating orthographic views for item description. The standard includes the multi-view system of drawing, selection, and arrangement of orthographic views, auxiliary views, sectional views, details, and conventional drawing practices. This allows engineers to view different angles and look at more-detailed pictures for the item (ASME 2003). The different views and symbols can be interpreted to extract the required information and the specifications for that item. For example, orthographic views show a top view, a front view, and a right side view. One view is not sufficient to describe the item in detail, and so additional views are required. The number of orthographic views needed to describe an object fully depends on the complexity of the object. For example, a simple metal washer can be fully described using only one orthographic view; however, an extremely complex object may require as many as six views

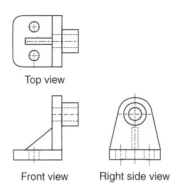

Top view

Front view   Right side view

Figure 14.9   Top, front, and right side views of an item.

(top, front, left side, right side, back, and bottom). Most objects can be sufficiently described using three views: top, front, and right side, as shown in Figure 14.9.

The symbols on the drawing have different representations based on the ASME standards. For example, each line style has its own interpretation. Figure 14.10 shows the different line symbols that can be used in an engineering drawing (Gunderson 1994).

Other symbols that are used in a feature control frame to specify a feature's description, tolerance, modifier, and datum(s) are shown in Table 14.1.

3. POSITION AND BONUS TOLERANCES

Bonus tolerance is an additional tolerance that is used for geometric control. Whenever a geometric tolerance is applied to a feature of size, and it contains a maximum material condition (MMC) or a least material condition (LMC) modifier in the tolerance portion of the feature control frame, a bonus tolerance is permissible (Effective Training 2012).

Tolerance of position control is a geometric tolerance that defines the location tolerance of a feature of size from its true position (Effective Training 2012).

If a position was identified exactly on a drawing, the tolerance is applied at LMC or MMC, or is applied regardless of feature size. If LMC or MMC is listed, we can calculate a wider tolerance, or bonus, depending on the actual size of the measured feature. When using the regardless-of-feature-size approach, we are not allowed to consider bonus tolerance, and the center of the measured feature must lie within the tolerance zone specified. For example, the symbols in Figure 14.11 on a drawing indicate that the diameter of a tolerance zone is 0.001" and the true point is in the middle.

The diameter is a tolerance of size. However, the location also affects the fit and function of the feature to its mating part(s). Bonus tolerances allow the tolerance amount not used in the diameter to be applied to the location. This allows the maximum use of tolerances while keeping the fit and function intact (Clark 2012).

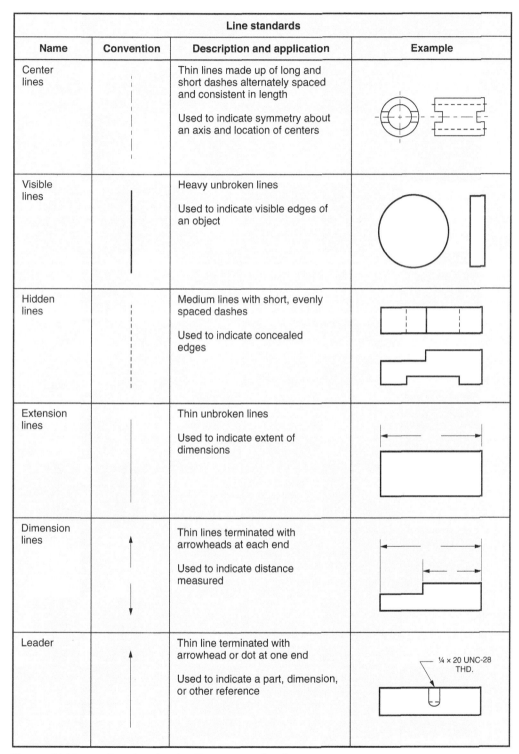

Line standards			
Name	**Convention**	**Description and application**	**Example**
Center lines		Thin lines made up of long and short dashes alternately spaced and consistent in length Used to indicate symmetry about an axis and location of centers	
Visible lines		Heavy unbroken lines Used to indicate visible edges of an object	
Hidden lines		Medium lines with short, evenly spaced dashes Used to indicate concealed edges	
Extension lines		Thin unbroken lines Used to indicate extent of dimensions	
Dimension lines		Thin lines terminated with arrowheads at each end Used to indicate distance measured	
Leader		Thin line terminated with arrowhead or dot at one end Used to indicate a part, dimension, or other reference	¼ × 20 UNC-28 THD.

Figure 14.10   Engineering drawing line types and styles.
Source: Gunderson (1994).

Line standards			
Name	**Convention**	**Description and application**	**Example**
Break (long)	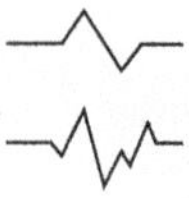	Thin solid ruled lines with freehand zig-zags Used to reduce size of drawing required to delineate object and reduce detail	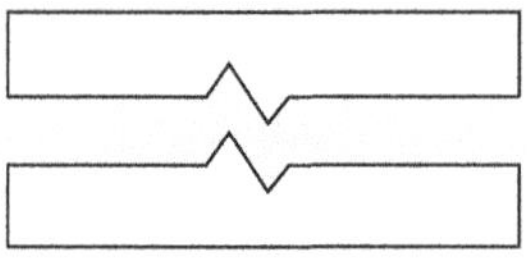
Break (short)		Thick solid freehand lines Used to indicate a short break	
Phantom or datum line		Medium series of one long dash and two short dashes evenly spaced ending with long dash Used to indicate alternate position of parts, repeated detail, or a datum plane	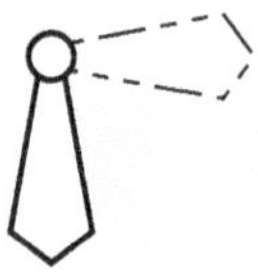
Stitch line		Medium line of short dashes evenly spaced and labeled Used to indicate stitching or sewing	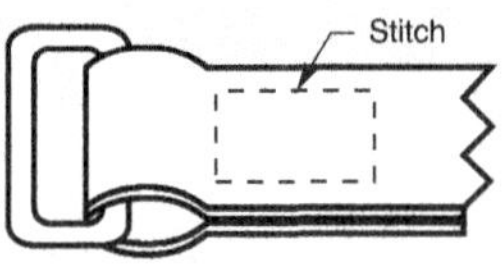 Stitch
Cutting-plane line		Used to designate where an imaginary cutting took place	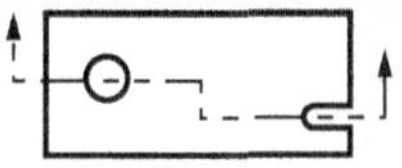
Viewing-plane line	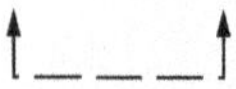	Used to indicate direction of sight when a partial view is used	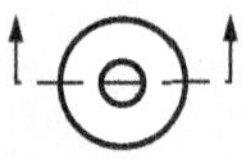
Section lines		Used to indicate the surface in the section view imagined to have been cut along the cutting-plane line	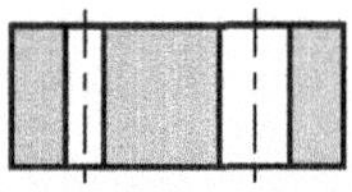
Chain line		Used to indicate that a surface or zone is to receive additional treatment or considerations	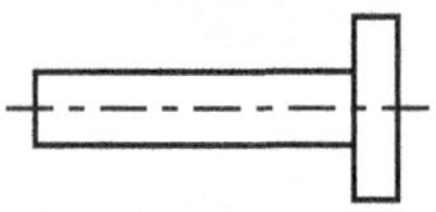

Figure 14.10   *Continued.*

Table 14.1 Other feature control symbols.

Symbol	Modifier
Ⓕ	Free state
Ⓛ	Least material condition
Ⓜ	Maximum material condition
Ⓟ	Projected tolerance zone
Ⓢ	Regardless of feature size
Ⓣ	Tangent plane
Ⓤ	Unilateral

Figure 14.11 Example of symbols on an engineering drawing.

EXAMPLE

Imagine we're trying to assemble a 5" long plug into a 4" deep bore. If the diameter of the bore is 2.0000" and the diameter of the plug is 1.9999", the plug would have to be straight within (or probably below) 0.0001" to ensure it would fit and function. On the contrary, if our plug diameter were 1.9995", it could have a straightness deviation of almost 0.0005" and still fit. This is an example of form, as opposed to location, but the concept is very similar (Clark 2012).

In our example we'll use an inside feature (see Figure 14.12). Our drawing states we have a diameter tolerance of 1.5000" + 0.0005" (so our MMC is 1.5000"). In addition, we have a positional location tolerance of 0.001" applied at MMC (Clark 2012).

The intent of positional location when applied at LMC or MMC is to ensure an acceptable amount of clearance between the part being made and its mating part. If the size of our inside feature is at MMC (smallest diameter), we need to be within 0.001" of the location for the mating part to fit (our part) properly. The larger we make our inside diameter, the more "room" we have for the location to be outside the 0.001" location tolerance zone, with the clearance remaining acceptable. Whatever amount above MMC (above our minimum) our diameter becomes is applied as a bonus to the tolerance of the positional location. If the diameter of our feature was 1.5005", the five-tenths we are above MMC would be applied to the location tolerance, which then becomes 0.0015" (Clark 2012).

Continued

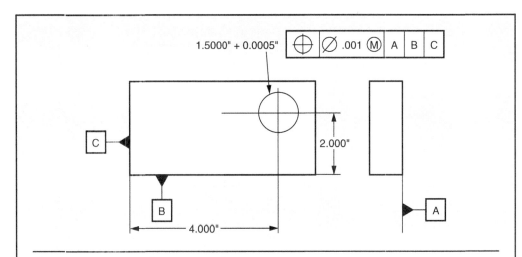

Figure 14.12 Form tolerance example.

If we look at the diameter tolerance and the location tolerance as two sides of a balanced equation, whatever we add to one side we also add to the other side to keep the two sides in balance (Clark 2012):

$$1.5000'' \text{ (Diameter at MMC)} = 0.001'' \text{ (Location)}$$

But if we were to add:

$$1.5000'' + 0.0003'' \text{ (Diameter)} = 0.001'' + 0.0003'' \text{ (Location)}$$
$$1.5003'' \text{ (Diameter)} = 0.0013'' \text{ (Location)}$$

4. PART ALIGNMENT AND DATUM STRUCTURE

Datums are points, lines, planes, cylinders, axes, and so on, from which the location, or geometric relationship, of other part features may be established or related.

Datum targets define the setup or fixture that will align the part to the datum reference frame. Datum targets do the same thing that a surface plate, angle plate, gauge pin, or a stack of gauge blocks does. They are all used to establish the datum points, axes, and planes. It would be like tolerancing the datum reference framework. If a fixture is built to establish the datum targets, there will be a drawing of the fixture, and this fixture drawing will be toleranced. But, rule of thumb (Y14.43) says the tolerances will usually be a factor of 10 better than the part tolerances (Tec-Ease 2012).

Part alignment is crucial for achieving accurate machine measurements. Knowing the software package that comes with a machine is not enough; operators of these machines must have good metrology skills, understand basic geometry, and, at a minimum, know how to read a blueprint and perform geometric dimensioning and tolerancing.

Incorrectly defining or failing to define a part alignment is the single most influential factor in gauge repeatability errors and incorrect measurements.

For example, consider that a perfectly round 1-in. diameter hole on a flat plate would show nearly 0.002 in. of form (roundness) error if measured as a circle and the part were 5° skewed from being parallel to the current CMM axis. Never assume that because a part sits on a CMM surface it can be measured without alignment.

A part alignment accomplishes two main objectives: (1) it defines the part function—usually depicted on the print via datum—and (2) it establishes the coordinate system or frame of reference for physically measuring the part.

To define a part alignment, the operator locks all three axes of the coordinate system to the part. This is done via machine software and requires establishing the directions of X, Y, and Z, as well as their intersection point, which can be taken as the origin. To build part alignment, we first do a level or spatial alignment, which separates feature types based on their dimensions. Second, we do a rotation or planar alignment. And third, we do axis translations (Nevado 2007).

REFERENCES

ASME (American Society of Mechanical Engineers). 1994. Y14.5M *Geometric Dimensioning and Tolerancing (GD&T)*. New York: ASME.

———. 2003. Y14.3-2003 *Multiview and Sectional View Drawings*. New York: ASME.

ASTM (American Society for Testing and Materials). 1996. D4356 *Standard Practice for Establishing Consistent Test Method Tolerances*. West Conshohocken, PA: ASTM.

Briggs, D., and T. Hendrix. 2003. *Recommended Practice Guide for Geometric Tolerances*. Chicago: Boeing Commercial Airplanes.

Cañas, A. J., and J. D. Novak, eds. 2006. "Geometric Tolerancing Explained by the Means of Concept Maps." *Proceedings of the Second International Conference on Concept Mapping*. San José, Costa Rica.

Clark, R. 2012. "Bonus Tolerances for GD&T: A True Balancing Act." HighBeam Research. February 1. Accessed May 15, 2018. Available at http://www.highbeam.com/doc/1G1-142386165.html.

Digital Design. 2012. "Drawing Sheet Layout." Accessed May 12, 2012, at http://www.metrication.com/drafting/layout.htm.

Dirks, A. L. 1995–2000. "Introduction to Technical Drawing." Accessed May 10, 2012, at http://webhost.bridgew.edu/adirks/ald/courses/design/desdraft.htm.

Effective Training. 2012. "GD&T Glossary." Accessed May 15, 2012, at http://www.etinews.com/gdt_glossary.html.

Fox, D. 2012. "Professional Skills." Department of Civil Engineering, University of Portsmouth. Accessed May 15, 2012, at http://www.scribd.com/doc/93761941/22248861-Professional-Skills-v1-1.

Gunderson, D. S., MMC (SW). 1994. *Blueprint Reading and Sketching*, NAVEDTRA 14040. NAVSUP Logistics Tracking Number 0504-LP-026-7150. Naval Education and Training Professional Development and Technology Center.

ISO (International Organization for Standardization). 2002. *ISO Standards Handbook, Technical Drawings, Volume 1: Technical Drawings in General*. Geneva: ISO.

Knoche, S. 2006. "Embrace Model Based Definition." *Quality Magazine,* July 1. Accessed November 27, 2018. Available at https://www.qualitymag.com/articles/84810-embrace-model-based-definition.

Lamit, L. G., and K. L. Kitto. 1994. *Principles of Engineering Drawing.* Minneapolis: West Publishing.

MTAG (Manufacturing Technology Advisory Group). 2001. "Core Competencies." Accessed May 2, 2012, at http://learningconnections.org/mtag/mtag_files/bio.htm.

Nevado, G. 2007. "Quality 101: CMM Part Alignment." *Quality Magazine,* October 30. Accessed November 27, 2018. Available at https://www.qualitymag.com/articles/85176-quality-101-cmm-part-alignment.

Pyzdek, T., and R. Berger, eds. 2003. *Quality Engineering Handbook.* Milwaukee: ASQ Quality Press; New York: Marcel Dekker.

Roymech, UK. 2007. "Drawing Title Blocks." Accessed May 2012, at http://www.roymech.co.uk/Useful_Tables/Drawing/Title_blocks.html.

Tec-Ease. 2012. "GD&T Training and Materials." Accessed May 12, 2012, at http://www.tec-ease.com.

Ware, M. 1999. *Cyanotype: The History, Science and Art of Photographic Printing in Prussian Blue.* London: NMSI Trading.

Chapter 15

B. Sampling

Define and interpret the following terms related to sampling. (Apply)

1. Acceptance quality limit (AQL)

2. Random sampling

3. Lot and sample size

4. Acceptance number

5. Sampling plans

                                                    Body of Knowledge III.B

INTRODUCTION

Acceptance sampling is a method for inspecting the product. Inspection can be done with screening (also called *sorting* or *100% inspection*), in which all units are inspected, or with sampling. *Acceptance sampling* is the process of inspecting a portion of the product in a lot for the purpose of making a decision regarding classification of the entire lot as either conforming or nonconforming to quality specifications.

Whether inspection is done with screening or with sampling, the results can be used for the following purposes:

1. To distinguish between good lots and bad lots using acceptance sampling plans (as in incoming material inspection and final product inspection).

2. To distinguish between good products and bad products.

3. To determine the status of process control and whether the process is changing. This is usually done in conjunction with control charts.

4. To evaluate process capability. In this case, inspection is used to determine whether the process exhibits excessive variation and whether it is approaching or exceeding the specification limits.

161

5. To determine process adjustment. Based on inspection results of process output—as depicted by a histogram, for example—the process mean may require adjustment, and/or process variation may need to be reduced. A process might require adjustment even though all the units produced to date conform to the quality standards agreed on with the customer.

6. To rate the accuracy of inspectors or inspection equipment by comparing the inspection results with corresponding standards. An inspection operation can result in two types of error: classification of a conforming unit as nonconforming and classification of a nonconforming unit as conforming. The probability of both types of error can be easily estimated using probability theory and other statistical methods.

7. To serve as a mechanism for evaluating vendors in terms of their products' quality. Vendors that consistently deliver high-quality products can receive preferred status involving reduced inspection and priority in bidding for new contracts, while vendors that do not stand up to quality requirements can be warned or discontinued altogether. This type of procedure is known as *vendor qualification* or *vendor certification*.

ADVANTAGES

Sampling provides the economic advantage of lower inspection costs due to fewer units being inspected. In addition, the time required to inspect a *sample* is substantially less than that required for the entire lot, and there is less damage to the product due to reduced handling. Most inspectors find that selection and inspection of a random sample is less tedious and monotonous than inspection of the complete lot. Another advantage of sampling inspection is related to the supplier/customer relationship. By inspecting a small fraction of the lot and forcing the supplier to screen 100% in case of lot rejection (which is the case for rectifying inspection), the customer emphasizes that the supplier must be concerned about quality. On the other hand, the variability inherent in sampling results in sampling errors: rejection of lots of conforming quality and acceptance of lots of nonconforming quality.

Acceptance sampling is most appropriate when inspection costs are high and when 100% inspection is monotonous and can cause inspector fatigue and boredom, resulting in degraded performance and increased error rates. Obviously, sampling is the only choice available for destructive inspection. Rectifying sampling is a form of acceptance sampling. Sample units detected as nonconforming are discarded from the lot, replaced with conforming units, or repaired. Rejected lots are subject to 100% screening, which can involve discarding, replacing, or repairing units detected as nonconforming.

In certain situations it is preferable to inspect 100% of the product. This would be the case for critical or complex products, where the cost of making the wrong decision would be too high. Screening is appropriate when the fraction nonconforming is extremely high. In this case, most of the lots would be rejected under acceptance sampling, and those accepted would be so as a result of statistical variations rather than better quality. Screening is also appropriate when the fraction nonconforming is not known and an estimate based on a large sample is needed.

SAMPLING CONCEPTS

Sampling may be performed according to the type of quality characteristics to be inspected. There are three major categories of sampling plans: sampling plans for attributes, sampling plans for variables, and special sampling plans.

Random Sampling

The simple random sampling design consists of selecting n (sample size) sampling units in such a way that each sampling unit has the same chance of being selected.

The Operating Characteristic Curve

No matter which type of attribute sampling plan is being considered, the most important evaluation tool is the operating characteristic (OC) curve.

The *OC curve* allows a sampling plan to be almost completely evaluated at a glance, giving a pictorial view of the probabilities of accepting lots submitted at varying levels of percent defective. The OC curve illustrates the risks involved in acceptance sampling. Figure 15.1 shows an OC curve for a sample size (n) of 50 drawn from an infinite lot size, with an acceptance number (c) of 3.

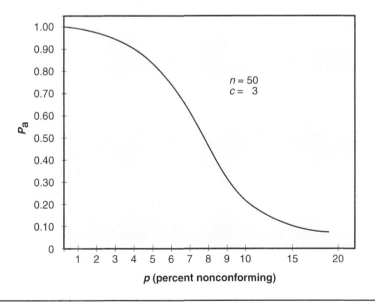

Figure 15.1   An OC curve.

As can be seen by the OC curve, if the lot were 100% to specifications, the probability of acceptance P_a would also be 100%. But if the lot were 13.4% defective, there would be a 10% probability of acceptance.

Acceptance Sampling by Attributes

Acceptance sampling by attributes is generally used for two purposes: (1) protection against accepting lots from a continuing process whose average quality deteriorates beyond an acceptance quality limit, and (2) protection against isolated lots that may have levels of nonconformances greater than can be considered acceptable. The most commonly used form of acceptance sampling plan is sampling by attributes. The most widely used *standard* of all attribute plans, although not necessarily the best, is ANSI/ASQ Z1.4-2008. The following sections provide more detail on the characteristics of acceptance sampling and discussion of military standards in acceptance sampling.

Acceptance Quality Limit

Acceptance quality limit (AQL) is defined as the quality level that is the worst tolerable process average when a continuing series of lots is submitted for acceptance sampling. This means that a lot that has a fraction defective equal to the AQL has a high probability (generally in the area of 0.95, although it may vary) of being accepted. As a result, plans that are based on AQL, such as ANSI/ASQ Z1.4-2008, favor the producer in getting lots accepted that are in the general neighborhood of the AQL for fraction defective in a lot.

Lot Tolerance Percent Defective

The *lot tolerance percent defective* (LTPD), expressed in percent defective, is the poorest quality in an individual lot that should be accepted. The LTPD has a low probability of acceptance. In many sampling plans, the LTPD is the percent defective having a 10% probability of acceptance.

Producer's and Consumer's Risks

There are two risks involved in using acceptance sampling plans: (1) producer's risk and (2) consumer's risk. These risks correspond with type 1 and type 2 errors in hypothesis testing and are defined as follows:

- *Producer's risk* (α). The producer's risk for any given sampling plan is the probability of rejecting a lot that is within the AQL (ASQ Statistics Division 2005). This means that the producer faces the possibility (at level of significance α) of having a lot rejected even though the lot has met the requirements stipulated by the AQL level.

- *Consumer's risk* (β). The consumer's risk for any given sampling plan is the probability of acceptance (usually 10%) for a designated numerical value of relatively poor submitted quality (ASQ Statistics Division 2005). The consumer's risk, therefore, is the probability of accepting a lot that has a quality level equal to the LTPD.

Average Outgoing Quality

The *average outgoing quality* (AOQ) is the expected average quality of outgoing products, including all accepted lots, plus all rejected lots that have been sorted 100% and have had all of the nonconforming units replaced with conforming units.

There is a given AOQ for specific fractions nonconforming of submitted lots sampled under a given sampling plan. When the fraction nonconforming is very low, a large majority of the lots will be accepted as submitted. The few lots that are rejected will be sorted 100% and will have all nonconforming units replaced with conforming units. Thus, the AOQ will always be less than the submitted quality. As the quality of submitted lots declines in relation to the AQL, the percentage of lots rejected increases in proportion to accepted lots. As these rejected lots are sorted and combined with accepted lots, an AOQ lower than the average fraction of nonconformances of submitted lots emerges. Therefore, when the level of quality of incoming lots is good, the AOQ is good; when the incoming quality is bad and most lots are rejected and sorted, the result is also good.

Average Outgoing Quality Limit

The AOQ is a variable dependent on the quality level of incoming lots. When the AOQ is plotted for all possible levels of incoming quality, a curve as shown in Figure 15.2 results. The *average outgoing quality limit* (AOQL) is the highest value on the AOQ curve.

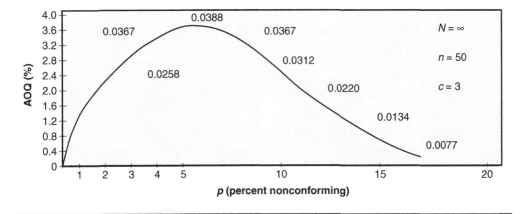

Figure 15.2   AOQ curve for $N = \infty, n = 50, c = 3$.

Lot Size, Sample Size, and Acceptance Number

For any single sampling plan, the plan is completely described by the lot size, sample size, and acceptance number.

TYPES OF ATTRIBUTE SAMPLING PLANS

There are several types of attribute sampling plans in use, with the most common being single, double, multiple, and sequential sampling plans. The type of sampling plan used is determined by ease of use and administration, general quality level of incoming lots, average sample number, and so on.

Single Sampling Plans

When single sampling plans are used, the decision to either accept or reject the lot is based on the results of the inspection of a single sample of n items from a submitted lot. In Figure 15.2, the OC curve and AOQ curve were calculated for a single sampling plan where $n = 50$ and $c = 3$. Single sampling plans have the advantage of ease of administration, but due to the unchanging sample size, they do not take advantage of potential cost savings of reduced inspection when incoming quality is either excellent or poor.

Double Sampling Plans

When using double sampling plans, a smaller first sample is taken from the submitted lot, and one of three decisions is made: (1) accept the lot, (2) reject the lot, or (3) draw another sample. If a second sample is to be drawn, the lot will either be accepted or rejected after the second sample. Double sampling plans have the advantage of a lower total sample size when the incoming quality is either excellent or poor, because the lot is either accepted or rejected on the first sample.

Multiple Sampling Plans

Multiple sampling plans work in the same way as double sampling with an increase in the number of samples to be taken up to seven, according to ANSI/ASQ Z1.4-2008. In the same manner that double sampling is performed, acceptance or rejection of submitted lots may be reached before the seventh sample depending on the acceptance/rejection criteria established for the plan.

SAMPLING STANDARDS AND PLANS

ANSI/ASQ Z1.4-2008

ANSI/ASQ Z1.4-2008 is probably the most commonly used standard for attribute sampling plans. The wide recognition and acceptance of the plan could be due to government contracts stipulating the standard, rather than its statistical importance. Producers submitting products at a nonconformance level within AQL have a high probability of having the lot accepted by the customer.

When using ANSI/ASQ Z1.4-2008, the characteristics under consideration should be classified. The general classifications are critical, major, and minor defects, and are described as follows:

- *Critical defect.* A *critical defect* is a defect that judgment and experience indicate is likely to result in hazardous or unsafe conditions for the individuals using, maintaining, or depending on the product, or a defect that judgment and experience indicate is likely to prevent performance of the unit. In practice, critical characteristics are commonly inspected to an AQL level of 0.40%–0.65% if not 100% inspected. One hundred percent inspection is recommended for critical characteristics if possible. Acceptance numbers are always zero for critical defects.

- *Major defect.* A *major defect* is a defect, other than critical, that is likely to result in failure or to materially reduce the usability of the unit of product for its intended purpose. In practice, AQL levels for major defects are generally about 1%.

- *Minor defect.* A *minor defect* is a defect that is not likely to materially reduce the usability of the unit of product for its intended purpose. In practice, AQL levels for minor defects generally range from 1.5% to 2.5%.

Levels of Inspection

There are seven levels of inspection used in ANSI/ASQ Z1.4-2008: reduced inspection, normal inspection, tightened inspection, and four levels of special inspection. The special inspection levels should only be used when small sample sizes are necessary and large risks can be tolerated. When using ANSI/ASQ Z1.4-2008, a set of switching rules must be followed as to the use of reduced, normal, and tightened inspection.

The following guidelines are taken from ANSI/ASQ Z1.4-2008:

- *Initiation of inspection.* Normal inspection Level II will be used at the start of inspection unless otherwise directed by the responsible authority.

- *Continuation of inspection.* Normal, tightened, or reduced inspection shall continue unchanged for each class of defect or defectives on successive lots or batches except where the following switching procedures require change. The switching procedures shall be applied to each class of defects or defectives independently.

Switching Procedures. Switching rules are graphically shown in Figure 15.3.

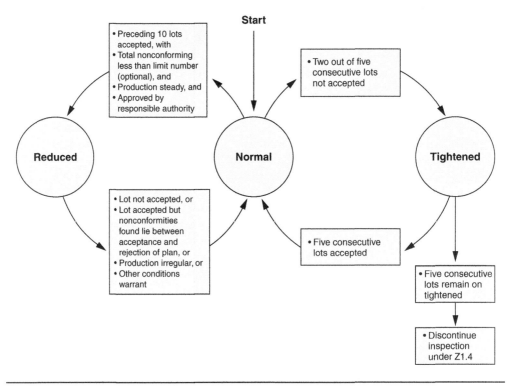

Figure 15.3   Switching rules for normal, tightened, and reduced inspection.

Types of Sampling

ANSI/ASQ Z1.4-2008 allows for three types of sampling plans:

1. Single sampling

2. Double sampling

3. Multiple sampling

The choice of the type of plan depends on many variables. Single sampling is the easiest to administer and perform but usually results in the largest average total inspection. Double sampling results in a lower average total inspection than single sampling but requires more decisions to be made, such as:

- Accept the lot after first sample

- Reject the lot after first sample

- Take a second sample

- Accept the lot after second sample

- Reject the lot after second sample

Multiple sampling plans further reduce the average total inspection but also increase the number of decisions to be made. As many as seven samples may be required before a decision to accept or reject the lot can be made. This type of plan requires the most administration.

A general procedure for selecting plans from ANSI/ASQ Z1.4-2008 is as follows:

1. Decide on an AQL

2. Decide on the inspection level

3. Determine the lot size

4. Find the appropriate sample size code letter

5. Determine the type of sampling plan to be used: single, double, or multiple

6. Using the selected AQL and sample size code letter, enter the appropriate table to find the desired plan to be used

7. Determine the normal, tightened, and reduced plans as required from the corresponding tables

VARIABLES SAMPLING PLANS

Variables sampling plans use the actual measurements of sample products for decision making rather than classifying products as conforming or nonconforming, as in attribute sampling plans. Variables sampling plans are more complex in administration than attribute plans, and thus they require more skill. They provide some benefits, however, over attribute plans:

1. The protection is equal to an attribute sampling plan with a much smaller sample size. There are several types of variables sampling plans in use, three of these being (1) σ known, (2) σ unknown but can be estimated using sample standard deviation s, and (3) σ unknown and the range R is used as an estimator. If an attribute sampling plan sample size is determined, the variables plans previously listed can be compared as a percentage to the attribute plan.

Plan	Sample size (percent)
Attribute	100
σ unknown, range method	60
σ unknown, s estimated from sample	40
σ known	15

2. Variables sampling plans allow the determination of how close to nominal or a specification limit the process is performing. Attribute plans either accept or reject a lot; variables plans give information on how well or poorly the process is performing.

Variables sampling plans, such as ANSI/ASQ Z1.9-2008, have some disadvantages and limitations:

1. The assumption of normality of the population from which the samples are being drawn.

2. Different characteristics on the same parts will have different averages and dispersions, resulting in a separate sampling plan for each characteristic.

3. Variables plans are more complex in administration.

4. Variables gauging is generally more expensive than attribute gauging.

ANSI/ASQ Z1.9-2008

The most common standard for variables sampling plans is ANSI/ASQ Z1.9-2008, which has plans for (1) variability known, (2) variability unknown—standard deviation method, and (3) variability unknown—range method. Using the afore-mentioned methods, this sampling plan can be used to test for a single specification limit, a double (or bilateral) specification limit, estimation of the process average, and estimation of the dispersion of the parent population.

Figure 15.4 summarizes the structure and organization of ANSI/ASQ Z1.9-2008.

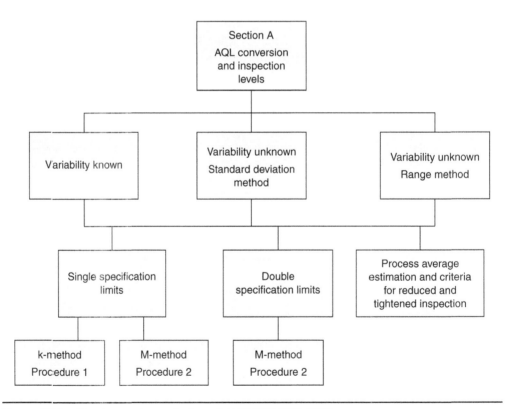

Figure 15.4 Structure and organization of ANSI/ASQ Z1.9-2008.

SEQUENTIAL SAMPLING PLANS

When tests are either destructive in nature or costly, it may be advantageous to use sequential sampling plans popularized by Wald (1973). These plans have the advantage of greatly reduced sample sizes while giving good protection.

To determine a sequential sampling plan, the following parameters must be defined:

α = Producer's risk

AQL = Acceptance quality limit = p_1

β = Consumer's risk

RQL = Rejectable (or unacceptable) quality level = p_2

Figure 15.5 shows the accept, reject, and continue testing areas for a sequential sampling plan. The y-axis represents the number of nonconforming items in the sample, and the x-axis scales the number of units inspected.

CONTINUOUS SAMPLING PLANS

Many production processes do not produce lots, and thus lot-by-lot acceptance sampling plans, discussed earlier, cannot be applied. In cases such as these, continuous sampling plans are developed. In continuous sampling plans, 100% inspection and sampling inspection are alternately applied. The most recent standard for developing continuous sampling plans is the military standard MIL-STD-1235B.

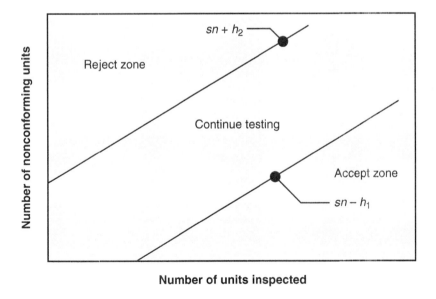

Figure 15.5   Decision areas for a sequential sampling plan.

MIL-STD-1235B

MIL-STD-1235B uses the same parameters, i and f, as previously defined. The standard includes CSP-1, CSP-2, CSP-F, CSP-T, and CSP-V plans.

CSP-1 and CSP-2 plans operate in the same way as Dodge's CSP-1 and CSP-2 plans, but they are selected based on a sample size code letter and an AQL value as a quality index. The sample size code letter is selected based on the number of units in the production interval.

CSP-F plans work the same way as CSP-1 plans, providing alternate sequences of 100% and sampling inspection procedures, but the difference is that AOQL and the number of units in the production interval are used in this case to characterize the plans. Once AOQL and f values are selected, go to the corresponding table to read i, the clearance number. CSP-F is a single-level continuous sampling scheme.

CSP-T plans include the provision of reduced sampling frequency once the product shows superior quality.

The CSP-T plan works as follows:

1. Start with 100% inspection.

2. When i (clearance number) consecutive number of units are found free from nonconformities, 100% inspection is replaced by sampling inspection.

3. A fraction of f units is randomly selected and then inspected.

   3.1. If one nonconformity is found, the inspector reinstates 100% inspection.

   3.2. If the inspector finds i consecutive units free from nonconformities, the fraction f is reduced to $f/2$.

      3.2.1. If one nonconformity is found, the inspector switches back to 100% inspection.

      3.2.2. If the inspector finds i consecutive units free from nonconformities, the fraction f is reduced to $f/4$.

         3.2.2.1. If one nonconformity is found, 100% inspection is reinstated.

CSP-V plans work the same way as CSP-T plans but with reduced i instead of reduced f. The procedure is as follows:

1. Start with 100% inspection.

2. When i (clearance number) consecutive number of units are found free from nonconformities, 100% inspection is replaced by sampling inspection.

3. A fraction of f units is randomly selected and then inspected.

   3.1. If one nonconformity is found, the inspector reinstates 100% inspection.

3.2. If the inspector finds *i* consecutive units free from nonconformities, the inspection continues with inspecting the same fraction *f*.

3.2.1. If one nonconformity is found, the inspector switches back to 100% inspection.

3.2.2. If the inspector finds i/3, the sampling inspection continues with the same fraction f.

REFERENCES

ANSI/ASQ (American National Standards Institute/American Society for Quality). 2008a. Z1.4-2008 *Sampling Procedures and Tables for Inspection by Attributes*. Milwaukee: ASQ Quality Press.

———. 2008b. Z1.9-2008 *Sampling Procedures and Tables for Inspection by Variables*. Milwaukee: ASQ Quality Press.

ASQ Statistics Division. 2005. *Glossary and Tables for Statistical Quality Control*. 4th ed. Milwaukee: ASQ Quality Press.

Wald, A. 1973. *Sequential Analysis*. New York: Dover Publications.

BIBLIOGRAPHY

Burr, W. 1976. *Statistical Quality Control Methods*. New York: Marcel Dekker.

Deming, W. E. 1986. *Out of the Crisis*. Cambridge, MA: MIT Center for Advanced Engineering.

Dovich, R. 1992. "Acceptance Sampling." In *Quality Engineering Handbook*, edited by T. Pyzdek and R. Berger. Milwaukee: ASQC Quality Press and New York: Marcel Dekker.

Duncan, A. J. 1974. *Quality Control and Industrial Statistics*. 4th ed. Homewood, IL: Richard D. Irwin.

Feigenbaum, A. V. 1991. *Total Quality Control*. 3rd ed., revised. New York: McGraw-Hill.

Gryna, F. M., R. C. H. Chua, and J. A. Defeo. 2007. *Juran's Quality Planning and Analysis for Enterprise Quality*. 5th ed. New York: McGraw-Hill.

Chapter 16

C. Inspection Planning and Processes

1. *Inspection types.* Define and distinguish between inspection types such as incoming material, first-article (first-piece), in-process, and final. (Apply)

2. *Inspection errors.* Identify potential inspection errors such as bias, fatigue, flinching, distraction, and poor time management. (Apply)

3. *Product traceability.* Identify methods to trace products and materials such as age control, shelf life, first-in first-out (FIFO), barcoding, date codes, and lot and part numbering. (Apply)

4. *Identification of nonconforming material.* Describe various methods of identifying nonconforming material such as tagging, labeling, and segregating. (Apply)

5. *Level of severity.* Define and describe levels of severity (critical, major, and minor) and apply them to product features and defects. (Apply)

6. *Disposition of nonconforming material.* Describe disposition methods including rework, reprocess, reinspect, scrap, and customer waiver, as determined by a material review board (MRB) or other authority. (Apply)

Body of Knowledge III.C

INTRODUCTION

Inspection is the evaluation of product quality by comparing the results of measuring one or several product characteristics with applicable standards. From this definition it is evident that the inspection function involves a number of tasks (Raz 1992):

1. Measurement, which could be on a qualitative or quantitative scale. The objective is to make a judgment about a product's conformance to specifications.

2. Comparison of the measurement results to certain standards that reflect the intended use of the product by the customer and the various production costs. If the product is found to be nonconforming,

175

a decision as to whether nonconforming products are fit for use may be reached.

3. Decision making regarding the disposition of the unit inspected and, under sampling inspection, regarding the lot from which the sample was drawn.

4. Corrective action(s) in order to improve the quality of the product and/or process based on the aggregate results of inspection over a number of units.

Inspection decisions for most products are shown in Figure 16.1.

INSPECTION PLANNING

Inspection planning includes the determination of the location of inspection and/ or quality control methods and procedures at the various points in the production process. It also involves the determination of the types of inspections to be carried out and the quality levels, identification of critical characteristics to be inspected, and classification of defects.

The location of inspection stations can be determined based on the following considerations (Raz 1992):

- Inspect incoming materials to prevent the entry of defective components into the production system. This step could be eliminated if the suppliers provide sufficient evidence of the use of process control techniques to maintain product quality.

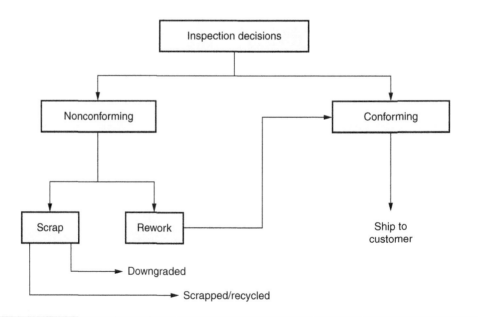

Figure 16.1 Inspection decisions.

- Inspect prior to costly operations in order to avoid further investment in an already nonconforming product.

- Inspect prior to processing operations that may mask defects; for example, surface finish should be inspected prior to painting.

- Inspect prior to processing operations that may cause an increase in repair costs. For example, inspect and test circuit boards prior to assembly into their enclosures.

- Inspect following operations known to have a relatively high defect rate.

- Inspect final or finished goods before moving the product to another department or plant prior to shipping to the customer.

- Inspect the first few units of each new batch in order to verify that the setup is correct.

The basic tool for choosing the location of inspection stations is the *flowchart*. The most common locations are as follows (Gryna 2001):

- At receipt of goods from suppliers, usually called "incoming inspection" or "supplier inspection."

- Following the setup of a process to provide added assurance against producing a defective batch. In some cases this "setup approval" also becomes approval of the batch.

- During the running of critical or costly operations, usually called "process inspection."

- Prior to delivery of goods from one department to another, usually called "lot approval" or "tollgate inspection."

- Prior to shipping completed products to storage or customers, usually called "finished goods inspection."

- Before performing a costly, irreversible operation, for example, pouring a melt of steel.

- At natural "peepholes" in the process.

A flowchart example is shown in Figure 16.2.

1. INSPECTION TYPES

Incoming Material Inspection

Incoming material inspection is performed when one company purchases materials or supplies from another company. This is considered a producer–supplier relationship, where the acceptance or rejection decisions on submitted lots are based on a certain criterion agreed on between both companies. The purpose of

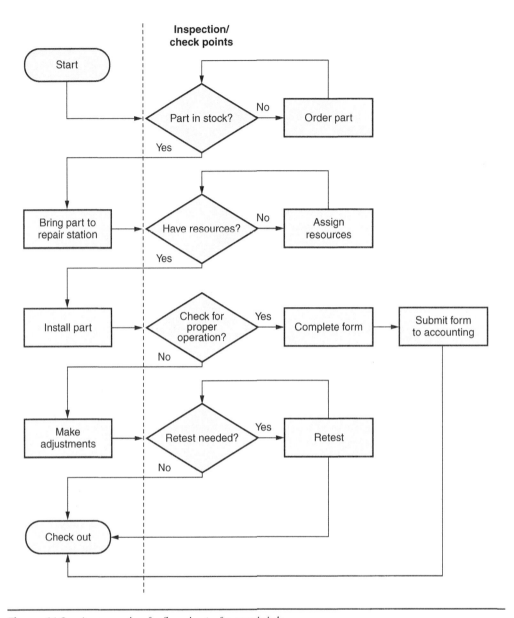

Figure 16.2 An example of a flowchart of a repair job.

incoming inspection is to distinguish between good lots and bad lots. The decision that follows an incoming inspection procedure falls into one of the following categories:

1. Accept the lot; that is, the lot conforms to specifications

2. Reject the lot; that is, the lot is considered nonconforming

3. The lot should go to a screening inspection (100% inspection)

First-Piece Inspection

In first-piece inspection, the operator is likely to carry out the inspection. The purpose is to make sure that all procedures and execution of work are properly employed according to a specified work standard or set of specifications.

In-Process Inspection

The purpose of in-process inspection is to determine the appropriateness of control techniques employed by the company to decide on the degree of conformance to a system of standard requirements. In many cases, sampling is employed. The results of in-process inspection are as follows:

1. Products are inspected and then classified into classes or grades depending on the degree of conformity to standards.

2. Nonconforming products may be classified as scrap or rework. In some cases the cost of reworking a product is more costly than producing it.

3. Nonconforming products may be analyzed to determine the root cause of the problem and the appropriate follow-up corrective action.

Final Inspection

Finished product inspection is carried out to confirm that the product conforms to the customer's specifications. It may include assembly, installation, and packaging. In all cases final inspection is thorough and complete and may be intensive and costly depending on the accuracy and severity of incoming inspection and in-process inspection.

Inspection planning also includes the preparation of a list of characteristics to be inspected. The following guidelines may prove helpful (Raz 1992):

• Inspect characteristics that affect the performance of the product. To the extent possible, product testing should be done under conditions that simulate actual use.

• Select characteristics that can be measured objectively, to the extent possible.

• Provide a seriousness classification in order to improve consistency for characteristics that are evaluated subjectively.

• Inspect characteristics that can be related to a specific production process in order to simultaneously obtain information about the process.

A detailed inspection plan should be prepared and approved by the customer and the production, engineering, and manufacturing departments prior to the start of full-scale production. The inspection plan should include the following items (Raz 1992):

- The location of each inspection station in the sequence of production operations

- The type of inspection or test to be carried out, including a description of the environment, equipment, and procedures

- Accuracy requirements from the measurements

- The conformance criteria, normally based on product specifications

- The sample size and procedure for drawing a sample in the case of sampling inspection

- The lot size and the criteria for lot acceptance, if applicable

- The disposition of nonconforming units (for example, repair, scrap, or salvage) and of rejected lots (for example, screen or return to vendor)

- The criteria for initiating a review of the process, vendor, or inspector

2. INSPECTION ERRORS

Errors are bound to happen in any system that has a combination of interrelated factors that make up an outcome. This is true in inspection, as the inspection process involves many factors that combine to determine the outcome of the inspection, often a decision. Major contributors to error sources are the following (Darmody 1967):

1. Human error or errors due to the physiology of the inspector

2. Inspection equipment errors due to accuracy, instrument selection, methodology, and so on

3. Errors due to the environment that surrounds the inspection location

4. Procedural errors due to the introduction of new processes, equipment, and so on

Inspection involves a measurement, which is comparing the actual value of the measured item, component, or material with a standard, and making the decision as a result of such comparison. Measurement by itself has different error sources that are often unavoidable.

Error in measurement is the difference between the indicated value and the true value of a measured quantity. The true value of a quantity to be measured is seldom known. Errors are classified as one of two types:

1. Random errors

2. Systematic errors

Random errors are accidental in nature. They fluctuate in a way that cannot be predicted from the detailed employment of the measuring system or from knowledge of its functioning. Sources of error such as hysteresis, ambient influences, or variations in the workpiece are typical but not all-inclusive in the random category.

Systematic errors are those not usually detected by repetition of the measurement operations. An error resulting from either faulty calibration of a local standard or a defect in contact configuration of an internal measuring system is typical but not completely inclusive in the systematic class of errors. It is important to know all the sources of error in a measuring system rather than merely to be aware of the details of their classification. Analysis of the causes of errors is helpful in attaining the necessary knowledge of achieved accuracy (Darmody 1967).

There are many different sources of errors that influence the precision of a measuring process in a variety of ways according to the individual situation in which such errors arise. The permutation of error sources and their effects, therefore, is quite considerable. In general, these errors can be classified under one of three main headings (Rashed and Hamouda 1974):

1. Process environment

2. Equipment limitation

3. Operator fallibility

These factors constitute an interrelated three-element system for the measuring process.

The requirement of any precision measuring instrument is that it be able to represent, as accurately as possible, the dimension it measures. This necessitates that the instrument itself have a high degree of inherent accuracy. Small inaccuracies will exist, however, due to the tolerances permitted in the instrument's manufacture. These inaccuracies will influence the degree of precision attainable in its application.

The areas in which operator fallibility arises can be grouped as follows:

1. Identification of the measuring situation

2. Analysis of alternative methods

3. Selection of equipment

4. Application (or measurement)

The identification of measuring situations becomes increasingly complex in modern metrology. As parts become smaller and more precise, greater attention has to be paid to geometric qualities such as roundness, concentricity, straightness, parallelism, and squareness. Deficiencies in these qualities may consume all of the permitted design tolerance, so that a simple dimensional check becomes grossly insufficient.

Operators have to be knowledgeable about what they have to measure and how satisfactorily the requirements of the situation will be met by the measuring instrument. Correct identification of the measuring situation will eliminate those methods unsuitable for the situation. Proper measuring equipment can therefore be selected from a smaller range of measuring process alternatives. Method analysis can then be applied to these alternatives to determine which best suits the situation. This usually involves examining each method for different characteristics and evaluating the relative accuracies of the different methods. Figure 16.3 depicts the factors that affect the performance of the measuring process.

```
┌─────────────────────────────────────────┐
│  Operator fallibility                    │
│     • Identification of the situation    │
│     • Analysis of alternative methods    │
│     • Selection of equipment             │
│     • Application/measurement            │
│  Measuring equipment                     │
│     • Sensitivity                        │
│     • Accuracy and precision             │
│     • Consistency                        │
│     • Repeatability                      │
│     • Gauge or instrument wear           │
│  Environmental conditions                │
│     • Temperature                        │
│     • Vibration                          │
│     • Structural instability             │
│     • Humidity                           │
│     • Factors of atmospheric pollution   │
│     • Atmospheric pressure               │
│     • Gravity                            │
└─────────────────────────────────────────┘
```

Figure 16.3   Factors affecting the measuring process.

Other common error sources in inspection include flinching, bias, distraction, and fatigue. *Flinching* is an unintended human observation in measurement that lies on the border between manipulation and approximation. Inspectors readily miscount a dial division or two to get a subconsciously desired reading (Kennedy et al. 1987).

Poor time management is another source of inspection error that is not commonly highlighted in many reference books.

Inspector Qualifications and Training

Basic requirements for inspection personnel include the following (Raz 1992):

1. The ability to perform the relevant measurements

2. Understanding of product specifications to the point of being capable of determining product quality

3. Basic mathematical skills for recording and analyzing data

4. Basic understanding of statistical concepts needed for sampling inspection and process characterization

5. Knowledge of measurements and measurement technology

6. Understanding of company's inspection policies, inspection procedure, products, materials, and processes

Training refers to the formal procedures used to improve job-related capability. Training programs for inspection personnel should be designed to address three main generic aspects:

1. *Attitude.* This includes developing a genuine concern for the product and for the customer, as well as fostering a positive self-image of the inspection function. To a significant extent, attitude is affected by the leadership of management and supervisory staff.

2. *Knowledge.* This includes not only knowledge directly related to the inspection function but also knowledge of the various production processes, materials, equipment, procedures, and so on.

3. *Skills.* This category refers to mastering the performance of the technical activities that are part of the inspector's job.

The Characteristics of a Quality Inspector

The quality inspector is involved in many aspects of product quality, including:

- Evaluating hardware documentation
- Performing laboratory procedures
- Inspecting products against specified standards
- Measuring process performance
- Recording data
- Preparing formal reports

Because of this, the quality inspector needs technical expertise in the field where they perform given tasks. This knowledge should be related to the processes where inspection is applied. The quality inspector should be aware of all applicable standards and regulations, and know how to systematically perform feature comparisons to prescribed requirements. The quality inspector should also be familiar with the products and processes, and how to use the inspection monitoring and measuring instruments. A quality inspector is required to understand and apply a variety of tools and techniques, including technical math, metrology, inspection and test techniques, and quality assurance and improvement methodologies. These are the essential features that determine the technical competency of the profession.

The level of excellence within the inspection field requires a specific personal skill set that distinguishes average from outstanding inspectors. The quality inspector must be attentive, objective, and detail oriented. This profession requires a high level of responsibility and accountability when performing quality inspection duties. Quality inspection activities are best performed by specialists who are accurate and error-free, analytical, consistent, confident, reliable, and organized.

Since quality inspectors need to work in cross-functional teams, solid interpersonal skills are essential. This interpersonal skill set includes verbal and nonverbal communication, listening, problem solving, and decision making (*Quality Magazine* 2016).

3. PRODUCT TRACEABILITY

Traceability is an explicit part of the ISO 9001 and ISO/TS 16949 standards. See paragraph 7.5.3 in ANSI/ISO/ASQ Q9001-2008, for example. Traceability is like a pedigree for a dog breed or the provenance of a painting. It allows one to learn the history of an item. Commodity products such as nuts and bolts have limited need for traceability. Complex products such as automobiles must have multiple paths that trace back through many levels and many different sources. Sensitive material such as pharmaceuticals and food products must be traceable at all times. Even in the case of nuts and bolts, however, wise manufacturers will keep different lots segregated and identified as long as it is economically possible.

The ISO 9001 standard requires product identification and traceability, where appropriate, for recall of nonconforming product, hazardous product, or product in conflict with laws, regulations, or statutes. Product identification must be provided when required by a customer. Properly identified items must have a unique number and are tracked by their location in the process. Differences between items and lots must be distinguishable.

Traceability, that is, the ability to preserve the identity of the product and its origins, should begin when the process is first designed. Today, appropriate software and database designs are available. Training of workers may be required in order to create the proper climate and means to accomplish this. Frank M. Gryna (1988) listed four reasons why traceability is needed:

1. To assure that only materials and components of adequate quality enter the final product, for example, sterility of drug materials, adequate metallurgical composition, and heat treatment of structural components.

2. To assure positive identification to avoid mix-up of products that otherwise look alike.

3. To permit recall of suspect product on a precise basis. Lacking traceability programs, huge recalls of automobiles and other products have been required in the past. The number of defectives in the recalled set was often quite small.

4. To localize causes of failure and take remedial action at minimal cost.

There are other uses of traceability—such as in inventory control and scheduling. Some of these uses also affect quality. For example, use of materials on a first-in, first-out basis reduces the risk of quality deterioration of perishable materials.

Factors to Consider

- What is the cost of the product? A more expensive product requires more accountability over time, and thus better traceability.

- How long will the product last? If it is going to be around a long time, there is more concern about its origin, as new discoveries are often made of chemical characteristics and environmental effects. The discovery that asbestos is a carcinogen after its routine use for decades is a good example.

- Will the product be built into another product?
- Does the product contain items or materials that have not been thoroughly evaluated over a long period of time?
- Is there a significant possible health hazard associated with the product?
- Are field modifications often required, with different replacement items required on different models? (Automobiles are a prime example.)

Ten items to consider in a traceability program are the following:

1. Product category
2. Product life
3. Unit cost
4. Recall or modification in the field
5. Product complexity
6. Level of downstream traceability
7. Documents providing traceability
8. Type of identification
9. Coded versus uncoded identification
10. Method of identification—tags, nameplates, ink stamps, other means

The use of a tracing code (Feigenbaum 1991) is required for efficient operation. This code is established at the beginning of material flow, and a traceability flowchart is established.

The major activities on the flowchart include the following:

1. Critical component selection and listing by part number.
2. Vendor part coding (recording vendor name and date of receipt).
3. Coding internally manufactured parts, subassembly, assembly, and storage in a daily tally. At the end of the assembly line, each shipping container is date coded. This sequential coding procedure provides sufficient data to tie critical components to specific dates of receiving inspection, manufacturing, and final assembly.
4. Computerized shipping records, including date codes, customer name, and destination. Correlation of these data with tracing code numbers results in very effective traceability of critical components.

Other methods that are commonly used to trace products and materials include age control, shelf life, first-in first-out (FIFO), barcoding, date codes, and lot and part numbering.

4. IDENTIFICATION OF NONCONFORMING MATERIAL

The only reason to identify anything is to be able to trace it. And the only reason to trace it is to be able to find out something about it later. These are two huge reasons in today's highly technological and litigious society. Without product traceability, many manufacturers would be exposed to unacceptable risk.

Principles of Identification

Modern technology has produced a wide array of identification methods. The physical application of markings and subsequent tracking by means of scanners and sensors provide many options. It is necessary to maintain records not only of items produced and their identification but also of how the record-keeping system itself is operated and modified. After all, information storage and retrieval is a rapidly changing field.

Mechanics

To illustrate the mechanics of product identification, consider the case of the Sauer Danfoss Company in Ames, Iowa. This company makes moderately complex mechanical products that require 100% testing and periodic design modifications. It recently improved its materials management system by creating a multifunctional task team of four people. The team collected data for two and a half years and finally decided to scrap the existing system for tracking material, which was dependent on manual entry into paper "move tags" and then manual keying into a computer database. Determination of current status required frequent physical counts of all items.

The team switched the company's system over to bar code and RFID (radio frequency identification) technologies. Now whenever an item of hardware moves, it is automatically accounted for, either by a bar code scanner or by an RFID receiver. A sophisticated database system automatically processes each scan. The database maintains a variety of characteristics about each unit, including:

- Model number
- Unit number
- Date produced
- Result of test
- Date of test
- Rework record

Product identification is vital when producing complex products, and often unnecessary for mundane commodities. However, an example of the lack of sufficient product identification and control is the Starlink seed corn problem of 2000. Starlink was a form of seed corn that was approved for growing animal feed but not for human consumption. Inadequate controls were put into place when the seed corn was sold to farmers, and as a result the animal feed corn was inextricably intermixed with human consumption corn at grain elevators throughout the

Midwest. At the time they were delivering the corn, neither the farmers nor the grain elevator operators realized there was a problem. But soon, consumer groups were testing products made out of this corn, and the use of the unacceptable corn was detected. A great outcry resulted, and many losses were incurred as the inter-mixed corn had to be converted to animal feed.

Lennox Industries in Marshalltown, Iowa, uses a 10-digit alphanumeric product identification code. This set of 10 digits allows traceability to a diverse set of factors, including the date of fabrication, the supplier of each subsystem, the product model, and the date of final assembly. Several things must be considered when setting up such a code:

- The amount of liability exposure.

- The number of levels of components and subcomponents.

- The process design must incorporate the ability to trace products back to their point of creation and installation.

5. LEVELS OF SEVERITY

In certain types of products more than one defect could be present, and a relatively small number of minor defects could be acceptable to the customer. Product quality in such cases may be judged by the total number of defects or the number of defects per unit. Control charts for attributes are a tool that may be used for this purpose. In such cases, the objective of inspection is to determine the number of defects or nonconformities present rather than to classify units as conforming or nonconforming.

A *nonconformity* is defined as the failure of a quality characteristic to meet its intended level or state, occurring with severity sufficient to cause the product not to meet a specification. A *defect* is a nonconformity severe enough to cause the product not to satisfy normal usage requirements. Thus, the difference between a nonconformity and a defect is based mainly on perspective. The former is defined according to specifications, while the latter is defined according to fitness for use. The numerical result generated by inspection consists of the number of defects or nonconformities for each product unit. Often, it is possible to classify the different types of defects according to their severity and then assign a weight to each class based on the importance of the affected quality characteristic regarding the product specifications. The selection of the weights should reflect the relative importance of the various defect categories and their likelihood of causing product failure or customer dissatisfaction. A typical seriousness classification includes four levels of defect seriousness:

1. A *critical* defect may lead directly to severe injury or catastrophic economic loss.

2. A *serious* defect may lead to injury or significant economic loss.

3. A *major* defect may cause major problems during normal use. A major defect will likely result in reduced usability of the product.

4. A *minor* defect may cause minor problems during normal use.

Training programs should be aimed at new inspection personnel as well as those with on-the-job experience. On-the-job training by a supervisor or a training coordinator could be the most prevalent and least costly approach to training. Other training methods include the following:

- Classroom instruction by in-house experts or outside consultants. Best suited for theoretical subjects such as basic mathematics, statistics, experimental design, and computer use.

- Self-study using audiovisual programs and self-instruction training manuals. This method allows the inspectors to study at their own pace and during convenient times.

- Outside programs offered by professional organizations and their local chapters, and by universities and community colleges through their extension divisions.

CONTROL OF NONCONFORMING MATERIALS

ISO 9001:2008 provides guidelines for control of nonconforming products (or materials) that are considered systematic courses of action in many organizations. The following is a summary of these guidelines.

Control of Nonconforming Product

- Product that does not conform to requirements is identified and controlled to prevent unintended use or delivery.

- Documented procedure defining the controls, responsibilities, and authorities.

- Shall deal with nonconforming product by one or more of the following:

  - Take action to eliminate nonconformity

  - Authorize use, release, or acceptance by concession of relevant authority (may be customer)

  - Take action to preclude its original intended use or application

- Record nature of conformities and actions taken, including any concessions obtained.

- When nonconforming product is corrected, it is subject to reverification to requirements.

- When detected after delivery, take action appropriate to effects, or potential effects, of the nonconformity.

- Should empower people at any stage in a process to report nonconformities.

- Should effectively and efficiently control nonconforming product identification, segregation, and disposition.

- Should establish effective and efficient process to provide review and disposition.

- Review should be conducted by authorized, competent people with authority to disposition and take appropriate corrective action.

Trends or patterns should be reviewed and should be considered for improvement.

Corrective Action

- Take action to eliminate the cause of nonconformities in order to prevent recurrence.

- Corrective actions shall be appropriate to the effects of the nonconformities encountered.

- Documented procedure to define requirements for:

  - Reviewing nonconformities (including customer complaints)

  - Determining the causes of nonconformities

  - Evaluating the need for action to ensure that nonconformities do not recur

  - Determining and implementing action needed

  - Records of the results of action taken (4.2.4)

  - Reviewing corrective action taken

- Should ensure the corrective action is used as improvement tool

- Should include evaluation of the significance of problems and potential impact on:

  - Operating cost

  - Costs of nonconformity

  - Product performance

  - Dependability

  - Safety

  - Customer satisfaction

- Corrective action should be focused on eliminating causes to avoid recurrence. Examples of sources for corrective action:

  - Customer complaints

  - Nonconformity reports

−Internal audit reports

−Outputs from management review

−Outputs from data analysis

−Organization's people

−Process measurements

Preventive Action

- Determine action to eliminate causes of potential nonconformities in order to prevent their occurrence.

- Preventive actions shall be appropriate to the effects of the potential problems.

- Documented procedure to define requirements for:
  - Determining potential nonconformities and their causes
  - Evaluating the need for action to prevent occurrence
  - Determining and implementing action needed
  - Records of results of action taken (4.2.4)
  - Reviewing preventive action

- Should plan to mitigate the effects of loss to organization in order to maintain performance of processes and products.

- Loss prevention in the form of planning should be applied to realization and support processes, activities, and product to ensure satisfaction of interested parties.

- Should be based on data from appropriate methods, including evaluation of data trends and criticality relative to the performance of the organization and its products. Data can be generated from:
  - Risk analysis tools, such as fault modes and effect analysis
  - Customer needs and expectations
  - Management review output
  - Outputs from data analysis
  - Satisfaction measurements
  - Results of self-assessment

- Results of the evaluation of the effectiveness and efficiency of loss prevention plans should be an output from management review.

- Should be used as input for the modification plans and as input to the improvement processes.

6. DISPOSITION OF NONCONFORMING MATERIAL

Material Segregation

There are two major situations that demand disposition of nonconforming products. The first is when a product fails to pass inspection or a test, and a decision regarding it must be made. This is the function of the material review board. The second situation, considerably more serious, is when a problem develops after the product is out of the plant, on store shelves, in dealer showrooms, and in use by customers. Now a product recall may be required. In view of the very negative aspects of product recall, all the prior work concerning product traceability and product integrity will pay off quite handsomely in organizing the recall.

Material Review Board

The *material review board* (MRB) is an appointed group of individuals with different backgrounds and expertise whose assignment is to determine what corrective actions must be taken after nonconforming parts or components are discovered. In a larger sense, the purposes of the MRB are to determine the disposition of nonconforming parts, components, and subassemblies, determine the causes of the nonconformance of these items, and take the necessary corrective actions to prevent such nonconformance from taking place in future production.

The basic function of an MRB is to (1) review material that does not conform to standards, (2) determine what its disposition should be, and (3) drive the development of effective corrective action to prevent recurrence. The MRB is a broad-based reviewing agency whose membership usually consists minimally of representatives from the following:

- *Engineering*. The cognizant designer is often the representative.

- *Quality assurance*. The representative is often from quality control engineering.

- *Customers*. The representative may be from the customer's organization (for example, the government inspector) or from marketing. In some companies the role of the MRB is solely one of judging fitness for use of nonconforming products. Bond (1983) discusses board composition, philosophy, and problem documentation.

In general, the MRB procedural steps can be summarized as follows: After a defect is discovered, verification by inspection may be needed. A complete description of any nonconformance is then initiated. A quality engineer picked by the MRB will review the facts and include the case in an appropriate tracking system. The MRB committee may then follow up with investigation and analysis. After this, the quality engineer takes the case again, recommending the appropriate corrective action(s) and steps for implementation. The term *standard repair* is common within the MRB framework. It signifies a procedure where a certain type of defect occurs time and time again. A standard repair procedure is then initiated, documented, and implemented for such situations. Minor defects are most likely to be

Table 16.1 Standards pertaining to MRB operations.

Standard	Purpose
MIL-STD-1520C	Sets "the requirements for cost-effective corrective action and disposition system for nonconforming material"
MIL-Q-9858A	Quality program requirements, Section 6.5, "Nonconforming Material," requires the contractor to establish "an effective and positive system for controlling nonconforming material"
MIL-STD-481B	Configuration control—engineering changes
MIL-I-8500	Establishes interchangeability and replaceability requirements
ANSI/ASQ Z1.4-2008	Sampling procedures and tables for inspection by attributes
ANSI/ASQ Z1.9-2008	Sampling procedures and tables for inspection by variables percent nonconforming

treated with a standard repair procedure. Minor defects, unlike major ones, may not adversely affect the integrity of the part, component, or assembly. In many cases, the MRB concludes that the lot containing nonconforming products should not be shipped as is.

The decision, concurred with by inspection personnel, may be to sort (100% inspection), downgrade, repair, rework, or scrap. A decision to ship may also be authorized by the MRB; in such cases, a unanimous decision should be reached by all members. The decision should also create factual data and thus is an important source of information. A successful MRB program requires that the board not only makes decisions about immediate disposition of rejected material, but also directs ongoing programs of root cause analysis to eliminate future rejections of the same type.

Several military documents are associated with the MRB concept. A partial list is shown in Table 16.1.

REFERENCES

Bond, T. P. 1983. "Basics of an MRB." *Quality*, November, 48.

Darmody, W. J. 1967. "Elements of a Generalized Measuring System." In *Handbook of Industrial Metrology*. Englewood Cliffs, NJ: Prentice-Hall.

Feigenbaum, A. V. 1991. *Total Quality Control*. 3rd ed., revised. New York: McGraw-Hill.

Gryna, F. M. 1988. "Manufacturing Planning." In *Juran's Quality Control Handbook*. 4th ed. Edited by J. M. Juran. New York: McGraw-Hill.

———. 2001. *Quality Planning and Analysis*. 4th ed. New York: McGraw-Hill.

Kennedy, C. W., E. G. Hoffman, and S. D. Bond. 1987. *Inspection and Gaging*. New York: Industrial Press.

Quality Magazine. 2016. "A Perfect Quality Inspector." *Quality Magazine*, September 1.

Rashed, A. F., and A. M. Hamouda. 1974. *Technology for Real Quality*. Alexandria, Egypt: Egyptian University House.

Raz, T. 1992. "Inspection." In *Quality Engineering Handbook*, edited by T. Pyzdek and R. Berger. Milwaukee, WI: ASQC Quality Press; New York: Marcel Dekker.

BIBLIOGRAPHY

ASQ Statistics Division. 2005. *Glossary and Tables for Statistical Quality Control*. 4th ed. Milwaukee: ASQ Quality Press.

Deming, W. E. 1986. *Out of the Crisis*. Cambridge, MA: MIT Center for Advanced Engineering.

Devor, R., T. Chang, and J. Sutherland. 2006. *Statistical Quality Design and Control*. 2nd ed. Upper Saddle River, NJ: Prentice Hall.

Dorris, A. L., and B. L. Foote. 1978. "Inspection Errors and Statistical Quality Control: A Survey." *AIIE Transactions* 10 (2): 184–92.

Dotson, C. 2006. *Fundamentals of Dimensional Metrology*. 5th ed. New York: Delmar Cengage Learning.

Juran, J. M., and F. N. Gryna Jr. 2005. *Juran's Quality Planning and Analysis for Enterprise Quality*. New York: McGraw-Hill.

Konz, S., G. Peterson, and A. Joshi. 1981. "Reducing Inspection Errors." *ASQC Quality Progress* 7: 24–26.

McKenzie, R. M. 1958. "On the Accuracy of Inspectors." *Ergonomics* 1: 258–72.

Megaw, E. D. 1979. "Factors Affecting Visual Inspection Accuracy." *Applied Ergonomics* 10: 27–32.

Chapter 17

D. Testing Methods

Define and use the following methods in various situations. (Apply)

1. *Nondestructive testing:* X-ray, eddy current, ultrasonic, dye penetrant, magnetic particle, optical, visual, and profile.

2. *Destructive testing:* tensile, force testing, and drop test.

3. *Functionality testing:* tension, torque, leak testing, and compression.

4. *Hardness testing:* Brinell, Rockwell, durometer, and micro-hardness scales.

Body of Knowledge III.D

1. NONDESTRUCTIVE TESTING

Definition

Nondestructive testing (NDT) is testing that does not destroy the test object. It is also referred to as *nondestructive evaluation* or *nondestructive examination* (NDE). The American Society for Nondestructive Testing (ASNT) defines NDT as "test methods used to examine or inspect a part or material or system without impairing its future usefulness" (Dettmers 2004; ASNT 2012).

NDT Applications and Objectives

The history of NDT started in the early 1900s, and it evolved over the years from being captive in the lab to becoming a very powerful production tool. NDT is now used worldwide to detect variation in product finish, product defects, and/or cracks. This type of testing is used in most stages of the production process, if not all. The Center for Nondestructive Evaluation at Iowa State University gives the following applications for NDT (Larson 2000):

- Screening and inspection of incoming material
- Product development

- Inspecting for in-service damage

- Verifying the proper process

- Monitoring and controlling manufacturing processes

- Verifying the proper assembly

The objectives of such testing are (ASNT 2012):

- To ensure customer satisfaction through ensuring product reliability and integrity

- To ensure the safety of the end user

- To compete with the current evolving market by maintaining reputation through high-quality products and better product design

- To minimize waste, which will lead to minimizing the overall manufacturing cost and maximizing the profit

- To ensure the flexibility and adaptation of product to market changes

Methods of NDT

The National Materials Advisory Board (NMAB) Ad Hoc Committee on Nondestructive Evaluation adopted a system that classifies methods into six major categories: visual, radiation, magnetic-electrical, mechanical vibration, thermal, and chemical-electrochemical (ASNT 2012; Wenk and McMaster 1987; McMaster and Wenk 1951). Within these categories the most identified methods are visual, X-ray, eddy current, ultrasonic, magnetic, and liquid penetrant.

Visual Method. The visual method is the oldest and most common method of examination. It has been used in a variety of industrial and commercial applications (Aircraft NDT 2005). The examiner usually follows a certain procedure that might vary in complexity from simple to very complex. Visual tools also vary, from the naked eye to very complex remote-controlled equipment. Figure 17.1 shows one piece of equipment that might be used to inspect products or materials. Some tools can be visual but controlled with a robot to inspect hazardous or tight areas, such as nuclear reactors. Video cameras and camcorders are considered tools for visual inspection.

Radiation. An X-ray machine or radioactive isotope is used as a source of radiation. The radiation is directed through the test part and onto a recording medium such as film. When the film is developed, a radiograph is obtained that shows the internal condition of a part (Aircraft NDT 2005). This radiation has higher energy and a shorter wavelength than visible light, which gives it the ability to penetrate the different objects and thus reveal cracks and other object defects (Larson 2000). Figure 17.2 shows the method of inspecting using X-ray.

The different shades on the film indicate the different thicknesses showing defects existing in the object. Figure 17.3 shows an example of an object that has been inspected by X-ray.

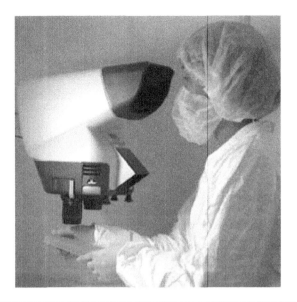

Figure 17.1   Visual inspection ensures consistency.
Source: Larson (2000).

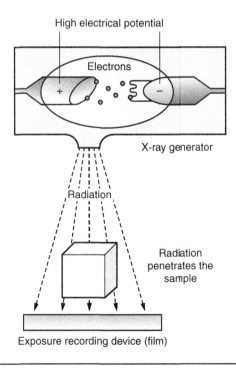

Figure 17.2   Inspection using X-ray.
Source: Larson (2000).

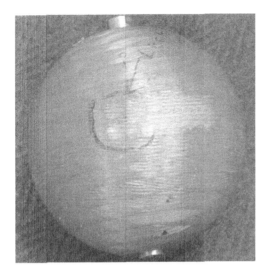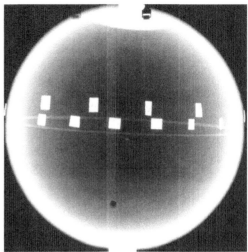

Figure 17.3 Example of an inspection using X-ray.
Source: Larson (2000).

X-ray and radiation testing in general affect the health of the people performing the test. Appropriate precautions and policies have to be followed in order to protect users. Radioactive waste should be taken into consideration for environmental and biological issues (NDT-ED.org 2012c).

Eddy Current. *Eddy current* is an electromagnetic NDT method in which electric currents are generated into a conductive material by an induced, varying magnetic field. Changes in the flow caused by variations in the object are reflected into a nearby coil or coils, where they are detected and measured by suitable instrumentation (Aircraft NDT 2005). Figure 17.4 depicts the eddy current method. This type of testing can be used to detect surface cracks but can also be used to make electrical conductivity and coating-thickness measurements (Larson 2000).

Eddy current can also be used for monitoring aircraft structural components and metallic structures such as aircraft fuselage. Some disadvantages of this type of testing are that it works only with conductive materials and that the surface of the material must be accessible. Other limitations are the depth of penetration, which is bounded to a certain extent, and the possibility that the finish of the product might provide a bad reading. Even with these limitations, however, this method still has many advantages, including portability and the ability to provide immediate feedback (Soleimani et al. 2006).

Ultrasonic. Ultrasonic testing uses high-frequency sound waves to conduct examinations and make measurements. The pulse echo technique is performed by introducing sound into the test object, and reflections (echoes) are returned to a receiver from internal imperfections or from geometrical surfaces of the part. It is typically used to detect subsurface defects, or defects originating from surfaces not accessible without disassembly or removal. It can also be used to detect laminations, lack of fusion, and corrosion of various materials (Aircraft NDT 2005; NDT-ED.org 2012a). Figure 17.5 shows the general inspection principle.

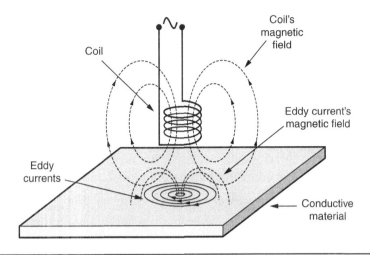

Figure 17.4   Eddy current method.
Source: Larson (2000).

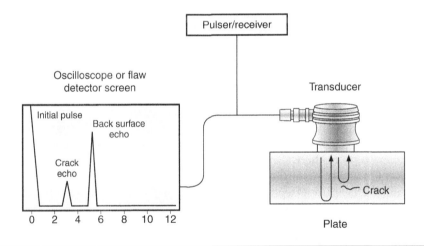

Figure 17.5   The general inspection principle for ultrasonic testing.
Sources: Aircraft NDT (2005); NDT-ED.org (2012a).

Some often-cited advantages of ultrasonic inspection include the following (NDT-ED.org 2012a):

- It is sensitive to both surface and subsurface discontinuities.

- The depth of penetration for flaw detection or measurement is superior to other NDT methods.

- Only single-sided access is needed when the pulse echo technique is used.

- It is highly accurate in determining reflector position and estimating size and shape.

- Minimal part preparation is required.

- Electronic equipment provides instantaneous results.

- Detailed images can be produced with automated systems.

- It has other uses, such as thickness measurement, in addition to flaw detection.

Like all NDT methods, ultrasonic inspection also has its limitations, which include (NDT-ED.org 2012a):

- Surface must be accessible to transmit ultrasound.

- Skill and training necessary are more extensive than with some other methods.

- It normally requires a coupling medium to promote the transfer of sound energy into the test specimen.

- Materials that are rough, irregular in shape, very small, exceptionally thin, or not homogeneous are difficult to inspect.

- Cast iron and other coarse-grained materials are difficult to inspect due to low sound transmission and high signal noise.

- Linear defects oriented parallel to the sound beam may go undetected.

- Reference standards are required for both equipment calibration and the characterization of flaws.

Magnetic. Magnetic particle inspection is an NDT method that is conducted on ferromagnetic material (material that can be magnetized) such as iron, nickel, cobalt, or some of their alloys. The test induces a magnetic field into the ferrous object, coating the surface with iron particles that are either dry or suspended in a liquid. Surface imperfections will distort the magnetic field, causing an accumulation of the iron particles near imperfections, thus indicating their presence in the material (Aircraft NDT 2005). Many industries use magnetic particle inspection for determining a component's fitness for use. Some examples of these are the structural steel, automotive, petrochemical, power generation, and aerospace industries. Underwater inspection is another area where magnetic particle inspection may be used to test items such as offshore structures and underwater pipelines (NDT-ED.org 2012b). Figure 17.6 is an example of testing using magnetic particle inspection.

One disadvantage, as mentioned earlier, is that it works only on ferromagnetic material. On the other hand, it has many advantages:

- It is a simple concept compared to other concepts.

- It is considered as a combination of two NDT methods—magnetic flux leakage testing and visual testing.

- It can be used underwater.

- It is easy to apply, and the object's surface preparation is not as critical as in other NDT methods (Larson 2000; Aircraft NDT 2005; NDT-ED.org 2012b).

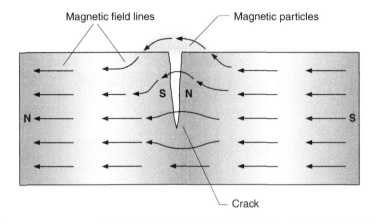

Figure 17.6 Magnetic particle inspection.
Sources: Larson (2000); NDT-ED.org (2012b).

Liquid Penetrant. Liquid or dye penetrant inspection is considered an extension of visual inspection and is used for detecting surface-breaking flaws on any non-absorbent material's surface. For this type of test, the object must be thoroughly cleaned to remove dirt and grease. The object is then soaked in a fluorescent or visible dye solution. After a specified dwell time, the excess penetrant is removed from the surface and a developer is applied. Often, a developer is applied to help draw penetrant out of imperfections open to the surface, making them much more visible. With fluorescent penetrants, the object must be viewed in a dark room with an ultraviolet lamp, which is sometimes not practical. Some industries use red dye in aerosol cans instead of the fluorescent material. This red dye doesn't need the ultraviolet light and can be viewed with the naked eye. Liquid penetrant inspections are able to detect only surface-breaking flaws (Larson 2000; Aircraft NDT 2005; Munns 2004). The steps for the liquid penetrant testing are shown in Figure 17.7.

Other nondestructive inspection methods include laser testing, leak testing, inspection, thermal/infrared testing, vibration testing and analysis, and profile testing.

2. DESTRUCTIVE TESTING

Definition

Destructive testing is a test that puts the sample object under certain circumstances until it actually fails. The failed pieces are then studied and compared with known standards to determine the quality of the object. This type of testing is generally much easier to carry out, more likely to yield more information, and much easier to interpret than NDT (Integrated Publishing 2012).

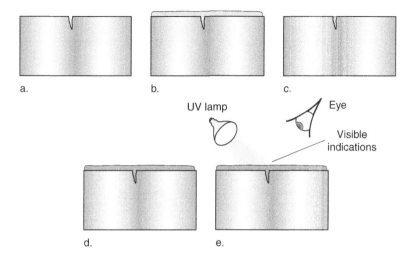

Figure 17.7 Liquid penetrant testing steps.
Source: Munns (2004).

Destructive Testing Applications and Objectives

Destructive testing usually provides a more reliable assessment for objects, but destruction of the test object usually makes this type of test more costly to the test object's owner than NDT. Destructive testing is also inappropriate in many circumstances, such as forensic investigation. A decision has to be made regarding the trade-off between the cost of the test and its reliability. If a nondestructive test can provide the required results, the destructive test can be waived. The destructive testing is performed on a sampling of test objects randomly drawn for the purpose of characterizing the testing reliability of the nondestructive test (Integrated Publishing 2012).

Destructive testing is used mostly in metal testing, especially to test the strength of welded parts. It is also used to determine the ability of a metal to stretch or pent. It is common in automobile manufacturing testing and other metal manufacturing industries.

Methods of Destructive Testing

Tensile Testing. A *tensile test*, also known as a *tension test*, is the method for determining the behavior of materials under axial stretch loading. Data from the test are used to determine elastic limit, stretching, modulus of elasticity, proportional limit, reduction in area, tensile strength, yield point, yield strength, and other tensile properties. This test is probably the most fundamental type of mechanical test that can be performed on a material. Tensile tests are simple, relatively inexpensive, and fully standardized. By pulling on something, you will very quickly determine how the material reacts to forces being applied in tension. As the material is being pulled, you will find its strength, along with how much it

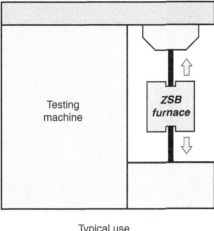

Typical use

Figure 17.8   Tensile test for a furnace.
Source: Micropyretics Heaters International (2012).

will stretch. Figure 17.8 shows a tensile test for a furnace (Integrated Publishing 2012; Instron 2012).

The results of tensile testing are used in selecting materials for engineering applications. Tensile properties are included in material specifications to ensure quality. Tensile properties are used to predict the behavior of materials under certain forms of tension (Davis 2004).

Force Testing. Force testing includes free-bend, guided-bend, nick-break, impact, and crash testing. The *free-bend* test is designed to measure the flexibility of the weld deposit and the heat-affected area adjacent to a weld. It is also used to determine the percentage of stretching of the weld metal (Integrated Publishing 2012). Figure 17.9 shows a free-bend test and the forces applied in the test to measure the flexibility.

The *guided-bend* test is used to determine the quality of weld metal at the face and root of a welded joint. The sample object is placed across the supports of the die. A plunger, operated from above by hydraulic pressure, forces the sample into the die. To fulfill the requirements of this test, the sample object has to be bent to 180° with no cracks on the surface greater than 1/8 inch (Integrated Publishing 2012).

The *nick-break* test is useful for determining the internal quality of the weld metal. This test is used for detecting whether internal defects exist, such as slag inclusions, gas pockets, lack of fusion, and oxidized or burned metal. For example, there should not be more than six pores or gas pockets per square inch of exposed broken surface of the weld (Integrated Publishing 2012).

The *impact* test is used to check the ability of a weld to absorb energy under impact without fracturing. This is a dynamic test in which a test specimen is broken by a single blow, and the energy used in breaking the piece is measured in foot-pounds. This test compares the toughness of the weld metal with the base

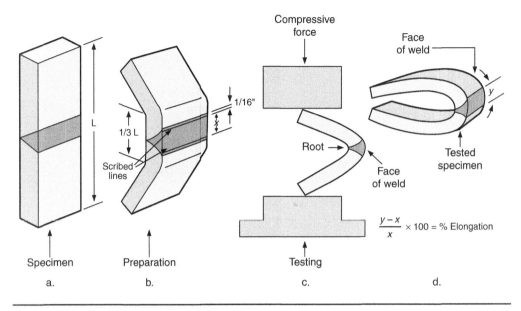

Figure 17.9 Free-bend test.
Source: Integrated Publishing (2012).

metal. It is useful for determining whether any of the mechanical properties of the base metal were destroyed by the welding process (Integrated Publishing 2012).

A *crash* test is usually performed in order to ensure safe design standards in crash compatibility for automobiles or related components, as shown in Figure 17.10.

Hardness Testing. *Hardness* is the property of a material that enables it to resist plastic deformation, usually by penetration. However, the term "hardness" may also refer to resistance to bending, scratching, abrasion, or cutting. Hardness is not an intrinsic material property dictated by precise definitions in terms of fundamental units of mass, length, and time. A hardness property value is the result of a defined measurement procedure. Relative hardness of minerals can be assessed by reference to the *Mohs scale*, which ranks the ability of materials to resist scratching by another material. Similar methods of relative hardness assessment are still used today.

Most hardness tests are limited in practical use and do not provide accurate numeric data or scales, particularly for modern-day metals and materials. The usual method to achieve a hardness value is to measure the depth or area of an indentation left by an indenter of a specific shape, with a specific force applied for a specific time. There are three principal standard test methods for expressing the relationship between hardness and the size of the impression: Brinell, durometer, and Rockwell (see Section 4, "Hardness Testing," for more details about these types of hardness testing). For practical and calibration reasons, each of these methods is divided into a range of scales, defined by a combination of applied load and indenter geometry (England 2012).

Figure 17.10   Crash testing.
Source: Integrated Publishing (2012).

Metallography. Metallography is the microscopic study of the structural characteristics of a metal or an alloy. The microscope is by far the most important tool of the metallurgist from both a scientific and a technical standpoint. It is possible to determine grain size and the size, shape, and distribution of various phases and inclusions, which have a great effect on the mechanical properties of the metal (ASM International 2005).

3. FUNCTIONALITY TESTING

Definition

Functionality testing is used to verify whether a product meets the intended design specifications and functional requirements stated in the development documentation (nResults 2008).

Functionality testing can identify potential product bugs, verify the success of the fixes, and ensure that the product is within standards.

Functionality Testing Objectives

Functionality testing provides products that have only a minimum number of bugs or problems. This type of test ensures that a product will function as intended. Minimizing the bugs in the product will minimize the cost of service and maintenance after the sale, which will build the reputation of the product and make it competitive in the market.

Methods of Functionality Testing

The most common functionality testing is performed on software packages. This topic is covered in Chapter 18. Other functionality testing is being performed in manufacturing facilities to ensure that products can be exposed to the maximum tension, torque, and/or compression.

Tension. *Tension* is the act of stretching an object using an external force. Test engineers use test equipment that can apply a large amount of force on an object and measure the magnitude and duration of the force on that object. A tension test machine is shown in Figure 17.11.

Torque. A *torque* is a vector that measures the tendency of a force to rotate an object about some axis (Serway and Jewett 2003). This type of test is performed on the object to measure the magnitude of torque that can be applied on that object before it breaks. The torque is calculated by multiplying the force applied to a lever by its distance from the lever's fulcrum (illustrated in Figure 17.12), which can be represented by the following formula:

$$\tau = r \times F$$

Compression. *Compression* is the act of applying axially directed pushing forces on an object, as shown in Figure 17.13. One example of such a functional test is

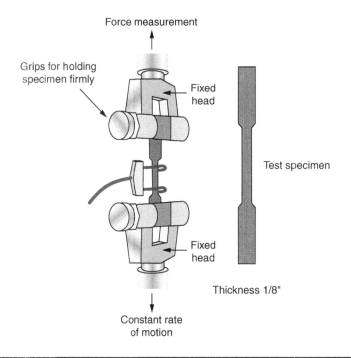

Figure 17.11   Tension test machine.
Source: ADMET Material Testing (2006).

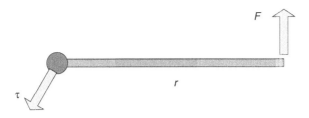

Figure 17.12 Torque can be calculated by multiplying the force applied to a lever by its distance from the lever's fulcrum.

Figure 17.13 Compression test.

compression exerted on a concrete block to test the ability of that block to withstand the pressure. Many concrete structures have compressive strengths in excess of 50 MPa.

The compressive strength of a material is the value of uniaxial compressive stress reached when the material fails completely.

4. HARDNESS TESTING

Brinell

The Brinell hardness test is based on applying forces on an object using a steel or carbide ball that has a 10 mm diameter and is subjected to a load of 6614 lb, which can be reduced for softer material to avoid excessive indentation (see Figure 17.14). The diameter of the indentation is measured after a certain amount of time using a low-powered microscope, and then the Brinell hardness number is calculated by dividing the load applied by the surface area of the indentation (England 2012).

Compared to the other hardness test methods, the Brinell ball makes the deepest and widest indentation, so the test averages the hardness over a wider amount of material, which will more accurately account for multiple grain structures and any irregularities in the uniformity of the material (England 2012).

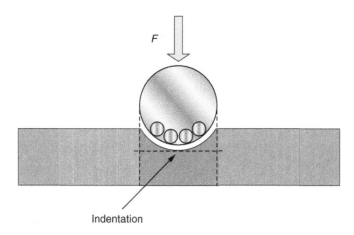

Indentation

Figure 17.14 Brinell hardness test method.

Rockwell

The Rockwell hardness test method (Figure 17.15) is also based on applying force on an object to create indentation, but it uses a diamond cone or hardened steel ball indenter. A preliminary force is applied on the indenter to be forced into the test material under minor load. When equilibrium has been reached, an additional major load is applied, with a resulting increase in penetration. When equilibrium has again been reached, the additional major load is removed, leaving the preliminary load as is. The removal of the additional major load allows a partial recovery. The indentation from that load is measured and is used to calculate the Rockwell hardness number (England 2012).

Advantages of the Rockwell hardness method include the direct Rockwell hardness number readout and rapid testing time. Disadvantages include many arbitrary nonrelated scales and possible effects from the iron sample object support block. The Vickers and Brinell methods don't suffer from this effect (England 2012).

Vickers

The Vickers hardness test (Figure 17.16) was developed as an alternative method to measure the hardness of materials. Unlike the Rockwell method, this method doesn't have the arbitrary nonrelated scales and is often easier to use than other hardness tests. The Vickers test can be used for all metals and can also be used on ceramic materials. It has one of the widest scales among hardness tests. The unit of hardness given by the test is known as the *Vickers pyramid number (HV)*. The hardness number is determined by the load over the surface area of the indentation and not the area normal to the force, and is therefore not a pressure. Like the Brinell and Rockwell tests, this test uses an indenter to test the metal, but this indenter is in the shape of a diamond with 136° between opposite faces (England 2012; Meyers and Chawla 1999; CALCE and the University of Maryland 2001).

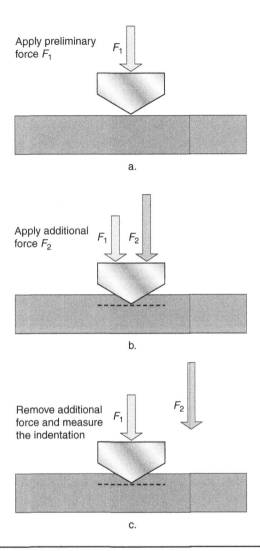

Figure 17.15   Rockwell hardness test method.

The two diagonals of the indentation left in the surface of the material after removal of the load are measured using a microscope, and their average is calculated. The area of the sloping surface of the indentation is calculated. The Vickers hardness is the quotient obtained by dividing the kgf load by the square mm area of indentation (England 2012; Meyers and Chawla 1999; CALCE and the University of Maryland 2001).

The advantages of the Vickers hardness test are that extremely accurate readings can be taken, and just one type of indenter is used for all types of metals and surface treatments. Although thoroughly adaptable and very precise for testing the softest and hardest of materials, under varying loads, the Vickers machine is a floor-standing unit that is more expensive than the Brinell or Rockwell machines (England 2012; Meyers and Chawla 1999).

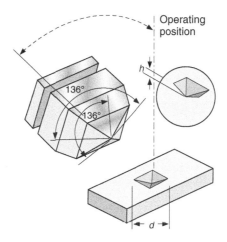

Figure 17.16   The Vickers hardness test.
Source: CALCE and the University of Maryland (2001).

Microhardness Test

Microhardness testing of metals, ceramics, and composites is useful for a variety of applications for which other test methods cannot be used: testing very thin materials like foils, measuring individual microstructures within a larger matrix, or measuring the hardness gradients of a part along the cross section. Microhardness testing gives an allowable range of loads for testing with a diamond indenter; the resulting indentation is measured and converted to a hardness value (England 2012; CALCE and the University of Maryland 2001).

The term "microhardness test" usually refers to static indentations made with loads not exceeding 1 kgf. The indenter is either the Vickers diamond pyramid or the Knoop elongated diamond pyramid. The procedure for testing is very similar to that of the standard Vickers hardness test except that it is done on a microscopic scale with higher-precision instruments. The surface being tested generally requires a metallographic finish; the smaller the load used, the higher the surface finish required. Precision microscopes are used to measure the indentations; these usually have a magnification of around ×500 and measure to an accuracy of ±0.5 micrometers (England 2012).

REFERENCES

ADMET Material Testing. 2006. "Tensile Property Testing of Plastics." Accessed May 2012. Available at http://asia.matweb.com/reference/tensilestrength.asp.

Aircraft NDT. 2005. "NDT Terminology at Level III NDT." Accessed May 2012 at http://www.aircraftndt.com/ndt_terms.htm.

ASM International. 2005. *Metallography and Microstructures*. Vol. 9 of *ASM Handbook*. Materials Park, OH: ASM International.

ASNT (American Society for Nondestructive Testing). 2012. Accessed May 2012 at http://www.asnt.org/ndt/primer1.htm.

CALCE and the University of Maryland. 2001. "Material Hardness." Accessed May 2012
    at http://www.calce.umd.edu/general/Facilities/Hardness_ad_.htm#rf11.

Davis, J. R. 2004. *Tensile Testing*. 2nd ed. Materials Park, OH: ASM International.

Dettmers, D. 2004. "NDT Methods for Mechanical Integrity." IRC. Best Practices
    Workshop, November.

England, G. 2012. "Hardness Testing." *Surface Engineering Forum*. Accessed May 2012.
    Available at http://www.gordonengland.co.uk/hardness/.

Instron. 2012. "Tensile Testing." *Material Testing Solutions*. Accessed May 2012. Available
    at http://www.instron.us/wa/applications/test_types/tension/default.aspx.

Integrated Publishing. 2012. "Destructive Testing." Accessed May 2012. Available at
    http://www.tpub.com/content/construction/14250/css/14250_169.htm.

Larson, B. 2000. PowerPoint Presentation. Center for NDE, Iowa State University.

McMaster, R. C., and S. A. Wenk. 1951. *A Basic Guide for Management's Choice of
    Nondestructive Tests*. Special Technical Publication No. 112. Philadelphia, PA:
    American Society for Testing and Materials.

Meyers, M. A., and K. K. Chawla. 1999. "Section 3.8." In *Mechanical Behavior of Materials*.
    Upper Saddle River, NJ: Prentice Hall.

Micropyretics Heaters International. 2012. Accessed May 2012. Available at http://www.
    mhi-inc.com/PG4/tensile.html.

Munns, I. 2004. "Liquid Penetrant Inspection." TWI World Centre for Materials Joining
    Technology.

NDT-ED.org. 2012a. "Basic Principles of Ultrasonic Testing." Education Resources.
    Accessed May 2012 at http://www.ndt-ed.org/EducationResources/Community
    College/Ultra sonics/Introduction/description.htm.

———. 2012b. "Introduction to Magnetic Particle Inspection." Education Resources.
    Accessed May 2012. Available at http://www.ndt-ed.org/EducationResources/
    CommunityCollege/MagParticle/Introduction/introduction.htm.

———. 2012c. "Present State of Radiology." Education Resources. Accessed May 2012.
    Available at http://www.ndt-ed.org/EducationResources/CommunityCollege/
    Radiography/Introduction/presentstate.htm.

nResults. 2008. "Functionality Testing." Accessed May 2012 at http://nresult.com/
    quality-assurance/functionality-testing/.

Serway, R. A., and J. W. Jewett Jr. 2003. *Physics for Scientists and Engineers*. 6th ed. Belmont,
    CA: Brooks Cole.

Soleimani, M., W. R. B. Lionheart, A. J. Peyton, X. Ma, and S. Higson. 2006. "A 3D Inverse
    Finite Element Method Applied to the Experimental Eddy Current Imaging Data."
    IEEE *Trans Magnetics* 42 (5): 1560–67.

Wenk, S. A., and R. C. McMaster. 1987. *Choosing NDT: Applications, Costs and Benefits of
    Nondestructive Testing in Your Quality Assurance Program*. Columbus, OH: American
    Society for Nondestructive Testing.

Chapter 18

E. Software for Test Equipment

Identify and describe basic tools (e.g., safeguarding, functional checks, comparison of test results, identification of attributes and parameters) used to ensure that the software for test equipment adequately and correctly performs its intended functions. (Remember)

Body of Knowledge III.E

SOFTWARE TESTING

Verification of software for the test equipment process determines whether the software fulfills the requirements, purpose, and accuracy of the test intended.

Software verification objectives include the following:

- Determine whether the software performs its intended functions correctly

- Ensure that the software performs no unintended functions

- Measure and assess the quality and reliability of the software

As a systems engineering discipline, software verification also assesses, analyzes, and tests the software on:

- How it interfaces with systems elements

- How it influences the performance of or reacts to stimuli from system elements

Basic principles for software testing include the following:

- Define the expected output or result, including the attributes and parameters

- Define how the software should function to get the results

- Compare test results with real results to ensure the consistency and accuracy of the software

- Include test cases for invalid or unexpected conditions

- Test the program to see if it does what it is not supposed to do as well as what it is supposed to do

- Debug the software to minimize errors

- Retest for functionality until you reach high precision

TESTING VERSUS INSPECTION

The objective of inspection is to find all the defects at each stage or process and to proceed to the next stage of the process with zero defects. Inspection methods can be developed to find more defects earlier and to be more effective by using the same method throughout the entire project. It is easier to find faults in code standard with inspection than with testing. Also, inspection can help more in debugging since it has the ability to find the fault in code, while testing only finds failure. One advantage with testing is that it is closer to the way the end user will use the system. The system will be more reliable by finding the most common failures. You can test the system by using multiple reruns using the same process of testing. So, we can say that inspection and testing complement each other, can be used to detect failure in different areas, and are used for different reasons and in different phases. Inspection is better in the initial stages, such as design, while testing is better at finding operational defects; both are needed for a better-quality product (Brykczynski et al. 1994; Daich et al. 1994).

FUNCTIONAL TESTING IN SOFTWARE DEVELOPMENT*

The internal structure of the program to be tested is not considered in functional testing. Functional testing ensures the performance and efficiency in a given environment. Functional testing is a bit different from system testing in that in system testing the program is tested against the data provided by the user or system requirements, while in functional testing the program is tested against the documented specifications and designed documents.

Functional testing normally consists of five major steps but can be altered according to the test documents prepared for a program. Following are the five steps:

1. Calculation and identification of the functions expected from the software to be tested.

2. On the basis of the functional specifications of the program, input data is created.

3. On the basis of the functional specifications, the output is determined for the program.

4. Execution of the test cases.

*Reprinted from C. Joe. "Functional Testing in Software Development" Accessed May 15, 2012 at http://www.articlesnatch.com/Article/Functional-Testing-In-Software-Development/3445230.

5. The output data are compared with the expected output prepared according to the specifications.

SOFTWARE TESTING TERMINOLOGY*

The following terms are used in software testing and may be useful for the purpose of this handbook.

Automated Software Testing

The use of software to control the execution of tests, the comparison of actual outcomes to predicted outcomes, the setting up of test preconditions, and other test control and test reporting functions, without manual intervention.

Automated Testing Tools

Software tools used by development teams to automate and streamline their testing and quality assurance process.

Basis Path Testing

A white-box test case design technique that fulfills the requirements of branch testing and also tests all of the independent paths that could be used to construct any arbitrary path through the computer program.

Basis Test Set

A set of test cases derived from basis path testing.

Bebugging

A popular software engineering technique used to measure test coverage. Known bugs are randomly added to a program source code and the programmer is tasked to find them. The percentage of the known bugs not found gives an indication of the real bugs that remain.

Benchmark Testing

Benchmark testing is a normal part of the application development life cycle. It is a team effort that involves both application developers and database administrators (DBAs), and should be performed against your application in order to determine current performance and improve it. If the application code has been written as efficiently as possible, additional performance gains might be realized from tuning the database and database manager configuration parameters.

*Reprinted from Original Software. 2007. *Glossary of Software Testing Terms.* Westmont, IL: Original Software. Available at http://www.origsoft.com.

You can even tune application parameters to meet the requirements of the application better.

You run different types of benchmark tests to discover specific kinds of information:

- A transaction per second benchmark determines the throughput capabilities of the database manager under certain limited laboratory conditions.

- An application benchmark tests the same throughput capabilities under conditions that are closer to production conditions.

Benchmarking is helpful in understanding how the database manager responds under varying conditions. You can create scenarios that test deadlock handling, utility performance, different methods of loading data, transaction rate characteristics as more users are added, and even the effect on the application of using a new release of the product.

Benchmark Testing Methods

Benchmark tests are based on a repeatable environment so that the same test run under the same conditions will yield results that you can legitimately compare. You might begin benchmarking by running the test application in a normal environment. As you narrow down a performance problem, you can develop specialized test cases that limit the scope of the function that you are testing. The specialized test cases need not emulate an entire application to obtain valuable information. Start with simple measurements, and increase the complexity only when necessary.

Characteristics of good benchmarks or measurements include:

- Tests are repeatable.

- Each iteration of a test starts in the same system state.

- No other functions or applications are active in the system unless the scenario includes some amount of other activity going on in the system.

- The hardware and software used for benchmarking match your production environment.

For benchmarking, you create a scenario and then applications in this scenario several times, capturing key information during each run. Capturing key information after each run is of primary importance in determining the changes that might improve performance of both the application and the database.

Compatibility Testing

The process of testing to understand if software is compatible with other elements of a system with which it should operate, for example, browsers, operating systems, or hardware.

Debugging

A methodical process of finding and reducing the number of bugs, or defects, in a computer program or a piece of electronic hardware, thus making it behave as expected. Debugging tends to be harder when various subsystems are tightly coupled, as changes in one may cause bugs to emerge in another.

Desk Checking

The testing of software by the manual simulation of its execution.

Design-Based Testing

Designing tests based on objectives derived from the architectural or detail design of the software (for example, tests that execute specific invocation paths or probe the worst-case behavior of algorithms).

Dynamic Testing

Testing of the dynamic behavior of code. Dynamic testing involves working with the software, giving input values, and checking if the output is as expected.

Functional Decomposition

A technique used during planning, analysis, and design that creates a functional hierarchy for the software. Functional decomposition broadly relates to the process of resolving a functional relationship into its constituent parts in such a way that the original function can be reconstructed (that is, recomposed) from those parts by function composition. In general, this process of decomposition is undertaken either for the purpose of gaining insight into the identity of the constituent components (which may reflect individual physical processes of interest, for example), or for the purpose of obtaining a compressed representation of the global function, a task that is feasible only when the constituent processes possess a certain level of modularity (that is, independence or noninteraction).

Functional Requirements

Define the internal workings of the software, that is, the calculations, technical details, data manipulation and processing and other specific functionality that show how the use cases are to be satisfied. They are supported by nonfunctional requirements, which impose constraints on the design or implementation (such as performance requirements, security, quality standards, or design constraints).

Manual Testing

The oldest type of software testing. Manual testing requires a tester to perform manual test operations on the test software without the help of test automation. Manual testing is a laborious activity that requires the tester to possess a certain set of qualities; to be patient, observant, speculative, creative, innovative, open-minded, resourceful, un-opinionated, and skillful.

As a tester, it is always advisable to use manual white-box testing and black-box testing techniques on the test software. Manual testing helps discover and record any software bugs or discrepancies related to the functionality of the product.

Manual testing can be augmented by test automation. It is possible to record and play back manual steps and write automated test script(s) using test automation tools. But test automation tools will only help execute test scripts written primarily for executing a particular specification and functionality. Test automation tools lack the ability of decision making and recording any unscripted discrepancies during program execution. It is recommended that one should perform manual testing of the entire product at least a couple of times before actually deciding to automate the more mundane activities of the product.

Manual testing helps discover defects related to the usability testing and GUI testing area. While performing manual tests the software application can be validated as to whether it meets the various standards defined for effective and efficient usage and accessibility. For example, the standard location of the OK button on a screen is on the left and the location of the Cancel button is on the right. During manual testing you might discover that on some screens they are not. This is a new defect related to the usability of the screen. In addition, there could be many cases where the GUI is not displayed correctly but the basic functionality of the program is correct. Such bugs are not detectable using test automation tools.

Repetitive manual testing can be difficult to perform on large software applications or applications having very large data set coverage. This drawback is compensated for by using manual black-box testing techniques, including equivalence partitioning and boundary value analysis. Using these, the vast data set specifications can be divided and converted into a more manageable and achievable set of test suites.

There is no complete substitute for manual testing. Manual testing is crucial for testing software applications more thoroughly.

Metric

A standard of measurement. Software metrics are the statistics describing the structure or content of a program. A metric should be a real objective measurement of something such as number of bugs per lines of code.

Modified Condition/Decision Coverage

The percentage of all branch condition outcomes that independently affect a decision outcome that has been exercised by a test case suite.

Modified Condition/Decision Testing

A test case design technique in which test cases are designed to execute branch condition outcomes that independently affect a decision outcome.

Monkey Testing

Testing a system or an application on the fly, that is, a unit test with no specific end result in mind.

Negative Testing

Testing a system or application using negative data. (For example, testing a password field that requires a minimum of 9 characters by entering a password of 6).

Portability Testing

The process of testing the ease with which a software component can be moved from one environment to another. This is typically measured in terms of the maximum amount of effort permitted. Results are expressed in terms of the time required to move the software and complete data conversion and documentation updates.

Positive Testing

Testing aimed at showing whether the software works in the way intended.

Recovery Testing

The activity of testing how well the software is able to recover from crashes, hardware failures, and other similar problems. Recovery testing is the forced failure of the software in a variety of ways to verify that recovery is properly performed.

Security Testing

Process to determine that an IS (information system) protects data and maintains functionality as intended.

The six basic concepts that need to be covered by security testing are confidentiality, integrity, authentication, authorization, availability, and non-repudiation.

Confidentiality. A security measure that protects against the disclosure of information to parties other than the intended recipient(s). Often ensured by means of encoding using a defined algorithm and some secret information known only to the originator of the information and the intended recipient(s) (a process known as *cryptography*), but that is by no means the only way of ensuring confidentiality.

Integrity. A measure intended to allow the receiver to determine that the information that it receives has not been altered in transit or by other than the originator of the information. Integrity schemes often use some of the same underlying technologies as confidentiality schemes, but they usually involve adding additional information to a communication to form the basis of an algorithmic check rather than the encoding of all of the communication.

Authentication. A measure designed to establish the validity of a transmission, message, or originator. Allows a receiver to have confidence that information it receives originated from a specific known source.

Authorization. The process of determining that a requester is allowed to receive a service or perform an operation.

Availability. Assuring information and communications services will be ready for use when expected. Information must be kept available to authorized persons when they need it.

Non-Repudiation. A measure intended to prevent the later denial that an action happened, or a communication took place, and so on. In communication terms this often involves the interchange of authentication information combined with some form of provable time stamp.

Traceability

The ability to identify related items in documentation and software, such as requirements with associated tests.

Validation Testing

Determination of the correctness of the products of software development with respect to the user needs and requirements.

REFERENCES

Brykczynski, B., R. Meeson, and D. A. Wheeler. 1994. *Software Inspection: Eliminating Software Defects.* Alexandria, VA: Institute for Defense Analyses.
Daich, G. T., G. Price, B. Ragland, and M. Dawood. 1994. *Software Test Technologies Report.* http://www.stsc.hill.af.mil/resources/tech_docs/tst_rpt.pdf.

BIBLIOGRAPHY

Groover, M. P. 2002. *Fundamentals of Modern Manufacturing.* New York: John Wiley & Sons.
Peled, D. A. 2010. *Software Reliability Methods.* New York: Springer-Verlag.
Pullum, L. L. 2001. *Software Fault Tolerance Techniques and Implementation.* Boston: Artech House Publishers.
Sommerville, I. 2006. *Software Engineering.* 8th ed. New York: Addison-Wesley.
Wallace, D. R., and R. U. Fujii. 1989. "Software Verification and Validation: An Overview." *IEEE Software,* May, 10–17.

Section IV
Quality Assurance

Chapter 19   A. Basic Statistics and Applications
Chapter 20   B. Statistical Process Control (SPC)
Chapter 21   C. Quality Improvement
Chapter 22   D. Quality Audits
Chapter 23   E. Quality Tools and Techniques
Chapter 24   F. Problem-Solving Tools and Continuous Improvement Techniques
Chapter 25   G. Resources

Chapter 19

A. Basic Statistics and Applications

1. *Measures of central tendency.* Calculate mean, median, and mode. (Apply)

2. *Measures of dispersion.* Calculate range, standard deviation, and variance. (Apply)

3. *Measures of proportion.* Calculate percentage and ratio measures for various data sets. (Apply)

4. *Graphical displays.* Define, interpret, and use scatter diagrams, tally sheets, and bar charts to display data effectively in various situations. (Apply)

5. *Normal distribution.* Define various characteristics of a normal distribution: symmetry, bell curve, and central tendency. (Understand)

Body of Knowledge IV. A

The first two sections of this chapter are devoted to describing methods known as *graphical methods* and *numerical methods,* while the third section of this chapter is devoted entirely to the *normal distribution.* The graphical methods and numerical methods come under the umbrella of *descriptive statistics.* Descriptive statistics are very commonly used in applied statistics to help understand the information contained in data sets that are usually encountered in many industrial and nonindustrial applications. The normal distribution, also commonly known as the *Bell-shaped distribution* or the *Gaussian distribution,* plays a very important role in all parts of mathematical statistics and applied statistics.

1. GRAPHICAL METHODS

We start our discussion of graphical methods by considering an important tool called the *frequency distribution table.* The frequency distribution table constitutes the first step in displaying data graphically.

Frequency Distribution Table

Graphical methods allow us to visually observe characteristics of the data, as well as to summarize pertinent information contained in the data. The frequency distribution table is a powerful tool that helps summarize both quantitative and qualitative data, enabling us to prepare additional types of graphics, which are discussed in the first part of this chapter.

Qualitative Data

A frequency distribution table for *qualitative* data consists of two or more categories along with the data points that belong to each category. The number of data points that belong to any particular category is called the *frequency* of that category. For illustration, let us consider Example 19.1.

Note that sometimes a *quantitative* data set is such that it consists of only a few distinct observations that occur repeatedly. These kinds of data are normally treated in the same way as the categorical data. The categories are represented by the distinct observations. We illustrate this scenario with Example 19.2.

Interpretation of a Frequency Distribution Table. Using row 2 of Table 19.3 as an example, column 1 gives the number of bypass surgeries (two) performed in 24 hours; column 2 shows the tally of the number of days when two bypass surgeries were performed; column 3 gives the number of days (13) when two bypass surgeries were performed; column 4 gives the proportion of days (13 out of 50) on which two bypass surgeries were performed; column 5 indicates that on 26% of the days two bypass surgeries were performed; and column 6 indicates that on 21 days the number of bypass surgeries performed was one or two.

Quantitative Data

So far, we studied the frequency distribution tables for qualitative data. Now we will study the frequency distribution tables for quantitative data.

Let $X_1, \ldots, X_n$ be a set of quantitative data. We would like to construct a frequency distribution table for this data set. To prepare such a table, we go through the following steps:

Step 1: Find the range of the data that is defined as

$$\text{Range } (R) = \text{Largest data point} - \text{Smallest data point} \tag{19.1}$$

Step 2: Divide the data set into an appropriate number of classes/categories. This number is commonly defined by using Sturgis's formula as follows:

$$m = 1 + 3.3 \log n \tag{19.2}$$

where n is the total number of data points in a given data set.

Step 3: Determine the width of classes as follows:

$$\text{Class width} = R/m \tag{19.3}$$

EXAMPLE 19.1

Consider a random sample of 110 small to midsize companies located in the Midwestern region of the United States, and classify them according to their annual revenues (in millions of dollars).

Solution

We can classify the annual revenues into five categories (1, 2, 3, 4, 5) as follows:

Under 250, 250–under 500, 500–under 750, 750–under 1000, 1000 or more

The data collected can then be represented as shown in Table 19.1.

After tallying the data and preparing the frequency distribution table, we find that of the 110 companies, 30 belong in the first category, 25 in the second category, 20 in the third category, 15 in the fourth category, and 20 in the last category. The frequency distribution table for these data is as shown in Table 19.2.

Table 19.1   Classification of annual revenues of 110 small to midsize companies located in the Midwestern region of the United States.

1 4 3 5 3 4 1 2 3 4 3 1 5 3 4 2 1 1 4 5 5 3 5 2 1 2 1 2 3 3 2 1 5 3 2 1 1
1 2 2 4 5 5 3 3 1 1 2 1 4 1 1 1 4 4 5 2 4 1 4 4 2 4 3 1 1 4 4 1 1 2 1 5 3
1 1 2 5 2 3 1 1 2 1 1 2 2 5 3 2 2 5 2 5 3 5 5 3 2 3 5 2 3 5 5 2 3 2 5 1

Table 19.2   Complete frequency distribution table for the 110 small to midsize companies.

Category no.	Tally	Frequency	Relative frequency	Percentage	Cumulative frequency
1	///// ///// ///// ///// ///// /////	30	30/110	27.27	30
2	///// ///// ///// ///// /////	25	25/110	22.73	55
3	///// ///// ///// /////	20	20/110	18.18	75
4	///// ///// /////	15	15/110	13.64	90
5	///// ///// ///// /////	20	20/110	18.64	110
Total		110	1	100	

Step 4: Finally, prepare the frequency distribution table by assigning each data point to an appropriate class or category. While assigning these data points to a class, be particularly careful to ensure that each data point is assigned to one, and only one, class and that the whole set is included in the table. Another important point is that the class on the lowest end of the scale must be started with a number that is less than or equal to the smallest

EXAMPLE 19.2

The following data show the number of graft surgeries for coronary artery bypasses performed at a hospital in a 24-hour period during the last 50 days. Bypass surgeries are usually performed when a patient has multiple blockages or when the left main coronary artery is blocked.

1 2 1 5 4 2 3 1 5 4 3 4 6 2 3 3 2 2 3 5 2 5 3 4 3

1 3 2 2 4 2 6 1 2 6 6 1 4 5 4 1 4 2 1 2 5 2 3 4 3

Construct a complete frequency distribution table for these data.

Solution

In this example, the variable of interest is the number of bypass surgeries performed at a hospital in a 24-hour period. Following the discussion in Example 19.1, we can see the frequency distribution table for the data in this example is as shown in Table 19.3.

This type of table is usually called a *single-valued* frequency distribution table.

Table 19.3 Complete frequency distribution table for the data in Example 19.2.

Category no.	Tally	Frequency	Relative frequency	Percentage	Cumulative frequency
1	///// ///	8	8/50	16	8
2	///// ///// ///	13	13/50	26	21
3	///// /////	10	10/50	20	31
4	///// ////	9	9/50	18	40
5	///// /	6	6/50	12	46
6	////	4	4/50	8	50
Total		50	1	100	

EXAMPLE 19.3

The following data define the lengths (in millimeters) of 40 randomly selected rods manufactured by a company:

145 140 120 110 135 150 130 132 137 115

142 115 130 124 139 133 118 127 144 143

131 120 117 129 148 130 121 136 133 147

147 128 142 147 152 122 120 145 126 151

Prepare a frequency distribution table for these data.

Continued

Solution

Following the steps described earlier, we have

1. Range (R) = 152 – 110 = 42

2. Number of classes = 1 + 3.3 log 40 = 6.29, which, by rounding, becomes 6.

3. Class width = R/m = 42/6 = 7

The six classes we use to prepare the frequency distribution table are as follows:

110–under 117, 117–under 124, 124–under 131, 131–under 138, 138–under 145, 145–152

Note that in the case of quantitative data, each class is defined by two numbers. The smaller of the two numbers is usually called the *lower limit*, and the larger is called the *upper limit*. Also, note that, except for the last class, the upper limit does not belong to the class. This means, for example, that data point 117 will be assigned to class two and not to class one. This way, no two classes will have any common point, ensuring that each data point belongs to one and only one class. For simplification, we will use mathematical notations to denote the above classes as

[110–117), [117–124), [124–131), [131–138), [138–145), [145–152]

where customarily the square bracket symbol implies that the beginning point belongs to the class and the parenthesis implies that the end point does not belong to the class. The frequency distribution table for the data in this example is shown in Table 19.4.

Table 19.4 Frequency table for the data on rod lengths.

Category no.	Tally	Frequency	Relative frequency	Percentage	Cumulative frequency
[110–117)	///	3	3/40	7.5	3
[117–124)	///// //	7	7/40	17.5	10
[124–131)	///// ///	8	8/40	20.0	18
[131–138)	///// //	7	7/40	17.5	25
[138–145)	///// /	6	6/40	15.0	31
[145–152]	///// ////	9	9/40	22.5	40
Total		40	1	100	

data point, and the class on the highest end of the scale must end with a number that is greater than or equal to the largest data point in the data set.

Notes:

1. Quite often when we determine the class width, the number obtained by dividing R by m is not an easy number to work with. In such cases we should always round this number up, preferably to a whole number. Never round it down.

2. When we use Sturgis's formula to find the number of classes, the value of *m* is usually not a whole number. In that case we must round it up or down to a whole number since the number of classes can only be a whole number.

Having discussed the frequency distribution table, we are now ready to study various graphical displays of a data set.

Dot Plot

A dot plot is one of the easiest graphs to construct, and this plot does not make use of the frequency distribution table. In a dot plot each observation is plotted on a real line. For illustration we consider Example 19.4.

Dot plots are more useful when the sample size is small. A dot plot gives us, for example, information about how far the data are scattered and where most of the observations are concentrated. For instance, in Example 19.4, we see that the minimum number of defective motors is 5 and the maximum number of defective motors received in any shipment is 29. Also, we can see that 75% of the time, the number of defective motors is between 8 and 21 for the shipment, and so on.

Pie Chart

Pie charts are commonly used to represent different categories of a population that are created by a characteristic of interest of that population, for example,

---

EXAMPLE 19.4

The following data give the number of defective motors received in 20 different shipments:

8 12 10 16 6 25 21 15 17 5

26 21 29 8 10 21 10 17 15 13

Construct a dot plot for these data.

Solution

To construct a dot plot, first draw a horizontal line, the scale of which begins at the smallest observation (5 in this case) or smaller and ends with the largest observation (29 in this case) or larger (see Figure 19.1).

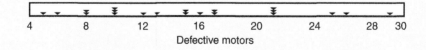

4	8	12	16	20	24	28	30

Defective motors

Figure 19.1   Dot plot for the data on defective motors received in 20 different shipments.

allocation of federal budget by sector, revenues of a large manufacturing company by region or by plant, technicians in a large corporation who are classified according to their basic qualification (that is, high school diploma, associate degree, undergraduate degree, or graduate degree), and so on. The pie chart helps to better show at a glance the composition of the population with respect to the characteristic of interest.

To construct a pie chart, divide a circle into slices such that each slice represents a category and is proportional to the size of that category. Remember, the total angle of the circle is 360°. The angle of a slice corresponding to a given category is determined as follows:

Angle of a slice = (Relative frequency of the given category) × 360

We illustrate the construction of a pie chart using the data in Example 19.5.

Note: In the example we just happen to use the total frequency equal to 361, the number of observations, which should not be confused with the total degrees in a circle, which equals 360.

Bar Chart

Bar charts are commonly used to study one or more populations when they are classified into various categories, for example, by sector, by region, or over different time periods. We may want or need to know more about the sales of a company

---

EXAMPLE 19.5

In a manufacturing operation, we are interested in better understanding defect rates as a function of our various process steps. The inspection points in the process are initial cutoff, turning, drilling, and assembly. These data are shown in the frequency distribution Table 19.5. Construct a pie chart for these data.

The pie chart for these data is now constructed by dividing the circle into four slices. The angle of each slice is given in the last column of Table 19.5. Thus, the pie chart is as shown in Figure 19.2. The construction of such a chart gives us a better understanding at a glance about the rate of defects occurring at different steps of the process.

Table 19.5 Understanding defect rates as a function of various process steps.

Process step	Frequency	Relative frequency	Angle size
Initial cutoff	86	86/361	85.75
Turning	182	182/361	181.50
Drilling	83	83/361	82.75
Assembly	10	10/361	10.00
Total	**361**	**1.000**	**360.00**

Continued

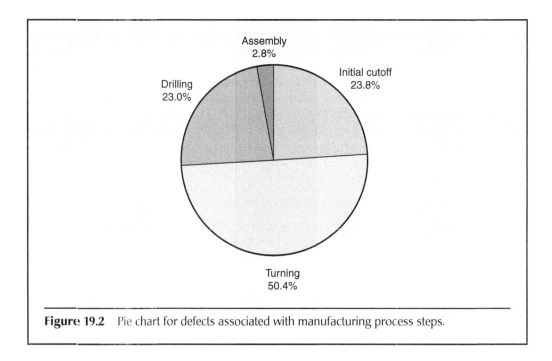

Figure 19.2 Pie chart for defects associated with manufacturing process steps.

by sector, by region, or over different time periods. Different sectors, different regions, or different time periods are usually labeled as different categories. A bar chart is constructed by creating categories that are represented by intervals of equal length on a horizontal axis, or x-axis. Within each category we indicate the number of observations as a frequency of the corresponding category, which is then represented by a rectangular bar of length proportional to the frequency. The construction of a bar chart is illustrated in Examples 19.6 and 19.7.

Pareto Chart

The Pareto chart is a very useful tool for learning more about attribute data quickly and visually. The *Pareto chart*—named after its inventor, Vilfredo Pareto, an early twentieth century economist who died in 1923—is simply a bar graph of attribute data in descending order of frequency by, say, defect type. For example, consider the data on defective rolls in Example 20.1, and, as shown in Figure 19.5, plot the frequency totals (row totals, see Table 20.1) of occurrence of each defect starting from highest to lowest frequency against the defect type.

The chart allows the user to quickly identify which defects occur more frequently and which occur less frequently. This allows the user to prioritize the use of his or her resources to eliminate first those defects that have the greatest effect on quality of the product. For instance, the Pareto chart in Figure 19.5 indicates that 40% of the paper rolls are rejected because of a corrugation problem. Corrugation and blistering together are responsible for 55.7% of the rejected paper. Corrugation, blistering, and streaks are responsible for 70%. To reduce the overall rejection rate, one should first attempt to eliminate or at least reduce defects due to corrugation, then blistering, streaks, and so on. By eliminating just these three

EXAMPLE 19.6

The following data give the annual revenues (in millions of dollars) of a company over a period of five years (1998–2002):

78 92 95 94 102

Construct a bar chart for these data.

Solution

Following the above discussion, we construct a bar chart for the data given in this example. The desired bar chart is shown in Figure 19.3.

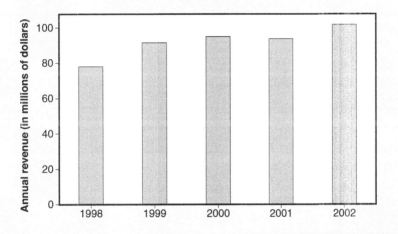

Figure 19.3   Bar chart for annual revenues of a company over a five-year period.

EXAMPLE 19.7

A company that manufactures auto parts is interested in studying the types of defects that occur in parts produced at a particular plant. The following data show the types of defects that occurred over a certain period:

B A C A B A E D C A B C D C A E A B A B

C E D D A E A E A D B C B A B E D B D B E A

C A B C E C B A B E

Construct a bar chart for the types of defects found in the auto parts.

Solution

In order to construct a bar chart for the data in this example, we first need to prepare a frequency distribution table. The data in this example are qualitative, and the categories are the types of defects, namely, A, B, C, D, and E. The frequency distribution table is shown in Table 19.6.

Continued

To construct the bar chart, we label the intervals of equal length on the *x*-axis with the types of defects, and then indicate the frequency of observations associated with each defect by a rectangular bar proportional to the corresponding frequency. The number of observations in each category is taken to be equal to the frequency of the corresponding category. Thus, the desired bar graph is as shown in Figure 19.4, which shows that type A defects occur most frequently, type B occur second most frequently, type C occur third most frequently, and so on.

Table 19.6 Frequency distribution table for the data in Example 19.7.

Category no.	Tally	Frequency	Relative frequency	Percentage	Cumulative frequency
A	///// ///// ////	14	14/50	14	30
B	///// ///// ///	13	13/50	27	55
C	///// ////	9	9/50	36	75
D	///// //	7	7/50	43	90
E	///// //	7	7/50	50	110
Total		50	1.00	100	

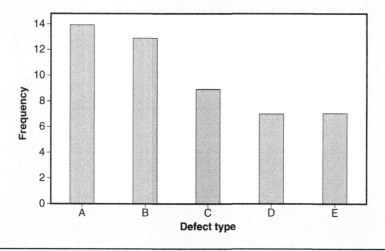

Figure 19.4 Bar graph for the data in Example 19.7.

types of defects, one would dramatically reduce the percentage of rejected paper and the resulting losses.

It is important to note that if one can eliminate more than one defect simultaneously, one should consider eliminating them even though some of them occur less frequently. Furthermore, after one or more defects are either eliminated or reduced, one should collect the data again and reconstruct the Pareto chart to determine whether the priority has changed (for example, another defect is now

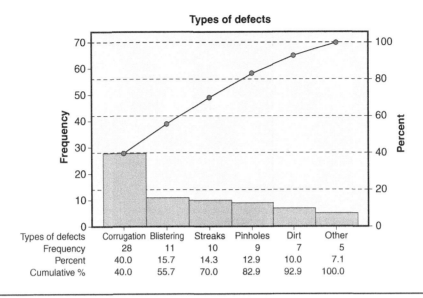

Types of defects

Types of defects	Corrugation	Blistering	Streaks	Pinholes	Dirt	Other
Frequency	28	11	10	9	7	5
Percent	40.0	15.7	14.3	12.9	10.0	7.1
Cumulative %	40.0	55.7	70.0	82.9	92.9	100.0

Figure 19.5   Pareto chart for the data in Example 20.1.

occurring more frequently), and thus one may divert the resources to eliminate such a defect next. Note that in Figure 19.5, the "Other" category may include several defects, such as porosity, grainy edges, wrinkles, or brightness, that do not occur frequently. So, one who has very limited resources should not use his or her resources on this category until all other defects have been eliminated.

Sometimes, all the defects are not equally important. This is particularly true when some defects are life threatening while other defects are merely a nuisance or a matter of inconvenience. It is quite common to allocate weights to each defect and then plot the weighted frequencies versus defects to construct the Pareto chart.

For example, consider the following scenario. A product has five types of defects, denoted by A, B, C, D, and E, where A is life threatening, B is not life threatening but very serious, C is serious, D is somewhat serious, and E is not serious or is merely a nuisance. We can assign a weight of 10 to A, 7.5 to B, 5 to C, 2 to D, and 0.5 to E. The data collected over a period of study are shown in Table 19.7.

Note that the Pareto chart in Figure 19.6 using weighted frequencies presents a completely different picture. That is, by using weighted frequencies, the order of priority for removing the defects is C, A, B, D, E, whereas without using the weighted frequencies this order would have been E, C, D, B, A.

Scatter Plot

When studying two variables simultaneously, the data obtained for such a study are known as *bivariate data*. In examining bivariate data, the first question to emerge is whether there is any association between the two variables of interest. One effective way to investigate such an association is to prepare a graph by plotting one variable along the horizontal scale (x-axis) and the second variable along the vertical scale (y-axis). Each pair of observations (x, y) is then plotted as a point

Table 19.7   Frequencies and weighted frequencies when different types of defects are not equally important.

Defect type	Frequency	Weighted frequency
A	5	50.0
B	6	45.0
C	15	75.0
D	12	24.0
E	25	12.5

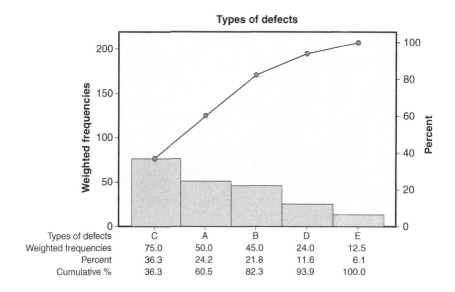

Figure 19.6   Pareto chart when weighted frequencies are used.

in the *xy* plane. The graph that is prepared is called a *scatter plot*. A scatter plot is a very useful graphical tool because it depicts the nature and strength of associations between the two variables. To illustrate, we consider Example 19.8.

Histograms

Histograms are very popular graphs used to represent quantitative data graphically, and they provide very useful information about a data set, for example, information about trends, patterns, location/center, and dispersion of the data. Such information is not particularly apparent from the raw data.

Construction of a histogram involves the following two major steps:

Step 1: Prepare a frequency distribution table for the given data.

EXAMPLE 19.8

The cholesterol levels and the systolic blood pressures of 30 randomly selected males in the United States in the age group of 40–50 years are given in Table 19.8. Construct a scatter plot of these data and determine whether there is any association between the cholesterol levels and the systolic blood pressures.

Solution

Figure 19.7 shows the scatter plot of the data in Table 19.8. This scatter plot indicates that there is a fairly good upward linear trend. Also, if we draw a straight line through the data points, we can see that they are concentrated around the straight line within a narrow band. The upward trend indicates a positive association between the two variables, and the width of the band indicates the strength of the association, which in this case is very strong. As the association between the two variables gets stronger and stronger, the band enclosing the plotted points becomes narrower and narrower. A downward trend indicates a negative association between the two variables. A numerical measure of association between two numerical variables is called the *Pearson correlation coefficient*, or simply the *correlation coefficient*, named after the English statistician Karl Pearson (1857–1936). The correlation coefficient between two numerical variables in sample data is usually denoted by r. The Greek letter ρ (rho) denotes the corresponding measure of association that is the correlation coefficient for a population data. The correlation coefficient is defined as

$$r = \frac{\Sigma(x_i - \bar{x})(y_i - \bar{y})}{\sqrt{\Sigma(x_i - \bar{x})^2 \Sigma(y_i - \bar{y})^2}} = \frac{\Sigma x_i y_i - \frac{(\Sigma x_i)(\Sigma y_i)}{n}}{\sqrt{\left(\Sigma x_i^2 - \frac{(\Sigma x_i)^2}{n}\right)\left(\Sigma y_i^2 - \frac{(\Sigma y_i)^2}{n}\right)}} \tag{19.4}$$

The correlation coefficient is a unitless measure that can attain any value in the interval $[-1,+1]$. As the strength of the association between the two variables grows, the absolute value of r approaches 1. When there is a perfect association between the two

Table 19.8 Cholesterol levels and systolic blood pressures of 30 randomly selected US males.

Subject	1	2	3	4	5	6	7	8	9	10
Cholesterol (x)	195	180	220	160	200	220	200	183	139	155
Systolic BP (y)	130	128	138	122	140	148	142	127	116	123
Subject	11	12	13	14	15	16	17	18	19	20
Cholesterol (x)	153	164	171	143	159	167	162	165	178	145
Systolic BP (y)	119	130	128	120	121	124	118	121	124	115
Subject	21	22	23	24	25	26	27	28	29	30
Cholesterol (x)	245	198	156	175	171	167	142	187	158	142
Systolic BP (y)	145	126	122	124	117	122	112	131	122	120

Continued

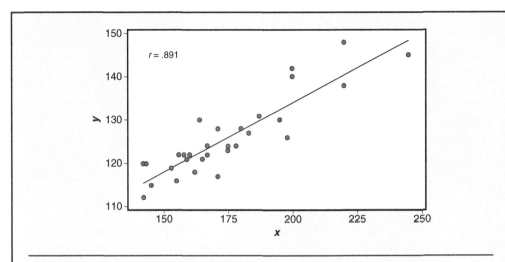

Figure 19.7 Scatter plot of the data in Table 19.8.

variables, then $r = 1$ or -1 depending on whether the association is positive or negative. In other words, $r = 1$ if the two variables are moving in the same direction (increasing or decreasing), and $r = -1$ if they are moving in opposite directions.

Perfect association means that if we know the value of one variable, the value of the other variable can be determined without any error. The other special case is when $r = 0$, which means that there is no association between the two variables. As a rule of thumb, the association is weak, moderate, or strong when the absolute value of r is less than 0.3, between 0.3 and 0.7, or greater than 0.7, respectively.

Step 2: Use the frequency distribution table prepared in step 1 to construct the histogram. From here, the steps involved in constructing a histogram are very similar to the steps taken to construct a bar chart except that in a histogram there is no gap between the intervals marked on the x-axis. We illustrate the construction of a histogram in Example 19.9.

Note that a histogram is called a *frequency histogram* or a *relative frequency histogram* depending on whether the heights of the rectangles erected over the intervals marked on the x-axis are proportional to the frequencies or to the relative frequencies. In both types of histograms the width of the rectangles is equal to the class width. In fact, the two types of histograms are identical except that the scales used on the y-axes are different. This point should also become clear from Example 19.9.

Another graph, which will become the basis of probability distributions that we will study later in this chapter, is called the *frequency polygon* or *relative frequency polygon* depending on which histogram is used to construct it.

To construct the frequency or relative frequency polygon, first mark the midpoints on the top ends of the rectangles of the corresponding histogram and then simply join these midpoints. Note that we include classes with zero frequencies

EXAMPLE 19.9

The following data give the survival time (in hours) of 50 parts involved in a field test under extreme operating conditions:

60 100 130 100 115 30 60 145 75 80 89 57 64 92 87 110 180

195 175 179 159 155 146 157 167 174 87 67 73 109 123 135 129 141

154 166 179 37 49 68 74 89 87 109 119 125 56 39 49 190

a. Construct a frequency distribution table for these data

b. Construct frequency and relative frequency histograms for these data

Solution A

1. Find the range of the data:

$$R = 195 - 30 = 165$$

2. Determine the number of classes:

$$m = 1 + 3.3 \log 50 = 6.57$$

By rounding, we consider the number of classes to be equal to 7.

3. Compute the class width:

$$\text{Class width} = R/m = 165/7 = 23.57$$

By rounding up this number, we have class width equal to 24. As noted earlier, we always round up the class width to a whole number or to any other convenient number that may be easy to work with. Note that if we round down the class width, some of the observations may be left out of our count and will not belong to any class. Consequently, the total frequency will be less than n. The frequency distribution table for the data in this example is shown in Table 19.9.

Table 19.9 Frequency distribution table for the survival time of parts.

Class	Tally	Frequency	Relative frequency	Cumulative frequency
[30–54)	/////	5	5/50	5
[54–78)	///// /////	10	10/50	16
[78–102)	///// ////	9	9/50	24
[102–126)	///// //	7	7/50	31
[126–150)	///// /	6	6/50	37
[150–174)	///// /	6	6/50	43
[174–198]	///// //	7	7/50	50
Total		**50**	**1**	

Continued

Solution B

Having completed the frequency distribution table, we are now ready to construct the histograms. To construct the frequency histogram, we first mark the classes on the x-axis and the frequencies on the y-axis. Remember that when we mark the seven classes on the x-axis we must ensure that no gaps exist between the classes. Then on each class marked on the x-axis, we place a rectangle whose height is proportional to the frequency of the corresponding class. The frequency histogram for the data with the frequency distribution given in Table 19.9 is shown in Figure 19.8.

To construct the relative frequency histogram, we just change the scale on the y-axis in Figure 19.8 so that instead of plotting the frequencies, we plot relative frequencies. The resulting graph, shown in Figure 19.9, is the relative frequency histogram for the data with the relative frequency distribution given in Table 19.9.

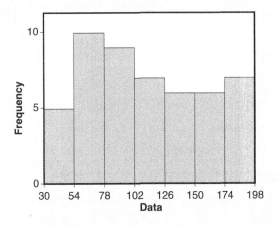

Figure 19.8   Frequency histogram for survival time of parts under extreme operating conditions.

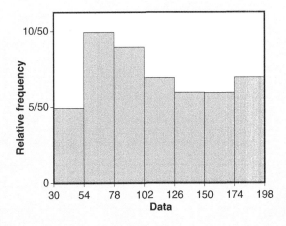

Figure 19.9   Relative frequency histogram for survival time of parts under extreme operating conditions.

at the lower end as well as at the upper end of the histogram so that we can connect the polygon with the *x*-axis. The curves obtained by joining the midpoints are called the *frequency* or *relative frequency polygons* as the case may be. The frequency polygon and the relative frequency polygon for the data in Example 19.9 are shown in Figure 19.10 and Figure 19.11, respectively.

Sometimes, a data set consists of a very large number of observations, which results in having a large number of classes of very small widths. In such cases frequency polygons or relative frequency polygons become very smooth curves. Figure 19.12 shows one such smooth curve.

Curves such as those shown in Figure 19.12 are usually called *frequency distribution curves*, and they represent the probability distributions of continuous random variables. Histograms eventually become the basis of probability distributions.

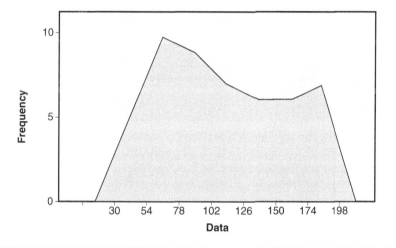

Figure 19.10   Frequency polygon for the data in Example 19.9.

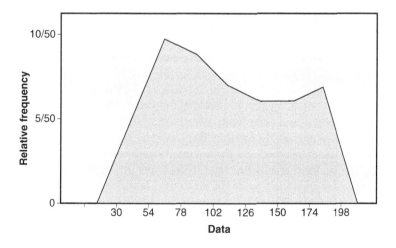

Figure 19.11   Relative frequency polygon for the data in Example 19.9.

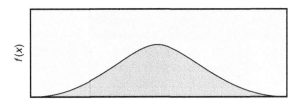

Figure 19.12   A typical frequency distribution curve.

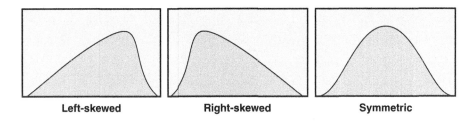

Figure 19.13   Three types of frequency distribution curves.

The shape of the frequency distribution curve depends on the shape of its corresponding histogram, which, in turn, depends on the given set of data. The shape of a frequency distribution curve, in fact, can be of any type, but in general we have three types of frequency distribution curves, shown in Figure 19.13.

Stem-and-Leaf Diagram

The stem-and-leaf diagram is a graphical tool used to display data using actual data values. Each value is split into two parts: the part with leading digits is called the *stem* and the rest is called the *leaf*. It is often used for exploratory data analysis, and the data analyzed are always quantitative data. Unlike the histogram, the stem-and-leaf diagram does not lose the identity of the actual value of the data point. The stem-and-leaf diagram is quite effective when the data set is small.

A stem-and-leaf diagram is a very powerful tool that is used to summarize quantitative data. The stem-and-leaf diagram has numerous advantages over the frequency distribution table and the frequency histogram. One major advantage of the stem-and-leaf diagram over the frequency distribution table is that we cannot retrieve the original data from a frequency distribution table whereas, as we will see later, we can easily retrieve data in their original form from a stem-and-leaf diagram. In other words, by preparing a stem-and-leaf diagram we do not lose any information, and that is not true in the case of frequency distribution tables. We illustrate the construction of the stem-and-leaf diagram in Example 19.10.

Note that in Figure 19.14 (a) leaves occur in the same order as observations in the raw data. In Figure 19.14 (b) leaves appear in ascending order, and that is why it is called an *ordered stem-and-leaf diagram*. By rotating the stem-and-leaf diagram counterclockwise through 90 degrees, we see that the diagram can serve the same

EXAMPLE 19.10

The following data give the survival time (in hours) of 50 parts when tested under certain conditions by a group of quality inspectors. Prepare a stem-and-leaf diagram for these data.

60	100	130	100	115	30	60	145	75	80	89	57	64	92	87	110	180
195	175	179	159	155	146	157	167	174	87	67	73	109	123	135	129
141	154	166	179	37	49	68	74	89	87	109	119	125	56	39	49	190

Solution

To create a stem-and-leaf diagram, we split each observation in the data set into two parts, called *stem* and *leaf*. For the data in this example, we split each observation at the unit place so that the digit at the unit place is a leaf and the remainder to the left is the stem. For example, for observations 60 and 100 the stems and leaves are

Stem	Leaf
6	0
10	0

To construct a complete stem-and-leaf diagram, list all the stems without repeating them in a column and then list all the leaves in a row against their corresponding stem. The data for this example are shown in Figure 19.14.

```
        (a)—ordinary                    (b)—ordered
      Stem   Leaf                     Stem   Leaf

   3    3    0 7 9                  3    3    0 7 9
   5    4    9 9                    5    4    9 9
   7    5    7 6                    7    5    6 7
  12    6    0 0 4 7 8             12    6    0 0 4 7 8
  15    7    5 3 4                 15    7    3 4 5
  21    8    0 9 7 7 9 7           21    8    0 7 7 7 9 9
  22    9    2                     22    9    2
 ( 4 )  10   0 0 9 9              ( 4 )  10   0 0 9 9
  24   11    5 0 9                 24   11    0 5 9
  21   12    3 9 5                 21   12    3 5 9
  18   13    0 5                   18   13    0 5
  16   14    5 6 1                 16   14    1 5 6
  13   15    9 5 7 4               13   15    4 5 7 9
   9   16    7 6                    9   16    6 7
   7   17    5 9 4 9                7   17    4 5 9 9
   3   18    0                      3   18    0
   2   19    5 0                     2   19    0 5
```

Figure 19.14   Ordinary and ordered stem–and–leaf diagram for the data on survival time for parts under certain conditions.

purpose as a histogram, with stems serving the role of classes, leaves as class frequencies, and rows of leaves as rectangles.

Unlike the frequency distribution table and histogram, the stem-and-leaf diagram can be used to answer questions such as what percentage of parts survived between 90 and 145 hours (inclusive). Using the stem-and-leaf diagram, we can see that 15 out of 50, or 30% of the parts, survived between 90 and 145 hours (inclusive), whereas using either a frequency table or a histogram, this type of question normally cannot be answered unless we have classes with their lower limit starting at 90 hours and the upper limit ending at 145 hours.

The first column in the graph is counting from the top and the bottom the number of parts that survived up to and beyond a certain number of hours, respectively. For example, the entry in the fifth row from the top indicates that 15 parts survived less than 80 hours, whereas the entry in the fifth row from the bottom indicates that 13 parts survived at least 150 hours. The entry with parentheses indicates the row that contains the *median* value of the data (to be discussed in the next section). It is clear that we can easily retrieve the original data from the stem-and-leaf diagram. For example, the first row in Figure 19.14 consists of data points 30, 37, and 39. Finally, we can say that the stem-and-leaf diagram is usually more informative than a frequency distribution table and/or a frequency histogram.

2. NUMERICAL METHODS

Numerical methods can be used to derive numerical measures for a sample of data as well as for data describing an entire population. Numerical measures computed by data describing an entire population are referred to as *parameters*. Numerical measures computed by using sample data are referred to as *statistics*.

It is standard practice to denote parameters by the letters of the Greek alphabet and statistics by the letters of the English alphabet.

We divide numerical measures into three categories: (1) measures of centrality, (2) measures of dispersion, and (3) measures of percentages. *Measures of centrality* give us information about the center of the data, *measures of dispersion* give us information about the variation within the data, and *measures of percentages* tell us what percentage of the data falls into some specific interval or intervals.

Measures of Centrality

Measures of centrality are also known as *measures of central tendency*. Whether referring to measures of centrality or central tendency, the following measures are of primary importance:

1. Mean

2. Median

3. Mode

The mean is also sometimes referred to as the *arithmetic mean*, and it is the most useful and most commonly used measure of centrality. The median is the second most used, and the mode is the least used measure of centrality.

Mean. The mean of a sample or a population data is calculated by taking the sum of the data measurements and dividing it by the number of measurements in the sample or the population data. The mean of a sample is called the *sample mean* and is denoted by $\overline{X}$ (read as "X bar"); the *population mean* is denoted by the Greek letter μ (read as "mu"). These terms are defined numerically as follows:

$$\text{Population mean } \mu = \frac{X_1 + X_2 + \ldots + X_N}{N} = \frac{\Sigma X_i}{N} \tag{19.5}$$

$$\text{Sample mean } \overline{X} = \frac{X_1 + X_2 + \ldots + X_n}{n} = \frac{\Sigma X_i}{n} \tag{19.6}$$

where Σ (read as "sigma") is symbolized as a summation over all the measurements, and where N and n denote the population size and sample size, respectively. See Examples 19.11 and 19.12.

Note that even though the formulas for calculating sample mean and population mean are very similar, it is very important to make a clear distinction between the sample mean $\overline{X}$ and the population mean μ for all application purposes.

Sometimes, a data set may include a few observations or measurements that are very small or very large. For example, the salaries of a group of engineers in a big corporation may also include the salary of its CEO, who also happens to be an engineer and whose salary is much larger than the salaries of the other engineers in that group. In such cases where there are some very small and/or very large observations, these values are referred to as *extreme* values. If extreme values are present in the data set, then their mean is not an appropriate measure of centrality. *It is important to note that any extreme value, large or small, adversely affects*

EXAMPLE 19.11

The data in this example give the hourly wages (in dollars) of some randomly selected workers in a manufacturing company:

$$8, 6, 9, 10, 8, 7, 11, 9, 8$$

Find the mean hourly wage of these workers.

Solution

Since the wages listed in these data are only for some of the workers in the company, they represent a sample. Thus, we have

$$n = 9$$

$$\Sigma x_i = 8 + 6 + 9 + 10 + 8 + 7 + 11 + 9 + 8 = 76$$

So, the sample mean is

$$\overline{X} = \frac{\Sigma x_1}{n} = \frac{76}{9} = 8.44$$

In this example the mean hourly wage of these employees is $8.44 an hour.

EXAMPLE 19.12

The following data give the ages of all the employees in the city hardware store:

$$22, 25, 26, 36, 26, 29, 26, 26$$

Find the mean age of these employees.

Solution

Since the data give the ages of all the employees of the hardware store, we are interested in a population. Thus, we have

$$N = 8$$

$$\Sigma x_i = 22 + 25 + 26 + 36 + 26 + 29 + 26 + 26 = 216$$

So, the population mean is

$$\mu = \frac{\Sigma x_i}{N} = \frac{216}{8} = 27 \text{ years}$$

In this example the mean age of the employees in the hardware store is 27 years.

---

the mean value. In such cases the median is a better measure of centrality since it is unaffected by a few extreme values. Next, we discuss the method for calculating the median of a data set.

Median. We denote the median of a data set by M_d. To determine the median of a data set we take the following steps:

Step 1: Arrange the measurements in the data set in ascending order and rank them from 1 to n.

Step 2: Find the rank of the median that is equal to $(n + 1)/2$.

Step 3: Find the value corresponding to the rank $(n + 1)/2$ of the median. This value represents the median of the data set.

Note that if the value of n is even, then the rank of the median is not an integer. In such cases the median is the average of the two middle measurements. See Examples 19.13 and 19.14.

It is important to note that the median may or may not be one of the values of the data set. Whenever the sample size is odd, the median is the center value, and whenever it is even, the median is always the average of the two middle values when the data are arranged in ascending order.

Finally, note that the data in Example 19.14 contain two values, 250 and 300, that seem to be the sales of the top-performing sales personnel. These two large values may be considered as extreme values.

In this case, the mean of these data is given by

$$\bar{X} = (7 + 8 + 10 + 12 + 12 + 15 + 15 + 16 + 17 + 18 + 19 + \\ 20 + 22 + 25 + 250 + 300)/16 = 47.875$$

EXAMPLE 19.13

To illustrate the method of determining the median in a data set, we consider a simple example. The following data give the length of an alignment pin for a printer shaft in a batch of production:

$$30, 24, 34, 28, 32, 35, 29, 26, 36, 30, 33$$

Find the median alignment pin length.

Solution

Step 1:   Write the data in ascending order and rank them from 1 to 11, since $n = 11$.

Observations in ascending order: 24 26 28 29 30 30 32 33 34 35 36

Rank: 1 2 3 4 5 6 7 8 9 10 11

Step 2:   Find the rank of the median.

Rank of the median = $(n + 1)/2 = (11 + 1)/2 = 6$

Step 3:   Find the value corresponding to rank 6 (this is the rank of the median). The value corresponding to rank 6 is 30.

The median alignment pin length is $M_d = 30$. This means that at the most, 50% of the alignment pins are of a length less than 30, and at the most, 50% are of a length greater than 30.

EXAMPLE 19.14

The following data describe the sales (in thousands of dollars) for 16 randomly selected sales personnel distributed throughout the United States:

$$10, 8, 15, 12, 17, 7, 20, 19, 22, 25, 16, 15, 18, 250, 300, 12$$

Find the median sales of these individuals.

Solution

Step 1:   Observations in ascending order: 7 8 10 12 12 15 15 16 17 18 19 20 22 25 250 300

Rank: 1 2 3 4 5 6 7 8 9 10 11 12 13 14 15 16

Step 2:   Rank of the median = $(16 + 1)/2 = 8.5$

Step 3:   Find the value corresponding to the 8.5th rank. In this case, since the rank of the median is not an integer or a whole number, the median is defined as the average of the values that correspond to the ranks 8 and 9 (since rank 8.5 is located between ranks 8 and 9).

The median of the data is $M_d = (16 + 17)/2 = 16.5$.

Thus, the median sales of the given individuals is $16,500.

Since the mean of 47.875 is so much larger than the median of 16.5, it is obvious that the mean of these data has been adversely affected by the extreme values. Since in this case the mean does not adequately represent the measure of centrality of the data set, the median would more accurately identify where the center of the data is located.

Furthermore, if we replace the extreme values of 250 and 300 with, for example, 25 and 30, respectively, the median will not change, whereas the mean becomes 16.937. The new data obtained by replacing 250 and 300 with 25 and 30, respectively, do not contain any extreme values. Therefore, the new mean value is more consistent with the true average sales. See Example 19.15.

Mode. The *mode* of a data set is the value that occurs most frequently. Mode is the least used measure of centrality. The mode or the modal values are mostly used in situations where products are produced via mass production. For example, in industries where clothes of certain sizes, rods of certain lengths, or chips with a certain amount of memory are being produced, the modal value is of great interest. Note that in any data set there may be no mode or, conversely, there may be multiple modes. We denote the mode of a data set by M_0. See Examples 19.16, 19.17, and 19.18.

Note that there is no mathematical relationship between the mean, mode, and median. However, the values of the mean, mode, and median do provide us important information about the potential type or shape of the frequency distribution of the data. Although the shape of the frequency distribution of a data set could be of any type, we see most frequently the three types of frequency distributions shown in Figure 19.15.

EXAMPLE 19.15

Elizabeth took five courses in a given semester with 5, 4, 3, 3, and 2 credit hours. The grade points she earned in these courses at the end of the semester were 3.7, 4.0, 3.3, 3.7, and 4.0, respectively. Find her grade point average (GPA) for that semester.

Solution

Note that in this example the data points 3.7, 4.0, 3.3, 3.7, and 4.0 have different weights attached to them, that is, credit hours for each course. So, to find Elizabeth's GPA, we cannot simply find the arithmetic mean. Rather, in this case we shall find the mean called the *weighted mean*, which is defined as

$$\bar{X}_w = \frac{w_1 X_1 + w_2 X_2 + \ldots + w_n X_n}{w_1 + w_2 + \ldots w_n} = \frac{\Sigma w_i X_i}{\Sigma w_i} \tag{19.7}$$

where $w_1, w_2, \ldots, w_n$ are the weights attached to $X_1, X_2, \ldots, X_n$, respectively. In this example, the weights are the number of credits. Thus, the GPA in this example is given by:

$$\bar{X}_w = \frac{5(3.7) + 4(4.0) + 3(3.3) + 3(3.7) + 2(4.0)}{5 + 4 + 3 + 3 + 2} = 3.735$$

EXAMPLE 19.16

Find the mode for the following data set:

$$3, 8, 5, 6, 10, 17, 19, 20, 3, 2, 11$$

Solution

In the given data set each value occurs once, except 3, which occurs twice. Thus, the mode for this set is:

$$M_0 = 3$$

EXAMPLE 19.17

Find the mode for the following data set:

$$1, 7, 19, 23, 11, 12, 1, 12, 19, 7, 11, 23$$

Solution

Note that in this data set each value occurs the same number of times. Thus, in this data set there is no mode.

EXAMPLE 19.18

Find the modes for the following data set:

$$5, 7, 12, 13, 14, 21, 7, 21, 23, 26, 5$$

Solution

In this data set 5, 7, and 21 occur twice, and the rest of the values occur only once. In this example there are three modes, that is,

$$M_0 = 5, 7, \text{ and } 21$$

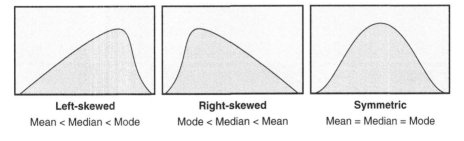

Left-skewed
Mean < Median < Mode

Right-skewed
Mode < Median < Mean

Symmetric
Mean = Median = Mode

Figure 19.15   Frequency distributions showing the shape and location of measures of central tendency.

The location of the measures of centrality or central tendency as shown in Figure 19.15 provide information about the type of data set. A data set is *symmetric* when the values in the data set that lie equidistant from the mean, on either side, occur with equal frequency. A data set is *left-skewed* when the values in the data set that are greater than the median occur with relatively higher frequency than those values that are smaller than the median. The values that are smaller than the median are scattered to the left far from the median. Finally, a data set is *right-skewed* when the values in the data set that are smaller than the median occur with relatively higher frequency than those values that are greater than the median. The values that are greater than the median are scattered to the right far from the median.

Measures of Dispersion

In the previous section we discussed measures of centrality. As we saw, they provide us information about the location of the center of frequency distributions of the data sets under consideration. However, measures of central tendency do not portray the whole picture of any data set. For example, this can be seen in Figure 19.16. The two frequency distributions have the same mean, median, and mode. Interestingly, however, the two distributions are significantly different from each other. The major difference between the two distributions is in the variation among the values associated with each distribution. It is important, then, for us to know about the variation among the values of the data set. Information about variation is provided by measures of dispersion. In this section we will study three measures of dispersion: range, variance, and standard deviation.

Range. The range of a data set is the easiest measure of dispersion to calculate. *Range* is defined as follows:

$$\text{Range} = \text{Largest value} - \text{Smallest value} \qquad (19.8)$$

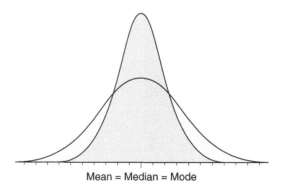

Mean = Median = Mode

Figure 19.16 Two frequency distribution curves with equal mean, median, and mode values.

EXAMPLE 19.19

The following data give the tensile strength (in psi) of a material sample submitted for inspection:

8538.24, 8450.16, 8494.27, 8317.34, 8443.99, 8368.04, 8368.94, 8424.41, 8427.34, 8517.64

Find the range for this data set.

Solution

The largest and the smallest values in the data set are 8538.24 and 8317.34, respectively. Therefore, the range for this data set is

$$\text{Range} = 8538.24 - 8317.34 = 220.90$$

Range is very sensitive to the influence of outliers and is not a very efficient measure of dispersion since it takes into consideration only the largest and the smallest values and does not take any account of the remaining observations. For example, if a data set has 100 distinct observations, it uses only two observations and ignores the remaining 98 observations. *As a rule of thumb, if the data set contains fewer than 10 observations, the range is considered a reasonably good measure of dispersion.* Otherwise, the range is not considered to be a very efficient measure of dispersion. See Example 19.19.

Variance. One of the most interesting pieces of information associated with any data is how the values in the data set vary from one another. A very important and widely used measure of dispersion is the *variance*, which focuses on how far the observations within a data set deviate from their mean, and thus gives an overall understanding about the variability of the observations within the data set.

For example, if the values in the data set are $x_1, x_2, x_3, \ldots, x_n$ and the mean is $\bar{x}$, then $x_1 = \bar{x}, x_2 = \bar{x}, x_3 = \bar{x}, \ldots, x_n = \bar{x}$, are the deviations from the mean. It is then natural to find the sum of these deviations and argue that if this sum is large, the values differ too much from one another; likewise, if this sum is small, they do not differ from one another too much.

Unfortunately, this argument does not hold since the sum of these deviations is always zero, no matter how much the values in the data set differ from one another. This is true because some of the deviations are positive and some are negative, and when we take their sum, they cancel each other. To avoid this cancellation process, we square these deviations and then take their sum. The variance is the average value of the sum of the squared deviations from the mean $\bar{x}$. If the data set represents a population, the deviations are taken from the population mean μ. So, the population variance, denoted by σ^2 (read as "sigma squared"), is defined as:

$$\sigma^2 = \frac{1}{N}\sum_{i=1}^{N}(X_i - \mu)^2 \tag{19.9}$$

And the sample variance, denoted by S^2, is defined as

$$S^2 = \frac{1}{n-1}\sum_{i=1}^{n}\left(X_i - \bar{X}\right)^2 \tag{19.10}$$

For computational purposes, equations (19.11) and (19.12) give the simplified forms of the formulas for population and sample variances:

$$\sigma^2 = \frac{1}{N}\left[\sum X_i^2 - \frac{\left(\sum X_i\right)^2}{N}\right] \tag{19.11}$$

$$S^2 = \frac{1}{n-1}\left[\sum X_i^2 - \frac{\left(\sum X_i\right)^2}{n}\right] \tag{19.12}$$

Note that one difficulty in using the variance as the measure of dispersion is that the units for measuring the variance are not the same as those used for data values. Rather, variance is expressed as a square of the units used for the data values. For example, if the data values are dollar amounts, then the variance will be expressed in squared dollars, which in this case is meaningless. For application purposes, therefore, we define another measure of dispersion, called the *standard deviation*, that is directly related to the variance. Standard deviation is measured in the same units as the data values.

Standard Deviation. Standard deviation is obtained by taking the positive square root (with positive sign) of the variance. See Example 19.20. The population standard deviation σ and the sample standard deviation s are defined as follows:

$$\sigma = +\sqrt{\frac{1}{N}\left[\sum x_i^2 - \frac{\left(\sum x_i\right)^2}{N}\right]} \tag{19.13}$$

$$S = \sqrt{\frac{1}{n-1}\left[\sum x_i^2 - \frac{\left(\sum x_i\right)^2}{n}\right]} \tag{19.14}$$

Empirical Rule. Now we see how the standard deviation of a data set helps in measuring the variability of the data. If the data have a distribution that is approximately bell shaped, the following rule, known as the *empirical rule*, can be used to compute the percentage of data that will fall within k standard deviations from the mean ($k = 1, 2, 3$).

1. Approximately 68% of the data will fall within one standard deviation of the mean, that is, between $\mu - 1\sigma$ and $\mu + 1\sigma$.

2. Approximately 95% of the data will fall within two standard deviations of the mean, that is, between $\mu - 2\sigma$ and $\mu + 2\sigma$.

3. Approximately 99.7% of the data will fall within three standard deviations of the mean, that is, between $\mu - 3\sigma$ and $\mu + 3\sigma$.

Figure 19.17 illustrates these features of the empirical rule. See also Examples 19.21 and 19.22.

EXAMPLE 19.20

The following data give the length (in millimeters) of material chips removed during a machining operation:

$$4, 2, 5, 1, 3, 6, 2, 4, 3, 5$$

Calculate the variance and the standard deviation for these data.

Solution

There are three simple steps involved in calculating the variance of any data set.

Step 1: Calculate ΣX_i, the sum of all the data values. Thus, we have

$$\Sigma x_i = 4 + 2 + 5 + 1 + 3 + 6 + 2 + 4 + 3 + 5 = 35$$

Step 2: Calculate ΣX^2_i, the sum of squares of all the observations, that is,

$$\Sigma x_i^2 = 4^2 + 2^2 + 5^2 + 1^2 + 3^2 + 6^2 + 2^2 + 4^2 + 3^2 + 5^2 = 145$$

Step 3: Since the sample size is $n = 10$, by inserting the values of ΣX_i and ΣX^2_i, calculated in step 1 and step 2, in equation (19.13), we have

$$S^2 = \frac{1}{10-1}\sum_{i=1}^{n}\left(145 - \frac{(35)^2}{10}\right)^2 = \frac{1}{9}(145 - 122.5) = 2.5$$

The standard deviation is obtained by taking the square root of the variance, that is,

$$S = \sqrt{2.5} = 1.58$$

Note: It is important to remember that the value of S^2, and therefore of S, is always greater than zero, except where all the data values are equal, in which case it is zero.

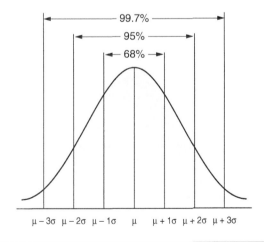

Figure 19.17   Application of the empirical rule.

EXAMPLE 19.21

A soft-drink filling machine is used to fill 16-oz soft-drink bottles. Since the amount of beverage varies slightly from bottle to bottle, it is believed that the actual amount of beverage in the bottle forms a bell-shaped distribution with a mean of 15.8 oz and a standard deviation of 0.15 oz. Use the empirical rule to find the percentage of bottles that contain between 15.5 oz and 16.1 oz of beverage.

Solution

From the information provided to us in this problem, we have

$$\mu = 15.8 \text{ oz} \qquad \sigma = 0.15 \text{ oz}$$

We are interested in finding the percentage of bottles that contain between 15.5 oz and 16.1 oz of beverage. Comparing Figure 19.18 with Figure 19.17, it is obvious that approximately 95% of the bottles contain between 15.5 oz and 16.1 oz of beverage, since 15.5 and 16.1 are two standard deviations away from the mean.

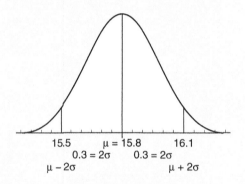

Figure 19.18   Amount of soft drink contained in a bottle.

Measures of Percentages

Measures of percentages divide the data into various parts of certain percentages or help to locate the place of any data value in the whole data set. For example, more commonly used measures of percentages are percentiles and quartiles, where *percentiles* divide the data into 100 parts such that each part contains at the most 1% of the data, and *quartiles* divide the data into four parts such that each part contains at the most 25% of the data. Then, from quartiles we can derive another measure, called the *interquartile range*, which gives the range of the middle 50% of the data values. The interquartile range may also be obtained by first writing the data in ascending order and then trimming 25% of the data values from both the lower end and the upper end.

Percentiles. Percentiles divide the data into 100 equal parts; each part contains at the most 1% of the data, and the percentiles are numbered from 1 to 99. For example, the median of a data set is the 50th percentile, which divides the data into two

EXAMPLE 19.22

At the end of every fiscal year, a manufacturer writes off or adjusts its financial records to reflect the number of units of bad production occurring over all lots of production during the year. Suppose the dollar values associated with the various units of bad production form a bell-shaped distribution with mean $\bar{x}$ = $35,700 and standard deviation S = $2500. Find the percentage of units of bad production that have a dollar value between $28,200 and $43,200.

Solution

From the information provided to us we have $\bar{x}$ = $35,700 and S = $2,500.

Since the limits $28,200 and $43,200 are three standard deviations away from the mean, comparing Figure 19.19 with Figure 19.17, we see that approximately 99.7% of the units of bad production had dollar values between $28,200 and $43,200.

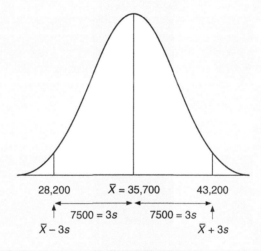

Figure 19.19 Dollar value of units of bad production.

equal parts such that at the most, 50% of the data fall below the median and at the most, 50% of the data fall above it. The procedure for determining the percentiles is similar to the procedure used for determining the median. We compute the percentiles as follows:

Step 1: Write the data values in ascending order and rank them from 1 to n.

Step 2: Find the rank of the pth percentile (p = 1, 2, . . . , 99), which is given by

$$\text{Rank of the } p\text{th percentile} = p \times [(n + 1)/100]$$

Step 3: Find the data value that corresponds to the rank of the pth percentile. We illustrate this procedure with Example 19.23.

EXAMPLE 19.23

The following data give the salaries (in thousands of dollars) of 15 engineers of a corporation:

$$62, 48, 52, 63, 85, 51, 95, 76, 72, 51, 69, 73, 58, 55, 54$$

Find the 70th percentile for these data.

Solution

Write the data values in ascending order and rank them from 1 to 15, since n is equal to 15.

Step 1: Salaries: 48, 51, 51, 52, 54, 55, 58, 62, 63, 69, 72, 73, 76, 85, 95

Rank: 1 2 3 4 5 6 7 8 9 10 11 12 13 14 15

Step 2: Find the rank of the 70th percentile, which is given by

$$70 \times [(15 + 1)/100] = 11.2$$

Step 3: Find the data value that corresponds to the rank 11.2, which will be the 70th percentile. From Figure 19.20, we can easily see that the value of the 70th percentile is given by

$$70\text{th percentile} = 72(.8) + 73(.2) = 72.2$$

Thus, the 70th percentile of the salary data is $72,200.

That is, at the most, 70% of the engineers are making less than $72,200, and at the most, 30% of the engineers are making more than $72,200.

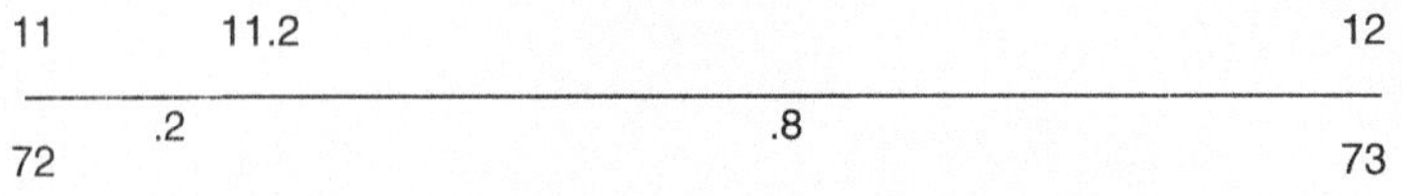

11	11.2		12
	.2	.8	
72			73

Figure 19.20   Percentile of salary data.

In our discussion we determined the value x of a given percentile p. Now we would like to find the percentile p corresponding to a given value x. This can be done by using the following formula:

$$p = \frac{(\#\text{ of data values} \leq x)}{(n+1)} \times (100) \qquad (19.15)$$

For instance, in Example 19.23 the percentile corresponding to the salary of $60,000 is

$$p = (7/(15 + 1)) \times 100 = 44$$

The engineer who makes a salary of $60,000 is at the 44th percentile. In other words, at most, 44% of the engineers are making less than $60,000, or at most, 56% are making more than $60,000.

Quartiles. In the previous discussion we studied percentiles, which divide the data into 100 equal parts. Some of the percentiles have special importance. These are the 25th, 50th, and 75th percentiles, which are known as the *first, second,* and *third quartiles* (denoted by Q_1, Q_2, and Q_3), respectively. These quartiles are sometimes also known as the lower, middle, and upper quartiles, respectively. Note that the second quartile is the same as the median. To determine the values of the different quartiles, one just has to find the 25th, 50th, and 75th percentiles (see Figure 19.21).

Interquartile Range. Often, we are more interested in finding information about the middle 50% of a population. A measure of dispersion relative to the middle 50% of the population or sample data is known as the *interquartile range*. This range is obtained by trimming 25% of the values from the bottom and 25% from the top (see Example 19.24). The interquartile range (IQR) is defined as

$$IQR = Q_3 - Q_1 \qquad (19.16)$$

Notes:

1. The interquartile range gives the range of variation among the middle 50% of the population.

	25%	25%	25%	25%
Quartiles	Q_1	Q_2	Q_3	
Percentiles	25th	50th	75th	

Figure 19.21 Quartiles and percentiles.

EXAMPLE 19.24

Find the interquartile range for the salary data in Example 19.23, that is:

Salaries: 48, 51, 51, 52, 54, 55, 58, 62, 63, 69, 72, 73, 76, 85, 95

Solution

In order to find the interquartile range, we first need to find the quartiles Q_1 and Q_3, or, equivalently, the 25th percentile and the 75th percentile. We can easily see that the ranks of 25th and 75th percentile are:

Rank of 25th percentile = (25/100) × (15 + 1) = 4

Rank of 75th percentile = (75/100) × (15 + 1) = 12

Thus, in this case, $Q_1 = 52$ and $Q_3 = 73$.

This means that the middle 50% of the engineers earn between $52,000 and $73,000. The interquartile range in this example is:

IQR = $73,000 − $52,000 = $21,000

2. The interquartile range is potentially a more meaningful measure of dispersion than the range since it is not affected by extreme values that may be present in the data. By trimming 25% of the data from the bottom and 25% from the top, we eliminate the extreme values that may be present in the data set. Very often, the interquartile range is used as a measure for comparing two or more data sets on similar studies.

Box-and-Whisker Plot

In our study of engineers' salaries, several mentions were made of extreme values. So, at some point we must know what values in a data set are extreme values, also known as *outliers*. A box-and-whisker plot—or simply, a *box plot*—helps us to answer this question. Figure 19.22 illustrates the construction of a box plot for any data set. See Examples 19.25 and 19.26.

Construction of a Box Plot

Step 1: For a given data set, find the quartiles Q_1, Q_2, and Q_3.

Step 2: Draw a box with its outer lines standing at the first quartile (Q_1) and the third quartile (Q_3), and then draw a line at the second quartile (Q_2). The line at Q_2 divides the box into two boxes, which may or may not be of equal size.

Step 3: From the center of the outer lines, draw straight lines extending outwardly up to three times the interquartile range (IQR) and mark them as shown in Figure 19.22. Note that each distance between the points A and B, B and C, D and E, and E and F is

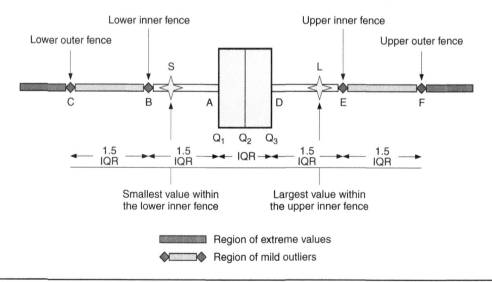

Figure 19.22 Box-and-whisker plot.

EXAMPLE 19.25

The following data give the noise level, measured in decibels (a normal conversation by humans produces a noise level of about 75 decibels), produced by different machines in a very large manufacturing plant:

$$85, 80, 88, 95, 115, 110, 105, 104, 89, 97, 96, 140, 75, 79, 99$$

Construct a box plot and determine whether the data set contains any outliers.

Solution

First, we arrange the data in ascending order and rank them from 1 to 15 ($n = 15$).

$$\text{Data values: } 75, 79, 80, 85, 88, 89, 95, 96, 97, 99, 104, 105, 110, 115, 140$$

$$\text{Rank: } 1\ 2\ 3\ 4\ 5\ 6\ 7\ 8\ 9\ 10\ 11\ 12\ 13\ 14\ 15$$

We now find the ranks of the quartiles Q_1, Q_2, and Q_3. Thus, we have

$$\text{Rank of } Q_1 = (25/100) \times (15 + 1) = 4$$

$$\text{Rank of } Q_2 = (50/100) \times (15 + 1) = 8$$

$$\text{Rank of } Q_3 = (75/100) \times (15 + 1) = 12$$

Therefore, the values of Q_1, Q_2, and Q_3 are

$$Q_1 = 85 \qquad Q_2 = 96 \qquad Q_3 = 105$$

The interquartile range is

$$\text{IQR} = Q_3 - Q_1 = 105 - 85 = 20$$

and

$$(1.5) \times \text{IQR} = (1.5) \times 20 = 30$$

Figure 19.23 shows the box plot for the data.
   Figure 19.23 shows that the given data set contains one outlier (140). In this case, action should be taken to reduce the activity that produces a noise level of 140 decibels.

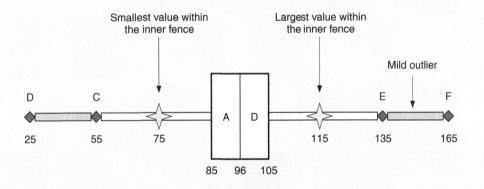

Figure 19.23   Box plot for the data in Example 19.25.

EXAMPLE 19.26

The following data give the number of persons who take the bus during the off-peak hours time schedule from Grand Central to Lower Manhattan in New York:

12 12 12 14 15 16 16 16 16 17 17 18 18 18 19 19 20 20 20 20

20 20 20 20 21 21 21 22 22 23 23 23 24 24 25 26 26 28 28 28

a. Find the mean, mode, and median for these data.

b. Prepare the box plot for the data.

c. Use the results of parts (a) and (b) to verify whether the data are symmetric or skewed. Examine whether the conclusions made using the two methods about the shape of the distribution are the same.

d. Use a box plot to check whether the data contain any outliers.

e. If in part (c) the conclusion is that the data are at least approximately symmetric, then find the standard deviation and verify whether the empirical rule holds.

Solution

a. The sample size in this problem is $n = 40$. So, we have

$$\text{Mean } \bar{X} = \sum x_i/n = 800/40 = 20$$

$$\text{Mode} = 20$$

$$\text{Median} = 20$$

Since the mean, median, and mode are equal, we may conclude that the data are symmetric.

b. To prepare the box plot, we first find the quartiles Q_1, Q_2, and Q_3.

$$\text{Rank of } Q_1 = (25/100) \times (40 + 1) = 10.25$$

$$\text{Rank of } Q_2 = (50/100) \times (40 + 1) = 20.50$$

$$\text{Rank of } Q_3 = (75/100) \times (40 + 1) = 30.75$$

Since the data presented in this problem are already in ascending order, we can easily see that quartiles Q_1, Q_2, and Q_3 are

$$Q_1 = 17 \qquad Q_2 = 20 \qquad Q_3 = 23$$

The interquartile range is

$$\text{IQR} = Q_3 - Q_1 = 23 - 17 = 6$$

$$1.5 \times (\text{IQR}) = 1.5 \times (6) = 9$$

The box plot for the data is shown in Figure 19.24. Evaluating the box plot, we may conclude that the data are symmetric.

c. Both parts (a) and (b) lead us to the same conclusion that the data are symmetric.

d. From the box plot in Figure 19.24 we see that the data do not contain any outliers.

Continued

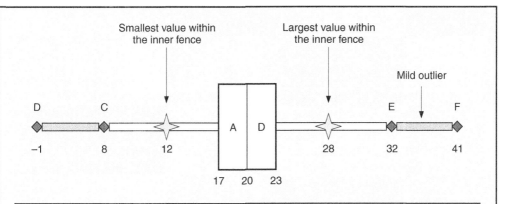

Figure 19.24   Box plot for the data shown in Example 19.26.

e. In part (c) we concluded that the data are symmetric and thus proceed to calculate the standard deviation and then verify whether the empirical rule holds.

$$S^2 = \frac{1}{40-1}\left[12^2 + \ldots + 28^2 - \frac{(12 + \ldots + 28)^2}{40}\right] = 18.1538$$

Thus, the standard deviation is $S = 4.26$, which is the square root of the variance 18.1538.

It can be seen that the intervals:

$$(\bar{X} - S, \bar{X} + S) = (15.74 - 24.26) \text{ contains } 72.5\% \text{ of the data}$$
$$(\bar{X} - 25, \bar{X} + 25) = (11.48 - 28.52) \text{ contains } 100\% \text{ of the data}$$

The data are slightly more clustered around the mean. But for all practical purposes, we may say that the empirical rule does hold.

equal to one and a half times the distance between the points A and D, or one and a half times the IQR. The points S and L are, respectively, the smallest and largest data points that fall within the inner fences. The lines from A to S and D to L are called the *whiskers*.

How to Use the Box Plot

About the outliers:

1. Data points that fall beyond the lower and upper outer fences are the extreme outliers. These points are usually excluded from the analysis.

2. Data points that fall between the inner and outer fences are the mild outliers. These points are excluded from the analysis only if we are convinced that they are in error.

About the shape of the distribution:

1. If the second quartile (median) is close to the center of the box and each of the whiskers is approximately of equal length, the distribution is symmetric.

2. If the right box is substantially larger than the left box and/or the right whisker is much longer than the left whisker, the distribution is right-skewed.

3. If the left box is substantially larger than the right box and/or the left whisker is much longer than the right whisker, the distribution is left-skewed.

3. NORMAL DISTRIBUTION

The normal distribution is one of the most important and widely used probability distributions. It forms the basis of modern statistical theory.

A random variable X is said to have a *normal probability distribution* if the density function of X is given by

$$f(x) = \frac{1}{\sqrt{2\pi}\sigma} e^{-(x-\mu)^2/2\sigma^2} \qquad -\infty \leq x \leq +\infty \qquad (19.17)$$

where $-\infty < \mu < +\infty$ and $\sigma > 0$ are the two parameters of the distribution, $\pi \cong 3.14159$ and $e \cong 2.71828$. Also, note that μ and σ are the mean and the standard deviation of the distribution. A random variable X having a normal distribution with mean μ and standard deviation σ is usually written as $X \sim N(\mu, \sigma^2)$.

Some characteristics of the normal probability function are the following:

1. The normal probability function curve is bell shaped and completely symmetric about its mean μ. For this reason the normal distribution is also known as a *bell-shaped distribution*.

2. The specific shape of the curve, whether it is more or less tall, is determined by the value of its standard deviation σ.

3. The tails of the probability function curve extend from $-\sigma$ to $+\sigma$.

4. The total area under the curve is 1.0. However, 99.73% of the area falls within three standard deviations of the mean μ.

5. The area under the normal curve to the right of μ is 0.5 and to the left of μ is also 0.5.

Figure 19.25 shows the normal probability function curve of a random variable X with mean μ and standard deviation σ.

Since 99.73% of the probability of a normal random variable with mean μ and standard deviation σ falls between $\mu - 3\sigma$ and $\mu + 3\sigma$, the 6σ distance between $\mu - 3\sigma$ and $\mu + 3\sigma$ is usually considered the range of the normal distribution. Figures 19.26 and 19.27 show that as the mean μ and the standard deviation σ change, the location and the shape of the normal curve also change.

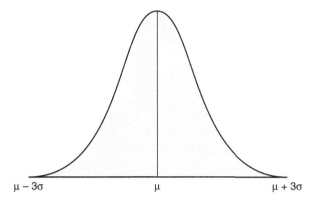

Figure 19.25   The normal probability function curve with mean μ and standard deviation σ.

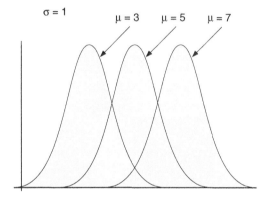

Figure 19.26   Curves representing the normal density function with different means, but with the same standard deviation.

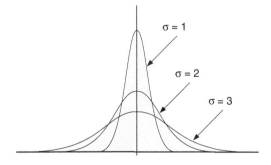

Figure 19.27   Curves representing the normal density function with different standard deviations, but with the same mean.

From Figure 19.27 we can observe an important phenomenon of the normal distribution; that is, as the standard deviation σ becomes smaller and smaller, the probability is concentrated more and more around the mean μ. We will see later that this property of the normal distribution is very useful in making inferences about populations.

To find the probabilities of a normal random variable, we need to introduce a new random variable, called the *standardized random variable*. The reason we have a standardized normal variable is so that we can have one table to determine probabilities rather than an infinite number of tables, which would be required without standardization. A *standard normal random variable*, denoted by Z, is defined as follows:

$$Z = \frac{X - \mu}{\sigma} \tag{19.18}$$

The new random variable Z is also distributed normally, but with a mean of 0 and a standard deviation of 1. The distribution of the random variable Z is generally known as the *standard normal distribution*, with mean 0 and standard deviation 1, and is usually written as $N(0,1)$.

The values of the standard normal random variable Z, denoted by the lower-case letter z, are called the z-scores. For example, in Figure 19.28 the points marked on the x-axis are the z-scores. The probability of the random variable Z falling in an interval (a,b) is shown by the shaded area under the standard normal curve in Figure 19.29. This probability is determined by using a standard normal distribution table (see Appendix D).

Standard Normal Distribution Table

The standard normal distribution table, shown in Appendix D, lists the probabilities of the random variable Z for its values between z = 0.00 and z = 3.09. A small portion of this table is reproduced in Table 19.10. The entries in the body of the table are the probabilities $P(0 \leq Z \leq z)$, where z is some point in the interval (0,3.09). These probabilities are also shown by the shaded area under the

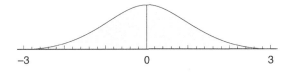

Figure 19.28   The standard normal density function curve.

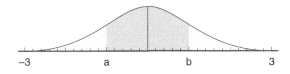

Figure 19.29   Probability ($a \leq Z \leq b$) under the standard normal curve.

normal curve given at the top of the table in Appendix D. To read this table, we mark the row and the column corresponding to the value of z to one decimal point and the second decimal point, respectively. The entry at the intersection of that row and column is the probability $P(0 \leq Z \leq z)$. For example, the probability $P(0 \leq Z \leq 2.09)$ is found by marking the row corresponding to $z = 2.0$ and the column corresponding to $z = 0.09$ (note that $z = 2.09 = 2.0 + 0.09$) and locating the entry at the intersection of the marked row and column, which in this case is equal to .4817. The probabilities for the negative values of z are found, due to the symmetric property of the normal distribution, by finding the probabilities of the corresponding positive values of z. For example, $P(-1.54 \leq Z \leq -0.50) = P(0.50 \leq Z \leq 1.54)$. See Examples 19.27, 19.28, and 19.29.

Table 19.10   A portion of the standard normal distribution table from Appendix D.

z	0.00	0.01	0.02	0.03	0.04	0.05	0.06	0.07	0.08	0.09
0.0	0.0000	0.0040	0.0080	0.0120	0.0160	0.0199	0.0239	0.0279	0.0319	0.0359
0.1	0.0398	0.0438	0.0478	0.0517	0.0557	0.0596	0.0636	0.0675	0.0714	0.0753
.	.									
.	.									
.	.									
1.0	0.3413	0.3438	0.3461	0.3485	0.3508	0.3531	0.3554	0.3577	0.3599	0.3621
1.1	0.3643	0.3665	0.3686	0.3708	0.3729	0.3749	0.3770	0.3790	0.3810	0.3830
.	.									
.	.									
.	.									
1.9	0.4713	0.4719	0.4726	0.4732	0.4738	0.4744	0.4750	0.4756	0.4761	0.4767
2.0	0.4772	0.4778	0.4783	0.4788	0.4793	0.4798	0.4803	0.4808	0.4812	.04817

EXAMPLE 19.27

Use the standard normal distribution table in Appendix D to find the following probabilities:

a. $P(1.0 \leq Z \leq 2.0)$

b. $P(-1.5 \leq Z \leq 0)$

c. $P(-2.2 \leq Z \leq -1.0)$

Solution

a. From Figure 19.30 it is clear that

$$P(1.0 \leq Z \leq 2.0) = P(0 \leq Z \leq 2.0) - P(0 \leq Z \leq 1.0)$$

$$= 0.4772 - 0.3413 = 0.1359$$

b. Since the normal distribution is symmetric about the mean, which in this case is 0, the probability of Z falling between -1.5 and 0 is the same as the probability of Z

Continued

falling between 0 and 1.5. Figure 19.31 also supports this assertion. Using the table in Appendix D, we have the following:

$$P(-1.5 \leq Z \leq 0) = P(0 \leq Z \leq 1.5) = 0.4332$$

c. By using the same argument as in part (b) and using the table in Appendix D (see Figure 19.32), we have that

$$P(-2.2 \leq Z \leq -1.0) = P(1.0 \leq Z \leq 2.2)$$
$$= P(0 \leq Z \leq 2.2) - P(0 \leq Z \leq 1.0)$$
$$= 0.4861 - 0.3413 = 0.1448$$

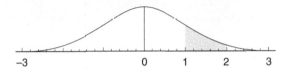

Figure 19.30   Shaded area equal to $P(1.0 \leq Z \leq 2.0)$.

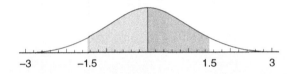

Figure 19.31   Two shaded areas showing $P(-1.5 \leq Z \leq 0) = P(0 \leq Z \leq 1.5)$.

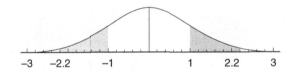

Figure 19.32   Two shaded areas showing $P(-2.2 \leq Z \leq -1.0) = P(1.0 \leq Z \leq 2.2)$.

EXAMPLE 19.28

Use the table in Appendix D to determine the following probabilities:

a. $P(-1.5 \leq Z \leq 0.8)$

b. $P(Z \leq 0.7)$

c. $P(Z \geq -1.0)$

Continued

Solution

a. Since the standard normal distribution table (Appendix D) gives the probabilities of z-values starting from zero to positive z-values, we have to break the interval −1.5 to 0.8 into two parts, that is, −1.5 to 0 plus 0 to 0.8 (see Figure 19.33), so that we get

$$P(-1.5 \leq Z \leq 0.8) = P(-1.5 \leq Z \leq 0) + P(0 \leq Z \leq 0.8)$$

Thus, we have

$$P(-1.5 \leq Z \leq 0.8) = P(-1.5 \leq Z \leq 0) + P(0 \leq Z \leq 0.8)$$

$$= P(0 \leq Z \leq 1.5) + P(0 \leq Z \leq 0.8)$$

$$= 0.4332 + 0.2881 = 0.7213$$

b. The probability $P(Z \leq 0.7)$ is shown by the shaded area in Figure 19.34. This area is equal to the sum of the area to the left of $z = 0$ and the area between $z = 0$ and $z = 0.7$, which implies that

$$P(Z \leq 0.7) = P(Z \leq 0) + P(0 \leq Z \leq 0.7) = 0.5 + 0.2580 = 0.7580$$

c. By using the same argument as in part (b) and Figure 19.35, we get

$$P(Z \geq -1.0) = P(-1.0 \leq Z \leq 0) + P(Z \geq 0)$$

$$= P(0 \leq Z \leq 1.0) + P(Z \geq 0)$$

$$= 0.3413 + 0.5 = 0.8413$$

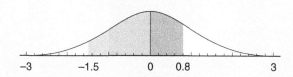

Figure 19.33   Shaded area showing $P(-1.5 \leq Z \leq 0.8) = P(-1.5 \leq Z \leq 0) + P(0 \leq Z \leq 0.8)$.

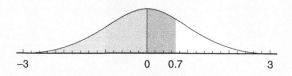

Figure 19.34   Shaded area showing $P(Z \leq 0.7)$.

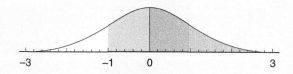

Figure 19.35   Shaded area showing $P(Z \geq -1.0)$.

EXAMPLE 19.29

Use the table in Appendix D to find the following probabilities:

a. $P(Z \geq 2.15)$

b. $P(Z \leq -2.15)$

Solution

a. The desired probability $P(Z \geq 2.15)$ is equal to the shaded area under the normal curve to the right of $z = 2.15$, shown in Figure 19.36. This area is equal to the area to the right of $z = 0$ minus the area between $z = 0$ and $z = 2.15$. Since the area to the right of $z = 0$ is 0.5, we have

$$P(Z \geq 2.15) = 0.5 - P(0 \leq Z \leq 2.15) = 0.5 - 0.4842 = 0.0158$$

b. Using the symmetric property of the normal distribution (see Figure 19.37) and using part (a), we have

$$P(Z \leq -2.15) = P(Z \geq 2.15) = 0.0158$$

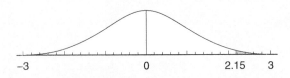

Figure 19.36 Shaded area showing $P(Z \geq 2.15)$.

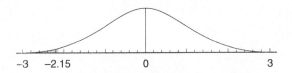

Figure 19.37 Shaded area showing $P(Z \leq -2.15)$.

So far in this section, we have considered the problems of finding probabilities of the standard normal variable Z, that is, a normal random variable with mean $\mu = 0$ and standard deviation $\sigma = 1$. In Examples 19.30 and 19.31 we consider the problems where $\mu \neq 0$ and $\sigma \neq 1$.

REFERENCES

Gupta, B. C., and H. Fred Walker. 2005. *Applied Statistics for the Six Sigma Green Belt.* Milwaukee: ASQ Quality Press.

Gupta, B. C., and I. Guttman. 2013. *Statistics and Probability with Applications for Engineers and Scientists.* Hoboken, NJ: John Wiley & Sons.

EXAMPLE 19.30

Let X be a random variable distributed normally with $\mu = 6$ and $\sigma = 4$. Then, determine the following probabilities:

$$P(8.0 \le X \le 14.0)$$

$$P(2.0 \le X \le 10.0)$$

$$P(0 \le X \le 4.0)$$

Solution

a. To find the probability $P(8.0 \le X \le 14.0)$, we first need to transform the random variable X into the standard normal variable Z, which is done by subtracting throughout the inequality the mean μ and dividing by the standard deviation σ. Thus, as shown in Figures 19.38 and 19.39, we get

$$P(8.0 \le X \le 14.0) = P\left(\frac{8-6}{4} \le \frac{X-6}{4} \le \frac{14-6}{4} \right)$$

$$= P(0.5 \le Z \le 2.0)$$

$$= P(0 \le Z \le 2.0) - P(0 \le Z \le 0.5)$$

$$= 0.4772 - 0.1915 = 0.2857$$

b. Proceeding in the same manner as in part (a) and using Figure 19.40, we have

$$P(2.0 \le X \le 10.0) = P\left(\frac{2-6}{4} \le \frac{X-6}{4} \le \frac{10-6}{4} \right)$$

$$= P(-1.0 \le Z \le 1.0)$$

$$= P(-1.0 \le Z \le 0) - P(0 \le Z \le 1.0)$$

$$= 2 \times P(0 \le Z \le 1.0) = 2 \times (0.3413) = 0.6826$$

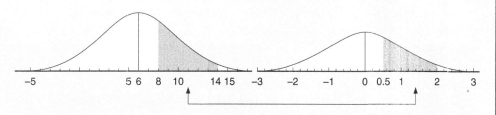

Figure 19.38   Converting normal $N(6,4)$ to standard normal $N(0,1)$.

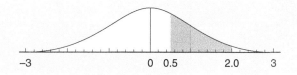

Figure 19.39   Shaded area showing $P(0.5 \le Z \le 2.0)$.

Continued

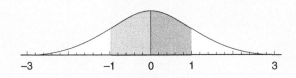

Figure 19.40   Shaded area showing $P(-1.0 \leq Z \leq 1.0)$.

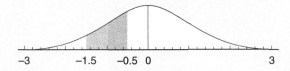

Figure 19.41   Shaded area showing $P(-1.5 \leq Z \leq -0.5)$.

c. Again, transforming X into Z and using Figure 19.41, we get

$$P(0 \leq X \leq 4.0) = P\left(\frac{0-6}{4} \leq \frac{X-6}{4} \leq \frac{4-6}{4}\right) = P(-1.5 \leq Z \leq -0.5)$$

$$= P(0.5 \leq Z \leq 1.5)$$

$$= P(0 \leq Z \leq 1.5) - P(0 \leq Z \leq 0.5)$$

$$= 0.4332 - 0.1915 = 0.2417$$

EXAMPLE 19.31

Suppose a quality characteristic of a product is normally distributed with mean $\mu = 18$ and standard deviation $\sigma = 1.5$. The specification limits furnished by the customer are (15, 21). Determine what percentage of the product meets the specifications set by the customer.

Solution

Let the random variable X denote the quality characteristic of interest. Then X is normally distributed with mean $\mu = 18$ and standard deviation $\sigma = 1.5$.

We are interested in finding the percentage of product with the characteristic of interest within the specification limits (15, 21), which is given by

$$P(15 \leq X \leq 21) = P\left(\frac{15-18}{1.5} \leq \frac{X-18}{1.5} \leq \frac{21-18}{1.5}\right)$$

$$= P(-2.0 \leq Z \leq 2.0)$$

$$= P(-2.0 \leq Z \leq 0) + P(0 \leq Z \leq 2.0)$$

$$= 2 \times P(0 \leq Z \leq 2.0) = 2 \times (0.4772) = 0.9544$$

Thus, the percentage of product that will meet the specifications set by the customer is equal to

$$95.44\% \ (= 0.9544 \times 100).$$

Chapter 20

B. Statistical Process Control (SPC)

1. *Common and special cause variation.* Explain the difference between these causes of variation. Determine whether a process is in statistical control by analyzing data patterns (runs, trends, and hugging), and identify what actions should be taken in response. (Evaluate)

2. *Control limits and specification limits.* Define, describe, and distinguish between these limits as used in SPC. (Apply)

3. *Variables charts.* Identify characteristics and uses of $\bar{X} - R$ and $\bar{X} - S$ charts. (Apply)

4. *Attributes charts.* Identify characteristics and uses of p, np, c, and u charts. (Apply)

5. *Process capability analysis.* Define and distinguish between C_p, C_{pk}, P_p, and P_{pk} studies and identify their application to various types of data. (Understand)

Body of Knowledge IV.B

The concept of quality is centuries old. However, the concept of *statistical quality control* (SQC) is less than a century old. SQC is merely a set of interrelated tools such as statistical process control (SPC), design of experiments (DOE), acceptance sampling plans, and other tools that are used to monitor and improve quality. SPC consists of several tools that are very useful for process monitoring. One of these tools is the quality control chart, which is the center of our discussion in this chapter. Walter A. Shewhart presented the first quality control chart in 1924.

1. BASIC CONCEPTS OF QUALITY AND ITS BENEFITS

Different authors have defined the concept of quality in different ways. We define it as Deming defined it: a product is of good quality if it meets the needs of a customer and the customer is glad that he or she bought that product. The customer may be internal or external, an individual or a corporation. If a product meets the needs of the customer, the customer is likely to buy that product again and again.

On the contrary, if a product does not meet the needs of the customer, the customer will not buy that product again even if he or she is an internal customer. Consequently, that product will be deemed of bad quality, and eventually it will disappear from the market.

Other components of a product's quality are its reliability, how much maintenance it demands, and, when the need arises, how easily and how quickly one can get it serviced. In evaluating the quality of a product, its attractiveness and rate of depreciation also play an important role.

As described by Deming in his telecast conferences, the benefits of better quality are numerous. First and foremost is that it enhances the overall image and reputation of the company by meeting the needs of its customers and making them happy. A happy customer is bound to buy the product again and again. Also, a happy customer is bound to share a good experience with a product with friends, relatives, and neighbors. Therefore, the company gets firsthand publicity without spending a dime, which results in more sales and higher profits. Higher profits lead to higher stock prices, which means higher net worth of the company. Better quality provides workers satisfaction and pride in their workmanship. A satisfied worker goes home happy, which makes his or her family happy. A happy family boosts the morale of a worker, which means more dedication and more loyalty to the company. Another benefit of better quality is decreased cost. This is due to the need for less rework, less scrap, fewer raw materials used, fewer production hours, and fewer machine hours wasted. All this ultimately means increased productivity, a better competitive position, and hence higher sales and higher market share for the company. On the other hand, losses due to poor quality are enormous. Poor quality not only affects sales and the competitive position, but also carries with it high hidden costs, which usually are not calculated and therefore are not known with precision. These costs include unusable product, product sold at a discounted price, and so on. In most companies the accounting departments provide only minimal information to quantify the actual losses incurred due to poor quality. Lack of awareness concerning the cost of poor quality could lead company managers to fail to take appropriate actions to improve quality.

2. FLOWCHART

Flowcharts were introduced by industrial engineers Frank and Lillian Gilbreth in the 1930s. A *flowchart* (also sometimes called a *process map*) shows a process or computer algorithm in various fields of application such as business, engineering, and various processes developed for quality improvement. It is a diagram that uses ovals, rectangles, and diamonds connected by arrows to represent the various steps of a process or an algorithm (see Figure 20.1).

3. WHAT IS A PROCESS?

A *process* may be defined as a series of actions or operations performed in producing manufactured or nonmanufactured products. A *process* may also be defined as a combination of workforce, equipment, raw material, methods, and environment that work together to produce output. The flowchart of a process in Figure 20.1 shows where each component of a process fits.

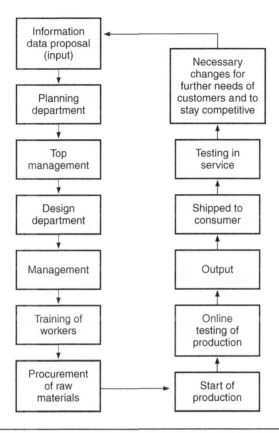

Figure 20.1 Flowchart of a process.

Note that SPC is very useful in any process, whether related to the manufacturing, service, or retail industry. There are several tools that are very valuable in achieving process stability. The set of all these tools, including the control charts, constitutes an integral part of SPC. These tools are as follows:

1. Histogram

2. Stem-and-leaf diagram

3. Scatter diagram

4. Pareto chart

5. Check sheet

6. Cause-and-effect diagram (also known as a *fishbone* or *Ishikawa* diagram)

7. Defect concentration diagram

8. Run chart (also known as a *line graph* or *time series graph*)

9. Control charts

We discussed several of these tools in Chapter 19, and we will discuss the remaining ones in this chapter.

4. CHECK SHEET

To improve the quality of a product, management must try to reduce the variation of all the quality characteristics; that is, the process must be brought to a stable condition. In any SPC procedure used to stabilize a process, it becomes essential to know precisely what types of defects are affecting the quality of the final product. The check sheet is an important tool in achieving this goal. We discuss this tool with the help of a real-life example. See Example 20.1.

The summary data in Table 20.1 not only give the total number of different types of defects but also provide a very meaningful source of trends and patterns of defects. These trends and patterns can help in finding possible causes for any particular defect or defects. Note that the column totals show the number of defects (rolls of paper rejected) occurring daily, whereas the row totals provide the number of defects by type occurring over the total period (four weeks) of study. It is important to remark here that these data become more meaningful if a logbook of all changes, such as change of raw material, calibration of machines, training of workers or new workers hired, and so on, is well maintained.

5. CAUSE-AND-EFFECT (FISHBONE OR ISHIKAWA) DIAGRAM

In implementing SPC, it is very important to identify and isolate the causes of any particular problem(s). A very effective tool for identifying such causes is the *cause-and-effect diagram*. This diagram is also known as both a *fishbone diagram*, because

---

EXAMPLE 20.1

In a paper mill a high percentage of paper rolls is discarded due to various types of defects. In order to identify these defects and their frequency, a study is launched. This study is done over a period of four weeks. The data are collected daily and are summarized in a *check sheet*, shown in Table 20.1.

Table 20.1   Check sheet summarizing the data of a study over a period of four weeks.

Defect type \ Day	1	2	3	4	5	6	7	8	9	10	11	12	13	14	15	16	17	18	19	20	21	22	23	24	25	26	27	28
Corrugation	1		2		1		3			1	1			2		1	1		1		3	2	1	2	2	1		3
Streaks			1			1						1				1		2			1		1				1	1
Pinholes	1			1	1			1	1						1	1											1	1
Dirt		1					1						1						1					2		1		
Blistering			2				2					2				2			1							1		1
Other	1				1															1	1							1
Total	3	1	5	1	3	1	6	1	1	1	1	3	1	2	1	5	1	2	3	1	5	2	2	4	2	3	2	7

of its shape, and an *Ishikawa diagram*, named after its inventor. Japanese manufacturers have widely used this diagram to improve the quality of their products. To prepare a cause-and-effect diagram, it is typical to first use a technique commonly known as *brainstorming*.

The brainstorming technique is a form of creative and collaborative thinking. Thus, this technique is used in a team setting. The team usually includes personnel from production, inspection, purchasing, design, and management, and any other members associated with the product under discussion. Some of the rules used in a brainstorming session include the following:

1. Each team member makes a list of ideas.

2. The team members sit around a table and take turns reading one idea at a time.

3. As the ideas are read, a facilitator displays them on a board so that all team members can see them.

4. Steps 2 and 3 are repeated until all of the ideas have been exhausted and displayed.

5. Cross-questioning is allowed only for clarification concerning a team member's idea.

6. When all ideas have been read and displayed, the facilitator asks each team member if he or she has any new ideas. This procedure continues until no team member can think of any new ideas.

Once all the ideas are presented, the next step is to analyze them. The cause-and-effect diagram is a graphical technique used to analyze these ideas. An initial structure of a cause-and-effect diagram is shown in Figure 20.2.

The five "bones" in Figure 20.2 indicate the five major factors or categories that could be the cause, or causes, of defect(s). In most workplaces, whether they are

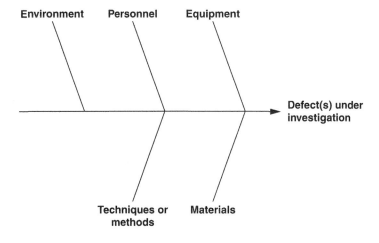

Figure 20.2   Initial form of a cause–and–effect diagram.

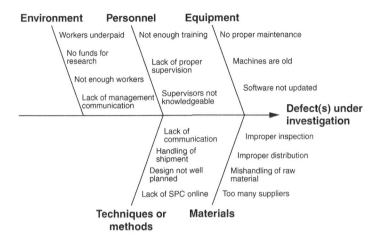

Figure 20.3   A completed cause-and-effect diagram.

manufacturing or nonmanufacturing, the causes of all problems usually fall into one or more of these categories.

Using a brainstorming session, the team brings up all possible causes under each category. For example, under the environment category, a cause could be management's attitude; perhaps top management is not willing to release any funds for research, not willing to change suppliers, not cooperating with middle management, or something similar. Under the personnel category, a cause could be lack of proper training for workers, supervisors who are not helpful in solving problems, lack of communication between workers and supervisors, and workers who are afraid of asking their supervisors questions, fearing repercussions in their jobs, promotions, or raises. Once all possible causes under each major category are listed in the cause-and-effect diagram, the next step is to isolate one or more common causes and then eliminate them. For example, a complete cause-and-effect diagram may appear as shown in Figure 20.3.

6. DEFECT CONCENTRATION DIAGRAM

A *defect concentration diagram* is a visual representation of the product under study that depicts all the defects. This diagram helps the workers determine whether there are any patterns or particular locations where the defects occur and what kinds of defects are occurring, minor or major. The patterns or particular locations may help the workers find the specific causes for such defects. It is important that the diagram show the product from different angles. For example, if the product is shaped as a rectangular prism and defects are found on the surface, the diagram should show all six faces to very clearly indicate the location of the defects. In Figure 20.4 the two diagonally opposite edges are damaged, which could have happened during transportation or when moving this item from the production area to the storage area.

The defect concentration diagram proved to be of great use when the daughter of one of the authors made a claim with a transportation company. In 2001 the

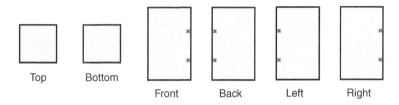

Figure 20.4   A damaged item shaped as a rectangular prism.

author shipped a car from Boston, Massachusetts, to his daughter in San Jose, California. After receiving the car, she found that the front bumper's paint was damaged. She filed a claim with the transportation company for the damage, but the company turned it down, simply stating that this damage was not caused by the company. A couple of days later, she found similar damage symmetrically opposite under the back bumper. She again called the company and explained that this damage had clearly been done by the belts used to hold the car in transport. This time the company could not turn down her claim since she could scientifically prove, using a defect concentration diagram, that the damage was caused by the transportation company.

7. RUN CHART

In any SPC procedure it is very important to detect any trends that may be present in the data. *Run charts* help identify such trends by plotting data over a certain period of time. For example, if the proportion of nonconforming parts produced from shift to shift is perceived to be a problem, we may plot the number of nonconforming parts against the shifts for a certain period of time to determine whether there are any trends. Trends usually help us identify the causes of nonconformities. This chart is particularly useful when the data from a production process are collected over a certain period of time.

A run chart for the data in Table 20.2 is shown in Figure 20.5, in which we have plotted the percentage of nonconforming units produced during different shifts over a period of 10 days, starting with the morning shift.

From this run chart we can easily see that the percentage of nonconforming units is the lowest during the morning shifts and the highest during the night shifts. There are some problems in the evening shifts, too, but they are not as severe as those in the night shifts. Since such trends or patterns are usually caused by special or assignable causes, the run chart will certainly prompt management to explore how the various shifts differ. Does the quality of the raw material differ from shift to shift? Are workers in the later shifts inadequately trained? Are evening- and late-shift workers more susceptible to fatigue? Are there environmental problems that increase in severity as the day wears on?

Deming (1982, 312) points out that sometimes the frequency distribution of a set of data does not give a true picture of the data, whereas a run chart can bring out the real problems in its display of the data. The frequency distribution gives us the overall picture of the data but does not show us any trends or patterns that may be present in the process on a short-term basis.

Table 20.2 Percentage of nonconforming units in 30 different shifts.

Shift number	1	2	3	4	5	6	7	8	9	10
Percent nonconforming	5	9	12	7	12	4	11	7	15	3
Shift number	11	12	13	14	15	16	17	18	19	20
Percent nonconforming	5	8	2	5	15	4	6	15	5	5
Shift number	21	22	23	24	25	26	27	28	29	30
Percent nonconforming	8	6	10	15	7	10	13	4	8	14

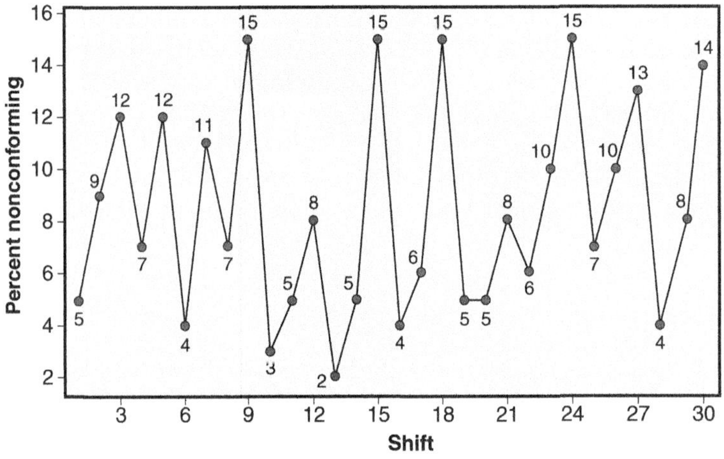

Figure 20.5 Run chart.

Control charts are perhaps the most important part of SPC. We first present some basic concepts of control charts and then study them in more detail in the following two sections.

8. CONTROL CHARTS

A *control chart* can be defined as:

1. A device for describing in concrete terms what a state of statistical control is.

2. A device for judging whether control has been attained and whether assignable causes are present.

3. A device for attaining a stable process.

Suppose that we take a sample of size n from a process at approximately regular intervals, and that for each sample we compute a sample statistic X. This

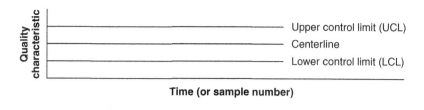

Figure 20.6 A pictorial representation of the components of a control chart.

statistic may be the sample mean, fraction of nonconforming product, or any other appropriate measure. Now, since X is a statistic, it is subject to some fluctuation or variation. If no special causes are present, the variation in X will have characteristics that can be described by some statistical distribution. By taking enough samples, we can estimate the desired characteristics of such a distribution. For instance, we now suppose that the statistic X is distributed as normal, and we divide the vertical scale of a graph in units of X and the horizontal scale in units of time or any other such characteristic. Then, we draw horizontal lines through the mean and the extreme values of X, called the *centerline* and the *upper* and *lower control limits*, respectively, which results in the tool known as a *control chart*. A typical control chart is shown in Figure 20.6.

The main goal of using the control charts is to reduce the variation in the process and bring the process target value to the desired level.

If we plot data pertaining to a process on a control chart, and if the data conform to a pattern of random variation that falls within the upper and lower limits, we say that the process is in *statistical control*. If, however, the data fall outside these control limits and/or do not conform to a pattern of random variation, the process is considered to be *out of control*. In the latter case, an investigation is launched to track down the special causes responsible for the process being out of control, and to correct them.

If any particular cause of variation is on the unfavorable side, an effort is made to eliminate it. If, however, the cause of variation is on the favorable side, an effort is made to detect such a cause and perpetuate it instead of eliminating it. In this manner, the process can eventually be brought into a state of statistical control.

Dr. Shewhart, the inventor of control charts, recommended very strongly that a process should not be judged to be in control unless the pattern of random variation has persisted for some time and for a sizable volume of output.

Note: If a control chart shows a process in statistical control, this does not mean that all special causes have been completely eliminated; rather, it simply means that for all practical purposes, it is reasonable to assume or adopt a hypothesis of common causes only.

Preparation for Use of Control Charts

For control charts to serve their intended purpose, it is important to take a few preparatory steps prior to their implementation:

1. *Establish an environment suitable for action.* Any statistical method will fail unless management has prepared a responsive environment.

2. *Define the process and determine the characteristics to be studied.* The process must be understood in terms of its relationship to the other operations/users and in terms of the process elements (for example, people, equipment, materials, methods, and environment) that affect it at each stage. Some of the techniques discussed earlier, such as the Pareto analysis or the fishbone chart, can help make these relationships visible. Once the process is well understood, the next step is to determine which characteristics affect the process, which characteristics should be studied in depth, and which characteristics should be controlled.

3. *Look for a correlation between characteristics.* For an efficient and effective study, take advantage of the relationships between characteristics. If several characteristics of an item tend to vary together, it may be sufficient to chart only one of them. If some characteristics are negatively correlated, a deeper study is required before any corrective action on such characteristics can be taken.

4. *Define the measurement system.* The characteristic must be operationally defined so that the findings can be communicated to all concerned in ways that have the same meaning today as they did yesterday. This includes specifying what information is to be gathered, where, how, and under what conditions. The operational definition is very important for collecting data since it can impact the control charts in many ways. Moreover, the analysis of data depends on how the data are collected. It is extremely important that the data contain the pertinent information and are valid (for example, appropriate sampling schemes are used) so that their analysis and the interpretation of the results is done appropriately. Moreover, one should always keep in mind that each measurement system has its own inherent variability. Thus, the accuracy of any measurement system is as important as the elimination of the special causes affecting the process.

5. *Minimize unnecessary variation.* Unnecessary external causes of variation should be reduced before the study begins. This includes overcontrolling the process or avoiding obvious problems that could and should be corrected even without the use of control charts.

6. *Meet the customer's needs.* This includes any subsequent processes that use the product or service as an input as well as the final end-item customer. For example, a computer manufacturing company is a customer of the semiconductor industry, a car manufacturing company is a customer of tire manufacturing companies, and in a paper mill the papermaking unit is a customer of the pulp-making unit.

Note that in all cases, a *process log* should be kept. It should include all relevant events (big or small), such as procedural changes, the use of new raw materials, or a change of operators. This will aid in subsequent problem analysis.

Benefits of Control Charts

Properly used, control charts can:

1. Be used by operators for ongoing control of a process

2. Help the process perform consistently and predictably

3. Allow the process to achieve higher quality, higher effective capacity (since there will be either no or fewer rejections), and hence lower cost per unit

4. Provide a common language for discussing process performance

5. Help distinguish special causes from common causes for variability and hence serve as a guide for management to take local action or action on the system

Rational Subgroups for a Control Chart

It is very important to note that the *rational subgroup* or *sample* used to prepare a control chart should represent subgroups of output that are as homogeneous as possible. In other words, the subgroups should be such that if special causes are present, they will show up in differences between the subgroups rather than in differences between the members of a subgroup. A natural subgroup, for example, would be the output of a given shift. It is not correct to take the product for an arbitrarily selected period of time as a subgroup, especially if it overlapped two or more shifts. This is because if a sample comes from two or more shifts, any difference between the shifts will be averaged out, and, consequently, the plotted point won't indicate the presence of any special cause due to shifts. As another example, if the process used six machines, it would be better to take a separate sample from the output of each machine than to have samples that consist of items from all six machines. This is because the difference between machines may be the special cause of variation. It will be hard to detect this special cause if the samples are not taken from individual machines. It is true to say that careful selection of a subgroup or sample is perhaps the most important item in setting up a control chart. The next question in the selection of a sample is to determine the sample size. Factors usually taken into consideration for determining the sample size and the frequency of the samples are the average run length and the operating characteristic curve, both of which we discuss here.

9. AVERAGE RUN LENGTH

A *run* is the number of successive items possessing the same characteristics. For example, the number of successive conforming or successive nonconforming items forms a run. An *average run length* (ARL) is the average number of points plotted, that is, the number of subgroups inspected, before a point falls outside the control limits, indicating that the process is out of control.

In Shewhart control charts the ARL can be determined by using the formula

$$ARL = \frac{1}{p} \qquad (20.1)$$

where p is the probability that any point falls outside the control limits. It is quite common to use the ARL as a benchmark to check the performance of a control chart.

As an illustration, consider a process quality characteristic that is normally distributed. Then, for an $\bar{X}$ control chart with 3-sigma control limits, the probability that a point will fall outside the control limits when the process is stable is $p = 0.0027$, which is the probability that a normal random variable deviates from the mean μ by at least 3σ. Thus, the ARL for the $\bar{X}$ control chart when the process is stable is

$$ARL_0 = \frac{1}{0.0027} = 370$$

In other words, when the process is stable, we should expect that, on average, an out-of-control signal or false alarm will occur once in every 370 samples. The ARL can also be used to determine how often a false alarm will occur by simply multiplying the ARL_0 by the time t between the samples. For example, if samples are taken every 30 minutes, a false alarm will occur, on average, once every 185 hours. On the other hand, the ARL can be used in the same manner to find how long it will take before a given shift in the process mean is detected. We illustrate this concept with Example 20.2 using an $\bar{X}$ control chart.

In practice, the decision of how large the samples should be and how frequently they should be taken is based on the cost of taking samples and how quickly we would like to detect the shift. Large samples taken more frequently would certainly give better protection against shifts, since it will take less time to detect any given shift. For instance, in Example 20.2, if the samples are taken every half hour instead of every hour, it will take only one hour (instead of taking two hours) to detect the shift of 1.5σ. Similarly, it can easily be shown that if larger samples are taken, the shifts can be detected more quickly. This means that if the large samples are taken more frequently, shifts in the process mean will be detected faster, and the process will produce fewer nonconforming units. Thus, when calculating the cost of taking samples, one must take into account how much money will be saved by detecting the shift more quickly and consequently producing fewer nonconforming units.

10. OPERATING CHARACTERISTIC CURVE

The *operating characteristic curve* (OC curve) is a graph characterizing the relationship between the probabilities of type II error (β) and the process shifts.

A set of OC curves for the $\bar{X}$ chart with 3-sigma limits, for different sample sizes n, is shown in Figure 20.7. The scale on the horizontal axis is in process standard deviation σ.

By carefully observing the OC curves in Figure 20.7, we see that

1. For a given sample size n and σ, where σ is the probability of a point exceeding the control limits when the process is stable, a larger shift corresponds to a smaller probability, β.

EXAMPLE 20.2

Suppose a process quality characteristic that is normally distributed is plotted in a Shewhart $\bar{X}$ control chart with 3-sigma control limits. Suppose that the process mean μ_0 experiences an upward shift of 1.5σ. Determine how long, on average, it will take to detect this shift if samples of size 4 are taken every hour.

Solution

Since the process mean has experienced an upward shift of 1.5σ, the new process mean will be $\mu_0 + 1.5\sigma$. Furthermore, since the sample size is 4, the upper control limit in this case is also

$$\mu_0 + 3\sigma_{\bar{x}} = \mu_0 + 3\frac{\sigma}{\sqrt{4}} = \mu_0 + 1.5\sigma$$

In other words, the centerline of the control chart will coincide with the upper control limit. Thus, the probability p that a point will fall beyond the control limits is

$$p = P(z \leq -6) + P(z \geq 0)$$
$$\cong 0.00000 + 0.5 = 0.5$$

Therefore, the ARL is given by

$$\text{ARL} = \frac{1}{0.5} = 2$$

In other words, it will take on average two hours to detect a shift of 1.5σ in the process mean.

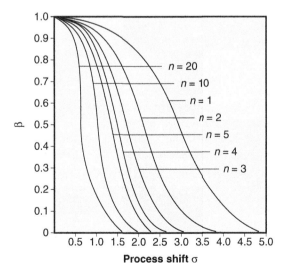

Figure 20.7   OC curves for the $\bar{X}$ chart with 3-sigma limits, for different sample sizes n.

2. With a larger sample size, there is a smaller probability (β) for a given process shift.

For a detailed discussion of the construction of an OC curve, refer to Gupta and Walker (2007a).

As mentioned earlier, OC curves are very helpful in determining the sample size needed to detect a shift of size $d\sigma$ with a given probability $(1 - \beta)$. For example, if we are interested in determining the sample size required to detect a shift of 1 sigma with probability 95%, then from Figure 20.7, with $d = 1$ and $\beta = 0.05$, we find the size n will be slightly higher than 20.

11. COMMON CAUSES VERSUS SPECIAL CAUSES

The quality of the final product depends on how well a process is designed and executed. However, no matter how perfectly a process is designed and how well it is executed, no two items produced by the process are identical. The difference between two items is called the *variation*. Such variation occurs due to two causes:

1. Common causes, or random causes

2. Special causes, or assignable causes

To better understand these causes, it is important to understand a process and to have a concrete plan for future actions that would be needed to improve the process.

Process Evaluation

Process evaluation includes the study of not only the final product but also all the *intermediate steps* or *outputs* that describe the actual operating state of the process. For example, in the paper production process, wood chips and pulp may be considered as intermediate outputs. If the data on process evaluation are collected, analyzed, and interpreted correctly, they can show where and when a corrective action is necessary to make the whole process work more efficiently.

Action on Process

Action on process is very important for any process, since it prevents the production of an out-of-specification product. An action on process may include changes in raw material, operator training, change of some equipment, change of design, or other measures. Effects of such actions on a process should be monitored closely and further action should be taken if necessary.

Action on Output

If the process evaluation does not indicate that any action on the process is necessary, the first action on the process is to ship the final product to its destination. Note that some people believe action on output consists of sampling plans and discarding out-of-specification product that has already been produced. Obviously, such action on the output is futile and expensive. We are interested in correcting the output before it is produced. This goal can be achieved through the use of control charts.

Variation

No process can produce two products that are exactly alike or that possess the same exact characteristics. Any process is bound to contain some sources of variation. A difference between two products may be very large, moderate, very small, or even undetectable depending on the source of variation, but certainly there is always some difference. For example, the moisture content in any two rolls of paper, the opacity in any two spools of paper, and the brightness of any two lots of pulp will always vary. Our aim is to trace back as far as possible the sources of such variation and eliminate them. The first step is to separate the common and special causes of such sources of variation.

Common Causes, or Random Causes

Common causes, or *random causes,* refer to the various sources of variation within a process that is in statistical control. They behave like a constant system of chance causes. While individual measured values may all be different, as a group they tend to form a pattern that can be explained by a statistical distribution that is generally characterized by:

1. Location parameter

2. Dispersion parameter

3. Shape (the pattern of variation—symmetrical, right-skewed, or left-skewed)

Special Causes, or Assignable Causes

Special causes, or *assignable causes,* refer to any source of variation that cannot be adequately explained by any single distribution of the process output, as otherwise would be the case if the process were in statistical control. Unless all the special causes of variation are identified and corrected, they will continue to affect the process output in an unpredictable way. *Any process with assignable causes is considered unstable and hence not in statistical control.* However, any process free of assignable causes is considered stable and therefore in statistical control. Assignable causes can be corrected by local actions, while common causes, or random causes, can be corrected only by actions on the system.

Local Actions and Actions on the System. The following are characteristics of local actions:

1. Are usually required to eliminate special causes of variation.

2. Can usually be taken by people close to the process.

3. Can correct about 15% of process problems.

4. Deming (1982) believed that as much as 6% of all system variations are due to special, or assignable, causes, while no more than 94% of the variations are due to common causes.

The following are characteristics of actions on the system:

1. Are usually required to reduce the variation due to common causes

2. Almost always require management's action for correction

3. Are needed to correct about 85% of process problems

Deming (1951) pointed out that there is an important relationship between the two types of variation and the two types of actions needed to reduce such variation. In the following we discuss this point in more detail.

Special causes of variation can be detected by simple statistical techniques. These causes of variation are not the same in all the operations involved. The detection of special causes of variation and their removal is usually the responsibility of someone who is directly connected with the operation, although management is sometimes in a little better position to correct them. The resolution of a special cause of variation usually requires local action.

The extent of common causes of variation can be indicated by simple statistical techniques, but the causes themselves need more exploration in order to be isolated. It is usually the responsibility of management to correct the common causes of variation, although other personnel directly involved with the operation are sometimes in a better position to identify such causes and pass them on to management for appropriate action. Overall, the resolution of common causes of variation usually requires action on the system.

We should note that about 15% (or according to Deming, 6%) of industrial process troubles are correctable by the local action taken by people directly involved with the operation, while 85% are correctable only by management's action on the system. Confusion about the type of action required is very costly to the organization in terms of wasted efforts, delayed resolution of trouble, and other aggravating problems. It would be totally wrong, for example, to take local action (for example, changing an operator or calibrating a machine) when, in fact, management action on the system is required (for example, selecting a supplier that can provide better and consistent raw material).

12. CONTROL LIMITS VERSUS SPECIFICATION LIMITS

It is common that confusion about specification limits and control limits exists in the minds of floor workers, technicians, inspectors, engineers, and managers. *However, we must make it clear that specification limits and control limits are two entirely different concepts and that there is no relationship between them.* Moreover, there is no analytical relationship between control limits and specification limits.

Control limits are defined by the process variability, which is usually determined by the process standard deviation, σ. Specification limits, however, are set by the manufacturing team, management, or the customer. *The most important point worth noting is that specification limits are used to evaluate the individual values, whereas control limits are used to evaluate the sample values.*

13. CONTROL CHARTS FOR VARIABLES

In this section we study various control charts for variables.

Shewhart $\bar{X}$ and R Control Chart

Certain rules are widely used in preparing Shewhart $\bar{X}$ and R control charts:

1. Take a series of samples from the process under investigation. Samples consisting of four or five items taken frequently are usually good, for the following reasons:

    a. Rational subgroups or samples of size 4 or 5 are more cost-effective.

    b. If samples are larger than 10, the estimate of process standard deviation obtained using the range is not very efficient. Moreover, the R chart is also not very effective.

    c. With samples of size 4 or 5, there are fewer chances for occurrence of any special causes during the collection of a sample. It is commonly known that if the type of variation is changing (special cause versus common cause variation), the sample size should be as small as possible so that the averages of samples do not mask the changes.

2. Enough samples should be collected so that the major source of variation has an opportunity to occur. Generally, at least 25 samples of size 4 or 5 are considered sufficient to give a good test for process stability.

3. During the collection of data, a complete log of any changes in the process—such as changes in raw materials, operators, or tools, or any calibration of tools or machines—must be maintained. Keeping a log is important for finding the special causes in a process (Duncan 1986).

Calculation of Sample Statistics

The sample statistics that need to be determined initially to prepare the Shewhart $\bar{X}$ and R control chart are the sample mean ($\bar{x}$) and the sample range (R). See Example 20.3. For example, let $x_1, x_2, \ldots, x_n$ be a random sample from the process under investigation. Then, we have

$$\bar{x} = \frac{x_1 + x_2 + \ldots + x_n}{n} \tag{20.2}$$

$$R = \text{Max}(x_i) - \text{Min}(x_i) \tag{20.3}$$

Calculation of Control Limits

Step 1: First calculate $\bar{x}_i$ and R_i for the ith sample, for $i = 1, 2, 3, \ldots, m$, where m is the number of samples collected during the study period.

EXAMPLE 20.3

Let 5, 6, 9, 7, 8, 6, 9, 7, 6, and 5 be a random sample from a process under investigation. Find the sample mean and the sample range.

Solution

Using the data, we have

$$\bar{x} = \frac{5+6+9+7+8+6+9+7+6+5}{10} = 6.8$$

$$R = \text{Max}(x_i) - \text{Min}(x_i) = 9 - 5 = 4$$

Step 2: Calculate

$$\bar{R} = \frac{R_1 + R_2 + \ldots + R_m}{m} \tag{20.4}$$

$$\bar{\bar{x}} = \frac{\bar{x}_1 + \bar{x}_2 + \ldots + \bar{x}_m}{m} \tag{20.5}$$

Step 3: Calculate the 3-sigma control limits for the $\bar{X}$ control chart:

$$\text{UCL} = \bar{\bar{x}} + 3\hat{\sigma}_{\bar{x}} \tag{20.6}$$

$$= \bar{\bar{x}} + 3\frac{\hat{\sigma}}{\sqrt{n}}$$

$$= \bar{\bar{x}} + 3\frac{\bar{R}}{d_2\sqrt{n}}$$

$$= \bar{\bar{x}} + A_2\bar{R}$$

$$\text{CL} = \bar{\bar{x}} \tag{20.7}$$

$$\text{LCL} = \bar{\bar{x}} = 3\hat{\sigma}_{\bar{x}} \tag{20.8}$$

$$= \bar{\bar{x}} - 3\frac{\hat{\sigma}}{\sqrt{n}}$$

$$= \bar{\bar{x}} - 3\frac{\bar{R}}{d_2\sqrt{n}}$$

$$= \bar{\bar{x}} - A_2\bar{R}$$

where the values of A_2 and d_2 for various sample sizes are given in Appendix E.

Note: Instead of calculating 3-sigma limits (common in the United States), we can calculate the probability limits (common in Europe) at the desired level of significance α simply by replacing 3 with $z_{\alpha/2}$ in equations (20.6) and (20.8). Thus, the control limits will be

$$UCL = \bar{\bar{x}} + z_{a/2}\frac{\hat{\sigma}}{\sqrt{n}} \qquad (20.9)$$

$$= \bar{\bar{x}} + z_{a/2}\frac{\bar{R}}{d_2\sqrt{n}}$$

$$LCL = \bar{\bar{x}} - z_{a/2}\frac{\hat{\sigma}}{\sqrt{n}} \qquad (20.10)$$

$$= \bar{\bar{x}} - z_{a/2}\frac{\bar{R}}{d_2\sqrt{n}}$$

Step 4: Calculate the control limits for the R control chart:

$$UCL = \bar{R} + 3\hat{\sigma}_R \qquad (20.11)$$

$$= \bar{R} + 3d_3\frac{\bar{R}}{d_2}$$

$$= \left(1 + 3\frac{d_3}{d_2}\right)\bar{R}$$

$$= D_4\bar{R}$$

$$CL = \bar{R} \qquad (20.12)$$

$$LCL = \bar{R} - 3\hat{\sigma}_R \qquad (20.13)$$

$$= \bar{R} - 3d_3\frac{\bar{R}}{d_2}$$

$$= \left(1 - 3\frac{d_3}{d_2}\right)\bar{R}$$

$$= D_3\bar{R}$$

where the values of D_3 and D_4 for various sample sizes are given in Appendix E.

The first implementation of control charts is referred to as *phase I*. In phase I it is important that we calculate the preliminary control limits. We do this to find the extent of variation in sample means and sample ranges if the process is stable. In other words, at this point only common causes would be affecting the process. If all the plotted points fall within the control limits and there is no evidence of any pattern, the control limits are suitable for the current or a future process. However, if some points exceed the control limits, then such points are ignored and every effort is made to eliminate any evident special causes that may be present in the process. Then, fresh control limits are calculated by using the remaining data, and the whole process is repeated. Remember that ignoring the points that exceed the control limits without eliminating the special causes may result in unnecessarily narrow control limits, which may cause different kinds of headaches such as the points falling beyond the control limits when, in fact, they should not be. Furthermore, it is highly recommended that for preliminary control limits, we use at least 25 samples of size 4 or 5. Otherwise, the control limits may not be suitable for the current or a future process. See Example 20.4.

A process is considered out of control not only when the points exceed the control limits but also when the points show some pattern of nonrandomness. The *Statistical Quality Control Handbook* gives a set of decision rules for determining nonrandom patterns on control charts (Western Electric 1956). In particular, it suggests the patterns are nonrandom if:

1. Two out of three successive points exceed the 2σ warning limits.

2. Four out of five successive points fall at a distance of σ or farther from the centerline.

3. Eight successive points fall on one side of the centerline.

4. Seven successive points run either upward or downward.

Interpretation of Shewhart $\bar{X}$ and R Control Charts

We should investigate any out-of-control points—that is, points on or beyond the 3σ control limits—or any patterns of nonrandomness on the R chart before interpreting the $\bar{X}$ chart. As discussed earlier, the reason for doing this is simple: it is not possible to bring the average under control without first bringing the variability under control. Normally, the $\bar{X}$ chart is placed above the R chart, and they are aligned with each other such that the average and the range for any sample are plotted on the same vertical line. Examine whether one chart, both charts, or neither chart indicates the process is out of control for any given sample. If any point exceeds the control limits on one or both charts, the sample did not come from a stable process. In other words, there are some special, or assignable, causes present in the system. More precisely, if the plotted point exceeds the control limits on the R chart, then it is evident that the variability of the process has changed. In such cases, before a full-blown investigation is launched, some preliminary checks should be made. For example:

1. Check that all the calculations are correct and that the data are entered into the computer correctly

2. Check whether there has been a change in workers, machines, or suppliers of raw material

If the points exceed the control limits in the $\bar{X}$ chart, the process mean has changed. Again, follow the preliminary checks before a full-blown investigation is launched.

If points exceed the limits in both the $\bar{X}$ chart and the R chart, this usually indicates that a sudden shift occurred in the lot from which the samples were

EXAMPLE 20.4

Table 20.3 provides data on the diameter measurements of ball bearings used in the wheels of heavy construction equipment. Twenty-five samples, each of size 4, are taken directly from the production line. Samples come from all three shifts, and no sample

Table 20.3   Diameter measurements (mm) of ball bearings used in the wheels of heavy construction equipment.

Sample	Observations				$\bar{x}_i$	R_i
1	15.155	15.195	15.145	15.125	15.155	0.070
2	15.095	15.162	15.168	15.163	15.147	0.073
3	15.115	15.126	15.176	15.183	15.150	0.068
4	15.122	15.135	15.148	15.155	15.140	0.033
5	15.148	15.152	15.192	15.148	15.160	0.044
6	15.169	15.159	15.173	15.175	15.169	0.016
7	15.163	15.147	15.137	15.145	15.148	0.026
8	15.150	15.164	15.156	15.170	15.160	0.020
9	15.148	15.162	15.163	15.147	15.155	0.016
10	15.152	15.138	15.167	15.155	15.153	0.029
11	15.147	15.158	15.175	15.160	15.160	0.028
12	15.158	15.172	15.142	15.120	15.148	0.052
13	15.133	15.177	15.145	15.165	15.155	0.044
14	15.148	15.174	15.155	15.175	15.155	0.027
15	15.143	15.137	15.164	15.156	15.150	0.027
16	15.142	15.150	15.168	15.152	15.153	0.026
17	15.132	15.168	15.154	15.146	15.150	0.036
18	15.172	15.188	15.178	15.194	15.183	0.022
19	15.174	15.166	15.186	15.194	15.180	0.028
20	15.166	15.178	15.192	15.184	15.180	0.026
21	15.172	15.187	15.193	15.180	15.183	0.021
22	15.182	15.198	15.185	15.195	15.190	0.016
23	15.170	15.150	15.192	15.180	15.173	0.042
24	15.186	15.194	15.175	15.185	15.185	0.019
25	15.178	15.192	15.168	15.182	15.180	0.024
					$\bar{\bar{x}} = 15.1628$	$\bar{R} = 0.03479$

Continued

contains data from two or more shifts. Use these data to construct an $\bar{X}$ and R chart and to verify that the process is stable.

Solution

From Appendix E, for a sample of size $n = 4$, we have $D_3 = 0$ and $D_4 = 2.282$. Thus, the control limits for the R chart are

$$LCL = D_3\bar{R} = 0 \times 0.03479 = 0$$

$$UCL = D_4\bar{R} = 2.282 \times 0.03479 = 0.07936$$

It is customary to prepare the R chart first and verify that all the plotted points fall within the control limits, and only then proceed to construct the $\bar{X}$ chart. In fact, the concept of first bringing the process variability under control and then proceeding to control the average does make a lot of sense. This is because it is almost impossible to bring the process average under control without controlling the process variability.

The R chart for the data is given in Figure 20.8, which shows that all the plotted points fall within the control limits and that there is no evidence of any special pattern. Thus, we may conclude that the only variation present in the process is due to common causes. In this case we can proceed further to calculate the control limits for the $\bar{X}$ chart. From Appendix E, for a sample of size $n = 4$, we get $A_2 = 0.729$. Hence, we have

$$LCL = \bar{\bar{x}} - A_2\bar{R} = 15.1628 - 0.729 \times 0.03479 = 15.13749$$

$$UCL = \bar{\bar{x}} + A_2\bar{R} = 15.1628 + 0.729 \times 0.03479 = 15.18814$$

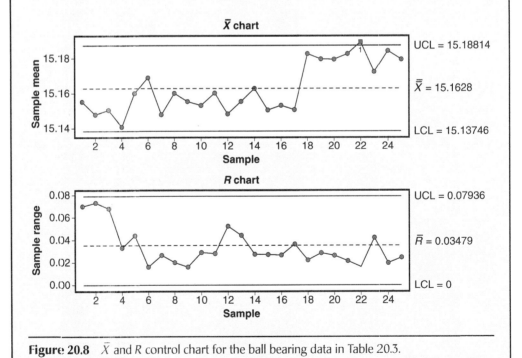

Figure 20.8 $\bar{X}$ and R control chart for the ball bearing data in Table 20.3.

Continued

> The $\bar{X}$ chart for the data is given in Figure 20.8, which shows that point 22 exceeds the upper control limits. Moreover, too many consecutive points fall below the centerline. This indicates that the process is not under control and that some special causes are present that are affecting the process average. Thus, a thorough investigation should be launched to find the special causes, and appropriate action should be taken to eliminate them before we proceed to recalculate the control limits for an ongoing process.

taken. In such cases, after the preliminary checks, there should be a full investigation concentrating on the period during which that lot was produced. Depending on the process, the possibility of stopping production until the special causes are detected should be considered.

In addition to points exceeding the control limits, nonrandom patterns—such as a run of seven points moving upward or downward, or a run of eight successive points falling above or below the centerline—should be checked.

An upward run or a run above the centerline in an R chart indicates:

1. A greater variability or a tendency of perpetuating a greater variability in the output of the process is occurring. This may be due to new material of undesirable low quality or a difference between the shifts. Immediate attention to detect special causes is warranted.

2. The measurement system has changed.

A downward run or a run below the centerline in an R chart indicates:

1. A smaller variability or a tendency of perpetuating a smaller variability in the output of the process is occurring. This is usually a good sign for the process. A thorough investigation should be made so that similar conditions are maintained as long as possible. Similar conditions should be implemented in the process elsewhere.

2. The measurement system has changed.

A run relative to the $\bar{X}$ chart indicates:

1. The process average has changed or is still changing.

2. The measurement system has changed.

Shewhart $\bar{X}$ and R Control Chart When Process Mean μ and Process Standard Deviation σ Are Known

Step 1: Calculate $\bar{x}_i$ and R_i for the ith sample for $i = 1, 2, 3, \ldots, m$, where m is the number of samples collected during the study period.

Step 2: Calculate the control limits for the $\bar{X}$ control chart

$$UCL = \mu + 3\frac{\sigma}{\sqrt{n}} \qquad (20.14)$$

$$CL = \mu \qquad (20.15)$$

$$LCL = \mu - 3\frac{\sigma}{\sqrt{n}} \qquad (20.16)$$

Note: Instead of calculating 3-sigma limits, we can calculate the probability limits at the desired level of significance α simply by replacing 3 with $z_{\alpha/2}$ in equations (20.14) and (20.16).

Step 3: Calculate the control limits for the R control chart

Recalling that $\sigma = R/d_2$ and $\sigma_R = d_3\sigma$, we have

$$UCL = d_2\sigma + 3\sigma_R \qquad (20.17)$$
$$= d_2\sigma + 3d_3\sigma$$
$$= (d_2 + 3d_3)\sigma$$
$$= D_2\sigma$$

$$CL = \sigma \qquad (20.18)$$

$$LCL = d_2\sigma - 3\sigma_R \qquad (20.19)$$
$$= d_2\sigma - 3d_3\sigma$$
$$= (d_2 - 3d_3)\sigma$$
$$= D_1\sigma$$

where the values of D_1 and D_2 for various sample sizes are given in Appendix E.

Shewhart $\bar{X}$ and S Control Chart

The $\bar{X}$ and S control charts, like the $\bar{X}$ and R control charts, are developed from a measured process's output data, and both the $\bar{X}$ chart and the S chart are used together. The standard deviation s is usually a more efficient indicator of process variability than the range, particularly when the sample sizes are large (10 or greater). The sample standard deviation s for the S chart is calculated using all the data points rather than just the maximum and minimum values in a data set, as is done for the R chart. S *charts are usually preferred over R charts in the following situations*:

- Samples are of size 10 or larger
- Sample size is variable
- The process is automated, so the s for each sample can be calculated easily

The sample standard deviation s is determined using the formula

$$s = \sqrt{\frac{1}{n-1}\left(\sum_{i=1}^{n}x_i^2 - \frac{1}{n}\left(\sum_{i=1}^{n}x_i\right)^2\right)} \qquad (20.20)$$

Then, the control limits for the $\bar{X}$ and S control charts are determined, as shown in the following section.

Calculation of Control Limits

Step 1: First, calculate $\bar{x}_i$ and s_i for the ith sample, for $i = 1, 2, 3, \ldots, m$, where m is the number of samples collected during the study period.

Step 2: Calculate

$$\bar{s} = \frac{s_1 + s_2 + \ldots + s_m}{m} \tag{20.21}$$

$$\bar{\bar{x}} = \frac{\bar{x}_1 + \bar{x}_2 + \ldots + \bar{x}_m}{m} \tag{20.22}$$

Step 3: Calculate the control limits for the $\bar{X}$ chart:

$$UCL = \bar{\bar{x}} + 3\frac{\hat{\sigma}}{\sqrt{n}} \tag{20.23}$$

$$= \bar{\bar{x}} + 3\frac{\bar{s}}{c_4\sqrt{n}}$$

$$= \bar{\bar{x}} + A_3\bar{s}$$

$$CL = \bar{\bar{x}} \tag{20.24}$$

$$LCL = \bar{\bar{x}} - 3\frac{\hat{\sigma}}{\sqrt{n}} \tag{20.25}$$

$$= \bar{\bar{x}} - 3\frac{\bar{s}}{c_4\sqrt{n}}$$

$$= \bar{\bar{x}} - A_3\bar{s}$$

where the values of A_3 and c_4 for various sample sizes are given in Appendix E.

Step 4: Calculate the control limits for the S chart:

$$UCL = \bar{s} + 3\hat{\sigma}_s \tag{20.26}$$

$$= \bar{s} + 3\frac{\bar{s}}{c_4}\sqrt{1 - c_4^2}$$

$$= \left(1 + 3\frac{1}{c_4}\sqrt{1 - c_4^2}\right)\bar{s}$$

$$= B_4\bar{s}$$

$$CL = \bar{s} \tag{20.27}$$

$$\text{LCL} = \bar{s} - 3\hat{\sigma}_s \qquad\qquad (20.28)$$

$$= \bar{s} - 3\frac{\bar{s}}{c_4}\sqrt{1 - c_4^2}$$

$$= \left(1 - 3\frac{1}{c_4}\sqrt{1 - c_4^2}\right)\bar{s}$$

$$= B_3\bar{s}$$

We illustrate the development of the $\bar{X}$ and S control charts with Example 20.5.

EXAMPLE 20.5

Use the ball bearing data in Table 20.3 to construct the $\bar{X}$ and S control charts.

Solution

From Appendix E, for a sample of size $n = 4$, we have $B_3 = 0$ and $B_4 = 2.266$. Hence, the control limits for the S control chart are

$$\text{LCL} = B_3\bar{s} = 0 \times 0.01557 = 0$$

$$\text{UCL} = B_4\bar{s} = 2.266 \times 0.01557 = 0.03527$$

It is customary to prepare the S control chart first and verify that all the plotted points fall within the control limits, and only then would we proceed to construct the $\bar{X}$ control chart. As described earlier, the concept of first bringing the process variability under control and then proceeding to control the average does make a lot of sense, since without controlling the process variability, it is practically impossible to bring the process average under control.

The S chart for the data is given in Figure 20.9, which shows that points 2 and 3 almost coincide with the upper control limit. Moreover, point 17 is almost on the centerline. If this point were clearly below the centerline, we would have had a run of nine points below the centerline. These observations indicate that the process variability is marginally under control and, therefore, the process should be carefully monitored. Since the process variability is under control, even though marginally, we can proceed further to calculate the control limits for the $\bar{X}$ chart. From Appendix E, for a sample of size $n = 4$, we get $A_3 = 1.628$. Hence, we have

$$\text{LCL} = \bar{\bar{x}} - A_3\bar{s} = 15.1628 - 1.628 \times 0.01557 = 15.13746$$

$$\text{UCL} = \bar{\bar{x}} + A_3\bar{s} = 15.1628 + 1.628 \times 0.01557 = 15.18814$$

The $\bar{X}$ chart for the data in Table 20.3 is given in Figure 20.9, which shows that point 22 exceeds the upper control limits. Moreover, too many consecutive points fall below the centerline. This indicates that the process is not under control and that some special causes are present that are affecting the process average. Thus, a thorough investigation should be launched to find the special causes, and appropriate action should be taken to eliminate them before we proceed to recalculate the control limits for an ongoing process.

Continued

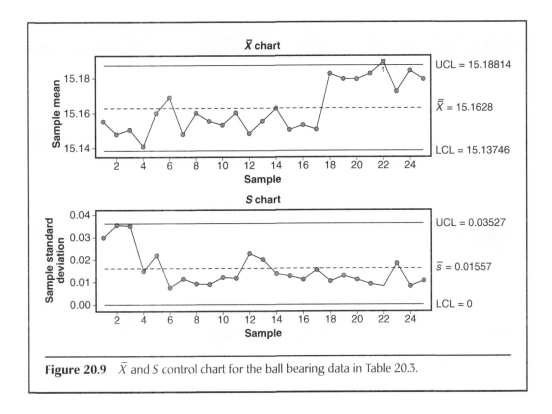

Figure 20.9 $\bar{X}$ and S control chart for the ball bearing data in Table 20.3.

14. CONTROL CHARTS FOR ATTRIBUTES

As noted earlier in this chapter, quality characteristics are usually of two types, called *variables* and *attributes*. In the previous section we studied control charts for variables for detecting large shifts. However, not all quality characteristics can be measured numerically. For example, we may be interested in finding whether new car paint meets specifications in terms of shine, uniformity, and scratches. Clearly, in this example we cannot quantify the shine, blemishes, and scratches. In other words, we cannot measure the shine, uniformity, or scratches numerically; consequently, to study the quality of paint on new cars, we cannot use control charts for variables. This type of situation can arise when a quality characteristic is measurable, but because of cost, time, or both we do not want to take the measurements. We may prefer to use a more economical method such as a go/no-go gauge. Therefore, it is important that we study control charts that are appropriate for quality characteristics that cannot be measured numerically. Such control charts are called *control charts for attributes*. In this section we study various control charts for attributes for detecting large shifts, which usually occur in phase I implementation of SPC.

When a quality characteristic cannot be measured numerically, we classify such product as defective or non-defective; in SPC it has become more common to use the terminology *conforming* or *nonconforming*. In this section, we shall continue use of the terminology *conforming* or *nonconforming*. A quality characteristic that classifies any product as conforming or nonconforming is called an *attribute*.

For instance, quality characteristics such as the determination that a soft drink can is not leaking, a stud has regular edges, a rod fits into a slot, a 100-watt light-bulb meets the desired standard, or a steel rivet meets the manufacturer's quality specifications are examples of attributes. Note that the data collected on a quality characteristic, which is an attribute, are simply count data. *Moreover, the sample sizes when using control charts for attributes are normally much larger (usually in the hundreds) than a sample of size 4 or 5, which we usually use in control charts for variables.*

In general, variables control charts are more informative and very effective in detecting a defect even before it occurs, whereas attribute charts are used only after the defects have occurred. There are cases, however, when variables control charts have limitations. For example, consider a product that is nonconforming due to any one of 10 quality characteristics that do not conform to specifications. Clearly, we cannot control all 10 quality characteristics by using one variables control chart, since one variables control chart can control only one quality characteristic at a time. Thus, in this case, to control all 10 quality characteristics, we will have to use 10 different variables control charts. *On the other hand, one attribute control chart can study all the quality characteristics because a nonconforming unit is nonconforming irrespective of the number of quality characteristics that do not conform to specifications.* Hence, we can conclude that both variables and attribute control charts have pros and cons.

In some cases the quality characteristic is such that instead of classifying a unit as conforming or nonconforming, it records the number of nonconformities per manufactured unit, for example, the number of holes in a roll of paper, the number of irregularities per unit area of a spool of cloth, the number of blemishes on a painted surface, the number of loose ends in a circuit board, the number of nonconformities per unit length of a cable, the number of nonconformities of all types in an assembled unit, and so on. In such cases we use control charts that fall under the category of control charts for attributes. These control charts are used to reduce the number of nonconformities per unit length, area, or volume of a single manufactured unit, or to reduce the number of nonconformities per manufactured or assembled unit.

The control charts for attributes are quite similar to the control charts for variables, that is, the centerline and the control limits of both charts are set in the same manner. However, it is important to note that the reasons for using control charts for variables and control charts for attributes are quite distinct. *As noted earlier, the purpose of using control charts for variables in any process is to reduce the variability due to special, or assignable, causes, whereas the control charts for attributes are used to reduce the number of nonconforming units, the number of nonconformities per manufactured or assembled unit, or simply the number of nonconformities per unit length, area, or volume of a single manufactured unit.*

In this section we will study four types of control charts for attributes: the *p* chart, *np* chart, *c* chart, and *u* chart. In Table 20.4 we give a very brief description of these charts, which can help determine the appropriate type of control chart that should be used for the quality characteristic under investigation.

The *p* Chart: Control Chart for Fraction of Nonconforming Units

The most frequently used attribute control chart is the *p* chart. It is used whenever we are interested in finding the fraction or percentage of units that do not conform

Table 20.4   Control charts for attributes.

Control chart	Quality characteristic under investigation
p chart	Percent or fraction of nonconforming units in a subgroup or a sample, where sample size can be variable
np chart	Number of nonconforming units in a sample
c chart	Number of nonconformities in a sample or in one or more inspection units
u chart	Number of nonconformities per unit, where sample size can be variable

to the specifications in a situation where the observed quality characteristic is an attribute or a variable measured by a go/no-go gauge. A p chart can be used to study one or more quality characteristics simultaneously. Since each inspected unit is classified as conforming or nonconforming and it is assumed that the conformity or nonconformity of each unit is defined independently, which is true only if the process is stable, the probability of occurrence of a nonconforming unit at any given time is the same. Then the basic rules of the p chart are governed by the binomial probability distribution with parameters n and p, where n is the sample size and p is the fraction of nonconforming units produced by the process under investigation.

The binomial probability distribution function of a random variable X with parameters n and p is defined by

$$P(X = x) = \binom{n}{x} p^x (1-p)^{n-x} \qquad x = 0, 1, \ldots, n \tag{20.29}$$

The mean and the standard deviation of the random variable X are given by np and

$$\sqrt{np(1-p)}$$

respectively. For more details on the binomial distribution, please refer to Gupta and Walker (2007a).

Control Limits for the p Chart

To develop a p control chart, proceed as follows:

1. From the process under investigation, select m ($m \geq 25$) samples of size n ($n \geq 50$) units. Note, however, if we have some prior information or any clue that the process is producing a very small fraction of nonconforming units, the sample size should be large enough that the probability that it contains some nonconforming units is relatively high.

2. Find the number of nonconforming units in each sample.

3. Find for each sample the fraction p_i of nonconforming units, that is

$$p_i = \frac{x}{n} \tag{20.30}$$

where x is the number of nonconforming units in the ith (i = 1, 2, ..., m) sample.

4. Find the average nonconforming $\bar{p}$ over the m samples, that is,

$$\bar{p} = \frac{p_1 + p_2 + \ldots + p_m}{m} \tag{20.31}$$

The value of $\bar{p}$ determines the centerline for the p chart and is an estimate of p, the process fraction of nonconforming units.

5. Using the well-known result that the binomial distribution with parameters n and p for large n can be approximated by the normal distribution with mean np and variance $np(1 - p)$, it can easily be seen that $\bar{p}$ will be approximately normally distributed with mean p and standard deviation

$$\sqrt{\frac{p(1-p)}{n}}$$

Hence, the upper and lower 3σ control limits and the centerline for the p chart are as shown in the following equations:

$$UCL = \bar{p} + 3\sqrt{\frac{\bar{p}(1-\bar{p})}{n}} \tag{20.32}$$

$$CL = \bar{p} \tag{20.33}$$

$$LCL = \bar{p} - 3\sqrt{\frac{\bar{p}(1-\bar{p})}{n}} \tag{20.34}$$

Note that in equations (20.32) and (20.34)

$$\sqrt{\frac{\bar{p}(1-\bar{p})}{n}}$$

is an estimator of

$$\sqrt{\frac{p(1-p)}{n}}$$

the standard deviation of $\bar{p}$. Furthermore, note that if the control charts are being implemented for the first time, the control limits given by equations (20.32)–(20.34) should be treated as the trial limits. In other words, before using these control limits any further, the points corresponding to all the samples used to determine these limits should be plotted and verified. Additionally, it should be established that all of the points fall within these control limits and that no pattern is evident. If any sample points exceed the control limits, or if there is any pattern, the possible special causes should be detected and eliminated before recalculating the control limits for future use. When recalculating the control limits, points that exceeded the trial control limits should be ignored, provided any special causes related to such points have been detected and eliminated.

Note: Sometimes for small values of $\bar{p}$, n, or both, the value of the lower control limit may turn out to be negative. In such cases, we always set the lower control limit at zero. This is because the fraction of nonconforming units can never go below zero.

Interpreting the Control Chart for Fraction Nonconforming

1. If any point or points exceed the upper or lower control limit, we conclude that the process is not stable and that some special causes are present in the process.

2. The presence of special causes, which may be favorable or unfavorable, must be investigated, and appropriate action(s) should be taken.

3. A point above the upper control limit is generally an indication that:

   • The control limit or the plotted point is in error.

   • The process performance has deteriorated or is deteriorating.

   • The measurement system has changed.

4. A point below the lower control limit is generally an indication that:

   • The control limit or the plotted point is in error.

   • The process performance has improved or is improving. This condition of the process should be investigated very carefully so that such conditions of improvement are implemented on a permanent basis at this location and elsewhere in the industry.

   • The measurement system has changed.

5. As in the case of the $\bar{X}$ and R or the $\bar{X}$ and S charts, the presence of any unusual patterns or trends is either an indication of an unstable process or an advance warning of conditions that, if left unattended or without any appropriate action, could make the process unstable.

6. If $\bar{p}$ is moderately high ($n\bar{p} \geq 5$), an approximately equal number of points should fall on either side of the centerline. Therefore, either of the following conditions could indicate that the process has shifted or a trend or shift has started:

   • A run of seven or more points going up or down.

   • A run of seven or more points falls either below or above the centerline.

7. A run above the centerline or a run going up generally indicates:

   • The process performance has deteriorated and may still be deteriorating.

• The measurement system has changed.

8. A run below the centerline or a run going down generally indicates:

• The process performance has improved and may still be improving.

• The measurement system has changed.

To illustrate the construction of the *p* chart, we consider the data in Table 20.5 of Example 20.6.

EXAMPLE 20.6

A semiconductor industry tracks the number of nonconforming computer chips produced each day. A team of Six Sigma Green Belts wants to improve the overall quality by reducing the fraction of nonconforming computer chips. To achieve this goal, the team decided to set up a *p* chart based on daily inspections of 1000 chips over a period of 30 days. Table 20.5 gives the number of nonconforming chips out of 1000 inspected chips each day during the study period of 30 days.

Table 20.5 Number of nonconforming computer chips out of 1000 inspected each day during the study period of 30 days.

Day	Number of nonconforming x	Sample fraction nonconforming p_i	Day	Number of nonconforming x	Sample fraction nonconforming p_i
1	9	0.009	16	12	0.012
2	5	0.005	17	5	0.005
3	6	0.006	18	6	0.006
4	11	0.011	19	12	0.012
5	11	0.011	20	10	0.010
6	12	0.012	21	6	0.006
7	7	0.007	22	7	0.007
8	11	0.011	23	11	0.011
9	6	0.006	24	11	0.011
10	6	0.006	25	9	0.009
11	8	0.008	26	5	0.005
12	5	0.005	27	12	0.012
13	8	0.008	28	11	0.011
14	5	0.005	29	7	0.007
15	8	0.008	30	9	0.009

Continued

Solution

Using the data in Table 20.5 we develop the trial control limits of the p chart as follows.

First, we calculate the sample fraction nonconforming values (p_i), which are listed in columns 3 and 6. Substituting the sample fraction nonconforming values in equation (20.31), we get

$$\bar{p} = 0.00837$$

Plugging the value of $\bar{p} = 0.00837$ and $n = 1000$ into equations (20.32)–(20.34), we get the control limits for the p chart, that is

$$UCL = 0.01701$$

$$CL = 0.00837$$

$$LCL = 0.0$$

The p control chart for the data in Table 20.5 is shown in Figure 20.10.

From the control chart in Figure 20.10 we observe that all the points are well within the control limits. We should note, however, that starting with point 9, seven successive points fall below the centerline. This indicates that from day 9 to day 15, the number of nonconforming chips was relatively low. The process conditions on these days should be investigated so that similar conditions may be implemented for future use. Otherwise, since all the points of the current data fall within the control limits, the trial control limits can be extended for use over the next 30 days, when the control chart should again be reevaluated.

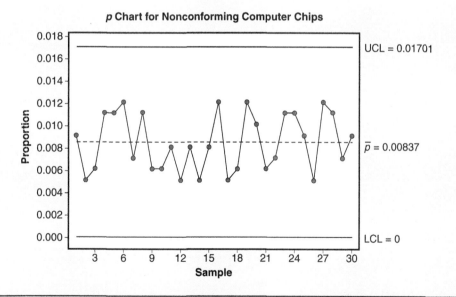

Figure 20.10 p chart for nonconforming computer chips, using trial control limits for the data in Table 20.5.

The *p* Chart: Control Chart for Fraction Nonconforming with Variable Samples

There are times when, for various reasons, it is not possible to select samples of equal sizes. This is particularly true when the samples consist of 100% inspection during a fixed period of time on each day of the study. The procedure for developing a *p* chart with variable sample sizes is very similar to the procedure for a *p* chart with constant sample size.

For example, suppose we have *m* samples of sizes $n_1, n_2, n_3, \ldots, n_m$. To develop a *p* chart for variable sample sizes, we proceed as follows:

1. From the process under investigation, select *m* ($m \geq 25$) samples of sizes $n_1, n_2, n_3, \ldots, n_m$ ($n_i \geq 50$) units.

2. Find the number of nonconforming units in each sample.

3. Find for each sample the fraction p_i of nonconforming units

$$p_i = \frac{x}{n_i} \tag{20.35}$$

where *x* is the number of nonconforming units in the *i*th ($i = 1, 2, \ldots, m$) sample.

4. Find the average fraction $\bar{p}$ of nonconforming units over the *m* samples, that is

$$\bar{p} = \frac{n_1 p_1 + n_2 p_2 + \ldots + n_m p_m}{n_1 + n_2 + n_3 + \ldots + n_m} \tag{20.36}$$

The value of $\bar{p}$ determines the centerline for the *p* chart and is an estimate of *p*, the process fraction of nonconforming units.

5. The control limits for *p* with variable sample sizes are determined for each sample separately. For example, the upper and lower 3-sigma control limits for the *i*th sample are

$$UCL = \bar{p} + 3\sqrt{\frac{\bar{p}(1-\bar{p})}{n_i}} \tag{20.37}$$

$$CL = \bar{p} \tag{20.38}$$

$$LCL = \bar{p} - 3\sqrt{\frac{\bar{p}(1-\bar{p})}{n_i}} \tag{20.39}$$

Note that the centerline is the same for all samples, whereas the control limits will be different for different samples.

To illustrate the construction of the *p* chart with variable sample size, we consider the data in Table 20.6 in Example 20.7.

EXAMPLE 20.7

Suppose in Example 20.6 that all the chips manufactured during a certain fixed period of time are inspected each day. However, the number of computer chips manufactured varies during that fixed period each day. The data collected for the study period of 30 days are shown in Table 20.6. Construct the p chart for these data and determine whether the process is stable.

Solution

Using the data in Table 20.6 and equations (20.37)–(20.39), we get the trial control limits as

$$UCL = 0.01675, CL = 0.00813, LCL = 0.0$$

The p chart for the data in Table 20.6 is shown in Figure 20.11.

From Figure 20.11 we see that all of the points are well within the control limits and that there is no apparent pattern or trend in the chart. Thus, the process is stable. Also, note that in Figure 20.10 we had a run of seven points that fell below the centerline, whereas in Figure 20.11 there is no such run even though we are dealing with the same process. Such differences are normal when samples are taken at different times.

Table 20.6 Number of nonconforming computer chips with different size samples inspected each day during the study period of 30 days..

Day	Number of nonconforming x	Sample size	Day	Number of nonconforming x	Sample size
1	7	908	16	7	962
2	11	986	17	11	926
3	8	976	18	7	917
4	7	991	19	9	978
5	7	944	20	7	961
6	5	906	21	6	970
7	11	928	22	9	905
8	5	948	23	9	962
9	10	994	24	8	900
10	8	960	25	11	998
11	7	982	26	5	935
12	6	921	27	6	970
13	7	938	28	6	967
14	10	1000	29	9	983
15	6	982	30	8	976

Continued

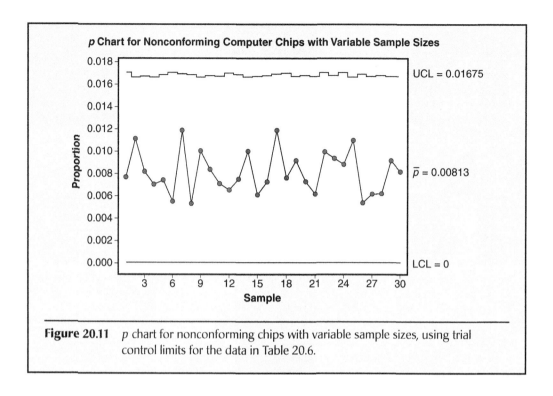

Figure 20.11 *p* chart for nonconforming chips with variable sample sizes, using trial control limits for the data in Table 20.6.

The *np* Chart: Control Chart for Number of Nonconforming Units

In the *np* chart we plot the number of nonconforming units in an inspected sample instead of the fraction of nonconforming units in the inspected sample; otherwise, the *np* chart is very similar to the *p* chart. *Note, however, that in* p *charts sample sizes can be equal or unequal, whereas in* np *charts sample sizes are equal.* Otherwise, both the *p* chart and the *np* chart can be implemented under the same circumstances. We summarize here some specific points that are pertinent for the *np* chart:

- The inspection sample sizes should be equal.
- The sample size should be large enough to include some nonconforming units.
- Record the sample size and the number of observed nonconforming in each sample, and plot the number of nonconforming on the control chart.

Control Limits for *np* Control Chart

Select *m* samples each of size *n* from the process under investigation and then determine the number of nonconforming units in each sample. Let the number of nonconforming units found be denoted by $x_1, x_2, x_3, \ldots, x_m$, respectively. Then the control limits are found as follows.

First, calculate $n\bar{p}$, the average number of nonconforming units per sample, that is

$$n\bar{p} = \frac{x_1 + x_2 + x_3 + \ldots + x_m}{m} \qquad (20.40)$$

Then the 3-sigma control limits and the centerline for the np control chart are given by

$$UCL = n\bar{p} + 3\sqrt{n\bar{p}(1-\bar{p})} \qquad (20.41)$$

$$CL = n\bar{p} \qquad (20.42)$$

$$LCL = n\bar{p} - 3\sqrt{n\bar{p}(1-\bar{p})} \qquad (20.43)$$

We illustrate construction of the np control chart with Example 20.8.

EXAMPLE 20.8

Consider the data on computer chips in Table 20.5. Construct an np chart for these data and verify whether the process is stable.

From the control chart in Figure 20.12 we observe that all the points are well within the control limits. However, as in Figure 20.10, starting from point 9, seven successive points fall below the centerline. This indicates that from day 9 to day 15, the number of nonconforming units was relatively low. The process conditions on these days should be investigated so that similar conditions may be extended for future use. Otherwise, since all the points of the current data fall within the control limits, the trial control limits can be extended for use over the next 30 days, when the control chart should again be reevaluated.

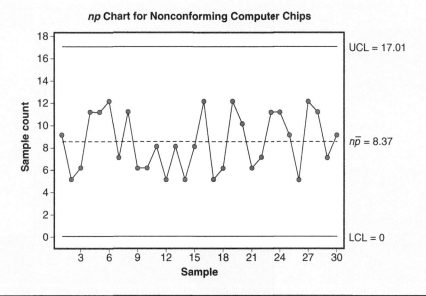

Figure 20.12 np chart for nonconforming computer chips, using trial control limits for the data in Table 20.5.

The *c* Chart (Nonconformities versus Nonconforming Units)

In many situations, we are interested in studying the number of nonconformities in a sample, which is also known as an *inspection unit*, rather than studying the fraction or total number of nonconforming units in a sample. This is particularly true when a unit is nonconforming due to various types of nonconformities. For example, we may be interested in studying the quality of electric motors, which could be nonconforming due to defective bearings, a defective gear, a defective seal, or a defective terminal connection of the winding.

As another example, suppose we are interested in studying the quality of printed circuit boards for laptops, which could be nonconforming due to shorted trace, an open via, cold solder joint, or a solder short. In these cases we may be more likely to study the nonconformities rather than the nonconforming units. The control chart that is most commonly used to study nonconformities is the *c* control chart. *The* p *control chart studies the fraction of nonconforming units, the* np *control chart studies the total number of nonconforming units in each sample, and the* c *chart studies the total number of nonconformities in each sample, or what is known as an inspection unit. The letter* c *in* c *control chart denotes the total number of nonconformities, which may be of one kind or of various kinds, in an inspection unit.*

To illustrate, suppose that to develop trial control limits for a *c* control chart for electric motors, we select samples of size 100 motors each, where each sample would be considered as one inspection unit or several inspection units depending on how the inspection units are defined. Note that the size of an inspection unit is purely a matter of convenience. But the *c* control charts are constructed with sample sizes or number of inspection units in a sample being equal. It can be shown that under certain conditions (such as those of a Poisson process, which are briefly discussed in Gupta and Walker [2007a]), the number of nonconformities, *c*, is distributed according to a Poisson probability distribution with parameter λ, where λ is the average number of nonconformities per inspection unit. The Poisson probability distribution is defined as

$$p(x) = \frac{e^{-1}1^x}{x!}, \qquad x = 0, 1, 2, 3, \ldots \tag{20.44}$$

where the mean and the variance of the Poisson distribution are given by λ. Now suppose that we select *m* samples, with each sample being one inspection unit, and let the number of nonconformities in these samples be $c_1, c_2, c_3, \ldots, c_m$, respectively. Then the parameter λ, which is usually unknown, is estimated by

$$\hat{\lambda} = \bar{c} = \frac{c_1 + c_2 + c_3 + \ldots + c_m}{m} \tag{20.45}$$

Then the 3-sigma control limits for the *c* control chart are defined as follows:

$$\text{UCL} = \bar{c} + 3\sqrt{\bar{c}} \tag{20.46}$$

$$\text{CL} = \bar{c} \tag{20.47}$$

$$\text{LCL} = \bar{c} - 3\sqrt{\bar{c}} \tag{20.48}$$

Note that for small values of $\bar{c}$ (≤ 5) the Poisson distribution is asymmetric; the value of a type I error (α) above the upper control limit and below the lower control limit is usually not the same. For small values of $\bar{c}$ it may be more prudent to use probability control limits rather than the 3-sigma control limits. The probability control limits can be found by using Poisson distribution tables.

To illustrate the construction of a c control chart using 3-sigma control limits, we consider the data in Table 20.7 of Example 20.9.

If the economic factors and time allow, one should take samples or inspection units large enough so that the lower control limit is positive. The lower control limit can be positive only if $\bar{c} > 9$. This means that the sample size should be such that it can catch nine or more nonconformities with high probability. An advantage of having a positive lower control limit is that it will allow us to see the conditions under which the nonconformities are very low and consequently will give us the opportunity to perpetuate these conditions on-site and implement them elsewhere in the industry.

As noted earlier, the size of the inspection unit is usually determined by what is convenient. However, to determine the actual inspection unit size, one should

EXAMPLE 20.9

A paper mill has detected that nonconformities of two types—holes and wrinkles in the paper—are responsible for almost 90% of rejected paper rolls. The Six Sigma Green Belt team in the mill decided to set up control charts to reduce or eliminate the number of these nonconformities. To set up the control charts, the team decided to collect some data by taking random samples of five rolls each day for 30 days and count the number of nonconformities (holes and wrinkles) in each sample. The data are shown in Table 20.7. Set up a c control chart using these data.

Table 20.7   Total number of nonconformities in samples of five rolls of paper.

Day	Total number of nonconformities	Day	Total number of nonconformities	Day	Total number of nonconformities
1	8	11	7	21	9
2	6	12	6	22	6
3	7	13	6	23	8
4	7	14	8	24	7
5	8	15	6	25	6
6	7	16	6	26	9
7	8	17	8	27	9
8	7	18	9	28	7
9	6	19	8	29	7
10	9	20	9	30	8

Continued

Solution

From the data in Table 20.7, the estimate of the population parameter is given by

$$\hat{\lambda} = \bar{c} = \frac{\sum\limits_{i=1}^{30} c_i}{30} = \frac{222}{30} = 7.4$$

Therefore, using equations (20.46)–(20.48), the 3-sigma control limits of the phase I c control chart are given by

$$UCL = 7.4 + 3\sqrt{7.4} = 15.56$$
$$CL = 7.4$$
$$LCL = 7.4 - 3\sqrt{7.4} = -0.76 = 0$$

Note that if the lower control limit turns out to be negative, as in this example, we set it at zero since the number of nonconformities cannot be negative. The c control chart for the data in Table 20.7 is shown in Figure 20.13.

From Figure 20.13, it is quite clear that the process is stable. In other words, no special causes are present, and the only causes that are affecting the process are common causes. To eliminate the imperfections in the paper, management must take action on the system, such as examining the quality of wood chips and pulp, changing old equipment, or providing more training for the workers. Also, to further enhance the process and eliminate the nonconformities, the quality engineers should use the techniques available via design of experiments.

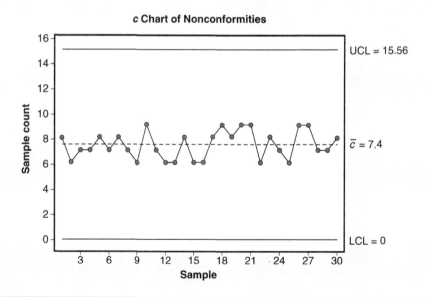

Figure 20.13 *c* control chart of nonconformities for the data in Table 20.7.

also take into consideration the statistical characteristics of the process, such as the average run length, the state of the process (that is, whether the process has deteriorated or improved), and other factors that may require us to increase or decrease the sample size. Thus, while using control charts for nonconformities, particularly in phase I, situations may arise when the sample size may vary. In such cases, we use the u control chart instead of the c control chart. We discuss the u control chart in the following section.

Note that if the samples consist of n inspection units, the control limits for the c control chart are given by

$$\text{UCL} = n\bar{c} + 3\sqrt{n\bar{c}} \tag{20.49}$$

$$\text{CL} = n\bar{c} \tag{20.50}$$

$$\text{LCL} = n\bar{c} - 3\sqrt{n\bar{c}} \tag{20.51}$$

The u Chart

The u control chart is essentially the c control chart except that the u control chart is always based on the number of nonconformities per inspection unit. In other words, the actual sample size may not be equal to one, or may vary, but the control limits of the u chart are always determined based on one inspection unit. Thus, if n is constant, one can use either a c chart or a u chart. For a u chart, the centerline is determined by $\bar{u} = \bar{c}/n$ and the 3-sigma control limits are given by

$$\text{UCL} = \bar{u} + 3\sqrt{\bar{u}/n} \tag{20.52}$$

$$\text{LCL} = \bar{u} - 3\sqrt{\bar{u}/n} \tag{20.53}$$

If the sample size varies, we define $\bar{u}$ as

$$\bar{u} = \frac{c_1 + c_2 + \ldots + c_m}{n_1 + n_2 + \ldots + n_m} = \frac{\bar{c}}{\bar{n}} \tag{20.54}$$

where m is the number of samples selected during the study period, $c_1, c_2, c_3, \ldots, c_m$ is the number of nonconformities in the m samples, and $\bar{n}$ is the average sample size, which is given by

$$\bar{n} = \frac{n_1 + n_2 + \ldots + n_m}{m} \tag{20.55}$$

Thus, in this case the centerline is fixed but the control limits are different; that is, the centerline and the 3-sigma control limits for the ith sample are given by

$$\text{UCL} = \bar{u} + 3\sqrt{\bar{u}/n_i} \tag{20.56}$$

$$\text{CL} = \bar{u} \tag{20.57}$$

$$\text{LCL} = \bar{u} - 3\sqrt{\bar{u}/n_i} \tag{20.58}$$

Sometimes, if the samples do not vary too much, the n_i's in equations (20.56) and (20.58) are replaced by $\bar{n}$ so that the control limits are

$$UCL = \bar{u} + 3\sqrt{\bar{u}/\bar{n}} \tag{20.59}$$

$$CL = \bar{u} \tag{20.60}$$

$$LCL = \bar{u} - 3\sqrt{\bar{u}/\bar{n}} \tag{20.61}$$

To illustrate the construction of the *u* chart, we consider the data in Table 20.8 of Example 20.10.

To illustrate the construction of the *u* chart when the sample sizes vary, we consider Example 20.11.

15. PROCESS CAPABILITY ANALYSIS

Earlier in this chapter we defined what a process is. Once the process is defined and brought under statistical control, the manufacturer's next concern is to deliver product that the consumer wants. In other words, the manufacturer must

---

EXAMPLE 20.10

A Six Sigma Green Belt team in a semiconductor industry found that the printed boards for laptops have nonconformities of several types, such as shorted trace, cold solder joint, and solder short, and the number of nonconformities is unacceptable. In order to reduce the number of nonconformities in the printed boards for laptops, the Six Sigma Green Belt team wants to set up a *u* chart. They collect some data by selecting samples of five inspection units, where each inspection unit consists of 30 boards. The data, shown in Table 20.8, were collected over a period of 30 days.

Solution

Using the data in Table 20.8, we have $\bar{c} = 41.333$
   Therefore,

$$\bar{u} = \frac{\bar{c}}{5} = \frac{41.333}{5} = 8.2667$$

Hence, the control limits are given by

$$UCL = \bar{u} + 3\sqrt{\bar{u}/n} = 8.2666 + 3\sqrt{8.2666/5} = 12.124$$
$$CL = \bar{u} = 8.2667$$
$$LCL = \bar{u} - 3\sqrt{\bar{u}/n} = 8.2666 - 3\sqrt{8.2666/5} = 4.409$$

The *u* chart for the data in Table 20.8 is shown in Figure 20.14.
   The *u* chart in Figure 20.14 shows that there are no assignable causes present in the process. In other words, only common causes are affecting the process. Therefore, management needs to take action on the system.

Continued

Table 20.8   Number of nonconformities on printed boards for laptops per sample; each sample consists of five inspection units.

Day	Number of nonconformities per sample	Day	Number of nonconformities per sample
1	48	16	42
2	49	17	34
3	38	18	30
4	49	19	49
5	43	20	44
6	37	21	47
7	45	22	33
8	48	23	37
9	39	24	33
10	46	25	34
11	40	26	49
12	44	27	50
13	43	28	49
14	35	29	35
15	31	30	39

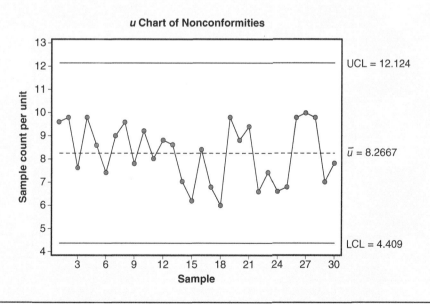

Figure 20.14 u chart of nonconformities for the data in Table 20.8, constructed using Minitab.

EXAMPLE 20.11

Suppose in Example 20.10, due to administrative reasons, it was not possible to examine five inspection units every day; in other words, the sample size varied. The data obtained are shown in Table 20.9. Construct and interpret a *u* chart for the data in Table 20.9.

Solution

Using the data in Table 20.9, we have

$$\bar{u} = \frac{33+40+38+...+40}{3+5+3+...+3} = \frac{1162}{126} = 9.22$$

The control limits are calculated for each individual sample. For example, the control limits for sample 1 are given by

$$UCL = \bar{u} + 3\sqrt{\bar{u}/n_1} = 9.22 + 3\sqrt{9.22/3} = 14.48$$

$$CL = \bar{u} = 9.22$$

$$LCL = \bar{u} - 3\sqrt{\bar{u}/n_1} = 9.22 - 3\sqrt{9.22/3} = 3.96$$

Table 20.9   Number of nonconformities on printed boards for laptops per sample, with varying sample size.

Day	Sample size	Number of nonconformities per sample	Day	Sample size	Number of nonconformities per sample
1	3	33	16	5	40
2	5	40	17	4	40
3	3	38	18	5	37
4	5	43	19	4	40
5	5	45	20	5	37
6	5	35	21	4	39
7	5	35	22	5	48
8	3	41	23	5	39
9	3	40	24	5	36
10	5	30	25	3	39
11	5	36	26	3	36
12	5	40	27	5	43
13	3	33	28	3	36
14	4	36	29	4	49
15	4	38	30	3	40

Continued

The control limits for the rest of the samples are calculated in the same manner. The centerline, however, remains the same. The u chart for the data in Table 20.9 is shown in Figure 20.15.

The u chart in Figure 20.15 shows that all the points are within the control limits. However, several points fall beyond the warning control limits. Moreover, points 8 and 9 fall very close to the upper control limits. All these observations about the process indicate that there may be some special causes present in the process. That is, the process may be on the verge of being unstable. Therefore, precautions should be taken to avoid the process becoming unstable, but certainly without overcontrolling it.

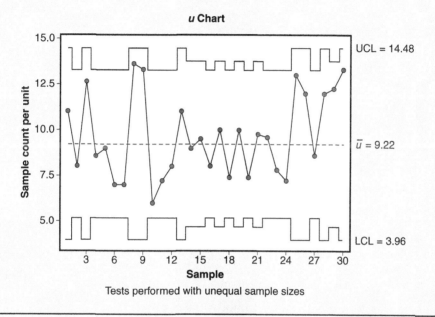

Figure 20.15 u chart of nonconformities for the data in Table 20.9, constructed using Minitab.

determine whether the process is capable of delivering the desired product. One way to address such a concern is to quantify the capability. A *process capability index* (PCI) is a unitless measure that quantifies the process capability, specifically the relationship between the output and the designed tolerances. This measure has become an important tool in process capability analysis. Moreover, since the PCI is a unitless measure of capability, it has become an easy tool of communication between the manufacturer and the supplier. More and more manufacturers and suppliers are using the PCI as an important part of their contract to ensure quality.

A *process capability analysis* is simply the comparison of the distribution of a process output with the product tolerances. As Kotz and Lovelace (1998) noted, the results of process capability analysis have proved very valuable in many ways.

Delleryd (1996) developed a list of the 13 most common ways of using the results of process capability analysis:

1. As a basis in the improvement process.

2. As an alarm clock.

3. As specifications for investments. By giving specifications for levels of process capability indices expected to be reached by new machines, the purchasing process is facilitated.

4. As a certificate for customers. The supplier is able to provide on delivery the results of the process capability studies conducted when the actual products were produced.

5. As a basis for new constructions. By knowing the capability of the production processes, the designer knows how to set reasonable specifications in order to make the product manufacturable.

6. For control of maintenance efforts. By continuously conducting process capability studies, it is possible to see if some machines are gradually deteriorating.

7. As specifications for introducing new products.

8. For assessing reasonableness of customer demands

9. For motivation of coworkers.

10. For deciding priorities in the improvement process.

11. As a base for inspection activities.

12. As a receipt for improvement.

13. For formulating quality improvement programs.

To implement a process capability analysis, one needs to consider the following:

1. The target value specification, which is usually defined by the customer.

2. The specification limits, which should be defined by the customer, or by their technical staff, and should be agreed on by the manufacturer. Furthermore, the specification limits should be such that they allow manufacturing variability without jeopardizing proper function of the product.

3. An analysis of the process that allows the manufacturer to determine whether the product produced meets the customer's specifications.

Once production starts, the manufacturer conducts capability studies to compare the measures of the quality characteristic of the manufactured product with the specification limits. This is the point where PCIs are used.

The first-generation PCIs were established by the Japanese in the 1970s. They used the following indices:

C_p Inherent capability of a process

k Position of the process in relation to the target value

C_{pk} Position of the 6σ process in relation to the target value

C_{pl} Position of the 6σ process in relation to the lower specification limit

C_{pu} Position of the 6σ process in relation to the upper specification limit

In this section we will study these and some other capability indices that are frequently used in the process capability analysis. We will not address every aspect of these indices; however, an excellent reference for a more detailed study of these indices is Kotz and Lovelace (1998).

Throughout the study of these indices we will assume that the process producing the desired quality characteristic is under control, and thus predictable.

Process Capability Index: C_p

Let X be the process quality characteristic that we want to monitor. Let USL and LSL be the *upper specification limit* and the *lower specification limit,* respectively. The performance of the process with respect to these limits is defined as follows:

Percentage of nonconforming produced
by the process at the upper end $= P(X > \text{USL})$

Percentage of nonconforming produced
by the process at the lower end $= P(X < \text{LSL})$

Thus, the total percentage of nonconforming produced by the process is defined as

$$P(X < \text{LSL or } X > \text{USL}) = 1 - P(\text{LSL} < X < \text{USL})$$

In the previous paragraph we saw the performance of the process with respect to the specification limits. Now we look at the performance of the process with respect to the *natural tolerance limits*, that is, the upper natural tolerance limit (UNTL) and the lower natural tolerance limit (LNTL).

The performance of the process with respect to the natural tolerance limits is the percentage of the product produced by the process with its quality characteristic falling within the interval $(\mu - 3\sigma, \mu + 3\sigma)$, where μ and σ are, respectively, the mean and the standard deviation of the process quality characteristic. Assuming that the process quality characteristic is normally distributed and that the process is under control, the percentage of the product produced by the process with its quality characteristic falling within the interval $(\mu - 3\sigma, \mu + 3\sigma)$ is approximately 99.73%. As noted earlier, a PCI is simply the comparison between what a process is expected to produce and what it is actually producing. Hence, we now define the PCI C_p, one of the first five indices used by the Japanese and proposed by Juran, Gryna, and Bingham (1974), as follows:

$$C_p = \frac{USL - LSL}{UNTL - LNTL} \tag{20.62}$$

$$= \frac{USL - LSL}{(\mu + 3\sigma) - (\mu - 3\sigma)}$$

$$= \frac{USL - LSL}{6\sigma}$$

Note that the numerator in equation (20.62) is the desired range of the process quality characteristic, whereas the denominator is the actual range of the process quality characteristic. From this we can see that a process can produce product of desired quality and that the process is capable only if the range in the numerator is at least as large as that in the denominator. In other words, the process is capable only if $C_p \geq 1$, and larger values of C_p are indicative of a process being more capable. For a 6σ process, $C_p = 2$. A predictable process, which is normally distributed with $C_p = 1$ and its mean located at the center of the specification limits, usually known as the target value of the process characteristic, is expected to produce 0.27% nonconforming units. Montgomery (2005) has given a comprehensive list of values of the PCI Cp and associated process nonconforming for one-sided specifications and two-sided specifications.

Since C_p is very easy to calculate, it is used widely in industry. However, the fact that it does not take into consideration the position of the process mean is a major drawback. A process could be incapable even if the value of C_p is large (> 1). That is, a process could produce 100% defectives, for example, if the process mean falls outside the specification limits and is far from the target value. Furthermore, note that the value of C_p will become even larger if the value of the process standard deviation σ decreases while the process mean moves away from the target value.

Note that the numerator in equation (20.62) is always known, but the denominator is usually unknown. This is because in almost all practical applications, the process standard deviation σ is unknown. Thus, to calculate C_p we must replace σ in equation (20.62) with its estimator $\hat{\sigma}$. Now we know that $\hat{\sigma}$ can be estimated either by the sample standard deviation s or by $\bar{R}/d_2$. However, remember that the estimator $\bar{R}/d_2$ is used only when the process is under control and the sample size is fewer than 10. Hence, an estimated value of C_p is given by

$$\hat{C}_p = \frac{USL - LSL}{6\sigma} \tag{20.63}$$

We illustrate the computation of $\hat{C}_p$ with Example 20.12.

Hence, even though the value of C_p did not change after the process mean experienced a shift, the process is producing nonconforming units at a rate that is 30 times higher than in the previous example. This implies that C_p did not measure the effect that the upward shift had on the ability of the process to produce products within the specification limits. This major drawback of C_p makes it less reliable than many other PCIs available in the literature. We will study some of them here. However, before we study other PCIs, let us see another alternative but

EXAMPLE 20.12

Table 20.10 gives the summary statistics on $\bar{X}$ and R for 25 samples of size $n = 5$ collected from a process producing tie rods for a certain type of cars. The measurement data are the lengths of tie rods, and the measurement scale is in millimeters.

The target value and the specification limits for the length of the rods are 272 and 272 ± 8, respectively. Calculate the value of $\hat{C}_p$ assuming that the tie rod lengths are normally distributed, and find the percentage of nonconforming tie rods produced by the process.

Solution

To find the value of $\hat{C}_p$ and the percentage of nonconforming tie rods produced by the process, we first need to estimate the process mean μ and the process standard deviation σ. These estimates may be found by using $\bar{\bar{X}}$ and $\bar{R}/d_2$, respectively. So that we get

$$\hat{\mu} = \bar{\bar{X}} = \frac{1}{m}\sum_{i=1}^{m} \bar{X}_i = \frac{1}{25}(274 + 265 + 269 + \ldots + 273) = 272$$

$$\hat{\sigma} = \frac{\bar{R}}{d_2} = \frac{\frac{1}{m}\sum_{i=1}^{m} R_i}{d_2} = \frac{\frac{1}{25}(6 + 8 + \ldots + 5 + 6)}{2.326} = \frac{6}{2.326} = 2.58$$

where the value of d_2 for different sample sizes is found in Appendix E. Substituting the values of USL, LSL, and $\hat{\sigma}$ in equation (20.63), we get

$$\hat{C}_p = \frac{280 - 284}{6(2.58)} = 1.03$$

Table 20.10   Data showing the lengths of tie rods for cars.

Sample number	$\bar{X}$	R	Sample number	$\bar{X}$	R
1	274	6	14	268	8
2	265	8	15	271	6
3	269	6	16	275	5
4	273	5	17	274	7
5	270	8	18	272	4
6	275	7	19	270	6
7	271	5	20	274	7
8	275	4	21	273	5
9	272	6	22	270	4
10	273	8	23	274	6
11	269	6	24	273	5
12	273	5	25	273	6
13	274	7			

Continued

which indicates that the process is capable. To find the percentage of nonconforming tie rods produced by the process, we proceed as follows:

$$\text{Percentage of nonconforming} = \left(1 - P(264 \le X \le 280)\right)100\%$$

$$= \left(1 - P(-3.1 \le Z \le 3.1)\right)100\%$$

$$= \left(1 - 0.9980\right)100\% = 0.2\%$$

Thus, in this example, the percentage of nonconforming tie rods is as expected when we consider the value of C_p. But, as noted earlier, this may not always be the case since C_p does not take into consideration where the process mean is located. To better explain this, we use Example 20.13.

EXAMPLE 20.13

Suppose that the process in Example 20.12 had a setback, and as a result, the process had an upward shift. Furthermore, suppose that after the process experienced this shift, we took another set of 25 random samples of size $n = 5$ and these samples produced $\bar{\bar{X}} = 276$ and $\bar{R} = 6$. Clearly, in this example the value of $\bar{\bar{X}}$ changed from 272 to 276, while $\bar{R}$ remained the same.

Solution

From the given values of $\bar{\bar{X}}$ and $\bar{R}$, we obtain

$$\hat{\mu} = 276 \text{ and } \hat{\sigma} = 2.58$$

Since the process standard deviation did not change, the value of $\hat{C}_p$ remained the same, that is, $\hat{C}_p = 1.03$. However, the percentage of nonconforming tie rods produced by the process will be

$$\text{Percentage of nonconforming} = \left(1 - P(264 \le X \le 280)\right)100\%$$

$$= \left(1 - P\left(\frac{264 - 276}{2.58} \le \frac{X - 276}{2.58} \le \frac{280 - 276}{2.58}\right)\right)100\%$$

$$= \left(1 - P(-4.65 \le Z \le 1.55)\right)100\% = 6.06\%$$

---

equivalent interpretation of C_p, which is given by finding the percentage of specification band used, that is

$$\text{Percentage of specification band used} = \frac{1}{C_p} \times 100$$

A smaller percentage of specification band used indicates a better process. Again, for reasons discussed earlier, this interpretation sometimes can also be misleading.

The other two PCIs first used by the Japanese are C_{pl} and C_{pu}. These indices are related to the lower specification limit and the upper specification limit, respectively, and are defined as follows:

$$C_{pl} = \frac{\mu - LSL}{3\sigma} \qquad (20.64)$$

$$C_{pu} = \frac{USL - \mu}{3\sigma} \qquad (20.65)$$

The estimates of C_{pl} and C_{pu} are given by

$$\hat{C}_{pl} = \frac{\bar{\bar{X}} - LSL}{3\hat{\sigma}} \qquad (20.66)$$

$$\hat{C}_{pu} = \frac{USL - \bar{\bar{X}}}{3\hat{\sigma}} \qquad (20.67)$$

To illustrate the computation of $\hat{C}_{pl}$ and $\hat{C}_{pu}$ we use the information in Examples 20.14 and 20.15.

Process Capability Index: C_{pk}

To overcome the centering problem in C_p discussed in the preceding section, the PCI C_{pk} was introduced. The PCI C_{pk}, which is again one of the first five used in Japan, is defined as

$$C_{pk} = \min (C_{pl}, C_{pu}) \qquad (20.68)$$

EXAMPLE 20.14

Using the information given in Example 20.12, compute $\hat{C}_{pl}$ and $\hat{C}_{pu}$.

Solution

$$\hat{C}_{pl} = \frac{\bar{\bar{X}} - LSL}{3\hat{\sigma}} = \frac{272 - 264}{3(2.58)} = 1.03$$

$$\hat{C}_{pu} = \frac{USL - \bar{\bar{X}}}{3\hat{\sigma}} = \frac{280 - 272}{3(2.58)} = 1.03$$

Note that both $\hat{C}_{pl}$ and $\hat{C}_{pu}$ are equal to $\hat{C}_p$, which will always be the case when the process mean is centered between the specification limits. Moreover, when both $\hat{C}_{pl}$ and $\hat{C}_{pu}$ are equal, the percentage of nonconforming units below the lower specification limit is the same as the percentage of nonconforming units above the upper specification limit.

EXAMPLE 20.15

Using the information given in Example 20.13, compute $\hat{C}_{pl}$ and $\hat{C}_{pu}$.

Solution

$$\hat{C}_{pl} = \frac{\bar{\bar{X}} - LSL}{3\hat{\sigma}} = \frac{276 - 264}{3(2.58)} = 1.55$$

$$\hat{C}_{pu} = \frac{USL - \bar{\bar{X}}}{3\hat{\sigma}} = \frac{280 - 276}{3(2.58)} = 0.52$$

In this case, the value of $\hat{C}_{pl}$ is much larger than 1, whereas the value of $\hat{C}_{pu}$ is much smaller than 1, which indicates that most of the nonconforming units produced by the process are falling above the upper specification limit. Finally, note that both $\hat{C}_{pl}$ and $\hat{C}_{pu}$ are sensitive to where the process mean is located.

The index C_{pk} is related to the index C_p as

$$C_{pk} = (1 - k)C_p \tag{20.69}$$

where

$$k = \frac{|(USL + LSL / 2 - \mu)|}{(USL - LSL) / 2} \tag{20.70}$$

Furthermore, it can easily be seen that $0 \leq k \leq 1$, so that C_{pk} is always less than or equal to C_p. Also, note that when the process mean μ coincides with the midpoint between the specification limits, $k = 0$, and therefore C_{pk} equals C_p.

Note that C_{pk} takes care of the centering problem only if the process standard deviation remains the same. If the process standard deviation changes, the value of C_{pk} may not change even when the process mean moves away from the center. It can easily be seen that this will always be the scenario, provided the distance of the process mean from the nearest specification limit in terms of σ remains the same. For example, in Table 20.11 we consider four processes with the same specification limits but with different process means (μ) and different standard deviations (σ) such that the value of C_{pk} in each case remains the same.

The value of C_{pk} for each of the four processes remains the same even though the process mean has been moving away from the center, since in each case the distance between the process mean and the nearest specification limit (in this example, the LSL) is three times the process standard deviation. Thus, we can say that in some ways C_{pk} is also not an adequate measure of centering. Assuming the process characteristic is normally distributed, Table 20.12 gives the parts per million (ppm) of nonconforming units for different values of C_{pk}.

From Table 20.12, we can see that each of the processes in Table 20.11 will produce 1350 nonconforming ppm. This is only possible if the process standard deviation is shrinking while the process mean is shifting, and the natural tolerance limits remain within the specification limits. In fact, in Table 20.11 the process with

Table 20.11   Different processes with the same value of C_{pk}.

Process	LSL	USL	Center	μ	σ	C_{pk}
1	12	36	24	24	4	1.00
2	12	36	24	22	3.33	1.00
3	12	36	24	20	2.67	1.00
4	12	36	24	18	2.00	1.00

Table 20.12   Parts per million of nonconforming units for different values of C_{pk}.

C_{pk}	1.00	1.33	1.67	2.00
ppm	1350	30	1	.001

standard deviation $\sigma = 2$ would be of Six Sigma quality if the process mean were at the center of the specification target. In this case, however, the process is producing 1350 nonconforming ppm because the process mean is off center by 3σ, a shift larger than 1.5σ, which would be tolerable only in a Six Sigma–quality process. For discussion on some other indices, see Gupta and Walker (2007b).

Process Capability Indices: P_p and P_{pk}

The capability indices we have studied so far have one characteristic in common: each one of them is used when the process is stable. In 1982 the Automotive Industry Action Group (AIAG), consisting of representatives from Ford Motor Company, General Motors Corporation, Daimler/Chrysler Corporation, and the American Society for Quality, was founded. This group standardized the supplier quality reporting procedure for the industry, and it advocated the use of two sets of PCIs—one consisting of C_p and C_{pk}, and the other consisting of P_p and P_{pk}. Furthermore, it advised using C_p and C_{pk} when the process is stable and P_p and P_{pk} when the process is not stable, where the two sets of indices P_p, P_{pk} and C_p, C_{pk} are defined in exactly the same manner and only differ in their estimates. Thus, we have

$$\hat{P}_p = \frac{USL - LSL}{6\hat{\sigma}_s} \tag{20.71}$$

$$\hat{C}_p = \frac{USL - LSL}{6\hat{\sigma}_{\bar{R}/d_2}} \tag{20.72}$$

and

$$\hat{P}_{pk} = \min\left(\frac{USL - \bar{\bar{X}}}{3\hat{\sigma}_s}, \frac{\bar{\bar{X}} - LSL}{3\hat{\sigma}_s}\right) \tag{20.73}$$

$$\hat{C}_{pk} = \min\left(\frac{USL - \bar{\bar{X}}}{3\hat{\sigma}_{\bar{R}/d_2}}, \frac{\bar{\bar{X}} - LSL}{3\hat{\sigma}_{\bar{R}/d_2}} \right) \tag{20.74}$$

In other words, they differ only in the method in which one estimates the standard deviation. The estimate $\hat{\sigma}_s$ is the usual standard deviation

$$s = \sqrt{\sum_{i=1}^{n}\sum_{j=1}^{m}\left(x_{ij} - \bar{\bar{x}}\right)^2 / (mn - 1)}$$

whereas $\hat{\sigma}_{\bar{R}/d_2} = \bar{R}/d_2$ is an estimate obtained using the subgroup ranges R_i, $i = 1, 2, \ldots, m$ and the corresponding value of d_2. Note that the estimate $\hat{\sigma}_s$ measures the process variability by using the variability within and between subgroups, whereas $\hat{\sigma}_{\bar{R}/d_2}$ uses only the variability within the subgroups. When the process is stable, there is very little variability between the subgroups, and the two sets of indices are essentially the same because the estimates $\hat{\sigma}_s$ and $\hat{\sigma}_{\bar{R}/d_2}$ are approximately equal. But if the process is not stable, there is potentially very large variability between the subgroups. This would mean that $\hat{\sigma}_{\bar{R}/d_2}$ underestimates the process standard deviation, and, consequently, C_{pk} would overestimate the process capability. Fortunately, this situation will not arise, because the use of C_{pk} is recommended only when the process is stable.

Kotz and Lovelace (1998, 253) strongly argued against the use of P_p and P_{pk}: They highly recommend against using these indices when the process is not in statistical control. Under these conditions, the P-numbers are meaningless with regard to process capability, have no tractable statistical properties, and infer nothing about long-term capability of the process. Worse still, they provide no motivation to the user companies to get their process in control. The P-numbers are a step backwards in the efforts to properly quantify process capability, and a step toward statistical terrorism in its undiluted form.

Montgomery (2005, 349) agrees with Kotz and Lovelace. He writes, "The process performance indices P_p and P_{pk} are more than a step backwards. They are a waste of engineering and management effort—they tell you nothing." The authors wholeheartedly agree with Kotz and Lovelace and Montgomery. No one can judge a process when its future behavior is so unpredictable.

REFERENCES

Deleryd, M. 1996. "Process Capability Studies in Theory and Practice." Licentiate thesis, Lulea University of Technology, Lulea, Sweden.

Deming, W. E. 1951. *Elementary Principles of the Statistical Control of Quality.* 2nd ed. Tokyo: Nippon Kagaku Gijutsu Remmei.

———. 1982. *Quality, Productivity, and Competitive Position.* Cambridge, MA: MIT, Center for Advanced Engineering Study.

Duncan, A. J. 1986. *Quality Control and Industrial Statistics.* 5th ed. Homewood, IL: Irwin.

Gupta, B. C., and H. F. Walker. 2007a. *Applied Statistics for the Six Sigma Green Belt.* Revised ed. Milwaukee: ASQ Quality Press.

———. 2007b. *Statistical Quality Control for the Six Sigma Green Belt.* Milwaukee: ASQ Quality Press.

Juran, J. M., F. M. Gryna, and R. S. Bingham, Jr. 1974. *Quality Control Handbook.* New York: McGraw-Hill.

Kotz, S., and C. R. Lovelace. 1998. *Process Capability Indices in Theory and Practice.* London/New York: Arnold.

Montgomery, D. C. 2005. *Introduction to Statistical Quality Control.* 5th ed. New York: John Wiley & Sons.

Western Electric. 1956. *Statistical Quality Control Handbook.* Indianapolis, IN: Western Electric Corporation.

Chapter 21

C. Quality Improvement

---

1. *Terms and concepts*. Define basic quality improvement concepts such as defect detection and prevention, the cost of poor quality, total quality management (TQM), and the importance of customer satisfaction, etc. (Understand)

2. *Products and processes*. Define and distinguish between products and processes. Describe the interrelationships of product design, materials used, manufacturing processes, and final output, and how individual steps in a process can affect the final product or the system as a whole. (Understand)

Body of Knowledge IV.C

---

1. TERMS AND CONCEPTS

Prevention versus Detection

Prevention versus detection is a quality improvement concept wherein it is far more desirable to prevent errors and mistakes prior to their occurrence than to attempt to detect errors after they are committed. The logic of prevention versus detection is generally acknowledged to be based on the following:

1. The avoidance of escalating costs

2. The likelihood of missing errors as part of the normal inspection process

In the case of avoiding escalating costs, the further into production or service delivery that an error passes, the more expensive it is to rework or scrap the product or service delivery due to the increasing value-added effort and materials consumed. In fact, much effort has been expended by industrial research and development organizations as well as in academic research to quantify exactly the financial resources consumed, and ultimately wasted, for each step or phase into production or the delivery of services that bad products or services cost. And while there are many mathematical models that quantify costs of errors in specific production or service delivery operations, the most common model is based on a factor of 10, wherein it is assumed that the cost to correct an error increases 10 times for each stage or step in a production or service delivery operation that is past the point where the original error was made.

In the case of missing errors as part of the normal inspection process, we know that the sampling methods used to support the inspection process are based on some form of rational subgrouping and assumed or calculated probabilities that errors will be detected. Since errors are assumed to be randomly distributed within samples, there is the likelihood that errors will not be detected. While it is beyond the scope of this section of the book to provide a mathematical basis for determining the probability of missing errors in a sample, the point is nonetheless important. Sampling and inspection simply do not guarantee that all errors will be detected.

The logic of prevention versus detection should, at this point, be clear. As quality professionals we prefer to prevent errors from happening rather than try to detect errors that have already occurred.

The Importance of Customer Satisfaction

Quality has been defined by many individuals to include two broad components:

1. Product or process characteristics and/or performance consistent with some form of specification

2. The perceptions of customers

These two component parts of quality, taken together, mean that customers in a contemporary, globally based market economy ultimately judge the quality of products and services, and their judgments are based on quantifiable (specifications) and nonquantifiable (perceptions) components. Customers in a contemporary global economy simply expect all the products and services they purchase to meet or exceed their expectations—even those expectations they are not yet aware they have. In the event that products and/or services do not meet customer expectations, customers are quite readily unsatisfied and react in a very predictable manner, including:

1. Sharing their dissatisfaction with vendors along with requested changes,

2. Not sharing their dissatisfaction with a selected vendor and changing to a new vendor (with and without telling others of the dissatisfaction), or

3. Sharing their dissatisfaction with a selected vendor and changing to a new vendor (with and without telling others of the dissatisfaction).

A key point relating to the importance of customer satisfaction is that dissatisfied customers don't buy products or services, and they commonly tell many other organizations and people when and why they are dissatisfied. And since a primary component in how we define quality is based on perceptions, we simply cannot afford to have dissatisfied customers.

The Cost of Poor Quality

The cost of quality is a topic that addresses costs associated with specific activities and events intended to ensure the quality of products and services. Gryna (2001) identifies four categories of quality costs:

1. *Prevention.* Costs associated with preventing errors (that is, training)

2. *Appraisal.* Costs associated with validating that errors have not occurred (that is, measurement and inspection)

3. *Internal failure.* Costs associated with correcting errors detected prior to customers' receipt of products or services (that is, correction of errors found during inspection and testing)

4. *External failure.* Costs associated with correcting errors detected after customers have received products or services (that is, warranty costs)

The true cost of quality is recognized to be misunderstood and understated. A common analogy associated with the cost of quality is an iceberg—wherein its tip, which is roughly 10%–15% of the iceberg, is what we typically can identify. In accordance with the analogy, some 85%–90% of the true cost of quality lies beneath the surface of the water and is thus misunderstood and understated.

Juran and Godfrey (1999) have continued a common use of the "cost of quality" concept to refer to the topic as the "cost of poor quality." The cost of poor quality, Juran and Godfrey note, applies differently to different people, but it does refer to the costs associated with ensuring customer satisfaction. In addition to the costs associated with the cost of quality, as identified earlier, the cost of poor quality generally refers to costs associated with lost goodwill when customers are dissatisfied with products or services. This lost goodwill influences customer perceptions, which, as explained earlier, influences a customer's willingness to buy products and services from a given vendor. It also influences the potential recommendations given by a customer to other customers. The costs associated with this occurrence are difficult to quantify, but they are very real costs nonetheless.

2. PRODUCTS AND PROCESSES

Product

For purposes of this book, and for the Certified Quality Inspector Body of Knowledge, a *product* is any tangible item intended for use by a customer. A product may be a physical item such as a unit of production, or a product may be the delivery of a service. Whether a physical item or the delivery of a service, some form of a process is required to produce a product.

Process

For purposes of this book, and for the Certified Quality Inspector Body of Knowledge, a *process* is a set of interrelated steps used to produce a product or deliver a service. A process may or may not require the use of tools and equipment.

The Interrelatedness of Products and Processes

Products and the processes used to produce them are integrally connected. Under a concept called *concurrent engineering*, customer expectations, product and/or service delivery designs, materials and procurement, process designs, packaging and distribution, and disposal are all considered simultaneously in acknowledgment of their interrelatedness.

REFERENCES

Gryna, F. M. 2001. *Quality Planning & Analysis: From Product Development through Use.* 4th ed. New York: McGraw-Hill.

Juran, J. M., and A. B. Godfrey. 1999. *Juran's Quality Handbook.* 5th ed. New York: McGraw-Hill.

BIBLIOGRAPHY

Arter, D., A. Cianfrani, and J. West. 2003. *How to Audit the Process-Based Quality Management System.* Milwaukee: ASQ Quality Press.

Defeo, J. A. 2017. *Juran's Quality Handbook: The Complete Guide to Performance Excellence.* 7th ed. New York: McGraw-Hill.

Kausek, J. 2006. *The Management System Auditor's Handbook.* Milwaukee: ASQ Quality Press.

Phillips, A. W. 2015. *ISO 9001:2015 Internal Audits Made Easy.* 4th ed. Milwaukee: ASQ Quality Press.

Russell, J.P., ed. 2012. *The Quality Auditing Handbook.* 4th ed. Milwaukee: ASQ Quality Press.

Chapter 22

D. Quality Audits

1. *Types of audits.* Define and describe various types of audits, including internal, external, system, product, and process. (Understand)

2. *Audit process.* Define and describe various stages of the audit process (planning, performance, and closure), including audit scope and purpose, resources needed, audit schedule, opening meeting, interviewing, data gathering, document and record review, analysis of results, closing meeting, audit documentation (reporting), recordkeeping, and verification of corrective actions. (Understand)

3. *Audit tools.* Define and describe the purpose of checklists, log sheets, sampling plans, record reviews, document reviews and forward—and backward—tracing. (Understand)

4. *Communication tools and techniques.* Define and describe the use of graphs, charts, diagrams, and other aids for written and oral presentations including interview techniques and listening skills. (Understand)

5. *Corrective action requests (CARs).* Describe how CARs from audits can support quality improvement. (Understand)

Body of Knowledge IV.D

Quality auditing is an important topic for the ASQ Certified Quality Inspector (CQI). While quality auditing is a career field in and of itself, and while there are three ASQ professional certifications pertaining to various aspects of quality auditing (ASQ Certified Quality Auditor, ASQ Certified Biomedical Auditor, and ASQ Certified HACCP Auditor), we will focus here only on the depth of content required for the ASQ CQI. Accordingly, in this section we will cover basic terms and definitions, types of audits, the audit process, audit tools, communication tools and techniques, and corrective action requests (CARs).

ASQ/ANSI/ISO 19011:2018 defines a quality audit as follows:

A systematic, independent and documented process for obtaining audit evidence and evaluating it objectively to determine the extent to which audit criteria are fulfilled.

A *quality audit* is a fact-finding process that compares actual results with specified standards and plans. The audit provides feedback for improvement and differs from inspection, which emphasizes acceptance or rejection, and from surveillance, which is ongoing continuous monitoring. There are several key terms and definitions that apply specifically to the preparation, conduct, and reporting of quality audits.

TERMS AND DEFINITIONS

auditee—The person or organization being audited.

auditor—The person or organization conducting the audit.

client—The person or organization requesting the audit.

interested party—A stakeholder to the audit process or results.

internal quality audit—Also known as a *first-party audit*. An audit conducted within a company or organization by one or more employees of that company or organization.

external quality audit—Also known as a *second-party audit*. An audit conducted within a company or organization by one or more employees from a different company or organization.

third-party audit—An audit conducted by a regulatory agency or registrar.

1. TYPES OF AUDITS

Quality audits may be classified according to the party conducting them or their scope.

When the auditor is an employee of the organization being audited (auditee), the audit is classified as an *internal quality audit*. For the purposes of maintaining objectivity and minimizing bias, internal auditors must be independent from the activity being audited. When the auditors are employees of the client or an independent organization, that is, a third party hired for the purpose, the audit is termed an *external quality audit*. In this case, the auditors are clearly independent of the auditee and are in a position to provide the client with an unbiased, objective assessment. This is the type of audit required to permit a listing in a register or to meet mandatory quality requirements. However, the time required and costs involved in an external audit are much higher compared to internal audits.

Another way to classify quality audits is by scope. An audit may be as comprehensive as needed or requested by a client. Arter (2003) identifies three types of audits, each with a different scope.

The most comprehensive type of audit is the quality *system audit*. System audits typically involve many areas and functions within a company or organization to examine the suitability and effectiveness of the quality system as a whole. System audits focus on the design and specification of specific controls and procedures, quality system documentation and interpretation by employees, and implementation aspects of the quality system. Reasons for initiating a system audit may range from evaluating a potential supplier to verifying an organization's own system.

Audits of specific elements of a system, such as processes and products/services, are also possible, but they are more limited in scope than the system audit.

The *process audit*, while more limited in scope than a system audit, is a more detailed audit focused on one or more processes. Russell (2012) explains that a "process audit is verification by evaluation of an operation or method against predetermined instructions or standards, to measure conformance to these standards and the effectiveness of the instructions." Accordingly, a process audit ensures the effectiveness of process controls designed, documented, and implemented to ensure customer satisfaction with products and services.

The *product/service audit*, even more limited in scope than the process audit, is conducted to ensure that finished products and services conform to customer expectations, specifications, and tolerances. A defining characteristic of a product or service audit is that such an audit is conducted after production or service delivery is complete. A product or service audit typically involves the use of measurement equipment to evaluate conformance to specifications and/or performance tests; in this regard, a product/service audit may be confused with final inspection. *Final inspection* is a normal step in production or service delivery operations by shop floor personnel or inspectors to ensure that the product or service meets customer expectations. Product/service audits are not a normal step in day-to-day production or service delivery operations by shop floor or inspection personnel; rather, they are audits conducted periodically by any interested party to ensure that the product or service meets customer expectations.

It is important to note that these classifications are not mutually exclusive, and, in practice, cross-classifications of a quality audit are possible.

The following purposes of quality audits are listed in ASQ/ANSI/ISO 19011:2018:

- To contribute to the improvement of a management system and its performance

- To fulfill external requirements (for example, certification to a management system standard)

- To verify conformity with contractual requirements

- To obtain and maintain confidence in the capability of a supplier

- To determine the effectiveness of the management system

- To evaluate the compatibility and alignment of the management system objectives with the management system policy and the overall organizational objectives

ROLES AND RESPONSIBILITIES IN AUDITS

Each of the three parties involved in an audit—the client, the auditor, and the auditee—plays a role that contributes to the success of the audit. The *client*, the party that initiates the audit, selects the auditor and determines the reference standard to be used. The client, typically the end user of the audit results, determines the type of audit needed (system, process, or product) as well as its time and duration.

The selected *auditor*, whether an individual or a group, needs to adhere to the role of a third party. That is, the auditor must maintain objectivity and avoid bias in conducting the audit. The auditor must comply with any confidentiality requirements mandated by the auditee. An experienced individual is appointed the lead auditor to communicate audit requirements, manage the auditing activities, and report the results. For rules, qualifications, and evaluation criteria for an auditor, see ASQ/ANSI/ISO 19011:2018.

Finally, the *auditee* has the responsibility of accommodating the audit, which entails providing the auditors access to the facilities involved and providing copies of all relevant documentation. The auditee is also expected to provide the resources needed and to select staff members to accompany the auditors.

2. AUDIT PROCESS

Proper planning is a key factor in achieving an efficient quality audit. Planning should be conducted with consideration of the client expectations. This includes the scope, depth, and time frame of the audit. The lead auditor has the responsibility of planning and conducting the audit and should be authorized to perform these activities.

Planning an audit, as with any activity, should address the questions of what, when, how, and who. That is, what elements of the quality system are to be audited? Against what document or reference standard should the quality system be audited? The answers to both questions are determined by the client and should be clearly communicated to the auditee. When should the audit start, and when should it conclude? A schedule of the audit activities needs to be prepared and communicated to both the client and the auditee. It is the lead auditor's responsibility to inform the client of any delays, report the reasons for the delays, and update the completion date of the audit.

The method of conducting the audit should also be addressed. Working documents need to be prepared, including checklists of the elements to examine, questions to ask, and activities to monitor. A number of references provide generic checklists that can be used as templates. However, it is best to design a checklist to suit the audit at hand and its specific scope and objectives. Forms for collecting auditors' observations and the supporting evidence should also be included in the working document. Working documents are typically reviewed by an experienced auditor and approved by the lead auditor before implementation. It is recommended that the auditor explain the methods planned to the auditee. This should help the organization better prepare for the audit and ease the fear usually attached to the process.

The question of who will examine specific elements, processes, or products addresses the qualifications and experience of the individual auditors (assessors) needed. With the client expectations in mind, the lead auditor should assign the various tasks among his or her team.

An audit is usually conducted in three steps. A pre-examination or opening meeting with the auditee marks the beginning of the process. During this meeting the lead auditor introduces team members to the senior management of the auditee and explains the objectives of the audit and the methods used. The auditee selects representative members of the organization to facilitate and assist in the process, and submits a documented description of the quality system or element to be examined. Issues regarding proprietary information are typically addressed and resolved before the audit is started.

The next step involves a suitability audit of the documented procedures against the selected reference standard. Observed nonconformities at this stage of the audit should be reported to both the client and the auditee for immediate action. The auditing process should pause to allow for corrective measures.

In the third step, the auditor examines in depth the implementation of the quality system. The auditor maintains records of all nonconformities observed and the supporting data. Provisions should be made in the audit plan to allow additional investigation of clues suggesting nonconformities revealed by the data collected. The auditee management should be made aware of, and acknowledge, all the nonconformities observed during the audit. This step concludes with a closing meeting with the auditee's management for a presentation of findings. In some cases the auditor may be required to recommend corrective measures for improving the system. However, it is up to the auditee to plan and implement these measures in a way that best suits the organization.

3. AUDIT TOOLS

To successfully complete any type of audit, several tools are required. Since many of these tools have been discussed in detail in other sections of this book, detailed discussions of tools already covered will not be repeated here.

Checklists

Checklists are used during audits to record tabular data such as the number of observations or occurrences of specific phenomena such as defects, errors, or mistakes. Checklists also commonly provide a rough graphic or illustration of a product, or flowchart of a service delivery operation, to provide auditors future reference as to where the phenomenon occurred. Data from checklists inform the audit process, particularly when making observations, reporting areas for improvement, and, later, verifying that corrective actions have been implemented and are effective.

Log Sheets

Log sheets are historical records of when specific actions were taken or functions were performed. Log sheets help identify who took specific actions, what actions were taken, and the timing and sequence of actions taken, and very commonly they refer to job instructions or procedures to be used. Log sheets are valuable sources of information and inform the audit process, ensuring that necessary tasks or functions are performed. Since many of the types of functions recorded on log sheets are related to maintenance activities, maintenance interval requirements, cleaning requirements, replenishment of materials and supplies, use of consumables, process adjustments, and identification of sources of variability or errors, log sheets are important audit tools.

Sampling Plans

Sampling plans are statistically based tools that provide guidance in terms of what, when, how frequently, and how much to sample. As sampling plans are covered elsewhere in this book, they will not be discussed in detail here; however, as sampling plans are related to quality auditing, we will address that application.

Sampling plans are used in quality audits primarily to identify key characteristics of when, where, how, and how much to sample the supplies, materials, consumables, components, subassemblies, and so on, of the products or service delivery applications being audited. Sampling plans are also used in audits to define when, where, how, and how much data auditors are to investigate. Regardless of whether sampling plans are used to look at products, processes, or functions to be audited, the sampling plans used are the same.

4. COMMUNICATION TOOLS AND TECHNIQUES

There has been extensive coverage of tools and techniques for communication and use in presentations throughout this book. For that reason we will not duplicate those discussions here. It is important to note that the many communication tools presented will be used by the ASQ CQI, and knowledge of these tools and techniques will be tested on the CQI exam. Of particular importance will be making sure the CQI understands the graphs, charts, and diagrams discussed throughout this book.

5. CORRECTIVE ACTION REQUESTS (CARS)

Corrective action requests (CARs) arising from audit processes are intended to address and correct deficiencies and improve processes. CARs create a historical record that (1) auditees can use to guide future work efforts, (2) individuals responsible for making repairs and process improvements can use as justification for resource requirements, and (3) auditors can use to verify that repairs and process improvements have been completed. CARs form an important part of the audit report for the auditee and the auditor.

AUDIT OUTCOMES

A set of documents used to guide any form of audit is called *working papers*. Working papers are used to ensure an efficient and effective review of selected systems, processes, and/or products and services. Included in the working papers are many examples and instances of discoveries, observations, and conversations, which become part of an audit. In particular, these discoveries, observations, and conversations are recorded during the information-gathering phase of an audit and are used later to provide the basis for comparisons with applicable standards, specifications, policies, procedures, and work instructions.

As a result of documenting the audit in the working papers, and in comparing actual operations with documentation of intended operations, two types of findings generally result: examples of effective or noteworthy accomplishments and examples of discrepancies. Examples of effective or noteworthy accomplishments, such as effective components of the quality system or innovative processes that prevent mistakes, are documented in the working papers as well as in the final audit report to encourage continued use or further implementation. Examples of discrepancies, such as inadequate instructions, incomplete training, and noncompliance with customer specifications, are documented in the working papers as well as in the final audit report to initiate corrective action.

When the need for corrective action is identified during an audit, a corrective action request (CAR) is generated. A CAR is a document that identifies a discrepant condition, the source or standard giving rise to the discrepant condition, when the discrepant condition was discovered and by whom, who is responsible for addressing the discrepant condition, the allowable time frame for corrective action, and so on. The primary intent of the CAR is to trigger action that either eliminates or reduces the negative effects of the condition. Ultimately, the CAR is intended to be the vehicle that drives process improvement. From this perspective, the CAR directly impacts customer satisfaction. So important are CARs, they are normally cited in the audit report with a required action to verify that the CAR was acted on and actually resulted in one or more process improvements.

Audit Reporting and Follow-Up

A final report is submitted to the client indicating the facts of the audit and conclusions regarding the ability of the subject system, element, process, or product to achieve quality objectives. Proper planning and execution of the audit facilitates the preparation of this report and provides data to support its conclusions. The lead auditor is responsible for the accuracy of the report and the validity of its conclusions. The report should be submitted to the client, who in turn is responsible for providing a copy to the auditee.

The audit final report should include, at a minimum, the following:

1. Type of audit conducted

2. Objectives of the audit

3. Identification of involved parties: auditor, auditee, and third party

4. Audit team members

5. Critical nonconformities and other observations (effective or noteworthy accomplishments)

6. Audit standards and reference documents used

7. Determination of proper corrective action(s)

8. Duration of audit

9. Audit report distribution and date

10. Audit results and recommendations

11. Audit-related records

Should the auditee initiate improvement efforts to correct nonconformities via CARs, the three parties should agree on a follow-up audit to verify the results. The plan, audit, report, and improve cycle may be repeated whenever systems and/ or requirements change. The results attained provide a measure of the effectiveness of the audit. Improvement efforts should also be directed toward identifying and eliminating the root causes of reported nonconformities and identifying the corrective action(s) to be taken. Root causes represent the main reason behind the occurrence of a nonconformance or an undesirable condition or status. The corrective actions may then be validated by performing tests, inspections, or even more audits.

REFERENCES

American Society for Quality (ASQ). 2018. ASQ/ANSI/ISO 19011:2018 *Guidelines for Auditing Management Systems*. Milwaukee: ASQ Quality Press.

Arter, D. 2003. *Quality Audits for Improved Performance*. 3rd ed. Milwaukee: ASQ Quality Press.

Russell, J.P., ed. 2012. *The ASQ Auditing Handbook*. 4th ed. Milwaukee: ASQ Quality Press.

BIBLIOGRAPHY

Bautista-Smith, J. 2012. *Auditing Beyond Compliance: Using the Portable Universal Quality Lean Audit Model*. Milwaukee: ASQ Quality Press.

Coleman, L. B. 2015. *Advanced Quality Auditing: An Auditor's Review of Risk Management, Lean Improvement, and Data Analysis*. 3rd ed. Milwaukee: ASQ Quality Press.

Chapter 23

E. Quality Tools and Techniques

Define and use the following quality tools and techniques. (Apply)

1. Pareto charts

2. Cause and effect diagrams

3. Flowcharts

4. Control charts

5. Check sheets

6. Scatter diagrams

7. Histograms

Body of Knowledge IV.E

An understanding of basic problem-solving and continuous improvement tools and techniques is critical for a quality inspector to be effective and to function within the larger quality community. It has been said many times that as much as 85% of the problems encountered in production or service delivery operations can be solved with these basic tools and techniques. We will begin our discussion with the seven quality control tools (see also Chapters 19 and 20), proceed in Chapter 24 with a discussion of PDCA/PDSA, and conclude with a discussion of the DMAIC and root cause analysis techniques.

SEVEN BASIC QUALITY CONTROL TOOLS

The seven basic quality control tools comprise the following:

1. Pareto charts

2. Cause-and-effect diagrams (also known as *fishbone* or *Ishikawa* diagrams)

3. Flowcharts

4. Control charts

5. Check sheets

6. Scatter diagrams

7. Histograms

Note that a detailed discussion of the Pareto chart, scatter plot, and histogram appeared in Chapter 19. The discussion of the remaining tools, that is, cause-and-effect diagram, flowcharts, control charts, and check sheets, appeared in Chapter 20. So, the discussion on these tools will not be repeated in this chapter.

These basic tools form a simple but very powerful structure for quality improvement. Once inspectors, technicians, and operators/service delivery personnel become fully familiar with these tools, management must get involved to sustain their use for an ongoing quality improvement process. Management must create an environment where these tools become part of the day-to-day production or service processes. Implementation of these tools without management's commitment portends an impending failure of continuous improvement efforts.

Every job, whether in a manufacturing company or in a service company, involves a process. As described, each process consists of a certain number of steps. Thus, no matter how well the process is planned, designed, and executed, there is always some potential for variability. In some cases this variability may be very little, while in other cases it may be very high. If the variability is very little, it is usually due to common causes, which are unavoidable and cannot be controlled. If the variability is too high, then, besides the common causes, there are other causes, usually known as *assignable causes*, present in the process. Any process working under only common causes or chance causes is considered to be in statistical control. If a process is working under both common and assignable causes, the process is considered unstable, or not in statistical control.

BIBLIOGRAPHY

Gupta, B. C., and H. F. Walker. 2007. *Statistical Quality Control for the Six Sigma Green Belt.* Milwaukee: ASQ Quality Press.

Chapter 24

F. Problem-Solving Tools and Continuous Improvement Techniques

Describe and use the following tools and techniques in various situations. (Apply)

1. Plan–do–check–act (PDCA) or plan–do–study–act (PDSA) cycles

2. Lean tools for eliminating waste: 5S, error-proofing, value-stream mapping; and lean concepts: kaizen, flow, pull

3. Six sigma phases: define, measure, analyze, improve, control (DMAIC)

4. Failure mode and effects analysis (FMEA)

5. 8D Methodology

6. 5 Why Analysis

7. Fault Tree Analysis

Body of Knowledge IV.F

Numerous tools and techniques are available to support problem solving and continuous improvement. These tools and techniques range from the most basic, such as the plan–do–check–act (PDCA) cycle, to the advanced, such as Six Sigma. It should be noted that a careful review of the current Certified Quality Inspector Body of Knowledge (CQI BoK) is required to assess the level of knowledge required for the CQI to master relative to *Bloom's Taxonomy*. For example, the CQI will be expected to know much more about the PDCA cycle than about Six Sigma and failure mode and effects analysis (FMEA).

1. PLAN–DO–CHECK–ACT (PDCA) OR PLAN–DO–STUDY–ACT (PDSA) CYCLES

The plan–do–check–act (PDCA) and the plan–do–study–act (PDSA) cycles are very common in use and in the language of the quality profession. Accordingly, we begin our discussion of these two cycles with a clarification. That clarification is that these two cycles were *not* created by the same person, the two cycles are not structurally the same, and the two cycles have different philosophical intents. As McKinley (2006) has documented, the original creators of the cycles are as follows:

- Walter Shewhart—Shewhart cycle—PDCA—development date late 1930s. It should be noted that Shewhart is credited with the "Shewhart cycle"; however, Shewhart did not label the steps of his cycle as PDCA, but rather used the terms "specification," "production," and "inspection."

- W. Edwards Deming—Deming cycle—PDSA—development date late 1950s.

Structurally, these cycles differ on the "check" step advocated by Shewhart as compared to the "study" step advocated by Deming. The primary emphasis of the *check* step is to verify that the desired results have been obtained. The primary emphasis of the *study* step is to gain quantitative knowledge of the process and its performance to learn how it may be further improved. This difference in emphasis between the check step and the study step explains the different philosophical intents of each cycle. It should also be noted that the points of difference explained here have been commonly confused, and PDCA and PDSA continue to be used interchangeably. Not only is this practice misleading and incorrect, but it obscures the points of origin and original intent of the two cycles.

Plan

Once a problem has been clearly defined, the first steps in solving it are to collect and analyze data, consider and analyze alternative solutions, and choose the best solution. These steps, although easy to state, can be extremely difficult and time-consuming to execute. Jointly, these steps constitute the *plan* phase in the PDCA cycle. One approach to this phase is to list the goals, the barriers to reaching those goals, and a strategy for coping with those barriers. This approach provides guidance for the next steps.

In most situations a team representing everyone affected by the problem and its solution should be formed and assigned the problem-solving task.

There is a strong tendency to jump to the *do* phase of the cycle rather than take the time to adequately execute the plan phase. Before moving to the do phase, however, careful plans should be made regarding the collection of information during that phase.

In some situations it may be useful to apply a quick-and-dirty or Band-Aid solution to allow time to focus on a permanent solution. Of course, this approach creates the tendency to move on to the next problem because this one is "solved."

Do

Once a solution to the problem has been decided on, and a data collection scheme has been determined, the next phase is to try it. If possible, this should be done on a small scale and/or off-line. Sometimes, the proposed solution can be tried in a laboratory setting or outside the regular production process. During the *do* phase as much data as possible should be collected. In some situations videotaping a process permits further data collection upon replay.

Check

The *check* phase is used to analyze the information collected during the *do* phase. The data must be validated using valid mathematical and statistical techniques.

Act

In the *act* phase, action is taken based on the conclusions reached in the *check* phase. If the data show that the proposed solution is a good solution for the problem, the act phase consists of integrating the solution into the standard way of doing things. If the data show that another proposed solution is needed, the act phase consists of initiating the search for another solution.

As the word "cycle" implies, the *act* phase is followed by the *plan* phase because quality improvement is a continuous journey, as shown in Figure 24.1.

The PDCA cycle is intended to be iterative. By *iterative* we mean the cycle is repeated until the desired improvement results have been achieved.

Gordon (2002) observes that many organizations are pretty good at the *do* and *check* phases but fall down on the *plan* and *act* phases. Perhaps this is partly due to the "Don't just stand there, do something" impulse. There is a tendency, for instance, to provide a service, process, or product to customers without adequate care in the design (plan) phase. The strategy is that customers will provide feedback, and much will be learned from the design mistakes. Automotive industries have attempted to combat this with such programs as advanced product quality planning (APQP), potential failure mode and effects analysis (PFMEA), and production part approval process (PPAP).

Figure 24.1   The plan–do–check–act cycle.

2. LEAN TOOLS FOR ELIMINATING WASTE

Lean production refers to a set of tools and techniques intended to improve efficiency and reduce or eliminate waste in manufacturing and service delivery. Lean production has often been characterized as "doing more with less." This concept of doing more with less is related to the fact that there is generally substantial waste in manufacturing and service delivery operations. As the concept of lean came from Japan in the late 1980s and early 1990s, the Japanese refer to this waste as *muda*. Taiichi Ohno originally identified seven types of waste:

1. Overproduction

2. Waiting

3. Unnecessary transportation of materials or products

4. Overprocessing

5. Inventory

6. Unnecessary employee movement

7. Production of defective parts

Ohno later identified an eighth waste, the underutilization of employees.

There are many tools that are considered applicable in lean operations; however, the most common lean tools are as follows.

5S

5S is an acronym and tool that focuses on cleanliness and order in the workplace. The concept of 5S is that if all elements in the workplace, such as tools, equipment, supplies, work surfaces, aisles, storage areas, and so on, are clean and organized, work will flow more rapidly through the work space and production or service delivery will be faster with less waste and, thus, more efficient. The five S's are *sort, set in order, shine, standardize*, and *sustain*.

Sort. *Sorting* refers to making sure that, as much as possible, only the things needed to perform specific and necessary work tasks—tools, equipment, supplies, instructions, paperwork, references, and so on—are in the area where the work is to be completed. By ensuring that only those things needed for the work are in the work space, clutter is removed. Clutter in the workplace slows production, adds to confusion and the potential for mistakes, and generally requires the unnecessary movement of material.

Set in Order. *Setting in order* refers to organization in the workplace that facilitates production. Setting in order applies to the physical arrangement of tools and equipment such that they are easily identifiable, located in predefined and easily accessible positions, and grouped in a way that improves the efficiency of their use when needed. Setting in order also refers to supplies in that parts, pieces, or other items such as forms needed in service delivery operations are readily positioned for access and use with minimal travel or movement within the work space.

Shine. Shine refers to keeping the work space clean. A clean work space improves productivity in at least three ways: (1) it ensures that when it is time to work, the work can begin promptly, (2) it contributes to safety by mitigating the potential for injuries, and (3) it improves employee morale.

Standardize. Standardize refers to making sure the basic principles of 5S are used consistently throughout the workplace. In many companies *standardize* means preparing and implementing policies, procedures, and instructions intended to ensure that all areas and work spaces use the same approaches to sorting, setting in order, and shining so that work spaces have certain elements of commonality and familiarity for all employees.

Sustain. Sustain refers to making sure each of the 5S elements remains in the workplace after initial implementation. Sustain is important because without a commitment to be diligent in implementing 5S, the workplace would likely revert back to the way things were done prior to the 5S implementation. Companies use a variety of other lean tools to help ensure that 5S is sustained. Many of these other lean tools focus on keeping key information and data visible and prominently displayed for employees in what are referred to as *visual controls*.

Error-Proofing

Error-proofing is commonly known as *fail-safing* and is derived from the Japanese term *poka-yoke*. Poka-yoke refers to efforts intended to eliminate human-based errors or mistakes before they occur. Poka-yoke concepts can be applied to the design, material selection, assembly or delivery, and handling and movement of products or service delivery.

ASQ provides guidance on when and how to implement error-proofing.

When to Use Mistake-Proofing

1. When a process step has been identified where human error can cause mistakes or defects to occur, especially in processes that rely on the worker's attention, skill, or experience.

2. In a service process, where the customer can make an error that affects the output.

3. At a hand-off step in a process, when output or (for service processes) the customer is transferred to another worker.

4. When a minor error early in the process causes major problems later in the process.

5. When the consequences of an error are expensive or dangerous.

Mistake-Proofing Procedure

1. Obtain or create a flowchart of the process. Review each step, thinking about where and when human errors are likely to occur.

2. For each potential error, work back through the process to find its source.

3. For each error, think of potential ways to make it impossible for the error to occur. Consider:

- *Elimination.* Eliminating the step that causes the error.

- *Replacement.* Replacing the step with an error-proof one.

- *Facilitation.* Making the correct action far easier than the error.

4. If you cannot make it impossible for the error to occur, think of ways to detect the error and minimize its effects. Consider inspection method, setting function, and regulatory function.

5. Choose the best mistake-proofing method or device for each error. Test it, then implement it. Three kinds of inspection methods provide rapid feedback:

- *Successive inspection* is done at the next step of the process by the next worker.

- *Self-inspection* means workers check their own work immediately after doing it.

- *Source inspection* checks, before the process step takes place, that conditions are correct. Often, it's automatic and keeps the process from proceeding until conditions are right.

Value Stream Mapping

Value stream mapping combines detailed flowcharting with key information to produce a thorough picture of manufacturing or service delivery operations. A key function of the value stream map is eliminating waste by identifying and categorizing operations that add value and those that do not add value (that is, waste, or *muda*). Operations that add value are those that change the form, fit, or function of a product or service, and customers are thus willing to pay for operations that add value. Operations that do not change the form, fit, or function of a product or service do not add value for the customer, and customers are thus not willing to pay for non-value-added operations. Non-value-added operations must be eliminated.

The process of developing a value stream map is much like that of developing a flowchart. While there are many approaches to value stream mapping, one approach is as follows:

1. Identify a product or service delivery operation for mapping

2. Perform a first-pass walk-through or inspection of the operation(s) to gain initial familiarity

3. Construct a map or diagram of the operation(s) in its current state using standard value-mapping symbology

4. Study the current-state map to identify areas of waste or non-value-added activity, and areas for improvement

5. Validate the areas of waste or non-value-added activity, or for improvement

6. Construct a map or diagram of the operation(s) in a desired future state using standardized value-mapping symbology

7. Gain consensus and/or approval on the desired future state of the operation(s)

8. Implement the changes needed for the desired future state of the operation(s)

9. Validate that the changes implemented for the desired future state of the operation(s) were effective and did not create new difficulties or waste

10. Monitor the desired state of the operation(s) to ensure that the improvements are sustained

Lean Concepts

Kaizen. ASQ defines *kaizen* as "a Japanese term that means gradual unending improvement by doing little things better and setting and achieving increasingly higher standards."

In operational terms, kaizen generally refers to major projects or events intended to dramatically improve processes. Kaizen events generally involve teams of people who, working from current- and future-state maps (mentioned in the material on value stream mapping), reconfigure work spaces to improve productivity and eliminate waste.

Push. *Push* is a concept that refers to the production of products before they are needed or are ordered by a customer. Products produced under a push system are placed in an inventory with the assumption that customers will buy the product in a reasonable period of time as it is configured; this is not always a reasonable assumption and can lead to a great deal of waste. The waste associated with push production is unnecessary material storage space, risk of damage or theft, and the inability to recover in a timely manner any compensation for the value added to the product(s).

Pull. *Pull* is a concept that refers to the production of products only when they are needed or are ordered by a customer. Products produced under a pull system are generally not placed in an inventory, which means the customer may define his or her own specifications or configurations. The pull system eliminates a great deal of waste.

Flow. ASQ defines *flow* as "the progressive achievement of tasks along the value stream so a product proceeds from design to launch, order to delivery, and raw to finished materials in the hands of the customer with no stoppages, scrap, or backflows."

3. SIX SIGMA PHASES

Quality is, in part, defined by consistency. By extension, *consistency* means an absence of variability. The CQI should take this to mean that the approach and techniques used to solve problems are essentially processes, and as a process, problem solving is no different from production or service delivery operations. To ensure consistent results in problem-solving efforts, a structured approach is required. Countless problem-solving approaches have been developed and reported in the press over many years—some specifically related to quality, some not. While it is not the intent of the authors to advocate for or against any particular problem-solving approach, it should be emphasized that for reasons of consistency and thoroughness, some standardized approach to problem solving should be adopted and used consistently to guide problem-solving efforts. Two problem-solving approaches are of interest to the CQI:

- The scientific method (a method not specifically related to quality)
- Six Sigma (a method specifically related to quality)

The Scientific Method

Perhaps the most noted and recognized approach to structured problem solving is the scientific method. The scientific method is used in many fields of inquiry to guide problem-solving efforts in accordance with standardized steps, which include:

- Asking a question
- Collecting data
- Posing hypotheses
- Testing hypotheses
- Analyzing data
- Drawing conclusions
- Communicating results

It is true that the scientific method can be used to guide problem-solving efforts in quality, and if used properly, it may be quite effective. Many of the tools and techniques used in continuous improvement can readily be applied to support and enhance the scientific method. What differentiates the scientific method from other problem-solving methods used specifically to support continuous improvement is an absence of the common language, tools, and techniques typically used in the quality community.

Six Sigma

Perhaps the most common problem-solving approach used within the quality community today is Six Sigma. Six Sigma is a five-step problem-solving approach comprising the following steps:

- Define

- Measure

- Analyze

- Improve

- Control

The five steps of Six Sigma are most commonly referred to as the DMAIC methodology. Upon further analysis, we can see that each of the outcomes of the scientific method are found within the DMAIC methodology. Two primary points differentiate the scientific method from Six Sigma: (1) Six Sigma's use of quality-specific language and tools, and (2) Six Sigma's use of the DMAIC methodology in quality-related problem solving when certain financial constraints or expectations have been met. The financial constraints or expectations are related to the amount of cost savings expected as a result of problem-solving activities to justify use of the comprehensive and systematic DMAIC methodology. It is beyond the scope of this book, and the CQI BoK, to provide further content on Six Sigma and the DMAIC methodology. It should be emphasized, however, that Six Sigma and the DMAIC methodology are, and will remain, critically important problem-solving approaches within the quality community. The CQI is strongly encouraged to continue his or her professional development by learning more about this topic.

The goal of all approaches to problem solving is to identify the reason(s) why a problem occurred. The process of identifying the true underlying reason(s) a problem occurred is known as *root cause analysis*.

Root Cause Analysis

Root cause analysis (RCA) is an approach to problem solving that is based on the identification of the true underlying reason(s) why a problem occurred. RCA is critically important because any corrective action taken on a non–root cause issue or item will result in the problem remaining active within a specific process. In other words, following some misapplied corrective action on a non–root cause issue or item may change the appearance or manifestation of the original problem, but the original problem still exists.

RCA is similar to the scientific method and Six Sigma in many ways: RCA makes use of many of the quality-related tools and techniques discussed thus far in this book, it is intended to be iteratively applied, wherein by iteration we contribute to continuous improvement, and it has a structured approach, which includes the following:

- Define the problem(s)

- Identify manifestations of the problem(s)

- Collect data

- Identify root causes

- Propose solutions

- Test solutions

- Verify effectiveness of solutions

4. FAILURE MODE AND EFFECTS ANALYSIS (FMEA)

Failure mode and effects analysis (FMEA) is a team-based problem-solving tool intended to help users identify and eliminate, or reduce the negative effects of, potential failures before they occur in systems, subsystems, product or process design, or the delivery of a service. FMEA can be used as a stand-alone tool or as part of comprehensive quality programs such as ISO/QS 9000, APQP, or Six Sigma. Accordingly, our goal is to familiarize readers with terminology, theory, mechanics, and applications of FMEA consistent with the CQI BoK requirements.

Selecting a Standard for FMEA

There are two primary standards for FMEA, the military standard (MIL-STD 1629A) and the Society of Automotive Engineers standard (SAE J1739). Both standards are limited in scope to address only design and process FMEAs. These standards provide general FMEA forms and documents, identify criteria for the quantification of risk associated with potential failures, and provide very general guidelines on the mechanics of completing FMEAs. MIL-STD 1629A and SAE J1739 may be obtained by contacting the Department of the Navy and the Society of Automotive Engineers at the following addresses, respectively:

> Department of the Navy
> Navy Publishing and Printing Services Office
> 709 Robbins Avenue
> Philadelphia, PA 19111-5094

> Society of Automotive Engineers
> 400 Commonwealth Drive
> Warrendale, PA 10596-0001

Planning for an FMEA

Planning for an FMEA involves a series of considerations that include, as a minimum, the following:

- *Selecting appropriate applications for the analysis.* An FMEA may be authorized by individuals at various levels within an organization, or it may be required by ISO/QS 9000, APQP, Six Sigma methodologies, internal quality programs, or customer requirements. However authorized or required, an FMEA is expensive to complete and should be completed only in those instances where the benefits of completing the analysis outweigh the costs.

- *Identifying and allocating resources.* These resources include FMEA team members and a reporting structure, physical space to conduct the analysis and store documentation, time, and clerical/communications support.

- *Defining scope.* Since an FMEA can be conducted at a high level (that is, the system level) or at a very detailed level (that is, the component level or service delivery level), and since a high-level FMEA may lead to additional FMEAs at more detailed levels, it is very important to set the scope of the analysis before beginning.

- *Expectations and deliverables.* The team-based nature of completing an FMEA means FMEA team members will have dual or multiple responsibilities and reporting structures in addition to the FMEA team. It is critical, therefore, to clearly define performance expectations for all FMEA team members and to communicate those expectations directly to appropriate supervisory or managerial personnel in reporting structures outside the FMEA team. It is equally important that all FMEA team members understand what deliverables will result from the analysis, and their respective roles in developing those deliverables.

- *Establishing milestones, due dates, and deadlines.* Key milestones for an FMEA include authorizing the analysis, establishing a reporting structure, allocating resources (particularly FMEA team members), gathering input for the analysis, completing the analysis, taking and monitoring corrective action, and preparing documentation, report-outs, and debriefings. To ensure effectiveness, an FMEA should be conducted as a project from the perspective of establishing a schedule specifying due dates and deadlines for each of the major milestones.

Establishing a Single Point of Responsibility

As mentioned earlier, FMEA is a team-based analysis. However, there is sufficient practical experience to support the idea that assigning responsibility to a cross-functional team rather than a single individual is not the most effective policy. For a variety of reasons, a single person should be assigned the responsibility of FMEA team leader, and that person needs the authority to make decisions and allocate resources to complete the FMEA as planned.

FMEA Team Members

The belief that only the one or two people closest to a system, subsystem, product or process design, or service delivery should be assigned to an FMEA violates the very intent of the analysis. FMEA is intended to be completed by team members representing a broad cross-section of expertise—technical and nontechnical. At a minimum, an FMEA should have representation from the following functional groups:

- Design engineering
- Manufacturing engineering

- Production

- Quality/reliability

- Purchasing/material control

- Sales and marketing

- Customers

It cannot be overemphasized that for an FMEA to be truly effective, the viewpoints and perspectives of every functional group listed here must be included—particularly customers. Excluding stakeholder input from the FMEA typically results in missed opportunities to detect and correct failure modes.

Inputs to an FMEA

To prepare for an FMEA it is necessary to gather information from several sources—and these inputs should be gathered prior to the initial FMEA team meeting so as to maximize the effectiveness of team members' time. Inputs to an FMEA include, as a minimum, the following:

- Process flowchart or functional block diagram

- Design specifications

- Customer requirements/specifications

- Testing data/results

- Data on similar process/design technology

- Warranty data

- Failure/rework data

- Design/configuration change data

- Prior FMEAs

- Results from quantitative analysis (design of experiments, statistical process control, process capability assessments, reliability assessments, and so on)

FMEA and Other Quality Tools

In addition to the inputs previously described, other quality tools are frequently used during the completion of an FMEA. These tools include, but are not limited to, the following:

- Cause-and-effect diagrams

- Process decision program charts

- Histograms

- Pareto diagrams
- Run charts
- Force-field analysis
- Fault tree diagrams
- Root cause analysis

Outputs from an FMEA

Outputs or deliverables from an FMEA include the following:

- FMEA documentation
- System, subsystem, design, process, and/or service delivery documentation
- Recommendation reports
- Corrective action reports
- Design changes
- Compliance reports
- Debriefings and presentations

Basic Steps in an FMEA

Complexity in an FMEA is directly related to the number of levels of analysis dictated by the situation or team members. At the most fundamental level, however, every FMEA consists of the same basic steps:

- Identify a starting point for the analysis; a starting point will be a system, subsystem, product or process design, or service delivery system of interest.
- Gather all relevant inputs to support the analysis; gathering inputs for an FMEA is a milestone to be completed prior to an initial FMEA meeting. It is far more effective, both from cost and efficiency perspectives, to have all team members at meetings participating in the analysis rather than leaving meetings to gather input.
- Identify potential failure modes related to the following:
  - Who would be impacted by a failure?
  - What would happen in the event of a failure?
  - When would the failure occur?
  - Where would the failure occur?

- Why would the failure occur?

- How would the failure occur?

- Quantify the risk associated with each potential failure; risk assessment is based on severity, occurrence, and detection of a potential failure.

- Develop a corrective action plan for the most significant risks.

- Iterate, or repeat, the analysis until all potential failures pose an "acceptable" level of risk; what constitutes an "acceptable" risk must be clearly defined by the individual or agent authorizing the FMEA.

- Document results.

- Report-out and/or present results.

Quantifying the Risk Associated with Each Potential Failure

To avoid confusion, the quantification of risk associated with potential failures will now be introduced—prior to detailed explanation of FMEA mechanics. While FMEA may appropriately be applied to systems, subsystems, product or process designs, and/or service delivery, risk assessment methods and metrics remain consistent regardless of analysis level. Where the actual criteria for risk assessment change (specifically between design and process FMEAs), the criteria will be provided as needed for the discussion. Readers are encouraged to familiarize themselves with this section on risk assessment, and be prepared to review this section once specific analysis levels are discussed.

Risk Components. For purposes of FMEA, risk has three components, which are multiplied to produce a risk priority number (RPN). The three components of risk are:

- *Severity* (S). An indicator of the severity of a failure should a failure occur. Severity is described on a 10-point scale.

- *Occurrence* (O). An indicator of the likelihood of a failure occurring. Occurrence is described on a 10-point scale.

- *Detection* (D). An indicator of the likelihood of detecting a failure once it has occurred. Detection is described on a 10-point scale.

$$RPNmin = 1, \text{ while } RPNmax = 1000$$

Taking Action Based on an RPN. A common mistake in assessing FMEA risk is prioritizing corrective action based on the descending order of RPNs. Logic would suggest that the largest RPNs represent the highest risk—which is true, but only to a point. When multiplying the three risk components together, their importance relative to each other becomes obscured. Consider the following example:

	(S)	×	(O)	×	(D)	=	RPN
Potential failure 1	2		10		5		100
Potential failure 2	10		2		5		100
Potential failure 3	2		5		10		100
Potential failure 4	10		5		2		100

In each case the resulting RPN is 100. Therefore, it is unclear which potential failure to take corrective action on first. There is, however, a generally accepted strategy when taking action on an RPN:

1. Eliminate the occurrence

2. Reduce the severity

3. Improve detection

Getting back to the example, with the additional information provided by the generally accepted strategy when taking action on an RPN, it becomes clear how to proceed.

1. Eliminating occurrences would, mathematically, reorder the RPNs.

2. Reducing severity next would focus our attention on potential failures 2 and 4. But then what? We still have two potential failures with the same level of risk.

3. Reducing occurrence as the next step in this process focuses our attention on potential failure 4, which has a higher occurrence rating than potential failure 2.

Now our attention can turn to evaluating the remaining potential failures since potential failures 2 and 4 have been ranked as the two most important. Of the two remaining potential failures (1 and 3), potential failure 1 has the higher occurrence rating and is therefore ranked as the third most important potential failure; potential failure 3 drops to the least important position by default. The rank order by which the potential failures should be investigated for corrective action is as follows:

1. First priority: Potential failure 4

2. Second priority: Potential failure 2

3. Third priority: Potential failure 1

4. Fourth priority: Potential failure 3

Do We Rate the Failure Mode or the Cause? A common point of confusion arises when considering what is actually rated as part of the risk assessment—the actual failure itself or the cause of a given failure. It is perfectly acceptable to rate either the failure or the cause—as long as the assumption is well documented (on actual FMEA charts, in written correspondence, and in all reports/presentations) and everyone on the FMEA team and in the reporting structure is aware of the assumption. Whether rating a failure itself or a cause of that failure, an FMEA should provide consistent results and corrective actions.

FMEAs Encountered by Quality Professionals

It was mentioned earlier in this chapter that FMEA can be applied to the system/ subsystem, design or process, or service delivery levels. A brief synopsis of each FMEA application follows:

- *System FMEA.* A *system*, or *subsystem*, is a collection of elements or components working together to accomplish a desired task or function. FMEA is applied at the system or subsystem level to identify potential failure modes and effects that could negatively impact system or subsystem performance. At the system or subsystem level, FMEA is focused at system or subsystem boundaries where potential failures are most likely to occur. The boundaries of interest for a system or subsystem FMEA include functional (that is, expected outcomes assuming normal operation) or operational (that is, specific outputs expected as compared with tolerances, specifications, and timing).

- *Design FMEA.* A *design*—or more accurately, a *product design*—is a set of specifications that describes all aspects of a product (that is, major functions, operating parameters and tolerances, materials, dimensions, and so on). FMEA is applied to product designs as early in the product design process as feasible to identify potential failure modes that could result from a design flaw. Design FMEAs are a normal part of key milestones in the product development process, such as concept reviews, concept approvals, preliminary design reviews, and final design reviews.

- *Process FMEA.* A *process design* is a set of specifications that describes all aspects of a process (that is, functional components, flow rates, process steps, equipment to be used, steps to be performed, operators or employees to be involved, and so on). Process design FMEA is applied to process designs at the earliest possible point to identify potential failure modes that could result from a design flaw. Process FMEAs, too, are a normal part of key milestones in the process development process.

- *Service delivery FMEA.* A *service delivery* is the completion of a set of tasks designed to meet one or more customer expectations. Service delivery FMEA is applied to service delivery designs to identify potential failure modes that, if experienced, would result in some level of dissatisfaction from customers. Service delivery FMEAs are also completed as early as possible in the design process and are a normal part of key milestones in the service delivery design process.

In most instances the practicing quality professional can be expected to work primarily on design and/or process FMEAs. A quality inspector would expect fewer opportunities, if any, to work on system/subsystem and/or service delivery FMEAs. Accordingly, this chapter focuses on design and process FMEAs and purposefully omits system/subsystem and service delivery FMEAs.

Design and Process FMEA

Following the steps outlined earlier describing the planning functions preceding an FMEA, the analysis proceeds as the FMEA team completes appropriate documentation such as the FMEA form. For purposes of this discussion, one form applicable to either a design or a process FMEA will be described. Where the criteria change between a design and a process FMEA, both criteria will be provided. Figures 24.2 and 24.3 are blank FMEA forms applicable to design and process FMEA—each component of the forms is identified and described in the following sections.

Heading Information and Documentation

Product or process name	Provide the formal and/or commonly used (if different) name for the product or process.
Product or process description	Provide a brief description of the product or process that is meaningful to the FMEA team members.
FMEA number	Assign an FMEA number to each FMEA for tracking and documentation purposes. There are no standards for numbering FMEAs; however, a numbering system that links the FMEA to a specific period of time and product/process family is preferred.
Design/process owner	Identify the individual or team assigned primary responsibility for the design or process for tracking and documentation purposes. This individual or team is also identified for reference, if needed, during the FMEA.
FMEA team leader	Identify the individual assigned primary responsibility for completion of the FMEA for documentation purposes. This individual is also identified so as to establish a point of contact should any stakeholder need information during or after the FMEA.
FMEA team	List each member of the FMEA team along with any key responsibilities relative to the FMEA.

Potential
Failure Mode and Effects Analysis
(Design FMEA)

____ System
____ Subsystem
____ Component ________________

Design responsibility ________________

FMEA number ________

Page ______ of ______

Prepared by ________________

Model year(s)/vehicle(s) ____________

Key date ________________

FMEA date (orig.) ________ (rev.) ________

Core team ________________________________

Item / Function	Potential failure mode	Potential effect(s) of failure	Sev	Class	Potential cause(s)/ mechanism(s) of failure	Occur	Current design controls	Detec	RPN	Recommended action(s)	Responsibility and target completion date	Action results				
												Actions taken	Sev	Occ	Det	RPN

Figure 24.2 Blank design FMEA form.

**Potential
Failure Mode and Effects Analysis
(Process FMEA)**

FMEA number _____
Page _____ of _____
Prepared by _____

Item _____
Process responsibility _____
Model year(s)/vehicle(s) _____
Key date _____
FMEA date (orig.) _____ (rev.) _____
Core team _____

Process function	Potential failure mode	Potential effect(s) of failure	C l a s s	Potential cause(s)/ mechanism(s) of failure	O c c u r	Current process controls	D e t e c	R P N	Recommended action(s)	Responsibility and target completion date	Action results				
Requirements			S e v								Actions taken	S e v	O c c	D e t	R P N

Figure 24.3   Blank process FMEA form.

FMEA date

Provide the date(s) during which the FMEA is completed to help establish a chronology of events. Revision dates should be noted here as well.

FMEA risk assessment based on

Indicate the basis of the risk assessment. The FMEA risk assessment may be based on either actual failures or failure causes. It is important to document the team's decision to assess risk based on failures or causes to ensure that everyone evaluating the FMEA understands exactly how risk was assessed.

Analysis Content and Documentation

DFMEA part name, #, function, or PFMEA process function

Identify the product (that is, part name, part number, and function) or process (that is, functions to be completed as part of the process).

Potential failure mode

List each of the potential failure modes associated with the design or process. Design failure modes may include dented, deformed, fractured, loosened, leaking, warped, and so on. Process failure modes may include overheating, inoperable, visual defect, and so on.

Potential effect of failure mode

For each potential failure mode, indicate the potential effect on customers or production/process personnel—it is entirely possible to have multiple effects for each potential failure mode.

Severity

Indicate the seriousness of the effect of the potential failure using the severity criteria defined in Tables 24.1 and 24.2. Note: The severity rating applies only to the effect of the potential failure.

Classification

Classify any special characteristics that may require additional process controls. SAE J1739 identifies classifications that include *critical*, *key*, *major*, and *significant.*

Potential cause of failure mode

For each potential effect of each failure mode, identify all possible causes; it is entirely possible to have more than one cause for each potential effect.

Occurrence

Indicate how frequently each failure is expected to occur using the occurrence criteria defined in Tables 24.3 and 24.4.

DFMEA design verifications, or PFMEA current process controls

For a design FMEA, identify the actions completed that ensure or verify the adequacy of the design. For a process FMEA, identify the control currently in place that prevents a failure mode from occurring.

Table 24.1   Design FMEA severity criteria.

Effect	Severity criteria	Ranking
Hazardous without warning	Very high ranking when potential failure mode affects safe operation and/or regulation noncompliance. Failure occurs without warning.	10
Hazardous with warning	Very high ranking when potential failure mode affects safe operation and/or regulation noncompliance. Failure occurs with warning.	9
Very high	Item or product is inoperable, with loss of function. Customer very dissatisfied.	8
High	Item or product is operable, with loss of performance. Customer dissatisfied.	7
Moderate	Item or product is operable, but comfort/convenience items inoperable. Customer experiences discomfort.	6
Low	Item or product is operable, but with loss of performance of comfort/convenience items. Customer has some dissatisfaction.	5
Very low	Certain characteristics do not conform. Noticed by most customers.	4
Minor	Certain characteristics do not conform. Noticed by average customers.	3
Very minor	Certain characteristics do not conform. Noticed by discriminating customers.	2
None	No effect.	1

$S \times O \times D$ = Risk priority number (RPN)

Derived from Technical Standard SAE J1739.

Reprinted by permission of The Society of Automotive Engineers (SAE).

Detection	Indicate the ability of design verification or current process controls to detect a potential failure mode in the event that failure actually occurs. Use the detection criteria defined in Tables 24.5 and 24.6.
Risk priority number (RPN)	For each potential failure mode, multiply the severity (S), occurrence (O), and detection (D) assessments together. Since each scale (S, O, and D) ranges from 1 to 10, RPNmin = 1 and RPNmax = 1000.
Recommended actions	For each potential failure mode, list one or more recommended corrective actions. For further direction and guidance on prioritizing recommended corrective actions, readers are encouraged to refer to the "Taking Action Based on an RPN" section of this chapter.

Table 24.2 Process FMEA severity criteria.

Effect	Severity criteria	Ranking
Hazardous without warning	May endanger machine or assembly operator. Very high severity ranking when a potential failure mode affects safe operation and/or involves noncompliance with regulation. Failure will occur without warning.	10
Hazardous with warning	May endanger machine or assembly operator. Very high severity ranking when a potential failure mode affects safe operation and/or involves noncompliance with regulation. Failure will occur with warning.	9
Very high	Major disruption to production line. 100% of product may have to be scrapped. Item inoperable, loss of primary function. Customer very dissatisfied.	8
High	Minor disruption to production line. A portion of product may have to be sorted and scrapped. Item operable, but at reduced level. Customer dissatisfied.	7
Moderate	Minor disruption to production line. A portion of product may have to be scrapped (no sorting). Item operable, but some comfort items inoperable. Customer experiences discomfort.	6
Low	Minor disruption to production line. 100% of product may have to be reworked. Item operable, but some comfort items operable at reduced level of performance. Customer experiences some dissatisfaction.	5
Very low	Minor disruption to production line. Product may have to be sorted and a portion reworked. Minor adjustments do not conform. Defect noticed by customer.	4
Minor	Minor disruption to production line. Product may have to be reworked online, but out of station. Minor adjustments do not conform. Defect noticed by average customer.	3
Very minor	Minor disruption to production line. Product may have to be reworked online, but out of station. Minor adjustments do not conform. Defect noticed by discriminating customer.	2
None	No effect.	1

Derived from Technical Standard SAE J1739.

Reprinted by permission of The Society of Automotive Engineers (SAE).

Individual/team responsible and completion date	For each recommended action, assign an appropriate individual or team and an expected completion date.
Actions taken	Provide a brief description of the actual actions taken and their respective action dates.

Table 24.3   Design FMEA occurrence criteria.

Probability of failure	Possible failure rates	Ranking
Very high: Failure almost inevitable	> 1 in 2 1 in 3	10 9
High: Repeated failures	1 in 8 1 in 20	8 7
Moderate: Occasional failures	1 in 80 1 in 400 1 in 2000	6 5 4
Low: Relatively few failures	1 in 15,000 1 in 150,000	3 2
Remote: Failure is unlikely	< 1 in 1,500,000	1

Derived from Technical Standard SAE J1739.

Reprinted by permission of The Society of Automotive Engineers (SAE).

Table 24.4   Process FMEA occurrence criteria.

Probability of failure	Possible failure rates	Ranking
Very high: Failure almost inevitable.	> 1 in 2 1 in 3	10 9
High: Generally associated with processes similar to previous processes that have often failed.	1 in 8 1 in 20	8 7
Moderate: Generally associated with processes similar to previous processes that have experienced occasional failures.	1 in 80 1 in 400 1 in 2000	6 5 4
Low: Isolated failures associated with similar processes.	1 in 15,000	3
Very low: Only isolated failures associated with almost identical processes.	1 in 150,000	2
Remote: Failure is unlikely. No failures associated with almost identical processes.	< 1 in 1,500,000	1

Derived from Technical Standard SAE J1739.

Reprinted by permission of The Society of Automotive Engineers (SAE).

Resulting RPN analysis   Following each action taken, reiterate the severity, occurrence, and detection assessments and calculate a new resulting RPN. Actions taken based on RPNs and resulting RPNs continue until the risk assessment for each potential failure is "acceptable" to the customer and/or authorizing agent for the FMEA.

Table 24.5 Design FMEA detection criteria.

Effect	Detection criteria	Ranking
Absolute uncertainty	Design control will not and/or cannot detect a potential cause/mechanism and subsequent failure mode or there is no design control.	10
Very remote	Very remote chance the design control will detect a potential cause/mechanism and subsequent failure mode.	9
Remote	Remote chance the design control will detect a potential cause/mechanism and subsequent failure mode.	8
Very low	Very low chance the design control will detect a potential cause/mechanism and subsequent failure mode.	7
Low	Low chance the design control will detect a potential cause/mechanism and subsequent failure mode.	6
Moderate	Moderate chance the design control will detect a potential cause/mechanism and subsequent failure mode.	5
Moderately high	Moderately high chance the design control will detect a potential cause/mechanism and subsequent failure mode.	4
High	High chance the design control will detect a potential cause/mechanism and subsequent failure mode.	3
Very high	Very high chance the design control will detect a potential cause/mechanism and subsequent failure mode.	2
Almost certain	Design control will almost certainly detect a potential cause/mechanism and subsequent failure mode.	1

Derived from Technical Standard SAE J1739.

Reprinted by permission of The Society of Automotive Engineers (SAE).

A Final Word on Taking Corrective Action

An FMEA represents an in-depth, objective, quantitative analysis of the risk associated with potential failures that results in the calculation of one or more RPNs. Once RPNs have been calculated and the FMEA team prepares to take corrective action, the analysis necessarily takes on a subjective element as FMEA team members use the risk assessment to guide prioritization of corrective actions.

As was mentioned earlier in this chapter, the most common practice used to prioritize corrective action is based on RPNs. Prioritization of corrective action based solely on RPNs works effectively, however, only as long as there is a "comfortable" difference between the RPN values. When there are clusters of RPN values that are the same, or very close (say within 25 to 50 points), taking action based on RPNs alone is not straightforward. In such cases, additional guidance in prioritizing corrective action is needed as follows:

1. Rank the RPNs in descending order.

2. For those RPNs that cluster within a predefined range of, say, 25 to 50 points, use the strategy suggested earlier in this chapter (that is,

Table 24.6   Process FMEA detection criteria.

Effect	Detection criteria	Ranking
Absolutely impossible	No known controls to detect failure mode.	10
Very remote	Very remote likelihood current controls will detect failure mode.	9
Remote	Remote likelihood current controls will detect failure mode.	8
Very low	Very low likelihood current controls will detect failure mode.	7
Low	Low likelihood current controls will detect failure mode.	6
Moderate	Moderate likelihood current controls will detect failure mode.	5
Moderately high	Moderately high likelihood current controls will detect failure mode.	4
High	High likelihood current controls will detect failure mode.	3
Very high	Very high likelihood current controls will detect failure mode.	2
Almost certain	Current controls will almost certainly detect a failure mode. Reliable detection controls are known with similar processes.	1

Derived from Technical Standard SAE J1739.

Reprinted by permission of The Society of Automotive Engineers (SAE).

first eliminate occurrence, then reduce severity, and finally improve detection).

3. Plan, take, and monitor corrective action on the largest non-clustered RPNs.

4. Plan, take, and monitor corrective action on RPN clusters as defined in step two.

5. Repeat steps 3 and 4 as needed to address all potential failures identified in the analysis.

As another means of eliminating the subjectivity in prioritizing corrective actions based on RPNs, the *criticality analysis* was developed as part of MIL-STD 1629A.

Assessing Criticality

MIL-STD 1629A defines two very important terms and concepts with respect to risk assessment:

Criticality—"A relative measure of the consequences of a failure mode and its frequency of occurrences."

Criticality analysis—"A procedure by which each potential failure mode is ranked according to the combined influence of severity and probability of occurrence."

When criticality is considered in an FMEA, the name is changed to *failure mode effects and criticality analysis* (FMECA). FMECA can be a qualitative or quantitative assessment of risk that leads to a prioritization of corrective action based on severity (S) and occurrence (O) assessments. In the qualitative approach to risk assessment in FMECA, risk is categorized as frequent, reasonably probable, occasional, remote, or extremely unlikely. In the quantitative approach to risk assessment in FMECA, failure rate data, failure effect probability data, individual part failure data, and operating time data are required as input to one or more protocols as defined in Military Handbook 217.

The key result of an FMECA is a criticality matrix that ranks potential failures with respect to severity. The matrix then identifies a prioritization scheme for corrective actions based on the severity of potential failure modes. As displayed on an FMECA criticality matrix, potential failures plotted farther away from the matrix origin on a diagonal line represent higher potential risk of failure and thus warrant increased need for corrective action.

For additional discussion of FMECA, readers are encouraged to consult MIL-STD 1629A for guidance in completing a criticality assessment.

A Caution about Using FMEA

FMEA can be a powerful and effective tool for system/subsystem, design or process, or service delivery improvement. It should be remembered, however, that completing an FMEA involves significant costs. One may be tempted to follow the results of an FMEA to further levels of refinement and specificity; readers are cautioned to remember that there is a cost/benefit relationship associated with the use of FMEA.

Design and Process FMEA Examples

Figures 24.4 and 24.5 are, respectively, examples of design and process FMEAs to help guide the reader through an actual analysis.

FMEA Summary

FMEA is a tool to help cross-functional teams identify, eliminate, and/or reduce the negative effects of potential failures—before they happen. FMEA is widely used as a stand-alone tool or as part of comprehensive quality systems/programs, which is why ASQ has incorporated FMEA into the CQI BoK.

Two standards were discussed in this chapter that relate to FMEA, namely, MIL-STD 1629A and SAE J1739. It is important to note that both standards have been designed such that they will lead to the same or very similar results when they are correctly used. Much of the preparation for, inputs to, and prioritization of corrective action guidance are not covered in the standards to support an FMEA.

5. 8D METHODOLOGY

The *8D methodology* is a problem-solving and analysis tool used to "identify, correct, and eliminate recurring problems" (ASQ Undated "What Are"). The term "8D"

**Potential
Failure Mode and Effects Analysis
(Design FMEA)**

System _____
X Subsystem _01.03/Body closures_ (2)
Component _____ (5)
Model year(s)/vehicle(s) _199X/Lion 4dr/wagon_
Core team _T. Fender—Car product dev., Childers—Manufacturing, J. Ford—Assy ops (Dalton, Fraser, Henley assembly plants)_

Design responsibility _Body engineering_ (3)
Key date _9X 03 01 ER_ (6)

FMEA number _1234_ (1)
Page _1_ of _1_
Prepared by _A. Tate—X6412—Body engr_ (4)
FMEA date (orig.) _8X 03 22_ (rev.) _8X 07 14_ (7)
(8)

Item / Function (9)	Potential failure mode (10)	Potential effect(s) of failure (11) (12)	Sev (13)	Class	Potential cause(s)/mechanism(s) of failure (13) (14)	Occur (15)	Current design controls (16)	Detec (17)	RPN	Recommended action(s) (18) (19)	Responsibility and target completion date (20)	Actions taken (21)	Sev	Occ	Det	RPN (22)
Front door L.H. H8HX-0000-A • Ingress to and egress from vehicle • Occupant protection from weather, noise, and side impact • Support anchorage for door hardware including mirror, hinges, latch, and window regulator • Provide proper surface for appearance items • Paint and soft trim	Corroded interior lower door panels	Deteriorated life of door leading to: • Unsatisfactory appearance due to rust through paint over time • Impaired function of interior door hardware	7		Upper edge of protective wax application specified for inner door panels is too low	6	Vehicle general durability test vah. T-118 T-109 T-301	7	294	Add laboratory accelerated corrosion testing	A Tate-Body Engrg 8X 09 30	Based on test results (Test No. 1481) upper edge spec raised 125mm	7	2	2	28
					Insufficient wax thickness specified	4	Vehicle general durability testing—as above	7	196	Add laboratory accelerated corrosion testing Conduct Design of Experiments (DOE) on wax thickness	Combine w/test for wax upper edge verification A Tate Body Engrg 9X 01 15	Test results (Test No. 1481) show specified thickness is adequate. DOE shows 25% variation in specified thickness is acceptable	7	2	2	28
					Inappropriate wax formulation specified	2	Physical and Chem Lab test—Report No. 1265	2	28	None						
					Entrapped air prevents wax from entering corner/edge access	5	Design aid investigation with non-functioning spray head	8	280	Add team evaluation using production spray equipment and specified wax	Body Engrg & Assy Ops 8X 11 15		7	1	3	21
					Wax application plugs door drain holes	3	Laboratory test using "worst case" wax application and hole size	1	21	None		Based on test 3 additional vent holes provided in affected areas				
					Insufficient room between panels for spray head access	4	Drawing evaluation of spray head access	4	112	Add team evaluation using design aid buck and spray head	Body Engrg & Assy Ops	Evaluation showed adequate access	7	1	1	7

SAMPLE

Figure 24.4   Design FMEA example.

**Potential
Failure Mode and Effects Analysis
(Process FMEA)**

Item　Front door L.H./H8HX-000-A　②

Model year(s)/vehicle(s) 199X/Lion 4dr/wagon　⑤

Core team　A. Tate—Body engrg., J. Smith—OC, R. James—Production, J. Jones—Maintenance

Process responsibility　Body engrg./assembly operations　③

Key date　9X 03 01 ER　　9X 08 26 Job #1　⑥

FMEA number　1450　①

Page　1　of　1

Prepared by J. Ford—X6521—Assy ops　④

FMEA date (orig.)　9X 05 17　(rev.)　9X 11 06　⑦

⑧

Process function ⑨ / Requirements	Potential failure mode ⑩	Potential effect(s) of failure ⑪	⑫	C l a s s	Potential cause(s)/ mechanism(s) ⑬ of failure ⑭	O c c u r ⑮	Current process controls ⑯	⑰ D e t e c	R P N	Recommended action(s) ⑲	Responsibility and target completion date ⑳	Action results ㉒

Process function ⑨ / Requirements	Potential failure mode ⑩	Potential effect(s) of failure ⑪	S e v	C l a s s	Potential cause(s)/ mechanism(s) of failure	O c c u r	Current process controls	D e t e c	R P N	Recommended action(s)	Responsibility and target completion date	Actions taken ㉑	S e v	O c c	D e t e c	R P N
Manual application of wax inside door	Insufficient wax coverage over specified surface	Deteriorated life of door leading to: • Unsatisfactory appearance due to rust through paint over time • Impaired function of interior door hardware	7		Manually inserted spray head not inserted far enough	8	Visual check each hour—1/shift for film thickness (depth meter) and coverage	5	280	Add positive depth stop to sprayer	MFG Engrg 9X 10 15	Stop added, sprayer checked on line	7	2	5	70
To cover inner door, lower surfaces at minimum wax thickness to retard corrosion										Automate spraying	Mfg Engrg 9X 12 15	Rejected due to complexity of different doors on same line				
					Spray heads clogged • Viscosity too high • Temperature too low • Pressure too low	5	Test spray pattern at start-up and after idle periods, and preventive maintenance program to clean heads	3	105	Use Design of Experiments (DOE) on viscosity vs. temperature vs. pressure	Mfg Eng'rg 9X 10 01	Temp and press limits were determined and limit controls have been installed—control charts show process is in control Cpk-1.85	7	1	3	21
					Spray head deformed due to impact	2	Preventive maintenance programs to maintain head	2	28	None						
					Spray time insufficient	8	Operator instructions and lot sampling (10 doors / shift) to check for coverage of critical areas	7	392	Install spray timer	Maintenance 9X 09 15	Automatic spray timer installed—operator starts spray, timer controls shut-off, control charts show process is in control Cpk-2.05	7	1	7	49

SAMPLE

Figure 24.5　Process FMEA example.

DO	Plan
D1	Create a team
D2	Define and describe the problem
D3	Contain the problem
D4	Identify, describe, and verify root causes
D5	Choose corrective actions
D6	Implement and validate corrective actions
D7	Take preventive measures
D8	Congratulate your team

Figure 24.6   List of the eight disciplines (8D).
Source: Duffy (2013).

refers to the eight (8) stages in the methodology, which initially were referred to as "disciplines." The term *disciplines* as intended with the 8D methodology refers to process steps to be consistently and deliberately followed versus organizational functions such as engineering, finance, marketing/sales, and so on.

The 8D methodology is useful in process improvement efforts in production operations as well as in service delivery applications. As a methodology, 8D is a step-by-step process to be followed while investigating and/or improving processes, so the 8D methodology brings together several other statistical (quantitative) and qualitative (graphical) tools to facilitate a more thorough understanding of process steps, performance characteristics, and paths to improvement.

The 8D methodology consists of the components presented in Figure 24.6.

6. 5 WHYS

The *5 whys* is a questioning methodology intended to help users understand the root cause(s) of a process failure or improvement opportunity. The underlying concept of the 5 whys methodology is that members of a process improvement team cannot get to the point of understanding a process failure or process improvement opportunity until they can ask and answer the question "Why" at least five times. The 5 whys then help users and team members develop a more thorough understanding of the process as well as process failures or improvement opportunities.

A second underlying concept of the 5 whys methodology is that making process adjustments or improvements without getting to the root cause(s) leads only to treating symptoms of the problems. What is critically important is that users or team members understand more than just symptoms by identifying the true root cause(s). A major concern for process owners is that premature interventions or treatments only cause additional problems.

Just as with the 5 whys methodology, the "5 hows" methodology is intended to help users understand just how an intervention or process improvement ultimately impacts the process operation or quality. Ultimately, asking *why* (a process failure occurred) at least five times, and asking at least five times *how* a proposed intervention might eliminate a root cause, users of the methodology will have a better chance of success in correcting problems or achieving success in implementing process improvements.

7. FAULT TREE ANALYSIS (FTA)

Fault tree analysis (FTA) is a tool and approach to reducing a system, even very complex systems, into one or more diagrams depicting the logic of the system represented by two primary logic gates (that is, symbols) including the ""AND" gate and the ""OR" gate. The AND gate appears to resemble most closely the letter "D," while the OR gate appears to resemble most closely the letter "C" written backwards. Figure 24.7, originally developed by author Simha Pilot (2002), shows both the AND as well as the OR gate along with the logic inputs required for the gate operation.

The AND gate triggers, or provides an output, only when both of the inputs are positive, meaning most often that both inputs are functioning and are operational. A matter of primary importance with the AND gate is that *both* inputs must be positive for the AND gate to have a positive output.

The OR gate triggers, or provides an output, if either of the inputs are positive, meaning that either or both of the inputs are functioning or are operational. A matter of primary importance with the OR gate is that *either or both* of the inputs may be positive for the OR gate to have a positive output.

Using a combination of the AND and OR gates, it is possible to develop a graphical representation (that is, fault tree) of even the most complex systems. Fault trees are particularly useful in analyzing how and where process failures may be expected to reveal, or manifest, themselves in system or process operation. FTA, originally developed at Bell Laboratories, remains particularly useful in digital circuit analysis where systems operate on five-volt logic, and a signal is present or absent based on the presence or absence of a digital five-volt signal.

The fault tree is sometimes said to be "top-down" because the diagram is commonly drawn vertically from top to bottom. A more correct understanding of why fault trees are referred to as top-down is that constructing the diagram starts at the output and works "upstream" toward the inputs.

Fault trees are said to be "deductive" because they are based on reason and logic (that is, represented by gates) generalized by a set of system or process characteristics (that is, the presence or absence of signals representing system or process operations).

In the example in Figure 24.7, the many conditions related to patient hazards during surgery are depicted. It should be noted when conducting a fault tree analysis that there are conditions under which any event occurring will result in a hazard, while there are other conditions that require two or more unsafe conditions occurring at the same time for a hazard to occur.

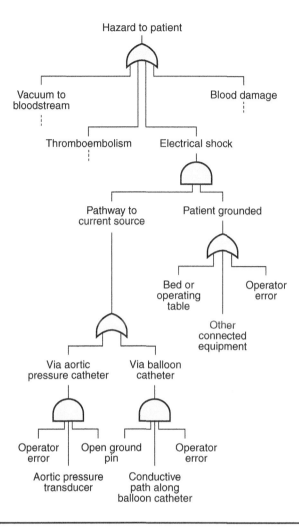

Figure 24.7   Fault tree depicting the root causes of hazard to patients during surgery.
Source: Pilot (2002).

REFERENCES

ASQ (American Society for Quality). Undated. "Quality Glossary—F," s.v. "flow."
    Accessed December 17, 2018. Available at http://asq.org/glossary/f.html.
———. Undated. "Quality Glossary—K," s.v. "kaizen." Accessed December 17, 2018.
    Available at http://asq.org/glossary/k.html.
———. Undated. "What Are the Eight Disciplines (8D)?" Quality Resources.
    Accessed December 18, 2018. Available at http://asq.org/learn-about-quality/
    eight-disciplines-8d/
———. Undated. "What Is Mistake Proofing?" Learn About Quality. Accessed December
    17, 2018. Available at http://asq.org/learn-about-quality/process-analysis-tools/
    overview/mistake-proofing.html.

Department of Defense (DoD), US. 1980. MIL-STD 1629A. *Military Standard: Procedures for Performing a Failure Mode, Effects and Criticality Analysis.* Washington, DC: DoD. Available at http://www.everyspec.com/MIL-STD/MIL-STD-1600-1699/MIL_STD_1629A_1556/.

Duffy, G. L. 2013. *Modern Kaizen: Continuous and Breakthrough Improvement.* Milwaukee: ASQ Quality Press.

Gordon, D. K. 2002. "Where Does Quality Begin?" ASQ *Quality Progress*, March.

McKinley, J. 2006. "Re: PDSA or PDCA?" Accessed January 2008 at http://deming.eng.clemson.edu/den/archive/2006.07/msg00055.html.

Pilot, S. 2002. "What Is a Fault Tree Analysis?" ASQ *Quality Progress*, March.

BIBLIOGRAPHY

AIAG (Automotive Industry Action Group) and ASQ (American Society for Quality) 2008. *Potential Failure Mode and Effects Analysis.* 4th ed. Milwaukee: AIAG and ASQ.

Andersen, B., and T. Fagerhaug. 2006. *Root Cause Analysis: Simplified Tools and Techniques.* 2nd ed. Milwaukee: ASQ Quality Press.

Anleitner, M. A. 2010. *The Power of Deduction: Failure Modes and Effects Analysis for Design.* Milwaukee: ASQ Quality Press.

Juran, J., and J. De Feo. 2010. *Juran's Quality Handbook.* 6th ed. New York: McGraw-Hill.

Keller, P. A. 2011. *Six Sigma Demystified: Hard Stuff Made Easy.* 2nd ed. New York: McGraw-Hill Professional.

Kubiak, T. M., and D. W. Benbow. 2012. *The Certified Six Sigma Black Belt Handbook.* 2nd ed. Milwaukee: ASQ Quality Press.

Lee, Q., and B. Snyder. 2008. *The Strategos Guide to Value Stream & Process Mapping: Genesis of Manufacturing Strategy.* Bellingham, WA: Enna Publishing.

Manos, A., and C. Vincent, eds. 2012. *The Lean Handbook: A Guide to the Bronze Certification Body of Knowledge.* Milwaukee: ASQ Quality Press.

McDermott, R. E., Mikulak, R. J., and M. R. Beauregard. 2008. *The Basics of FMEA.* New York: Productivity Press.

Meisel, R. M., S. J. Babb, S. F. Marsh, and J. P. Schlichting. 2007. *The Executive Guide to Understanding and Implementing Lean Six Sigma: The Financial Impact.* Milwaukee: ASQ Quality Press.

Ohno, T. 1988. *Toyota Production System: Beyond Large-Scale Production.* Portland, OR: Productivity Press.

Okes, D. 2009. *Root Cause Analysis: The Core of Problem Solving and Corrective Action.* Milwaukee: ASQ Quality Press.

Robitaille, D. 2009. *The Corrective Action Handbook.* 2nd ed. Chico, CA: Paton Press.

Rogers, D. 2011. *The Future of Lean Sigma Thinking in a Changing Business Environment.* Boca Raton, FL: CRC Press.

Stamatis, D. 2003. *Failure Mode and Effect Analysis: FMEA Theory to Execution.* 2nd ed. Milwaukee: ASQ Quality Press.

Wilson, L. 2009. *How to Implement Lean Manufacturing.* New York: McGraw-Hill Professional.

Chapter 25

G. Resources

> 1. *Environmental and safety support.* Define and use various resources related to personal and environmental safety: safety data sheets (SDS), material data sheet (MDS), and personal protective equipment (PPE). (Apply)
>
> 2. *Reference documents.* Identify and use national and international standards (ISO, ANSI, ASTM, QS) and customer requirements as authorities that support processes and procedures used to assure quality products. (Apply)
>
> 3. *Employees as resources.* Describe how employees can be empowered and the value they add to project teams or quality improvement teams. Describe typical team roles and responsibilities: facilitator, ground rules, project or team charter. Describe the four stages of team development: forming, storming, norming, performing. (Remember)
>
> 4. *Quality documentation.* Basic quality documentation including correct form/revision for the process (ISO9100, FAIR, ISIR, PPAPs). Proper usage of policy, procedure, work instructions and forms, proper documentation practices such as document control, filling out forms completely, correcting misspellings, and initialing changes. (Apply)
>
> **Body of Knowledge IV.G**

As we begin to conclude our discussion of the CQI BoK, it is important that we consider four remaining topics: environmental and safety support, reference documents, technical reports, and employees as resources. As we have done with all the other topics in this book, we will keep the scope of our discussion consistent with the ASQ CQI BoK. It is important to realize, however, that these four topics are the focus of three different career fields: environmental safety and health, professional communications, and human resources. Accordingly, there are a great many text and electronic resources available that provide additional depth and detail about these topics.

1. ENVIRONMENTAL AND SAFETY SUPPORT

Protection of employee safety and health while in the workplace is the obligation of employers. Provisions for employee safety and health are set forth in the many local, regional, and federal codes and statutes. The Occupational Safety and Health Administration (OSHA) is responsible for all safety and health regulation. The primary regulation for safety and health is the OSHA Code of Federal Regulations (CFR) Title 29. CFR Title 29 has three major sections:

1910—Occupational Safety and Health Standards

1915—Occupational Safety and Health Standards for Shipyard Employment

1926—Occupational Safety and Health Regulations for Construction

Where safety and health are concerned, CFR Title 29 requires that protections be afforded employees as they relate to the areas in the list following. Further, if some form of employee protection is required, CFR Title 29 requires that a safety program be developed and implemented wherein the safety program address hazards present; the selection, maintenance, and use of protections; training of employees; and program monitoring.

It cannot be overemphasized that employees do ultimately bear at least some responsibility in protecting their personal safety and health while at work. As a responsible professional, you should not take for granted that your safety and health are protected in the work environment.

There are at least six different areas of concern for employee safety and health:

- *Material safety data sheets* (MSDSs). MSDSs provide employees and emergency response personnel with documentation of hazardous or potentially hazardous substances. MSDSs must be made available to all employees, informing them of the type and nature of substances used in the workplace. Every employee is encouraged to review these MSDSs as it may not be obvious what types of substances are in use. While there are several formats acceptable for MSDSs, they all contain the same basic information as it relates to physical data (melting point, boiling point, flash point, and so on), toxicity, health effects, first aid, reactivity, storage, disposal, protective equipment, and spill/leak procedures (ILPI Undated).

- *Personal protective equipment* (PPE). PPE is equipment used to ensure the safety of employees in the workplace. PPE is required by OSHA to "reduce employee exposure to hazards when engineering and administrative controls are not feasible or effective in reducing these exposures to acceptable levels. Employers are required to determine if PPE should be used to protect their workers" (OSHA Undated).

  PPE may include, but is not limited to, items such as safety glasses, gloves, footwear, ear plugs/muffs, respirators, and safety helmets. PPE may also include, but is not limited to, equipment such as air filters, gas detectors, fire alarms, and exit signs. As with MSDSs, employers are required to disclose PPE available for use.

- *Ergonomics.* Ergonomics refers to the study of the interface between humans and their work spaces, tools, and equipment. OSHA provides protections pertaining to ergonomics under CFR Title 29 (guidelines, enforcement, and outreach and assistance). Through application of basic ergonomic principles, many repetitive-motion injuries can be avoided; hence, it is an employee's responsibility to identify any discomfort or pain arising from his or her working conditions. Once an employee identifies the need for assistance, it is the responsibility of the employer to meet the spirit of CFR Title 29 in implementing a remedy.

- *Hearing conservation.* Excessive noise in the workplace can lead to hearing loss. Noise is measured on the decibel (dB) scale, wherein exposure to 85 dB or more for an extended period of time can lead to hearing loss. The dB scale is not linear, which means the increase in noise magnitude from, say, 4 dB to 5 dB is not the same as the increase from 10 dB to 11 dB. Protection of hearing is provided by CFR Title 29 under the subject "Hearing Conservation."

- *Confined spaces.* A confined space is defined as any enclosure that limits entry or egress. Confined spaces typically have restricted airflow and tend to trap gases. In accordance with CFR Title 29, some confined spaces are required to limit entry by untrained and/or unequipped employees. Make no mistake about it, confined spaces are dangerous and should be avoided. Where access to a confined space is required, CFR Title 29 and many local regulations require specific procedures to be followed in terms of checking for hazardous gases, provision of breathable air, and so on. As employers are required to clearly mark and limit access to confined spaces, employees are strongly advised not to enter these spaces.

- *Lock-out/tag-out.* Lock-out/tag-out refers to removal of electrical power from tools, equipment, or other electrical circuits. It may be necessary to remove electrical power for safety, to facilitate maintenance, or to stop the use of selected pieces of equipment or work spaces. When power is removed for any application, a locking device is affixed to wires and/or electrical connections to prevent reconnection of power—intentional or inadvertent. When power is removed and an appropriate lock-out device is installed, it is strictly forbidden under CFR Title 29 to reconnect power. Under CFR Title 29, the only person authorized to reconnect power is the person who disconnected the power and installed the lock-out device. Reconnecting power to equipment or work spaces where it has been removed puts at risk not only the life of the person reconnecting the power but also anyone who may potentially come in contact with the reconnected equipment or work space.

2. REFERENCE DOCUMENTS

As has been noted throughout this book, customer expectations help to define quality. An extension of customer expectations is a customer requirement wherein customers formalize their expectations in terms of the existence of selected quality systems, use of selected standards, and/or compliance with certain policies and procedures. These customer expectations may be set in the interest of standardization across multiple vendors or facilities. These customer expectations may also be set in the interest of communicating values or goals to customers as well as consumers.

Several sets of documents, reference documents, are used to specify customer expectations. While it is beyond the scope of this book to provide an exhaustive list of all reference standards, the standards can be accessed via the Internet at the addresses provided. These documents originate from organizations such as the following:

- *International Organization for Standardization* (ISO). ISO 9000 is a series of standards pertaining to research and development, manufacturing, and service delivery organizations. The ISO standards articulate requirements for the design, structure, implementation, operation, maintenance, and documentation of comprehensive quality systems (www.iso.org).

- *Quality Systems* (QS). QS 9000 was a set of standards for quality systems based on the ISO 9000 series of standards as tailored for the automotive industry. The QS 9000 quality standards for the automotive industry were replaced by the TS 16949 standards in 2006 (https://16949store.com/iatf-16949-standards/what-is-qs-9000/). The current version of TS 16949 was adopted in 2016 (https://16949store.com/iatf-16949-standards/what-is-ts-16949/), and more information about the TS 16949 standard can be accessed at https://16949store.com/iatf-16949-standards/what-is-iatf-16949/.

  AS 9100 is a set of standards for quality systems based on the ISO 9000 series of standards (ISO 9001:2000) as tailored for the aerospace industry. Information about the AS 9100 standards can be obtained from https://www.sae.org/standards/content/as9100/.

- *US Department of Defense* (MIL-*). The US Department of Defense (DoD) established and maintains a set of reference documents that includes, but is not limited to, defense specifications, handbooks, and standards. Military Specifications (MIL-SPECs) "describe the physical and/or operational characteristics of a product," Military Standards (MIL-STDs) "detail the processes and materials to be used to make the product," and Military Handbooks (MIL-HDBKs) provide information and/or guidance (http://www.asq.org).

- *American National Standards Institute* (ANSI). ANSI is an organization that coordinates, maintains, archives, and distributes voluntary standards. These voluntary standards have applications in virtually every type of industry (http://www.ansi.org).

- *American Society for the Testing of Materials* (ASTM). ASTM serves as an international standards organization. ASTM develops procedures and protocols for the testing of all types of materials and applications (http://www.astm.org).

3. EMPLOYEES AS RESOURCES

Employees bring tremendous value to the workplace in terms of their knowledge, skills, abilities, and creativity. This value is so great that employees have come to be considered assets, in many cases of equal or greater value than buildings or equipment. Considering employees to be resources and assets is a relatively new phenomenon that has gained popularity, particularly during the past two decades. When we manage the collective knowledge brought into the workplace by employees, we refer to this practice as "knowledge management" (Frappaolo 2006).

In addition to inventorying employee knowledge and allocating it to where it is most needed within an organization, there are other practices that facilitate employees making the best possible contributions in the work environment. These practices include empowering employees and employee involvement.

Empowering Employees

When we say we are "empowering employees," we mean that we are giving employees the latitude—in fact, the responsibility—to take ownership of certain aspects of their daily work life and to use their creativity in making certain types of decisions (Woods 2005). Empowering employees requires trust between leadership team members and staff/operators. That trust is developed over time (Blanchard et al. 2010) and requires significant effort in articulating and negotiating the boundaries within which employees are enabled to make decisions. A greater reliance on the input and participation of employees characterizes the work environment, particularly that of the CQI.

The CQI is well advised to learn as quickly as possible the amount of decision-making authority/empowerment he or she has as part of his or her normal work responsibilities. It is important to exercise the expected level of decision-making authority/empowerment but not to exceed it. As more workplace experience is gained, and as a history of making effective decisions is accumulated, additional empowerment will normally result, up to some point where leadership involvement is required. Where is that "point" where leadership involvement is required? That depends completely on the level of employee involvement in the decision-making process, for which the leadership team ultimately has final responsibility.

Employee Involvement

As noted in the preceding section, the amount of employee involvement in day-to-day business, production, or service delivery operations depends on a balance of employee competence and leadership authorization. Certainly, the trend is to enable employees to be more, rather than less, involved with decision-making processes.

There are a variety of ways to practice employee involvement (Ichniowski et al. 2001). It is likely that the CQI will, in fact, become involved with some form of employee involvement, and the form of involvement most likely for the CQI is serving on one or more types of teams. Common teams for the CQI are Six Sigma project teams, self-directed work teams, quality circles, and continuous improvement teams. It is beyond the scope of this book to explain the many different types of teams; however, we will cover basic elements of team formation and stages of development that are contained within the CQI BoK.

Team Roles and Responsibilities

Several characteristics are common to most team types:

- Teams have a clearly defined charter (assigned task or area of concern).

- Teams typically have a defined amount of time in which to complete their work.

- Teams are provided with the resources needed (time, finances, access to equipment, access to information, and so on).

- Teams are normally provided with a list of expected outcomes.

- Teams are composed of employees from as many stakeholder groups as possible.

- Team size is kept to a minimum to accomplish assigned tasks (4–10 members is common).

In addition to the team characteristics just described, teams are composed of members who have different roles and responsibilities, such as the following:

- *Champion.* The team champion is an organization or company leader who has convened the team. The champion is responsible for ensuring that there is a clear path of communication to the company leadership, that the team functions effectively, and that the team has the resources it needs to complete its work.

- *Team leader.* The team leader is responsible for articulating strategy, formalizing and assigning work tasks, supervising day-to-day operation of the team, and documenting team activities. The team leader also typically tracks and monitors resources used and required by the team.

- *Facilitator.* The facilitator helps balance participation of team members, particularly during team meetings. The facilitator does not take an active role in the substance of team meeting agenda items or conversations; rather, the facilitator ensures that meetings remain productive by enforcing team operating rules, practicing professional courtesy and collegiality, and effectively managing meeting time. The facilitator also may provide training in selected problem-solving approaches and tools or techniques that may be needed by members of the team.

- *Team members.* Team members are selected to serve on teams based on their ability to contribute to the solution of a problem or exploit an opportunity, as well as their proximity to, or involvement with, a problem or opportunity. Team members are purposefully selected from as many areas as possible within or outside a work unit or company to ensure that all stakeholders are represented. A stakeholder is someone who is directly or indirectly affected by any given problem or opportunity.

No matter how experienced the members of a team may be within their areas of expertise, or in working on teams, team performance is very predictable based on stages of development. Each time a team is created, members of the team progress through these stages of development. The amount of time needed to progress through each stage depends on many factors; in fact, it is possible that a dysfunctional team may not be able to progress through these stages.

Stages of Team Development

The following are the stages of team development:

- *Forming.* During the forming stage, the team comes together, and members learn the rules of operation, strategy, and expected outcomes. Team members also learn to work with one another, so this stage commonly is a bit frustrating for team members.

- *Storming.* During the storming stage, team members come to grips with the project assignment. They begin to question the strategy, specific tasks, and expected outcomes. Team members may express many differences of opinion, and there is a tendency for some team members to withdraw from the work of the team while other team members begin to try to take charge. If the forming stage is a bit frustrating for team members, the storming stage can be downright difficult to manage—certainly more difficult than the forming stage (Scholtes et al. 2003).

- *Norming.* During the norming stage, team members begin to reach agreement on strategy, specific tasks, and expected outcomes. Team members begin to work collectively to accomplish common tasks. Once team development reaches the stage of norming, much of the frustration and difficulty experienced during the forming and storming stages of development subside, and the day-to-day work atmosphere becomes much more congenial.

- *Performing.* During the performing stage, team members become efficient in completing tasks, they refine working relationships, and they work in unison to accomplish any remaining work. Team members gain a sense of pride and belonging with the team, which greatly helps prevent or minimize internal conflict.

Conflict Resolution

Regardless of how effective a team may be, and regardless of what stage of development a team may have obtained, conflicts will inevitably arise. A conflict involves a difference of opinion. Differences of opinion, while they have their merit and value, can be disruptive to any team. When working with teams, it is not a question of *if* a conflict will arise, it is a question of *when* a conflict will arise. Because the topic of conflict resolution is complex, it involves many experts and many approaches. While it is beyond the scope of this book to cover all the details of conflict management, we would be remiss if we did not provide at least some simple guidelines to help handle a conflict:

- All team members must be heard (one at a time).
- Team members must respect others' opinions and ideas.
- Rely on facts and data where possible. If the data aren't available, reach agreement on a method to obtain them.
- Bring in outside expertise if needed.
- If necessary, test more than one solution and collect data on each.

Consensus

Although it is sometimes necessary to put things to a team vote, it is usually advisable to reach agreement by continued discussion. Although this method, referred to as *consensus building*, takes more time than voting, it reduces the tendency for some team members to feel left out. Reaching a consensus means that people have to "give a little" in order for the team to make progress.

Brainstorming

In the early stages of problem solving it is useful to get a large number of ideas. The brainstorming technique does this by asking each person to first express just one idea. This idea is written down so all can see it, and then the next person expresses one thought. After all team members have had a turn, each is asked for a second idea, and so on. One of the rules of a brainstorming session is that no idea is to be criticized or judged. Often, members will piggyback on a previous idea and come up with a new or modified thought. The theory of brainstorming is that if all ideas are documented, it is likely that the best idea or solution is on the list somewhere. The next step is to compress the list. It may be possible to combine two or more ideas into one. Sometimes the ideas can be grouped into categories such as machining problems, supplier problems, painting problems, and so on. The team may elect to prioritize the items on the list, agreeing to study the highest-priority items first. Individuals may be assigned the task of pursuing individual ideas further and reporting on them at the next team meeting.

Meeting Management

The hours spent in team meetings are a very valuable resource. Well-managed meetings make the most of the time spent together. Barriers to effective use of meeting time include the following:

- Lack of a clear agenda

- Tendency to digress from the subject

- Feeling on the part of team members that the meeting is a waste of time or has a lower priority than other responsibilities

- Strong disagreement among team members

- Tendency for some members to dominate the discussion and others to withdraw participation

It is the responsibility of the team leader to minimize these and other barriers that may impede the team. Techniques that have proved useful include:

- Distribute the agenda in advance of the meeting. Begin the meeting by reviewing the agenda.

- Call the team back to the agenda when members stray too far or for too long.

- Keep the meeting moving. If an agenda item can't be adequately addressed, it may be best to postpone it for later consideration. Start and end on time. If the business of the meeting has been completed, end the meeting early.

- When conflicts among members arise, help them find a middle ground of agreement. Even an agreement on how to collect data is better than no agreement at all.

- Frequently go around the room and ask for input from each member to maintain an even level of participation.

Experience and training in meeting management will help the leader in using these techniques. When the team leader doesn't have the requisite skills, it may be useful to have a team facilitator assist with meeting management.

4. QUALITY DOCUMENTATION

Quality documentation section VI.G.4 was a new addition to the CQI BoK in 2018. There are two components to the new material on quality documentation—use of correct forms and revision control—as well as the proper use of policy, procedure, work instructions, forms, and proper documentation practices.

The CQI is expected to apply concepts requiring that particular information be documented on particular forms, with particular expectations for revision control, as they relate to four primary quality systems and/or major quality processes, including ISO 9001, first article inspection reports, initial sample inspection reports (ISIR), and the production part approval process (PPAP). Key concepts relating to "proper use" include document control, filling out forms completely, correcting misspellings, and initialing changes.

ISO 9001

ISO is an acronym that stands for the International Organization for Standardization. ISO sponsors multiple quality systems, of which ISO 9001 is but one standard. As an organization, ISO has developed very comprehensive expectations for the documentation of quality systems in all of the standards they sponsor. It is important to note that documentation requirements are established by the ISO, and these documentation requirements are standardized in most applications, which means that individuals and organizations implementing any given ISO standard generally are not at liberty to make choices about what information can or must be documented; that has been defined by ISO, and compliance with documentation requirements is a centerpiece of quality audits. Said another way, companies choose whether or not to become ISO certified, and if they do choose to become ISO certified, they must comply with the documentation requirements specified by ISO.

General information about ISO 9001, and information about ISO 9001 documentation requirements in particular, may be accessed electronically at https://committee.iso.org/sites/tc176sc2/home/page/iso-9001-auditing-practices-grou.html.

Stojanovic (Undated) identified mandatory documentation requirements for ISO 9001, which, at the time of this writing, included the following:

- Monitoring and measuring equipment calibration records (clause 7.1.5.1)

- Records of training, skills, experience, and qualifications (clause 7.2)

- Product/service requirements review records (clause 8.2.3.2)

- Records about design and development outputs review (clause 8.3.2)

- Records about design and development inputs (clause 8.3.3)

- Records of design and development controls (clause 8.3.4)

- Records of design and development outputs (clause 8.3.5)

- Design and development changes records (clause 8.3.6)

- Characteristics of product to be produced and service to be provided (clause 8.5.1)

- Records about customer property (clause 8.5.3)

- Production/service provision change control records (clause 8.5.6)

- Record of conformity of product/service with acceptance criteria (clause 8.6)

- Record of nonconforming outputs (clause 8.7.2)

- Monitoring and measurement results (clause 9.1.1)

- Internal audit program (clause 9.2)

- Results of internal audits (clause 9.2)

- Results of the management review (clause 9.3)

- Results of corrective actions (clause 10.1)

Similarly, Stojanovic identified non-mandatory documentation requirements related to ISO 9001:

- Procedure for determining context of the organization and interested parties (clauses 4.1 and 4.2)

- Procedure for addressing risks and opportunities (clause 6.1)

- Procedure for competence, training, and awareness (clauses 7.1.2, 7.2, and 7.3)

- Procedure for equipment maintenance and measuring equipment (clause 7.1.5)

- Procedure for document and record control (clause 7.5)

- Sales procedure (clause 8.2)

- Procedure for design and development (clause 8.3)

- Procedure for production and service provision (clause 8.5)

- Warehousing procedure (clause 8.5.4)

- Procedure for management of nonconformities and corrective actions (clauses 8.7 and 10.2)

- Procedure for monitoring customer satisfaction (clause 9.1.2)

- Procedure for internal audit (clause 9.2)

- Procedure for management review (clause 9.3)

First Article Inspection Report (FAI)

A first article inspection report (commonly referred to simply as an "FAI") is related to manufacturing, particularly for the assurance of quality prior to shifting from process setup to production:

> *The purpose of the FAI is to provide objective evidence that all engineering design and specification requirements are properly understood, accounted for, verified, and documented. . . . It is intended that the documentation generated will be a quality record of the supplier and customer for review of accountability and planning, for performing periodic surveillance and audits to verify conformance, for evaluating root cause and corrective action for any nonconformances, and for problem investigations (https://www.sae.org/standards/content/as9102/).*

Differing from the ISO family of standards, which apply in a standardized form and implementation to multiple industries, the FAI is generally guided by a standard produced for or by specific industries such as the aerospace and auto-motive industries. FAI standards generally apply to industries that use produc-tion operations to produce parts (that is, articles, pieces, and so on) in quantity. It is important to remember that the documentation requirements for FAI in one industry may not be the same as the documentation requirements in another industry. It is reasonable to expect commonalities in documentation, particularly with respect to a set of characteristics such as part numbers, quality requirements, engineering design specifications, part drawings, identification of specific manu-facturing equipment required in production, and so on.

There are many vendors providing FAI software. Querying the term "first arti-cle inspection" on the Internet will produce multiple FAI products and vendors. Examples of FAI templates are readily available via the Internet as well. Figure 25.1 shows an example set of working papers for FAI as utilized by the Moog company. A thorough review of the example, and comparison with other FAI software, tem-plates, and examples, will reveal the commonalities and differences noted above.

The example shown in Figure 25.1 can be accessed at http://www.moog.com/literature/Corporate/Suppliers/First_Article_Inspection-_Aerospace_Forms.pdf. It should be noted that this example is illustrative of comprehensive FAI docu-mentation based on the AS9102 standard as applied to the aerospace industry by the Moog company.

Initial Sample Inspection Report (ISIR)

The ISIR differs from the FAI in the scope of documentation provided. Let us be clear—the FAI provides more detail and support information than does the ISIR. Also important for clarity is that there are many opinions communicated as fact that are not necessarily true implying that the FAI and the ISIR are the same thing. While there are many examples in online forums where dialogue participants interchange the FAI and ISIR, it should be noted that the FAI is more comprehensive than the ISIR in that, among other things, the FAI contains more information/documentation about the production process whereas the ISIR is typically less comprehensive than the FAI. Also, the ISIR is frequently, and correctly, referring to part layout and spec-ification information/documentation separate from production information/documentation.

It was noted in the discussion about FAI that the FAI is generally guided by a standard produced for/by specific industries such as the aerospace and/or auto-motive industries. FAI standards generally apply to industries that use produc-tion operations to produce parts (that is, articles, pieces, and so on) in quantity. It is important to know that ISIR standards, content, and procedures also differ by industry and company. It is common when ordering parts and generating pur-chase contracts that the details of what is, and what is not, included in an ISIR is specified. In this case, as was the case with the FAI, what one industry or company may stipulate to be included in an ISIR may not be the same as the documentation requirements in another industry or company. It is reasonable to expect common-alities in documentation among different ISIR documents.

As noted above in the FAI discussion, there are many vendors providing ISIR software. Querying the term "initial sample inspection report" on the Internet

Page 1 of 6

MOOG	First Article Inspection Report Approval Form	Report No:	FAI

Supplier Name & Address		Supplier Ref. No./ Cert of Conformity	
		Supplier Code	
Part Number/ Scheme Number		Drawing/Scheme Issue/Revision	
Part Description		Previous FAIR No.	N/A
Classification	Unclassified Critical Sensitive	Previous FAIR Date	
Component Weight	Any Special Ref.	Key Characteristics (CCF's) Specified	Yes No
Type of FAIR	Full FAIR	Repeat FAIR	Partial FAIR

Reason for FAIR	New Part/Drawing/Scheme	Change of Source or Location	Change of Method or Sequence
	Drawing issue change	Lapse in Production (> 24 months)	Request by MOOG
	Description of Reason	NEW PART	

Supplier Declaration: **This is to certify that:**
- This FAIR demonstrates conformance of the product to all requirements and that the information is a true record of the production method.
- Where conformance control features (key characteristics) are specified, stage 2 data collection has commenced.

| Name: | | Date: | | Signature : | |
| Phone No. | | Fax No. | | E-Mail | |

FAIR Stage 1 Approval	Decision Signature			Name (printed)	Date
	Satisfactory	Conditional	Reject		
Final Approval by Authorised Supplier					
Dimensional Report					
Materials Function e.g. Lab./Eng. etc.					
Final Approval					
Comments					

FAIR Stage 2 Approval	Decision Signature		Name (printed)	Date
	Satisfactory	Reject		
Engineering				
Final Approval				
Comments				

First Article Inspection Process, Approval Form: Issue 1 06/09/2006
C:\Temp\notesD30550\AS9102_Blank_forms.doc

Figure 25.1a   First article inspection process—First Article Inspection Report Approval Form.
Source: Moog 2006.

MOOG	First Article Inspection Report Content/Check Sheet	Part Number: FAI Purchase Order:

Use comments section to list multiple documents

	Contents – Stage 1	Included Yes	Not Applicable	Comments
1	First Article Inspection Report (FAIR) - Approval Form			
2	FAIR Approval Forms for referenced FAIR's.			
3	FAIR Approval Forms for relevant parts within a kit of parts			
4	AS/EN/SJAC9102 Form 1			
5	Cascade Diagram			
6	Classified Part Plan Approved Sheet. Repair Approvals.			
7	Copies of Approved Concession(s), Waivers, Production Permits.			
8	AS/EN/SJAC 9102 Form 2			
9	Approved Data Cards for special processes.			
10	Special Process substantiation reports			
11	Certificates of Raw Material Validation			
12	Functional Test Reports/Certificates (e.g. Hardness/Flow/Pressure Testing & Balancing - as applicable).			
13	Supplier Release Note (Certificate of Conformance), inc. sub-tier certification & documentation - as applicable			
14	AS/EN/SJAC 9102 Form(s) 3			
15	Released for Manufacture Drawing(s), or Repair Scheme - with feature numbering (Ballooned Print)			
16	Part Marking Verification (e.g. digital image)			
17	Method of Manufacture/Repair Router - as applicable.			
18	AS/EN/SJAC 9103 Process Control Document (page 1 and 2) to be submitted with Stage 1 for all CCF's / KC's			
19	*Bill of Material Part List*			
	Contents – Stage 2	Yes	Not Applicable	
1	AS/EN/SJAC 9103 Process Control Document Page 1 (Stage 5 achieved and Cpk >=1.33 for mandated CCF's / KC's)			
2	AS/EN/SJAC9103 Process Control Document Page 2 (Stage 5 achieved and Cpk >= 1.33 for mandated CCF's / KC's)			
3	Control Chart(s) and Capability Studies			

First Article Inspection Process, Content/Check Sheet: Issue 1 06/09/2006
C:\Temp\notesD30550\AS9102_Blank_forms.doc

Figure 25.1b First article inspection process–First Article Inspection Report Content/Check Sheet.
Source: Moog 2006.

AS9102 Rev A: First Article Inspection
Form 1: Part Number Accountability

Sheet 3 of 6

1. Part Number	2. Part Name	3. Serial Number	4. FAI Report Number
			FAI
5. Part Revision Level	6. Drawing Number	7. Drawing revision level	8. Additional Changes
9. Manufacturing Process Reference	10. Organization Name	11. Supplier Code	12. P.O. Number

13. Detail FAI Detail FAI Assembly FAI	14. Full FAI Partial FAI *Reason for Partial FAI:*	*Baseline Part Number including revision level*	

a)   if above part number is a detail part only, go to Field 19
b)   if above part number is an assembly, go to the "INDEX" section below.
INDEX of part numbers or sub-assembly numbers required to make the assembly noted above.

15. Part Number	16. Part Name	17. Part Serial Number	18. FAI Report Number

1) Signature indicates that all characteristics are accounted for; meet drawing requirements or are properly documented for disposition.
2) Also indicate if the FAI is complete per Section 5.4:   FAI complete   FAI not Complete

19. Signature	20. Date
21. Reviewed By	22. Date
23. Customer Approval	24. Date

AS9102 Form 1
C:\Temp\notesD30550\AS9102_Blank_forms.doc

Figure 25.1c   First article inspection process–Form 1: Part Number Accountability.
Source: Moog 2006.

AS91 02 Rev A: First Article Inspection   Sheet 4 of 6
Form 2: Product Accountability – Raw Material, Specifications and Special Process(s), Functional Testing

1. Part Number	2 Part Name		3. *Serial Number*		4. FAI Report Number FAI
5. *Material or Process Name*	6. *Specification Number*	7. Code	8. *Special Process Supplier Code*	9. *Customer Approval Verificatio n (Yes/No/NA)*	10. *Certificate of Conformance number*
11. *Functional Test Procedure Number*	12. *Acceptance report number, if applicable*				
13. Comments					
14. Prepared By			15. Date		

AS91 02 Form 2
C:\Temp\notesD30550\AS9102_Blank_forms.doc

Figure 25.1d   First article inspection process–Form 2: Product Accountablity–Raw Material, Specifications and Special Process(es), Functional Testing.

Source: Moog 2006.

AS9102 Rev A: First Article Inspection
Form 3: Characteristic Accountability, Verification and Compatibility Evaluation

Sheet 5 of 6

| 1. Part Number : | | | 2. Part Name : | | | 3. Serial Number: | 4. FAI Report |

Characteristic Accountability			Inspection/Test Results			Optional Fields	
5. Char No.	6. Reference Location	7. Characteristic Designator	8. Requirement	9. Results	10. Designed Tooling	11. Non-Conformance Number	Comments
							14

Form 3, AS9102 Rev A
C:\Templadded\D3055\0AS9102_Blank_forms.doc

MOOG

Figure 25.1e First article inspection process—Form 3: Characteristic Accountability, Verification and Compatibility Evaluation.
Source: Moog 2006.

AS9102 Rev A: First Article Inspection
Form 3: Characteristic Accountability, Verification and Compatibility Evaluation

1. Part Number :	2. Part Name :	3. *Serial Number:*	4. FAI Report	Sheet 6 of 6

*** NON-TOLERANCED DIMENSIONS ARE FOR REFERENCE ONLY AND MEASUREMENTS RECORDED ARE ONLY FOR GUIDANCE ***

The signature indicates that all characteristics are accounted for; meet drawing requirements or are properly documented for disposition.

12. Prepared By	13. Date

MOOG

Form 3, AS9102 Rev A
C:\Templocated\D30550\AS9102_Blank_forms.doc

Figure 25.1f First article inspection process—Form 3: Characteristic Accountability, Verification and Compatibility Evaluation.
Source: Moog 2006.

will produce multiple ISIR products and vendors. Examples of ISIR templates are readily available via the Internet as well.

A final comment on the FAI as compared to the ISIR: These reports do differ in the amount of information contained. The FAI is the more comprehensive document. Both the FAI and the ISIR are used in different industries and within different companies. Inclusion or exclusion of an FAI or an ISIR should be addressed in a purchase contract, and prudent practice would have the elements or pieces of information to be included in an FAI or ISIR should be specified in a purchase contract as well.

Production Part Approval Process (PPAP)

PPAP was designed as part of a nationwide effort within the United States to regain manufacturing competitiveness. The PPAP is applied when producing large volumes of complex products. The PPAP process, accordingly, is used primarily within the automotive industry, not only in the United States, but worldwide.

The automotive industry professional organization, the Automotive Industry Action Group (AIAG), publishes several very important standards and documents that the CQI is encouraged to know and understand. These standards and documents cover topics such as measurement systems analysis, FMEA, advanced product quality planning and control plans, and statistical process control, to name only a few. These resources can be accessed electronically at http://www.aiag.org/store/quality/publications.

When considering PPAP relative to ISO 9001, FAI, and ISIR, as discussed in this section of the *CQI Handbook* and the CQI BoK, these processes would be ranked on a scale of complexity and cost to implement in the following descending order: ISO 9001, PPAP, FAI, ISIR.

A primary intent of the PPAP is to ensure that there is a sufficiently robust quality system and documentation effort to ensure that product designs can be produced at a large scale. It is one thing to consider, and ensure, overall product quality in smaller-scale operations, but ensuring that a quality system exists and is fully functional across large-scale production operations, often at multiple plants and facilities, and often spanning multiple countries, requires a significant amount of support infrastructure and documentation.

PPAP is composed of 19 components as follows (Automotive Engineering HQ 2014):

1. Design documentation

2. Engineering change documentation

3. Engineering approvals

4. Design failure mode and effects analysis (DFMEA)

5. Process flow diagrams

6. Process failure mode and effects analysis (PFMEA)

7. Control plans

8. Measurement systems analysis

9. Dimensional results

10. Records of material/performance tests

11. Initial sample inspection reports

12. Initial process studies

13. Qualified laboratory documentation

14. Appearance approval reports

15. Sample production parts

16. Master production samples

17. Checking aides

18. Customer-specific requirements

19. Part submission warrants

A final comparison of FAI, ISIR, and PPAP should confirm the relationship discussed earlier in this chapter. Ranging from more complex to less complex are PPAP, then FAI, and then ISIR. In particular, it should now be clear that, while sometimes confused when used interchangeably, FAI and ISIR are commonly components of the more detailed and robust PPAP. The CQI should remember, however, that the FAI encompasses more content and information than does the ISIR.

BASIC QUALITY DOCUMENTATION

The last major section of the 2018 CQI BoK, section IV.G.4, relates to "proper use." As intended in the BoK, proper use of policy, procedure, work instructions and forms, and proper documentation practices requires that forms are filled out completely, all spelling is correct, all changes are initialed, and so on).

As we are nearing the end of this chapter, we wish to highlight several important points as follows:

1. Producing high-quality parts or services does not occur by happenstance.

2. The more complex the parts produced, or the services delivered, the more robust the quality systems must be to ensure quality.

3. There are four particularly important approaches to quality, namely, ISO 9001, FAI, ISIR, and PPAP.

4. Each of these four approaches to quality are heavily dependent on documentation.

5. There are very clear expectations related to how, why, when, where, and under what circumstances appropriate documentation is generated, used, stored, and revised.

6. Quality documentation serves not only as historical records, but also as the basis of communications, contracts, and performance expectations.

7. As historical records, quality documentation serves as a permanent record of your professional performance, and the ASQ code of ethics calls for your professional practice as a CQI to produce high-quality work as reflected in your generation and use of quality documentation.

REFERENCES

Automotive Engineering HQ. 2014. "Production Part Approval Process (PPAP)." August 31. Accessed September 3, 2018. Available at https://www.automotiveengineeringhq.com/production-part-approval-process-ppap/.

Blanchard, K., J. P. Carlos, and A. Randolph. 2010. *Empowerment Takes More Than a Minute.* 2nd ed. San Francisco: Berrett-Koehler.

Frappaolo, C. 2006. *Knowledge Management.* New York: John Wiley & Sons.

Ichniowski, C., D. I. Levine, C. Olson, and G. Strauss. 2001. *The American Workplace: Skills, Pay, and Employee Involvement.* Cambridge, UK: Cambridge University Press.

ILPI. Undated. "The Safety Data Sheet (SDS) FAQ: Introduction." The SDS FAQ. Accessed May 5, 2012. Available at http://www.ilpi.com/msds/faq/parta.html#whatis.

OSHA (Occupational Safety and Health Administration). Undated. "Personal Protective Equipment." Safety and Health Topics. Accessed May 5, 2012. Available at http://www.osha.gov/SLTC/personalprotectiveequipment/index.html.

Scholtes, P. R., B. L. Joiner, and B. J. Streibel. 2003. *The Team Handbook.* 3rd ed. Madison, WI: Oriel.

Stojanovic, S. Undated. "List of Mandatory Documents Required by ISO 9001:2015." Advisera. ISO 9001 Knowledge Base. Accessed September 3, 2018. Available at https://advisera.com/9001academy/knowledgebase/list-of-mandatory-documents-required-by-iso-90012015/.

Woods, E. 2005. *Employee Development at the Workplace: Achieving Empowerment in a Continuous Learning Environment.* Dubuque, IA: Kendall and Hunt.

BIBLIOGRAPHY

AIAG (Automotive Industry Action Group). Undated. AIAG Store. Quality Publication Listing. Accessed December 19, 2018. Available at http://www.aiag.org/store/quality/publications.

Alred, G., C. Brusaw, and W. Oliu. 2012. *The Handbook of Technical Writing.* 10th ed. New York: Bedford/St. Martin's.

Ancona, D., and H. Bresman. 2007. *X-Teams: How to Build Teams That Lead, Innovate, and Succeed.* Boston: Harvard Business School Press.

Bednarz, T. F. 2011. *Organizational Empowerment: Pinpoint Leadership Skill Development Training Series.* Stevens Point, WI: Majorium Business Press.

Cobb, A. T. 2012. *Leading Project Teams: The Basics of Project Management and Team Leadership.* 2nd ed. London: Sage.

Gerson, S. J., and S. M. Gerson. 2011. *Technical Communication: Process and Product.* 8th ed. New York: Prentice Hall.

Moog. 2006. First Article Inspection Documentation. Accessed September 3, 2018. Available at http://www.moog.com/literature/Corporate/Suppliers/First_Article_Inspection-_Aerospace_Forms.pdf.

Noe, R. A. 2010. *Employee Training and Development*. 5th ed. New York: McGraw-Hill.

O'Dell, C., and C. Hubert. 2011. *The New Edge in Knowledge: How Knowledge Management Is Changing the Way We Do Business*. New York: John Wiley & Sons.

Reep, D. C. 2010. *Technical Writing: Principles, Strategies, and Readings*. 8th ed. New York: Longman Publishing.

Synergy Global Sourcing. Undated. "Initial Sample Inspection Report." Accessed September 3, 2018 at https://www.synergyglobal.in%2fimages%2fquality_inspection_docs%2fsynergy_inspection_report.jpg&exph=1616&expw=1392&q=Initial+Sample+Inspection+Report+Template&simid=607997707581262268&selectedIndex=29&ajaxhist=0.

Tague, N. 2005. *The Quality Toolbox*. 2nd ed. Milwaukee: ASQ Quality Press.

West, M. A. 2012. *Effective Teamwork: Practical Lessons from Organizational Research*. 3rd ed. New York: John Wiley & Sons/BPS Blackwell.

Section V
Appendices

Appendix A American Society for Quality
Certified Quality Inspector (CQI)
Body of Knowledge 2018

Appendix B Computer Resources to Support the
CQI Handbook

Appendix C General Tables of Units of
Measurement

Appendix D Standard Normal Distribution

Appendix E Factors Helpful in Constructing
Control Charts for Variables

Appendix F Values of K_1 for Computing
Repeatability Using the Range
Method

Appendix G Values of K_2 for Computing
Reproducibility Using the Range
Method

Appendix H Sample Tables of ANSI/ASQ Z1.4-2008
and ANSI/ASQ Z1.9-2008 Standards

Appendix A

American Society for Quality Certified Quality Inspector (CQI) Body of Knowledge 2018

The topics in this body of knowledge include additional detail in the form of subtext explanations and the cognitive level at which the questions will be written. This information will provide useful guidance for both the Exam Development Committee and the candidate preparing to take the exam. The subtext is not intended to limit the subject matter or be all-inclusive of what might be covered in an exam. It is meant to clarify the type of content to be included in the exam. The descriptor in parentheses at the end of each line of subtext refers to the maximum cognitive level at which the topic will be tested. A complete description of cognitive levels is provided at the end of this document.

Note: Approximately 20% of the questions in each exam will require calculation.

I. Technical Mathematics (19 Questions)

   A. *Basic Shop Math.* Solve basic shop math problems using addition, subtraction, multiplication, division of fractions and decimals, squares and square roots. Use methods such as truncating and rounding to obtain significant digits for positive and negative numbers. (Apply)

   B. *Basic Algebra.* Solve or simplify first-degree and single-variable equations. (Apply)

   C. *Basic Geometry.* Calculate general parameters such as area, circumference, perimeter, and volume for basic geometric shapes. Calculate complementary and supplementary angles. (Apply)

   D. *Basic Trigonometry.* Solve for angles and lengths using trigonometric functions such as sine, cosine, tangent, and the Pythagorean Theorem. (Apply)

   E. *Measurement Systems.* Convert units within and between English and metric measurement systems (SI) such as inch to micro-inch, liter to quart, and meter to millimeter. (Apply)

   F. *Numeric Conversions.* Use various numbering methods such as scientific notation, decimals, and fractions, and convert values between these systems. (Apply)

II. Metrology (26 Questions)

A. *Common Gauges and Measurement Instruments*

1. *Variable gauges.* Identify and use variable gauges, including micrometers, calipers, dial indicators, and Coordinate Measuring Machines (CMM). Understand linear scales, such as steel rule, and gage blocks. Use borescopes, thermometers, and temperature probes. (Apply)

2. *Attribute gauges.* Identify and use attribute gauges, including thread plugs, progressive rings, flush pins, pin gauges, and radius gauges. (Apply)

3. *Transfer gauges.* Identify and use transfer gauges, including small-hole gauges, telescoping gauges, and spring calipers. (Apply)

4. *Measurement scales.* Describe and distinguish between dial, digital, and vernier scales. (Remember)

B. *Special Gauges and Applications.* Identify and describe the following basic tools and components. (Remember)

1. *Electronic gauging tools:* oscilloscopes, multimeters, and pyrometers.

2. *Automatic gauging components:* machine vision, ultrasonic, X-ray, and laser.

3. *Pneumatic gauging components:* air columns, probes, and rings.

4. *Force gauging:* torque wrenches.

5. *Environment instrumentation:* hygrometers, chart recorders, and data loggers.

C. *Gauge Selection, Handling, and Use*

1. *10:1 rule.* Understand the 10:1 rule: inspection measurements require better than the tolerance of a dimension by a factor of 10, and calibration standards require better than the inspection measurements by a factor of 10. (Understand)

2. *Gauge selection.* Select gauges according to the feature or characteristic to be measured, the applicable tolerance and the accuracy, environment, and the resolution and capability of the test instrument. Determine whether the type of measurement should be direct, differential, or transfer. (Apply)

3. *Gauge handling, preservation, and storage.* Identify and apply various methods of cleaning, handling, and storing gauges. (Apply)

4. *Gauge correlation.* Identify and apply methods for establishing the correlation between measurement instruments such as gauge-to-gauge or manual-to-automated process. (Apply)

D. *Surface Plate Tools and Techniques*

1. *Surface plate equipment.* Select and use height gauges, V-blocks, and other indicators, to measure various types of features. Understand the care, cleaning, calibration, and lapping of a surface plate. (Apply)

2. *Angle measurement instruments.* Identify and use protractors, sine bars, and angle blocks. (Apply)

E. *Specialized Inspection Equipment*

1. *Measuring mass.* Describe and apply weights, balances, and scales. (Apply)

2. *Measuring finish.* Describe and apply profilometers, and fingernail comparators. (Apply)

3. *Measuring shape and profile.* Describe and apply mechanical comparators, roundness testers, precision spindles, and profile tracers. (Apply)

4. *Optical equipment.* Describe and apply optical comparators, optical flats, and microscopes. (Apply)

5. *Software-based measurement systems.* Define and describe the use of digital cameras, in-line optical sensors, vision inspection systems (white light/blue light), articulating arms, laser trackers, contracers, and other digital systems for product inspection. Recognize software limitations with regard to locating functional datums, target points and areas, hole positions and the basic operation of the x, y, and z axes. (Understand)

6. *Measuring Inclination.* Define and describe the measurement of the slope or slant of various equipment (mechanical/laser). (Understand)

F. *Calibration*

1. *Calibration systems.* Describe the principles and purpose of a calibration system, including the importance of establishing calibration intervals and uncertainty. Identify and use basic tracking and identification methods such as logs, stickers, radio frequency identifications (RFID), barcodes, and other identification codes to control calibration equipment. (Apply)

2. *Calibration standards and equipment traceability.* Describe the hierarchy of standards, from working standards through international standards and the documentation process of a measurement device traceable to the international standards. (Remember)

3. *Gauge calibration environment.* Describe the effects that environmental conditions have on the calibration process, such as temperature, humidity, vibration, and cleanliness of the gauge. (Apply)

4. *Out-of-calibration effects.* Describe the effects that out-of-calibration instruments can have on product acceptance and the actions to take in response to this situation. (Apply)

G. *Measurement System Analysis (MSA).* Define and describe the following elements of MSA. (Remember)

1. Bias

2. Stability

3. Precision

4. Accuracy

5. Linearity

6. Repeatability and reproducibility (R&R) studies

III. Inspection and Test (33 Questions)

    A. *Blueprints, Drawings, Geometric Dimensioning & Tolerancing (GD&T) & Model Based Definitions*

        1. *Blueprints, engineering drawings and model based definitions.* Define and interpret various sections of technical drawings: title blocks, tolerances, change or revision blocks, including notes, scale, and size details. (Apply)

        2. *Terminology and symbols.* Define and interpret drawing views and details for product specifications or other controlling documents. Define and use various terms and symbols from the ASME Y14.5M Standard. (Analyze)

        3. *Position and bonus tolerances.* Calculate position and bonus tolerances from various drawings. (Analyze)

        4. *Part alignment and datum structure.* Determine part alignment and setup using the datum structure. (Analyze)

    B. *Sampling.* Define and interpret the following terms related to sampling. (Apply)

        1. Acceptance quality limit (AQL)

        2. Random sampling

        3. Lot and sample size

        4. Acceptance number

        5. Sampling plans

    C. *Inspection Planning and Processes*

        1. *Inspection types.* Define and distinguish between inspection types such as incoming material, first-article (first-piece), in-process, and final. (Apply)

        2. *Inspection errors.* Identify potential inspection errors such as bias, fatigue, flinching, distraction, and poor time management. (Apply)

        3. *Product traceability.* Identify methods to trace products and materials such as age control, shelf life, first-in first-out (FIFO), barcoding, date codes, and lot and part numbering. (Apply)

4. *Identification of nonconforming material.* Describe various methods of identifying nonconforming material such as tagging, labeling, and segregating. (Apply)

5. *Level of severity.* Define and describe levels of severity (critical, major, and minor) and apply them to product features and defects. (Apply)

6. *Disposition of nonconforming material.* Describe disposition methods including rework, reprocess, reinspect, scrap, and customer waiver, as determined by a material review board (MRB) or other authority. (Apply)

D. *Testing Methods.* Define and use the following methods in various situations. (Apply)

1. *Nondestructive testing:* X-ray, eddy current, ultrasonic, dye penetrant, magnetic particle, optical, visual, and profile.

2. *Destructive testing:* tensile, force testing, and drop test.

3. *Functionality testing:* tension, torque, leak testing, and compression.

4. *Hardness testing:* Brinell, Rockwell, durometer, and micro-hardness scales.

E. *Software for test equipment.* Identify and describe basic tools (safeguarding, functional checks, comparison of test results, identification of attributes and parameters) used to ensure that the software for test equipment adequately and correctly performs its intended functions. (Remember)

IV. Quality Assurance (22 Questions)

A. *Basic Statistics and Applications*

1. *Measures of central tendency.* Calculate mean, median, and mode. (Apply)

2. *Measures of dispersion.* Calculate range, standard deviation, and variance. (Apply)

3. *Measures of proportion.* Calculate percentage and ratio measures for various data sets. (Apply)

4. *Graphical displays.* Define, interpret, and use scatter diagrams, tally sheets, and bar charts to display data effectively in various situations. (Apply)

5. *Normal distribution.* Describe various characteristics of a normal distribution: symmetry, bell curve, and central tendency. (Understand)

B. *Statistical Process Control (SPC).*

1. *Common and special cause variation.* Explain the difference between these causes of variation. Determine whether a process is in statistical control by analyzing data patterns (runs, trends, and hugging), and identify what actions should be taken in response. (Evaluate)

2. *Control limits and specification limits.* Define, describe, and distinguish between these limits as used in SPC. (Apply)

3. *Variables charts.* Identify characteristics and uses of $\bar{X} - R$ and $\bar{X} - S$. (Apply)

4. *Attributes charts.* Identify characteristics and uses of p, np, c, and u charts. (Apply)

5. *Process capability analysis.* Define and distinguish between C_p, C_{pk}, P_p, and P_{pk} studies and identify their application to various types of data. (Understand)

C. *Quality Improvement*

1. *Terms and concepts.* Define basic quality improvement concepts such as defect detection and prevention, the cost of poor quality, total quality management (TQM), and the importance of customer satisfaction. (Understand)

2. *Products and processes.* Define and distinguish between products and processes. Describe the interrelationships of product design, materials used, manufacturing processes, and final output, and how individual steps in a process can affect the final product or the system as a whole. (Understand)

D. *Quality Audits*

1. *Types of audits.* Define and describe various types of audits, including internal, external, system, product, and process. (Understand)

2. *Audit process.* Define and describe various stages of the audit process (planning, performance, and closure), including audit scope and purpose, resources needed, audit schedule, opening meeting, interviewing, data gathering, document and record review, analysis of results, closing meeting, audit documentation (reporting), recordkeeping, and verification of corrective actions. (Understand)

3. *Audit tools.* Define and describe the purpose of checklists, log sheets, sampling plans, record reviews, document reviews and forward—and backward—tracing. (Understand)

4. *Communication tools and techniques.* Define and describe the use of graphs, charts, diagrams, and other aids for written and oral presentations including interview techniques and listening skills. (Understand)

5. *Corrective action requests (CARs).* Describe how CARs from audits can support quality improvement. (Understand)

E. *Quality Tools and Techniques.* Define and use the following quality tools and techniques. (Apply)

1. Pareto charts

    2. Cause and effect diagrams

    3. Flowcharts

    4. Control charts

    5. Check sheets

    6. Scatter diagrams

    7. Histograms

F. *Problem-solving Tools and Continuous Improvement Technique.* Describe and use the following tools and techniques in various situations. (Apply)

    1. *Plan-do-check-act (PDCA) or plan-do-study-act (PDSA) cycles*

    2. *Lean tools for eliminating waste:* 5S, error-proofing, value-stream mapping; and lean concepts: kaizen, flow, pull

    3. *Six sigma phases:* define, measure, analyze, improve, control (DMAIC)

    4. *Failure mode and effects analysis (FMEA)*

    5. *8D Methodology*

    6. *5 Why Analysis*

    7. *Fault Tree Analysis*

G. Resources

    1. *Environmental and safety support.* Define and use various resources related to personal and environmental safety: safety data sheets (SDS), material data sheet (MDS), and personal protective equipment (PPE). (Apply)

    2. *Reference documents.* Identify and use national and international standards (ISO, ANSI, ASTM, QS) and customer requirements as authorities that support processes and procedures used to assure quality products. (Apply)

    3. *Employees as resources.* Describe how employees can be empowered and the value they add to project teams or quality improvement teams. Describe typical team roles and responsibilities: facilitator, ground rules, project or team charter. Describe the four stages of team development: forming, storming, norming, performing. (Remember)

    4. *Quality documentation.* Basic quality documentation including correct form/revision for the process (ISO9100, FAIR, ISIR, PPAPs). Proper usage of policy, procedure, work instructions and forms, proper documentation practices such as document control, filling out forms completely, correcting misspellings, and initialing changes. (Apply)

LEVELS OF COGNITION—BASED ON *BLOOM'S TAXONOMY*—REVISED (2001)

In addition to content specifics, the subtext for each topic in this BoK also indicates the intended complexity level of the test questions for that topic. These levels are based on "Levels of Cognition" (from *Bloom's Taxonomy*—Revised, 2001) and are presented below in rank order, from least complex to most complex.

Remember

Recall or recognize terms, definitions, facts, ideas, materials, patterns, sequences, methods, principles, etc.

Understand

Read and understand descriptions, communications, reports, tables, diagrams, directions, regulations, etc.

Apply

Know when and how to use ideas, procedures, methods, formulas, principles, theories, etc.

Analyze

Break down information into its constituent parts and recognize their relationship to one another and how they are organized; identify sublevel factors or salient data from a complex scenario.

Evaluate

Make judgments about the value of proposed ideas, solutions, etc., by comparing the proposal to specific criteria or standards.

Create

Put parts or elements together in such a way as to reveal a pattern or structure not clearly there before; identify which data or information from a complex set is appropriate to examine further or from which supported conclusions can be drawn.

Appendix B

Computer Resources to Support the CQI Handbook

USING MINITAB SOFTWARE

In the past two decades, use of technology to analyze complicated data has increased substantially, which not only has made the analysis very simple, but also has reduced the time required to complete such analysis. To facilitate statistical analysis, many companies have acquired personal computer–based statistical application software. Several PC-based software packages are available, including BMDP, JMP, Minitab, SAS, SPSS, and SYSTAT just to name a few. A great deal of effort has been expended in the development of these software packages to create graphical user interfaces that allow software users to complete statistical analysis activities without having to know a computer programming or scripting language. We believe that publishing a book discussing applied statistics without acknowledging and addressing the importance and usefulness of statistical software would simply not be in the best interests of our readers. Accordingly, here we briefly discuss one very popular statistical package, Minitab. It is our explicit intent not to endorse any specific software package. Each package has its strengths and weaknesses.

USING MINITAB—VERSION 18

Minitab provides the options of using commands from the menu bar, typing in Session commands, or using both. As shown in Figure B.1, in the Windows environment it has the look and feel of most other Windows applications, where the menu options help you to easily navigate through the package.

Once in the Minitab environment you will see the heading *Minitab-Untitled* and three windows:

1. The *Data window (worksheet)* is used to enter data in columns denoted by C1, C2, C3, . . . , C4000.

2. The *Session window* displays the output and also allows the user to enter commands when using the command language.

3. The *Project manager window* (minimized at startup) displays project folders, which enable one to navigate through them and manipulate as necessary.

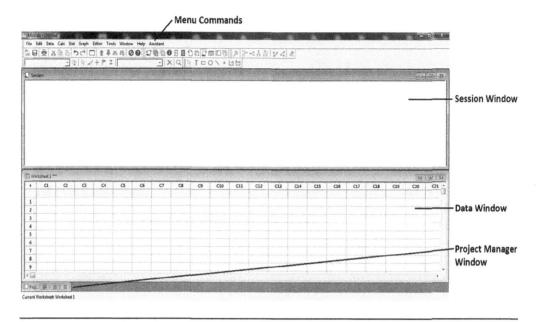

Figure B.1   The screen that appears first in the Minitab environment.

Getting Started with Minitab

In this chapter we discuss briefly how to use Minitab pull-down menus to analyze statistical data. Once you log on to your personal computer and get into the Minitab environment, you will see the picture in Figure B.1 on your PC screen. The pull-down menu appears at the top of the screen.

Menu Commands. Menu commands include:

File Edit Data Calc Stat Graph Editor Tools Window Help Assistant

By clicking any of the above menu commands, we see the options included in that command. For example, if we click on the *File* menu we get the drop-down menu as shown in Figure B.2. The first option, *New*, allows us to create a new worksheet.

Creating a New Worksheet. Creating a new worksheet means to enter new data in the worksheet or data window. The data window consists of 4000 columns, which are labeled C1, C2, . . . , C4000. The data can be entered in one or more columns depending on the setup of the problem. In each column, immediately below the labels C1, C2, and so on, there is one cell that is not labeled, whereas the rest of the cells are labeled 1, 2, 3, and so on. In the unlabeled cell you can enter the variable name such as part name, shift, lot number, and so on. In the labeled cells you enter data, using one cell for each data point. If a numerical observation is missing, Minitab will automatically replace the missing value with a star (*).

From the Menu bar select *File > New.* This gives two options: to create either a new worksheet or a project.

Selecting *Minitab Worksheet* opens a new worksheet (an empty data window) that is added to the current project.

Figure B.2   Minitab window showing the menu command options.

Selecting *Minitab Project* opens a new project and closes the existing project.

Saving a Data File. First, click anywhere on the worksheet window, then, using the command *File > Save Worksheet As* will allow you to save the current data file. When you enter this command, a dialog box entitled *Save Worksheet As…* appears. Type the file name in the box next to *File Name*, select the drive location for the file, and then click *Save*.

Retrieving a Saved Minitab Data File. Using the command *File > Open* will prompt the dialog box *Open* to appear. Select the drive and directory where the file was saved. Click on the file name twice; the file (Worksheet/Project) will open in the Minitab environment. Once the file opens, you can modify it any you want and then save it as explained above.

Saving a Minitab Project. Using the command *File > Save Project* saves the ongoing project in a Minitab Project (MPJ) file to the designated directory with the name you choose. Saving the project saves all windows opened in the project, along with the contents of each window. If it is a new project, use the command *File > Save Project As…*. This will allow you to save the current project. When you enter this command, a dialog box entitled *Save Project As…* appears. Type the file name in the box next to *File Name*, select the drive location for the file, and then click *Save*.

Print Options. To print the contents in any specific window, you need to make the specific window active by clicking on it and then using the command *File > Print Session Window (Graph, Worksheet)*.

If you want to print multiple graphs on a single page, highlight the multiple graphs in the *Graph* folder in the *Project Manager Window* by right-clicking on each and choose *Print*. The *Print Multiple Graphs* dialog box appears. To change the page orientation of the multiple graphs, you need to use *File > Page Setup* to adjust printing options.

Calculating Descriptive Statistics

Descriptive statistics can be calculated either one statistic or multiple statistics at a time. If you are interested in calculating only one statistic, you use either the *Column Command* or *Row Command* depending on whether you have entered your data in a column or in a row. For calculating multiple statistics at a time, you use the *Descriptive Statistics* command. Following, we consider all these cases one by one.

Column Statistics. First, enter the desired data in the *Worksheet Window*. Then, from the command menu select *Calc > Column Statistics*. The statistics that can be displayed for the selected columns include sum, mean, standard deviation, minimum, maximum, range, median, sum of squares, N total, N non-missing, and N missing. All these choices of statistics appear in the dialog box shown in Figure B.3. This dialog box appears immediately after you select the command *Calc > Column Statistics*. Note that when using this command you can choose only one statistic at a time. See Example B.1.

EXAMPLE B.1

Use the following steps to calculate any one of the statistics listed in the *Column Statistics* dialog box, using the following data:

8 9 7 6 5 6 8 9 8 9

Solution

1. Enter the data in column C1 of the data window.

2. Select *Calc* from the command menu.

3. Click *Column Statistics* from the pull-down menu available in the Calc command menu.

4. In the *Column Statistics* dialog box, check the circle next to the desired statistics; here we will use standard deviation.

5. Enter C1 in the box next to the input variable.

6. Click *OK*. The Minitab output will appear in the session window as shown in Figure B.3.

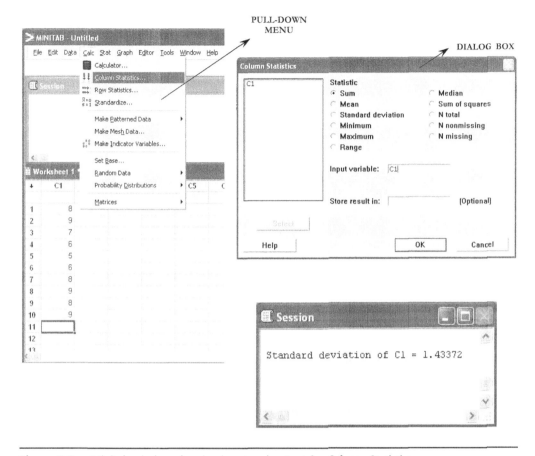

Figure B.3   Minitab window showing input and output for *Column Statistics*.

Row Statistics. From the menu bar select *Calc > Row Statistics*. The statistics that can be displayed for the selected rows include sum, mean, standard deviation, minimum, maximum, range, median, sum of squares, *N* total, *N* non-missing, and *N* missing.

Note that *Column Statistics* and *Row Statistics* give you exactly the same choices. So, use the appropriate command, *Column Statistics* or *Row Statistics*, depending on the format of your data and whether they are arranged in columns or rows.

Descriptive Statistics. From the menu bar select *Stat > Basic Statistics > Display Descriptive Statistics*. Statistics available for display include mean, standard deviation of mean, standard deviation, variance, coefficient of variation, trimmed mean, sum, minimum, maximum, range, *N* non-missing, *N* missing, *N* total, cumulative *N*, percent, cumulative percent, first quartile, median, third quartile, interquartile range, sum of squares, skewness, kurtosis, and MSSD.

The benefit of the command *Stat > Basic Statistics > Display Descriptive Statistics* over the commands *Column Statistics* and *Row Statistics* is that it provides all the statistics listed in the above paragraph in one step rather than one at a time. See Example B.2.

EXAMPLE B.2

Use the following steps to calculate any one of the statistics listed in the *Basic Statistics* dialog box, using the following data:

$$8 \quad 9 \quad 7 \quad 6 \quad 5 \quad 6 \quad 8 \quad 9 \quad 8 \quad 9$$

Solution

Enter the data in column C1 of the data window.

1. Select *Stat* from the command menu.

2. Click on *Basic Statistics > Display Descriptive Statistics* from the pull-down menu available under the *Stat* command menu (see Figure B.4).

3. Enter C1 in the box below *Variables* and click the *Statistics* button; a new dialog box pops up with various statistics to choose from. You may select only a few or all of them and then click OK.

4. Again click *OK*. The Minitab output will appear in the session window as shown in Figure B.4.

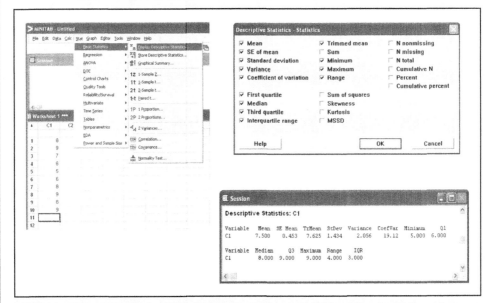

Figure B.4   Minitab window showing various options available under the Stat menu.

Graphs

From the menu bar select *Graph* and then select the graph of your choice. Some of the choices include scatter plot, histogram, dot plot, box plot, bar chart, stem-and-leaf, time series plot, pie chart, and others. We discuss some of these graphs following.

Histogram. First, enter the data in one or more columns of the worksheet depending on whether you have data on one or more variables. See Example B.3. For each variable, use only one column. Then use the menu command *Graph > Histogram.* This prompts the *Histograms* dialog box to appear, which has four different options to choose from. Choose the desired option and then click *OK.* For example, choose

EXAMPLE B.3

Prepare a histogram for the following data:

23	25	20	16	19	18	42	25
28	29	36	26	27	35	41	18
20	24	29	26	37	38	24	26
34	36	38	39	32	33		

Solution

Use the following steps to draw any one of the graphs listed in the pull-down menu available under the *Graph* menu.

1. Enter the data in column C1 of the data window.

2. Select from the command menu *Graph > Histogram > Simple* then click *OK.*

3. The *Histogram Simple* dialog box will pop up. In this dialog box enter C1 in the box under *Graph Variables* and click *OK.*

4. The Minitab output will appear in the graph window as shown in Figure B.5.

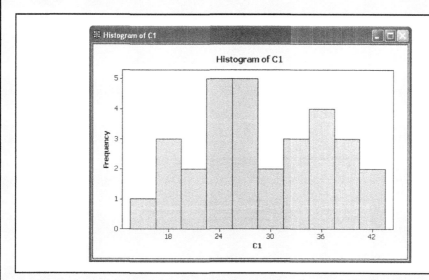

Figure B.5   Minitab display of the histogram for the data given in Example B.3.

the option *Simple* and click *OK*. The *Histogram Simple* dialog box appears. In this dialog box enter one or more variables in the box under *Graph Variables*. If you have not entered the names of the variables in the data columns, then under *Graph Variables* just enter C1, C2, and so on, and then click *OK*. A separate graph is displayed for each variable. To display more than one graph, select the *Multiple Graphs* option and then choose the desired display option.

Sometimes, we are interested in constructing a histogram with a particular number of classes or intervals, say five. Right-click on one of the bars in the default histogram to bring up the *Edit Bars* dialog box shown in Figure B.6.

In the *Edit Bars* dialog box select the *Binning* tab, and then under *Interval Type* check the circle next to *Midpoint*. Then, under *Interval Definition* check the circle next to *Number of Intervals*, and enter the number of desired intervals in the box next to it, five in this example. Click *OK*. The output will appear in the graph window as shown in Figure B.7.

Dot Plot. First, enter the data in one or more columns of the worksheet depending on how many variables you have. For each variable use only one column. Then use the menu command *Graph > Dotplot*. This command prompts the *Dotplots* dialog box to pop up, which has seven different options to choose from. Choose the desired graph option and then click *OK*. Another dialog box appears, entitled *Dotplot–One Y, Simple*. In this dialog box enter one or more variables under the *Graph Variables* box. If you have not entered the names of the variables in the data columns, in the box under *Graph Variables* just enter C1, C2, and so on, and then click *OK*. A separate graph is displayed for each variable. To display more than one graph, select the *Multiple Graphs* option and then choose the desired display option. See Example B.4.

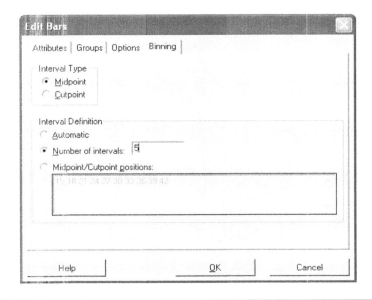

Figure B.6   Minitab window showing *Edit Bars* dialog box.

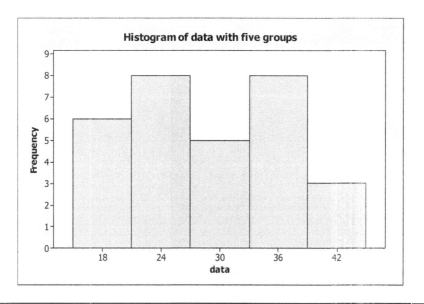

Figure B.7   Minitab display of a histogram with five classes for the data in Example B.3.

EXAMPLE B.4

Prepare a dot plot for the following data:

$$
\begin{array}{cccccccc}
23 & 25 & 20 & 16 & 19 & 18 & 42 & 25 \\
28 & 29 & 36 & 26 & 27 & 35 & 41 & 18 \\
20 & 24 & 29 & 26 & 37 & 38 & 24 & 26 \\
34 & 36 & 38 & 39 & 32 & 33 & &
\end{array}
$$

Solution

1. Enter the data in column C1 of the data window (the same as Example B.3).

2. Select *Graph* from the command menu.

3. Click *Dotplot* from the pull-down menu available under the *Graph* command menu.

4. Select the *Simple* dot plot and click *OK*.

5. Enter C1 in the box under *Graph Variables* and click *OK*.

6. The Minitab output will appear in the graph window as shown in Figure B.8.

Continued

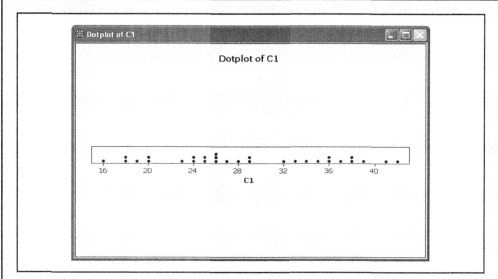

Figure B.8   Minitab dot plot output for the data in Example B.4.

Scatter Plot. First, enter the data in one or more columns of the worksheet depending on how many variables you have. For each variable use only one column. Then use the menu command *Graph > Scatterplot.* This command prompts the *Scatterplots* dialog box to appear, which has seven different options to choose from. Choose the desired graph option and then click *OK.* Another dialog box appears, entitled *Scatterplot–Simple.* In this dialog box enter the names of the variables under the *y* variable and the *x* variable. If you have not entered the names of the variables in the data columns, then under the *y* variable and the *x* variable just enter the columns where you have entered the data, say C1, C2, and so on, and then click *OK.* A separate graph is displayed for each set of variables. To display more than one graph, select the *Multiple Graphs* option and then choose the desired display option. See Example B.5.

The graph in Figure B.9 shows that although the plotted points are not clustered around the line, they still fall around the line going through them. This indicates that there is only a moderate correlation between the test scores and the job evaluation scores of the Six Sigma Green Belts.

Box-and-Whisker Plot. First, enter the data in one or more columns of the worksheet depending on how many variables you have. For each variable use only one column. Then use the menu command *Graph > Boxplot.* This command prompts the *Boxplot* dialog box to appear, with four different graph options. Choose the desired option and then click *OK.* Then the *Boxplot–One Y, Simple* dialog box appears. In this dialog box enter one or more variables in the box under *Graph Variables.* If you have not entered the names of the variables in the data columns,

EXAMPLE B.5

The following data show the test scores (x) and the job evaluation scores (y) of 16 Six Sigma Green Belts. Prepare a scatter plot for these data and interpret the result you observe in this graph.

x	45	47	40	35	43	40	49	46
y	9.2	8.2	8.5	7.3	8.2	7.5	8.2	7.3
x	38	39	45	41	48	46	42	40
y	7.4	7.5	7.7	7.5	8.8	9.2	9.0	8.1

Solution

1. Enter the data in columns C1 and C2 of the data window.

2. Select *Graph* from the command menu

3. Click *Scatterplot* from the pull-down menu available under the *Graph* command menu.

4. Select the simple scatter plot and click *OK*.

5. Enter C2 and C1 under the *y* variable and *x* variable, respectively, and click *OK*.

6. The Minitab output will appear in the graph window as shown in Figure B.9.

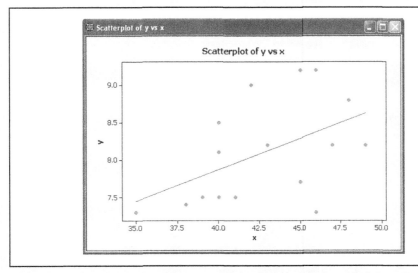

Figure B.9   Minitab scatter plot output for the data given in Example B.5.

then under *Graph Variables* just enter C1, C2, and so on, and then click *OK*. A separate graph is displayed for each variable. To display more than one graph, select the *Multiple Graphs* option and then choose the desired display option. The box plot will appear in the graph window as shown in Figure B.10a. See Example B.6.

EXAMPLE B.6

Prepare a box plot for the following data:

23	25	20	16	19	55	42	25
28	29	36	26	27	35	41	55
20	24	29	26	37	38	24	26
34	36	38	39	32	33		

Solution

1. Enter the data in column C1 of the data window (the same as in Example B.3).

2. Select *Graph* from the command menu.

3. Click on *Boxplot* from the pull-down menu available in the *Graph* command menu.

4. Select the *Simple* box plot.

5. Enter C1 in the box under *Graph Variables* and click *OK*.

6. The Minitab output will appear in the graph window as shown in Figure B.10.

The box plot for the data in this example will appear in the graph window as shown in Figure B.10a. Figure B.10b shows the box plot rotated through 90° so that the whiskers are horizontal.

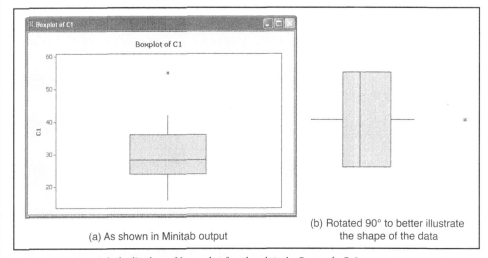

(a) As shown in Minitab output

(b) Rotated 90° to better illustrate the shape of the data

Figure B.10   Minitab display of box plot for the data in Example B.6.

Graphical Summary. First, enter the data in one or more columns of the worksheet depending on how many variables you have. For each variable use only one column. Then use the menu command *Stat > Basic Statistics > Graphical Summary.* See Example B.7. This command prompts the *Graphical Summary* dialog box to appear. In this dialog box enter the names of the variables you want summarized under *Variables.* If you have not entered the names of the variables in the data columns, then in the box under *Variables* just enter C1, C2, and so on. In the box next

---

EXAMPLE B.7

Prepare the graphical summary for the following data:

$$23 \quad 25 \quad 20 \quad 16 \quad 19 \quad 55 \quad 42 \quad 25$$

$$28 \quad 29 \quad 36 \quad 26 \quad 27 \quad 35 \quad 41 \quad 55$$

$$20 \quad 24 \quad 29 \quad 26 \quad 37 \quad 38 \quad 24 \quad 26$$

$$34 \quad 36 \quad 38 \quad 39 \quad 32 \quad 33$$

Solution

1. Enter the data in column C1 of the data window (the same as in Example B.3).

2. Select *Stat* from the command menu.

3. Select *Basic Statistics* and then *Graphical Summary* from the pull-down menu available under the *Stat* command menu.

4. Enter C1 in the box under *Graph Variables* and click *OK*.

5. The Minitab output will appear in the summary window as shown in Figure B.11.

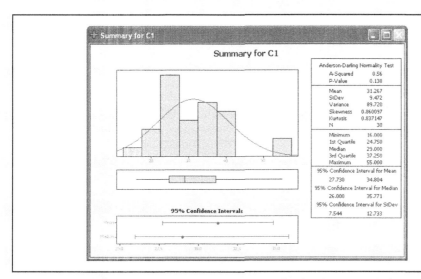

Figure B.11   Minitab display of graphical summary for the data in Example B.7.

to *Confidence Level* enter the appropriate value of the confidence level and then click *OK*. This option provides both graphical and numerical descriptive statistics. A separate graph and summary statistics are displayed for each variable.

Bar Chart. Enter the data containing categories and frequencies in separate columns C1 and C2; if the categories and frequencies are not given, then enter all the categorical data in column C1 per Example B.8. Then, from the menu select *Graph > Bar Chart*. In the *Bar Charts* dialog box there appear three options under *Bars Represent*. Select option (1) *Counts of Unique Values* if you have one or more columns of categorical data (as is the case in Example B.8); option (2) *A Function of a Variable* if you have one or more columns of measurement data; or option (3) *Values from a Table* if you have one or more columns of summary data. For each of these options there are several other options for representation of the graph. Choose one of the appropriate choices and then click OK. Now another dialog box appears entitled *Bar Chart–[Description]*. In this dialog box enter the variable name(s) under *Categorical Variables*. If you have not entered the names of the variables in the data columns, then under *Graph Variables* just enter C1, C2, and so on, and then click *OK*. A separate graph is displayed for each variable. To display more than one graph, select the *Multiple Graphs* option and then choose the desired display option.

Pie Chart. Enter the data containing categories and frequencies in columns C1 and C2; if the categories and frequencies are not given, then enter the categorical data in column C1 as in Example B.9. From the command menu select *Graph > Pie Chart*. Choose *Chart Raw Data* when each row in the column represents a single observation, and choose *Chart Variables from a Table* if the categories and frequencies are given. Each slice in the pie is proportional to the number of occurrences of a value in the column or the frequency of each category. Enter C1 in the box next to *Categorical Variables*. A separate pie chart for each column is displayed on the same graph. To display more than one graph, select the *Multiple Graphs* option and then choose the required display option. When category names exist in one column and summary data exist in another column, use the *Chart Values from a Table* option. Enter the columns for *Categorical Variables* and *Summary Variables*.

Probability Distributions

To calculate various probabilities, select *Calc > Probability Distributions* from the command menu and then the probability of choice. This will prompt a dialog box to appear where the choice of how the probabilities are calculated—that is, probability density, cumulative probability, or inverse probability—can be selected. Based on the probability distribution being calculated, appropriate parameter entries need to be made. The choices of probability distribution include uniform, binomial, *t*, chi-square, normal, *f*, Poisson, exponential, and others. We discuss several of these examples following. The technique for other distributions is quite similar and self-explanatory.

Normal Distribution. Using Minitab we can calculate three values related to the normal distribution:

1. *Probability density*, which means finding an area under the normal distribution curve

EXAMPLE B.8

Prepare a bar chart for the following categorical data:

$$2 \quad 3 \quad 5 \quad 4 \quad 2 \quad 3 \quad 5 \quad 4$$

$$6 \quad 6 \quad 5 \quad 4 \quad 2 \quad 3 \quad 4 \quad 5$$

$$4 \quad 2 \quad 5 \quad 6 \quad 4 \quad 2 \quad 3 \quad 6$$

$$5 \quad 4 \quad 2 \quad 3 \quad 5 \quad 6$$

Solution

1. Enter the data in column C1 of the data window.

2. Select *Graph* from the command menu.

3. Click on *Bar Chart* in the pull-down menu available under the *Graph* command menu.

4. Select *Counts of Unique Values* and *Simple* from the options and click *OK*.

5. Enter C1 in the box under *Categorical Variables* and click *OK*.

6. The Minitab output will appear in the graph window as shown in Figure B.12.

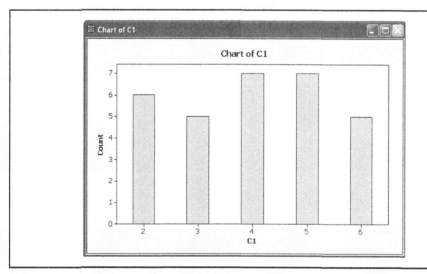

Figure B.12   Minitab display of the bar chart for the data in Example B.8.

2. *Cumulative probability*, which means finding an area under the normal distribution curve below a certain value of x

3. *Inverse cumulative probability*, which means that the area under the normal distribution curve below x is given, and we want to find out the corresponding value of x

EXAMPLE B.9

Prepare a pie chart for the following categorical data:

$$2 \quad 3 \quad 5 \quad 4 \quad 2 \quad 3 \quad 5 \quad 4$$

$$6 \quad 6 \quad 5 \quad 4 \quad 2 \quad 3 \quad 4 \quad 5$$

$$4 \quad 2 \quad 5 \quad 6 \quad 4 \quad 2 \quad 3 \quad 6$$

$$5 \quad 4 \quad 2 \quad 3 \quad 5 \quad 6$$

Solution

1. Enter the data in column C1 of the data window.

2. Select *Graph* from the command menu.

3. Select *Pie Chart* from the pull-down menu available under the *Graph* command menu.

4. Select *Chart Raw Data* from the options.

5. Enter C1 in the box under *Categorical Variables* and click *OK*.

6. The Minitab output will appear in the graph window as shown in Figure B.13.

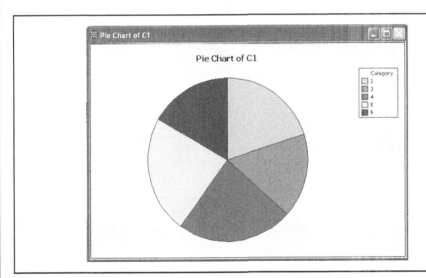

Figure B.13   Minitab display of the pie chart for the data in Example B.9.

To calculate any of the above probabilities, proceed as follows. From the menu bar select *Calc > Probability Distributions > Normal*. This will prompt the *Normal Distribution* dialog box to appear. In this dialog box click one of the options available: *Probability Density, Cumulative Probability,* or *Inverse Cumulative Probability*. Then enter the value of the *Mean* and the *Standard Deviation* to define the normal distribution. Check the circle next to *Input Column* (if you have more than one value of

---

EXAMPLE B.10

Let a random variable be distributed as normal with mean μ = 6 and standard deviation σ = 4. Determine the probability $P(8.0 \leq X \leq 14.0)$.

Solution

In order to determine the probability $P(8.0 \leq X \leq 14.0)$, we have to first find the probabilities $P(X \leq 8.0)$ and $P(X \leq 14.0)$. Then $P(8.0 \leq X \leq 14.0) = P(X \leq 14.0) - P(X \leq 8.0)$. Thus, to find probabilities $P(X \leq 8.0)$ and $P(X \leq 14.0)$ using Minitab, we proceed as follows:

1. Enter the test values of 8 and 14 in column C1.

2. From the menu bar select *Calc > Probability Distribution > Normal*.

3. In the dialog box that appears, check the circle next to *Cumulative Probability*.

4. Enter 6 (the value of the mean) in the box next to *Mean* and 4 (the value of the standard deviation) in the box next to *Standard Deviation*.

5. Click on the circle next to *Input Column* and type C1 in the box next to it.

6. Click *OK*.

7. In the session window, text will appear as follows, indicating values of $P(X \leq 14.0)$ = 0.977250 and $P(X \leq 8.0)$ = 0.691462 will appear. Hence, $P(8.0 \leq X \leq 14.0) = P(X \leq 14.0) - P(X \leq 8.0) = 0.977250 - 0.691462 = 0.285788$.

Normal with mean = 6 and standard deviation = 4

x	$P(X \leq x)$
8	0.691462
14	0.977250

---

x that you must enter in one of the data columns, say C1), and enter C1 in the box next to it. Or select *Input Constant Field* if you have only one value of *x*, and enter the value of that constant in the box next to it. If desired, in the *Optional Storage* field enter the column in which you want to store the output. Then click *OK*.

Shewhart $\bar{X}$ and R Control Chart. First, enter the data in one column of the *Worksheet* window. Then, from the command menu select *Stat > Control Charts > Variable Charts for Subgroups > Xbar-R*. The *Xbar-R Chart* dialog box shown in Figure B.14 appears immediately. We illustrate the construction of the *X-bar* and *R* chart in Example B.11.

Shewhart $\bar{X}$ and R Control Chart When Process Mean μ and Process Standard Deviation σ Are Known. Follow the first eight steps given in Example B.11. Then in step 9, click *X bar-R Options*. A new dialog box, shown in Figure B.15, will appear. Enter the specified values of the mean and the standard deviation in the boxes next to *Mean* and *Standard Deviation*, respectively, and then click *OK*. Then,

---

EXAMPLE B.11

Consider the data on the diameter measurements of ball bearings used in the wheels of heavy construction equipment shown in Table 20.3 of Example 20.4 in Chapter 20. Then use the following steps to construct the $\bar{X}$ and R control chart.

Solution

1. Enter all the data in column C1 of the *Worksheet* window. Note that one has the option to enter the data in rows of columns such that each row contains data from one subgroup. This option is usually preferred when the sample size is variable. Thus, we shall consider this option for constructing an $\bar{X}$ and R control chart with unequal sample sizes.

2. Click *Stat* from the command menu.

3. Select *Control Charts* in the pull-down menu under the *Stat* command menu.

4. Select *Variable Charts for Subgroups* from the *Control Charts* command menu.

5. Click on *Xbar-R* in the *Variable Charts for Subgroups* command menu. The *Xbar-R Chart* dialog box shown in Figure B.14 appears immediately.

6. In the *Xbar-R Chart* dialog box choose the option "All observations for a chart are in one column."

7. Enter C1 in the next box.

8. Enter the sample size in the box next to the *Subgroup Sizes.*

9. In the *Xbar-R Chart* dialog box there are several options available such as *Scale* and *Labels*. For instance, if you select the *Label* option, a new dialog box will appear where you can enter the title of the $\bar{X}$ and R chart and any footnotes that you would like to see on the output of the $\bar{X}$ and R chart and then click *OK*. By default, the title will be, for example, *X bar and R Chart for C1* or *X bar and R Chart for "name of the variable"* if you have given such a name in column C1 of the data window. Use the option *X bar-R Options*, for example, if you want to specify the values of the population mean and population standard deviation instead of estimating the population mean and population standard deviation by using the given data. Then click *OK* in the *Xbar-R Chart* dialog box. The desired $\bar{X}$ and R control chart will appear in the *Session* window. In our example the *Xbar-R Chart* dialog box will look as shown in Figure B.14.

Continued

---

again, click *OK* in the *X bar-R Chart* dialog box. The desired $\bar{X}$ and R control chart will appear in the *Session* window.

Shewhart $\bar{X}$ and S Control Chart—Equal Sample Size. First, enter the data in one column, say C1, of the *Worksheet* window. Then from the command menu select *Stat > Control Charts > Variable Charts for Subgroups > Xbar-S*. The *Xbar-S Chart* dialog box shown in Figure B.16 appears immediately. We illustrate the construction of a Shewhart $\bar{X}$ and S control chart in Example B.12.

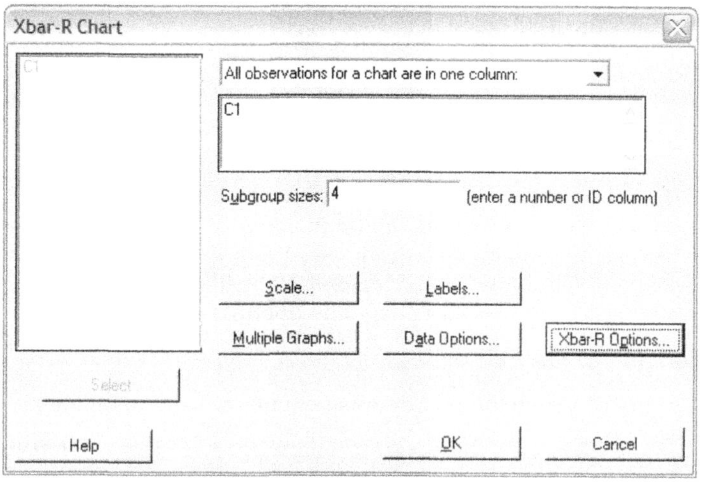

Figure B.14   Minitab window showing the *Xbar–R Chart* dialog box.

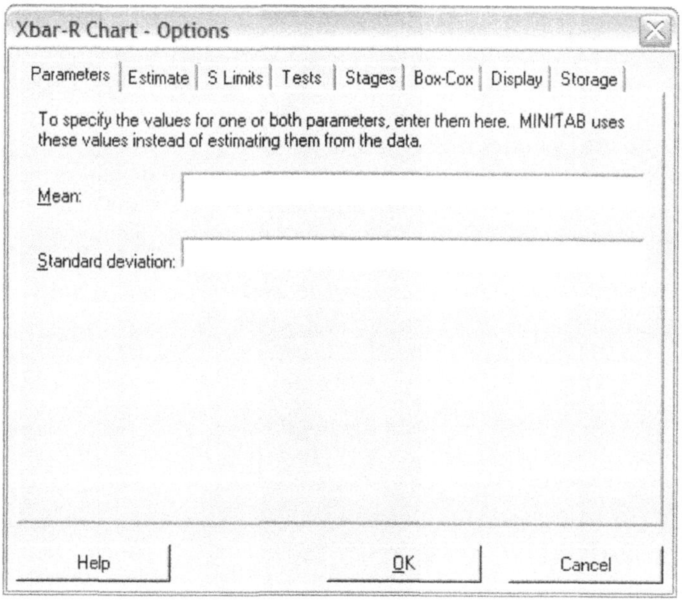

Figure B.15   Minitab window showing the *Xbar-R Chart–Options* dialog box.

EXAMPLE B.12

Consider the data on the diameter measurements of ball bearings used in the wheels of heavy construction equipment shown in Table 20.3 of Example 20.4 in Chapter 20. Then use the following steps to construct the $\bar{X}$ and S control chart.

Solution

1. Enter all the data in column C1 of the *Worksheet* window. Note that as in the case of the $\bar{X}$ and R chart, one has the option to enter the data in rows of columns such that each row contains data from one subgroup. This option is usually preferred when the sample size is variable. We shall consider this option for constructing an $\bar{X}$ and S control chart with unequal sample sizes.

2. Click *Stat* in the command menu.

3. Select *Control Charts* in the pull-down menu under the *Stat* command menu.

4. Select *Variable Charts for Subgroups* from the *Control Charts* command menu.

5. Click on *Xbar-S* from the *Variable Charts for Subgroups* command menu. The *Xbar-S Chart* dialog box shown in Figure B.16 appears immediately.

6. From the *Xbar-S Chart* dialog box choose the option "All observations for a chart are in one column."

7. Enter C1 in the next box.

8. Enter the sample size in the box next to *Subgroup Sizes*.

9. In the *Xbar-S Chart* dialog box there are several options available such as *Scale* and *Labels*. For instance, if you select the *Label* option, a new dialog box will appear where you can enter the title of the $\bar{X}$ and S chart and any footnotes that you would like to see on the output of the $\bar{X}$ and S chart, and then click *OK*. By default, the title will be, for example, Xbar-S Chart for C1 or Xbar-S Chart for "name of the variable" if you have given such a name in column C1 of the data window. Use the option *Xbar-S Options*, for example, if you want to specify the values of the population mean and population standard deviation instead of estimating the population mean and population standard deviation by using the given data. Then click *OK* in the *Xbar-S Chart* dialog box. The desired $\bar{X}$ and S control chart will appear in the *Session* window. In our example the *Xbar-S Chart* dialog box will look as shown in Figure B.16, and the output of the $\bar{X}$ and S chart will appear as shown in Figure 20.9 in Chapter 20.

Continued

PROCESS CAPABILITY ANALYSIS

First, enter the data in one column, say C1, of the *Worksheet* window. Then from the command menu select *Stat > Quality Tools > Capability Analysis > Normal*. The *Capability Analysis (Normal Distribution)* dialog box shown in Figure B.17 appears immediately. We illustrate the *capability analysis of a process* in Example B.13.

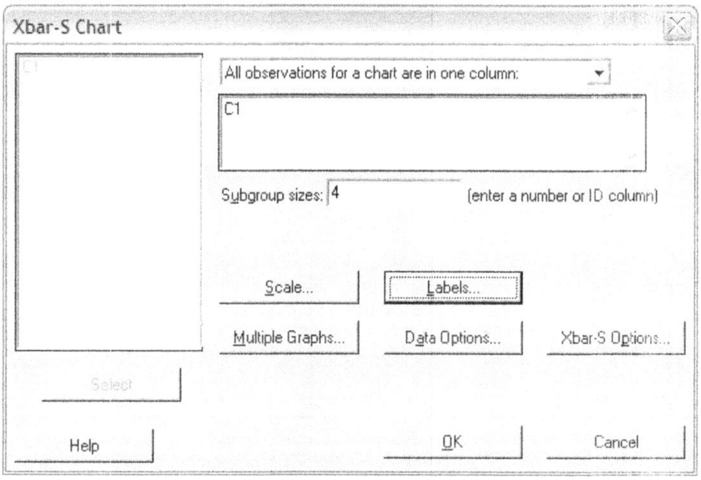

Figure B.16   Minitab window showing the *Xbar-S Chart* dialog box.

EXAMPLE B.13

Consider a quality characteristic of a process that is normally distributed. Suppose that the process is stable with respect to the 3-sigma control limits. Furthermore, suppose that the data for 25 samples each of size five from this process are as shown in Table B.1. Also, we are given that LSL = 0.95 and USL = 1.05. Perform the capability analysis of the process.

Solution

1. Enter all the data in columns C1 through C5 of the *Worksheet* window. Note that in this case one has the option to enter the data in one column, say C1.

2. Click on *Stat* from the command menu.

3. Select *Quality Tools > Normal* from the pull-down menu under the *Stat* command menu.

4. Select *Capability Analysis* from the *Control Charts* command menu.

5. Click on *Normal* (or the distribution of the process characteristic) from the *Capability Analysis* command menu. The *Capability Analysis (Normal Distribution)* dialog box shown in Figure B.17 appears immediately.

6. In the *Capability Analysis* dialog box under *Data Are Arranged As* select *Single Column* or *Subgroups Across Rows* depending on how you have entered the data in step 1, and then enter the columns or column in which you have entered the data.

7. Click *OK*. The capability analysis output will appear as shown in Figure B.18.

Continued

Table B.1 Data for 25 samples each of size five from a given process.

Sample number	Observations (mm)				
1	0.97076	0.98518	1.01204	0.97892	0.99094
2	0.99455	0.96904	0.99770	0.97502	0.98483
3	0.99538	0.99765	0.96011	1.03059	0.98048
4	1.00332	0.98891	0.98018	1.01699	1.00391
5	1.03023	0.98663	1.01498	0.97483	0.99836
6	0.98491	1.00487	0.96951	0.99613	1.03365
7	0.98894	1.00631	0.98630	0.98115	0.96755
8	0.93771	0.99017	1.03221	1.01045	1.01297
9	1.00103	1.01641	0.97683	1.00149	1.03012
10	1.01493	1.02220	1.00179	1.01556	1.01080
11	1.01606	0.96502	1.00546	0.99259	0.96857
12	0.98266	0.99031	0.99349	1.00499	1.03806
13	0.95560	1.00033	1.01098	0.99380	1.04496
14	0.97406	1.01305	0.97556	0.98493	1.00347
15	1.03027	0.97009	1.00151	0.99929	0.98366
16	1.02527	1.01652	1.02743	0.99951	0.99565
17	1.02837	1.01676	0.97056	0.95207	1.03254
18	0.98646	0.99434	1.00163	0.98811	1.01234
19	0.96072	1.02716	1.01030	1.04141	0.96355
20	1.03511	0.94637	1.00852	0.99454	1.00620
21	0.99550	0.98307	1.00948	1.00793	1.04035
22	0.98397	1.03082	0.98643	1.00540	0.97880
23	0.99934	0.99544	1.00959	1.00664	1.02905
24	1.00286	1.00777	1.01661	0.99793	1.03805
25	0.96557	0.98535	0.99911	1.03566	1.00453

Continued

The p Chart: Control Chart for Fraction Nonconforming Units. First, enter the data (number of nonconforming) in one column, say C1, of the *Worksheet* window. Then from the command menu select *Stat > Attributes Charts > P*. The *P Chart* dialog box shown in Figure B.19 appears immediately. We illustrate the construction of the *p chart* in Example B.14.

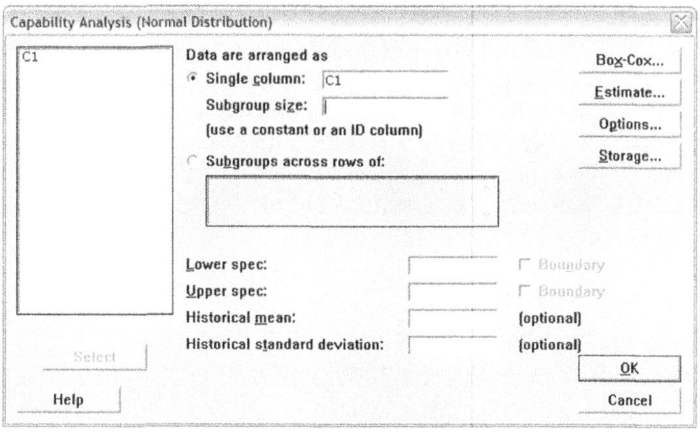

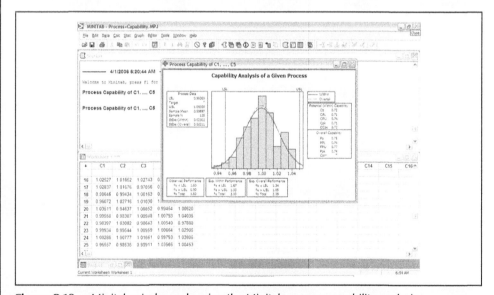

Figure B.17   Minitab window showing the *Capability Analysis (Normal Distribution)* dialog box.

Figure B.18   Minitab windows showing the Minitab process capability analysis.

The p Chart: Control Chart for Fraction Nonconforming Units with Variable Sample Sizes. The procedure for constructing a *p* chart with variable sample size is the same as for a *p* chart with fixed sample size except in this case we enter the data on number of nonconforming in column C1 and the corresponding sample sizes in column C2, and in step 6 instead of entering the sample size in the box next to *Subgroup Size*, we enter C2.

EXAMPLE B.14

A semiconductor manufacturer tracks the number of nonconforming computer chips produced each day. A team of Six Sigma Green Belt engineers wants to improve the overall quality by reducing the fraction of nonconforming computer chips. To achieve this goal, the team decided to set up a *p* chart, and in order to do so they decided to inspect a sample of 1000 chips each day over a period of 30 days. Table 20.5 in Chapter 20 gives the number of nonconforming chips out of 1000 inspected chips each day during the study period of 30 days.

Solution

1. Enter all the data (number of nonconforming given in Table 20.5) in column C1 of the *Worksheet* window. Click on *Stat* from the command menu.

2. Select *Control Charts* in the pull-down menu under the *Stat* command menu.

3. Select *Attributes Charts* from the *Control Charts* command menu.

4. Click on *P* from the *Attributes Charts* command menu. The *P Chart* dialog box shown in Figure B.19 appears immediately.

5. Enter C1 in the box under *Variables*.

6. Enter the sample size in the box next to *Subgroup Sizes*.

7. In the *P Chart* dialog box there are several options available such as *Scale* and *Labels*. For instance, if you select the *Label* option, a new dialog box will appear where you can enter the title of the *p* chart and any footnotes that you would like to see on the output of the *p* chart, and then click *OK*. By default, the title will be, for example, P Chart for C1 or P Chart for "name of the variable" if you have given

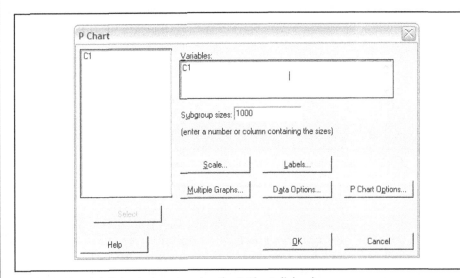

Figure B.19   Minitab window showing the *P Chart* dialog box.

Continued

such a name in column C1 of the data window. Use the option *P Chart Options*, for example, if you want to specify the values of fraction of nonconforming in the population instead of estimating it using the given data. Then, click *OK* in the *P Chart* dialog box. The desired *p* control chart will appear in the *Session* window. Hence, in our example the output of the *p* chart is as shown in Figure 20.10 of Chapter 20.

The np Chart: Control Chart for Nonconforming Units. In an *np* chart we plot the number of nonconforming units in an inspected sample. The *np* chart is very similar to the *p* chart except that in the *p* chart we plot the fraction of nonconforming units in each inspected sample. Moreover, in the *p* chart the sample sizes could be equal or unequal, whereas in the *np* chart the sample sizes are equal. Otherwise, both the *p* chart and the *np* chart can be implemented under the same circumstances. We summarize some specific points that are important for the *np* chart:

- The inspection sample sizes should be equal.

- The sample size should be large enough to include some nonconforming units.

- Record the sample size and number of nonconforming (*np*) in each sample, and plot the number of nonconforming on the control chart.

- To construct an *np* control chart, follow all the steps for the *p* control chart.

The c Chart. In many situations, we are interested in studying the number of nonconformities in a sample, which is also called the *inspection unit*, rather than studying the fraction nonconforming or total number of nonconforming in the sample. To construct the *c* chart, first enter the data (number of nonconformities) in one column, say C1, of the *Worksheet* window. Then from the command menu select *Stat > Attributes Charts > C*. The *C Chart* dialog box shown in Figure B.20 appears immediately. We illustrate the construction of a c chart in Example B.15.

The u Chart. The *u* chart is essentially the c chart except that the u chart is always based on the number of nonconformities per inspection unit. In other words, the actual sample size may be other than 1 or may vary, but the control limits of the *u* chart are always determined based on one inspection unit. For example, if *n* is constant, one can use either the *c* chart or the *u* chart. We illustrate the construction of the *u* chart in Example B.16.

The u Chart—Variable Sample Sizes. The procedure for constructing a *u* chart with variable sample size is the same as for the *u* chart with fixed sample size, except in this case we enter the data on number of nonconforming in column C1 and the corresponding sample sizes in column C2, and in step 6 instead of entering the sample size in the box next to the *Subgroup Sizes*, we enter C2. For an example, see the *u* chart of nonconformities for the data in Table 20.9 in Example 20.11 and Figure 20.15 of Chapter 20.

EXAMPLE B.15

A paper mill has detected that almost 90% of rejected paper rolls are due to nonconformities of two types: holes and wrinkles in the paper. The Six Sigma Green Belt team in the mill decided to set up control charts to reduce or eliminate these nonconformities. To set up control charts, the team decided to collect some data by taking a random sample of five rolls each day for 30 days and counting the number of nonconformities (holes and wrinkles) in each sample. The data are shown in Table 20.7 in Chapter 20. Set up a *c* control chart using these data.

Solution

1. Enter all the data (number of nonconformities given in Table 20.7) in column C1 of the *Worksheet* window. Click on *Stat* in the command window.

2. Select *Control Charts* in the pull-down menu under the *Stat* command menu.

3. Select *Attributes Charts* from the *Control Charts* command menu.

4. Click *C* in the *Attributes Charts* command menu. The *C Chart* dialog box shown in Figure B.20 appears immediately.

5. Enter C1 in the box under *Variables*.

6. In the *C Chart* dialog box there are several options available such as *Scale* and *Labels*. For instance, if you select the *Label* option, a new dialog box will appear where you can enter the title of the *c* chart and any footnotes that you would like to see on the output of the *c* chart, and then click *OK*. By default, the title will be, for example, C Chart for C1 or C Chart for "name of the variable" if you have given such a name (say, nonconformities) in column C1 of the data window. Use the option *C Chart Options*, for example, if you want to specify the mean value of

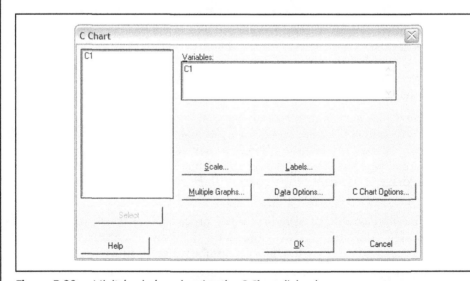

Figure B.20   Minitab window showing the *C Chart* dialog box.

Continued

nonconformities in the population instead of estimating it using the given data. Then click *OK* in the *C Chart* dialog box. The desired *c* control chart will appear in the *Session* window. Thus, in our example the output of the *c* chart is as shown in Figure 20.13 in Chapter 20.

EXAMPLE B.16

A Six Sigma Green Belt team at a semiconductor manufacturer found that the printed circuit boards for laptops have too many nonconformities of several types, such as shorted trace, open trace, cold solder joint, and solder short. In order to monitor non-conformities in the printed boards for laptops, the Six Sigma Green Belt team wants to set up a *u* chart. Therefore, they collected some data by selecting samples of five inspection units, each inspection unit consisting of 30 boards. The data, which are shown in Table 20.8 in Chapter 20, were collected over a period of 30 days.

Solution

1. Enter all the data (number of nonconformities given in Table 20.8) in column C1 of the *Worksheet* window. Click on *Stat* in the command menu.

2. Select *Control Charts* in the pull-down menu under the *Stat* command menu.

3. Select *Attributes Charts* from the *Control Charts* command menu.

4. Click on *U* in the *Attributes Charts* command menu. The *U Chart* dialog box shown in Figure B.21 appears immediately.

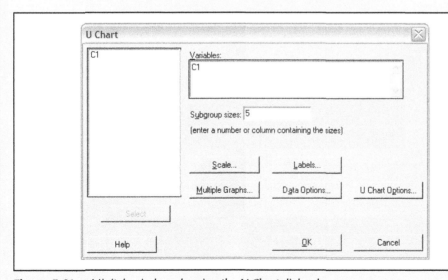

Figure B.21   Minitab window showing the *U Chart* dialog box.

Continued

5. Enter C1 in the box under *Variables*.

6. Enter the sample size in the box next to *Subgroup Sizes*.

7. In the *U Chart* dialog box there are several options available such as *Scale* and *Labels*. For instance, if you select the *Label* option, a new dialog box will appear where you can enter the title of the *u* chart and any footnotes that you would like to see on the output of the *u* chart, and then click *OK*. By default, the title will be, for example, U Chart for C1 or U Chart for "name of the variable" if you have given such a name (say, nonconformities) in column C1 of the data window. Use the option *U Chart Options*, for example, if you want to specify the mean value of nonconformities per unit in the population instead of estimating it using the given data. Then, click *OK* in the *U Chart* dialog box. The desired *u* control chart will appear in the *Session* window. Hence, in our example the output of the u chart is as shown in Figure 20.14 in Chapter 20.

REFERENCES

Gupta, B. C., and H. F. Walker. 2005. *Applied Statistics for the Six Sigma Green Belt.* Milwaukee: ASQ Quality Press.

Gupta, B. C., and I. Guttman. 2013. *Statistics and Probability with Applications for Engineers and Scientists.* Hoboken, NJ: John Wiley & Sons.

Gupta, B. C., and H. F. Walker. 2007. *Statistical Quality Control for the Six Sigma Green Belt.* Milwaukee: ASQ Quality Press.

Appendix C

General Tables of Units of Measurement

$\top$hese tables have been prepared for the benefit of those requiring tables of units for occasional ready reference. In Section 4 of this Appendix, the tables are carried out to a large number of decimal places and exact values are indicated by underlining. In most of the other tables, only a limited number of decimal places are given, therefore making the tables better adopted by the average user.

1. TABLES OF METRIC UNITS OF MEASUREMENT

In the metric system of measurement, designations of multiples and subdivisions of any unit may be arrived at by combining with the name of the unit the prefixes deka, hecto, and kilo, meaning, respectively, 10, 100, and 1000, and deci, centi, and milli, meaning, respectively, one-tenth, one-hundredth, and one-thousandth. In some of the following metric tables, some such multiples and subdivisions have not been included for the reason that these have little, if any, currency in actual usage.

In certain cases, particularly in scientific usage, it becomes convenient to provide for multiples larger than 1000 and for subdivisions smaller than one-thousandth. Accordingly, the following prefixes have been introduced and these are now generally recognized:

yotta	(Y)	meaning 10^{24}	deci	(d)	meaning 10^{-1}
zetta	(Z)	meaning 10^{21}	centi	(c)	meaning 10^{-2}
exa	(E)	meaning 10^{18}	milli	(m)	meaning 10^{-3}
peta	(P)	meaning 10^{15}	micro	(μ)	meaning 10^{-6}
tera	(T)	meaning 10^{12}	nano	(n)	meaning 10^{-9}
giga	(G)	meaning 10^{9}	pico	(p)	meaning 10^{-12}
mega	(M)	meaning 10^{6}	femto	(f)	meaning 10^{-15}
kilo	(k)	meaning 10^{3}	atto	(a)	meaning 10^{-18}
hecto	(h)	meaning 10^{2}	zepto	(z)	meaning 10^{-21}
deka	(da)	meaning 10^{1}	yocto	(y)	meaning 10^{-24}

Thus a kilometer is 1000 meters and a millimeter is 0.001 meter.

---

* Reproduced by permission of NIST. http://ts.nist.gov/WeightsAndMeasures/Publications/ upload/h4402_appenc.pdf.

Units of Length

10 millimeters (mm)	= 1 centimeter (cm)
10 centimeters	= 1 decimeter (dm) = 100 millimeters
10 decimeters	= 1 meter (m) = 1000 millimeters
10 meters	= 1 dekameter (dam)
10 dekameters	= 1 hectometer (hm) = 100 meters
10 hectometers	= 1 kilometer (km) = 1000 meters

Units of Area

100 square millimeters (mm²)	= 1 square centimeter (cm²)
100 square centimeters	= 1 square decimeter (dm²)
100 square decimeters	= 1 square meter (m²)
100 square meters	= 1 square dekameter (dam²) = 1 are
100 square dekameters	= 1 square hectometer (hm²) = 1 hectare (ha)
100 square hectometers	= 1 square kilometer (km²)

Units of Liquid Volume

10 milliliters (mL)	= 1 centiliter (cL)
10 centiliters	= 1 deciliter (dL) = 100 milliliters
10 deciliters	= 1 liter[1] = 1000 milliliters
10 liters	= 1 dekaliter (daL)
10 dekaliters	= 1 hectoliter (hL) = 100 liters
10 hectoliters	= 1 kiloliter (kL) = 1000 liters

Units of Volume

1000 cubic millimeters (mm³)	= 1 cubic centimeter (cm³)
1000 cubic centimeters	= 1 cubic decimeter (dm³) = 1,000,000 cubic millimeters
1000 cubic decimeters	= 1 cubic meter (m³) = 1,000,000 cubic centimeters = 1,000,000,000 cubic millimeters

---

[1] By action of the 12th General Conference on Weights and Measures (1964) the liter is a special name for the cubic decimeter.

Units of Mass

10 milligrams (mg)	= 1 centigram (cg)
10 centigrams	= 1 decigram (dg) = 100 milligrams
10 decigrams	= 1 gram (g) = 1000 milligrams
10 grams	= 1 dekagram (dag)
10 dekagrams	= 1 hectogram (hg) = 100 grams
10 hectograms	= 1 kilogram (kg) = 1000 grams
1000 kilograms	= 1 megagram (Mg) or 1 metric ton (t)

2. TABLES OF U.S. UNITS OF MEASUREMENT[2]

In these tables where <u>foot</u> or <u>mile</u> is underlined, it is survey foot or U.S. statute mile rather than international foot or mile that is meant.

Units of Length

12 inches (in)	= 1 foot (ft)
3 feet	= 1 yard (yd)
16-1/2 <u>feet</u>	= 1 rod (rd), pole, or perch
40 rods	= 1 furlong (fur) = 660 <u>feet</u>
8 furlongs	= 1 U.S. statute mile (mi) = 5280 <u>feet</u>
1852 meters	= 6076.11549 feet (approximately) = 1 international nautical mile

Units of Area[3]

144 square inches (in^2)	= 1 square foot (ft^2)
9 square feet	= 1 square yard (yd) = 1296 square inches
272-1/4 square <u>feet</u>	= 1 square rod (sq rd)
160 square rods	= 1 acre = 43,560 square <u>feet</u>
640 acres	= 1 square <u>mile</u> (mi^2)
1 <u>mile</u> square	= 1 section of land
6 <u>miles</u> square	= 1 township = 36 sections = 36 square miles

---

[2] This section lists units of measurement that have traditionally been used in the United States. In keeping with the Omnibus Trade and Competitiveness Act of 1988, the ultimate objective is to make the International System of Units the primary measurement system used in the United States.

[3] Squares and cubes of customary but not of metric units are sometimes expressed by the use of abbreviations rather than symbols. For example, sq ft means square foot, and cu ft means cubic foot.

Units of Volume[4]

1728 cubic inches (in³)	= 1 cubic foot (ft³)
27 cubic feet	= 1 cubic yard (yd³)

Gunter's or Surveyor's Chain Units of Measurement

0.66 <u>foot</u> (ft)	= 1 link (li)
100 links	= 1 chain (ch) = 4 rods = 66 <u>feet</u>
80 chains	= 1 U.S. statute mile (mi) = 320 rods = 5280 <u>feet</u>

Units of Liquid Volume[5]

4 gills (gi)	= 1 pint (pt) = 28.875 cubic inches
2 pints	= 1 quart (qt) = 57.75 cubic inches
4 quarts	= 1 gallon (gal) = 231 cubic inches = 8 pints = 32 gills

Apothecaries Units of Liquid Volume

60 minims (min or ♏)	= 1 fluid dram (fl dr or ℨ) = 0.2256 cubic inch
8 fluid drams	= 1 fluid ounce (fl oz or ℨ) = 1.8047 cubic inches
16 fluid ounces	= 1 pint (pt or o) = 28.875 cubic inches = 128 fluid drams
2 pints	= 1 quart (qt) = 57.75 cubic inches = 32 fluid ounces = 256 fluid drams
4 quarts	= 1 gallon (gal) = 231 cubic inches = 128 fluid ounces = 1024 fluid drams

Units of Dry Volume[6]

2 pints (pt)	= 1 quart (qt) = 67.200 6 cubic inches
8 quarts	= 1 peck (pk) = 537.605 cubic inches = 16 pints
4 pecks	= 1 bushel (bu) = 2150.42 cubic inches = 32 quarts

---

[4] Squares and cubes of customary but not of metric units are sometimes expressed by the use of abbreviations rather than symbols. For example, sq ft means square foot, and cu ft means cubic foot.

[5] When necessary to distinguish the *liquid* pint or quart from the *dry* pint or quart, the word "liquid" or the abbreviation "liq" should be used in combination with the name or abbreviation of the *liquid* unit.

[6] When necessary to distinguish *dry* pint or quart from the *liquid* pint or quart, the word "dry" should be used in combination with the name or abbreviation of the dry unit.

Avoirdupois Units of Mass[7]

The "grain" is the same in avoirdupois, troy, and apothecaries units of mass.

27-11/32 grains	= 1 dram (dr)
16 drams	= 1 ounce (oz) = 437-1/2 grains
16 ounces	= 1 pound (lb) = 256 drams = 7000 grains
100 pounds	= 1 hundredweight (cwt)[8]
20 hundredweights	= 1 ton = 2000 pounds[8]

In "gross" or "long" measure, the following values are recognized:

112 pounds	= 1 gross or long hundredweight[8]
20 gross or long hundredweights	= 1 gross or long ton = 2240 pounds[8]

Troy Units of Mass

The "grain" is the same in avoirdupois, troy, and apothecaries units of mass.

24 grains	= 1 pennyweight (dwt)
20 pennyweights	= 1 ounce troy (oz t) = 480 grains
12 ounces troy	= 1 pound troy (lb t) = 240 pennyweights = 5760 grains

Apothecaries Units of Mass

The "grain" is the same in avoirdupois, troy, and apothecaries units of mass.

20 grains	= 1 scruple (s ap or Э)
3 scruples	= 1 dram apothecaries (dr ap or ʒ) = 60 grains
8 drams apothecaries	= 1 ounce apothecaries (oz ap or ℥) = 24 scruples = 480 grains
12 ounces apothecaries	= 1 pound apothecaries (lb ap) = 96 drams apothecaries = 288 scruples = 5760 grains

[7] When necessary to distinguish the *avoirdupois* dram from the *apothecaries* dram, or to distinguish the *avoirdupois* dram or ounce from the *fluid* dram or ounce, or to distinguish the *avoirdupois* ounce or pound from the *troy* or *apothecaries* ounce or pound, the word "avoirdupois" or the abbreviation "avdp" should be used in combination with the name or abbreviation of the *avoirdupois* unit.

[8] When the terms "hundredweight" and "ton" are used unmodified, they are commonly understood to mean the 100-pound hundredweight and the 2000-pound ton, respectively; these units may be designated "net" or "short" when necessary to distinguish them from the corresponding units in *gross* or *long* measure.

3. NOTES ON BRITISH UNITS OF MEASUREMENT

In Great Britain, the yard, the avoirdupois pound, the troy pound, and the apothecaries pound are identical with the units of the same names used in the United States. The tables of British linear measure, troy mass, and apothecaries mass are the same as the corresponding United States tables, except for the British spelling "drachm" in the table of apothecaries mass. The table of British avoirdupois mass is the same as the United States table up to one pound; above that point the table reads:

14 pounds	= 1 stone
2 stones	= 1 quarter = 28 pounds
4 quarters	= 1 hundredweight = 112 pounds
20 hundredweight	= 1 ton = 2240 pounds

The present British gallon and bushel—known as the "Imperial gallon" and "Imperial bushel"—are, respectively, about 20 percent and 3 percent larger than the United States gallon and bushel. The Imperial gallon is defined as the volume of 10 avoirdupois pounds of water under specified conditions, and the Imperial bushel is defined as 8 Imperial gallons. Also, the subdivision of the Imperial gallon as presented in the table of British apothecaries fluid measure differs in two important respects from the corresponding United States subdivision, in that the Imperial gallon is divided into 160 fluid ounces (whereas the United States gallon is divided into 128 fluid ounces), and a "fluid scruple" is included. The full table of British measures of capacity (which are used alike for liquid and for dry commodities) is as follows:

4 gills	= 1 pint
2 pints	= 1 quart
4 quarts	= 1 gallon
2 gallons	= 1 peck
8 gallons (4 pecks)	= 1 bushel
8 bushels	= 1 quarter

The full table of British apothecaries measure is as follows:

20 minims	= 1 fluid scruple
3 fluid scruples	= 1 fluid drachm = 60 minims
8 fluid drachms	= 1 fluid ounce
20 fluid ounces	= 1 pint
8 pints	= 1 gallon (160 fluid ounces)

4. TABLES OF UNITS OF MEASUREMENT

All underlined figures are exact.

Units of Length—International Measure[9]

Units		Inches	Feet	Yards	Miles	Centimeters	Meters
1 inch	=	1	0.08333333	0.02777778	0.00001578283	2.54	0.0254
1 foot	=	12	1	0.3333333	0.0001893939	30.48	0.3048
1 yard	=	36	3	1	0.0005681818	91.44	0.9144
1 mile	=	63,360	5280	1760	1	160,934.4	1609.344
1 centimeter	=	0.3937008	0.03280840	0.01093613	0.000006213712	1	0.01
1 meter	=	39.37008	3.280840	1.093613	0.0006213712	100	1

Units of Length—Survey Measure[9]

Units		Links	Feet	Rods	Chains	Miles	Meters
1 link	=	1	0.66	0.04	0.01	0.000125	0.2011684
1 foot	=	1.515152	1	0.06060606	0.01515152	0.0001893939	0.3048006
1 rod	=	25	16.5	1	0.25	0.003125	5.029210
1 chain	=	100	66	4	1	0.0125	20.11684
1 mile	=	8000	5280	320	80	1	1609.347
1 meter	=	4.970960	3.280833	0.1988384	0.04970960	0.0006213699	1

Units of Area—International Measure[10]

All underlined figures are exact.

Units		Square inches	Square feet	Square yards
1 square inch	=	1	0.006944444	0.0007716049
1 square foot	=	144	1	0.1111111
1 square yard	=	1296	9	1
1 square mile	=	4,014,489,600	27,878,400	3,097,600
1 square centimeter	=	0.1550003	0.001076391	0.0001195990
1 square meter	=	1550.003	10.76391	1.195990

---

[9] One international foot   = 0.999998 survey foot (exactly)
   One international mile   = 0.999998 survey mile (exactly)

   Note: 1 survey foot   = 1200/3937 meter (exactly)
          1 international foot = 12 × 0.0254 meter (exactly)
          1 international foot = 0.0254 × 39.37 survey foot (exactly)

[10] One square survey foot   = 1.000004 square international feet
   One square survey mile   = 1.000004 square international miles

Units		Square miles	Square centimeters	Square meters
1 square inch	=	0.0000000002490977	6.4516	0.00064516
1 square foot	=	0.00000003587006	929.0304	0.09290304
1 square yard	=	0.0000003228306	8361.2736	0.83612736
1 square mile	=	1	25,899,881,103.36	2,589,988.110336
1 square centimeter	=	0.00000000003861022	1	0.0001
1 square meter	=	0.0000003861022	10,000	1

Units of Area—Survey Measure[11]

Units		Square feet	Square rods	Square chains	Acres
1 square foot	=	1	0.003673095	0.0002295684	0.00002295684
1 square rod	=	272.25	1	0.0625	0.00625
1 square chain	=	4356	16	1	0.1
1 acre	=	43,560	160	10	1
1 square mile	=	27,878,400	102,400	6400	640
1 square meter	=	10.76387	0.03953670	0.002471044	0.0002471044
1 hectare	=	107,638.7	395.3670	24.71044	2.471044

Units		Square miles	Square meters	Hectares
1 square foot	=	0.00000003587006	0.09290341	0.000009290341
1 square rod	=	0.000009765625	25.29295	0.002529295
1 square chain	=	0.00015625	404.6873	0.04046873
1 acre	=	0.0015625	4046.873	0.4046873
1 square mile	=	1	2,589,998	258.9998
1 square meter	=	0.0000003861006	1	0.0001
1 hectare	=	0.003861006	10,000	1

Units of Volume

All underlined figures are exact.

Units		Cubic inches	Cubic feet	Cubic yards
1 cubic inch	=	1	0.0005787037	0.00002143347
1 cubic foot	=	1728	1	0.03703704
1 cubic yard	=	46,656	27	1
1 cubic centimeter	=	0.06102374	0.00003531467	0.000001307951
1 cubic decimeter	=	61.02374	0.03531467	0.001307951
1 cubic meter	=	61,023.74	35.31467	1.307951

[11] One square survey foot = 1.000004 square international feet
One square survey mile = 1.000004 square international miles

Units		Milliliters (cubic centimeters)	Liters (cubic decimeters)	Cubic meters
1 cubic inch	=	16.387064	0.016387064	0.000016387064
1 cubic foot	=	28,316.846592	28.316846592	0.028316846592
1 cubic yard	=	764,554.857984	764.554857984	0.764554857984
1 cubic centimeter	=	1	0.001	0.000001
1 cubic decimeter	=	1000	1	0.001
1 cubic meter	=	1,000,000	1000	1

Units of Capacity or Volume—Dry Volume Measure

All underlined figures are exact.

Units		Dry pints	Dry quarts	Pecks	Bushels
1 dry pint	=	1	0.5	0.0625	0.015625
1 dry quart	=	2	1	0.125	0.03125
1 peck	=	16	8	1	0.25
1 bushel	=	64	32	4	1
1 cubic inch	=	0.0297616	0.0148808	0.00186010	0.000465025
1 cubic foot	=	51.42809	25.71405	3.214256	0.80356395
1 liter	=	1.816166	0.9080830	0.1135104	0.02837759
1 cubic meter	=	1816.166	908.0830	113.5104	28.37759

Units		Cubic inches	Cubic feet	Liters	Cubic meters
1 dry pint	=	33.6003125	0.01944463	0.5506105	0.0005506105
1 dry quart	=	67.200625	0.03888925	1.101221	0.001101221
1 peck	=	537.605	0.311114	8.809768	0.008809768
1 bushel	=	2150.42	1.244456	35.23907	0.03523907
1 cubic inch	=	1	0.0005787037	0.01638706	0.00001638706
1 cubic foot	=	1728	1	28.31685	0.02831685
1 liter	=	61.02374	0.03531467	1	0.001
1 cubic meter	=	61,023.74	35.31467	1000	1

Units of Capacity or Volume—Liquid Volume Measure

All underlined figures are exact.

Units		Minims	Fluid drams	Fluid ounces	Gills
1 minim	=	1	0.01666667	0.002083333	0.0005208333
1 fluid dram	=	60	1	0.125	0.03125
1 fluid ounce	=	480	8	1	0.25
1 gill	=	1920	32	4	1
1 liquid pint	=	7680	128	16	4
1 liquid quart	=	15,360	256	32	8
1 gallon	=	61,440	1024	128	32
1 cubic inch	=	265.9740	4.432900	0.5541126	0.1385281
1 cubic foot	=	459,603.1	7660.052	957.5065	239.3766
1 milliliter	=	16.23073	0.2705122	0.03381402	0.008453506
1 liter	=	16,230.73	270.5122	33.81402	8.453506

Units		Liquid pints	Liquid quarts	Gallons	Cubic inches
1 minim	=	0.0001302083	0.00006510417	0.00001627604	0.003759766
1 fluid dram	=	0.0078125	0.00390625	0.0009765625	0.22558594
1 fluid ounce	=	0.0625	0.03125	0.0078125	1.8046875
1 gill	=	0.25	0.125	0.03125	7.21875
1 liquid pint	=	1	0.5	0.125	28.875
1 liquid quart	=	2	1	0.25	57.75
1 gallon	=	8	4	1	231
1 cubic inch	=	0.03463203	0.01731602	0.004329004	1
1 cubic foot	=	59.84416	29.92208	7.480519	1728
1 milliliter	=	0.002113376	0.001056688	0.0002641721	0.06102374
1 liter	=	2.113376	1.056688	0.2641721	61.02374

Units		Cubic feet	Milliliters	Liters
1 minim	=	0.000002175790	0.06161152	0.00006161152
1 fluid dram	=	0.0001305474	3.696691	0.003696691
1 fluid ounce	=	0.001044379	29.57353	0.02957353
1 gill	=	0.004177517	118.2941	0.1182941
1 liquid pint	=	0.01671007	473.1765	0.4731765
1 liquid quart	=	0.03342014	946.3529	0.9463529
1 gallon	=	0.1336806	3785.412	3.785412
1 cubic inch	=	0.0005787037	16.38706	0.01638706
1 cubic foot	=	1	28,316.85	28.31685
1 milliliter	=	0.00003531467	1	0.001
1 liter	=	0.03531467	1000	1

Units of Mass Not Less Than Avoirdupois Ounces

All underlined figures are exact.

Units		Avoirdupois ounces	Avoirdupois pounds	Short hundredweights	Short tons
1 avoirdupois ounce	=	1	0.0625	0.000625	0.00003125
1 avoirdupois pound	=	16	1	0.01	0.0005
1 short hundredweight	=	1600	100	1	0.05
1 short ton	=	32,000	2000	20	1
1 long ton	=	35,840	2240	22.4	1.12
1 kilogram	=	35.27396	2.204623	0.02204623	0.001102311
1 metric ton	=	35,273.96	2204.623	22.04623	1.102311

Units		Long tons	Kilograms	Metric tons
1 avoirdupois ounce	=	0.00002790179	0.028349523125	0.000028349523125
1 avoirdupois pound	=	0.0004464286	0.45359237	0.00045359237
1 short hundredweight	=	0.04464286	45.359237	0.045359237
1 short ton	=	0.8928571	907.18474	0.90718474
1 long ton	=	1	1016.0469088	1.0160469088
1 kilogram	=	0.0009842065	1	0.001
1 metric ton	=	0.9842065	1000	1

Units of Mass Not Greater Than Pounds and Kilograms

All underlined figures are exact.

Units		Grains	Apothecaries scruples	Pennyweights	Avoirdupois drams
1 grain	=	1	0.05	0.04166667	0.03657143
1 apoth. scruple	=	20	1	0.8333333	0.7314286
1 pennyweight	=	24	1.2	1	0.8777143
1 avdp. dram	=	27.34375	1.3671875	1.139323	1
1 apoth. dram	=	60	3	2.5	2.194286
1 avdp. ounce	=	437.5	21.875	18.22917	16
1 apoth. or troy oz.	=	480	24	20	17.55429
1 apoth. or troy pound	=	5760	288	240	210.6514
1 avdp. pound	=	7000	350	291.6667	256
1 milligram	=	0.01543236	0.0007716179	0.0006430149	0.0005643834
1 gram	=	15.43236	0.7716179	0.6430149	0.5643834
1 kilogram	=	15,432.36	771.6179	643.0149	564.3834

Units		Apothecaries drams	Avoirdupois ounces	Apothecaries or troy ounces	Apothecaries or troy pounds
1 grain	=	0.01666667	0.002285714	0.002083333	0.0001736111
1 apoth. scruple	=	0.3333333	0.04571429	0.04166667	0.003472222
1 pennyweight	=	0.4	0.05485714	0.05	0.004166667
1 avdp. dram	=	0.4557292	0.0625	0.5696615	0.004747179
1 apoth. dram	=	1	0.1371429	0.125	0.01041667
1 avdp. ounce	=	7.291667	1	0.9114583	0.07595486
1 apoth. or troy ounce	=	8	1.097143	1	0.083333333
1 apoth. or troy pound	=	96	13.16571	12	1
1 avdp. pound	=	116.6667	16	14.58333	1.215278
1 milligram	=	0.0002572060	0.00003527396	0.00003215075	0.000002679229
1 gram	=	0.2572060	0.03527396	0.03215075	0.002679229
1 kilogram	=	257.2060	35.27396	32.15075	2.679229

Units		Avoirdupois pounds	Milligrams	Grams	Kilograms
1 grain	=	0.0001428571	64.79891	0.06479891	0.00006479891
1 apoth. scruple	=	0.002857143	1295.9782	1.2959782	0.0012959782
1 pennyweight	=	0.003428571	1555.17384	1.55517384	0.00155517384
1 avdp. dram	=	0.00390625	1771.8451953125	1.7718451953125	0.0017718451953125
1 apoth. dram	=	0.008571429	3887.9346	3.8879346	0.0038879346
1 avdp. ounce	=	0.0625	28,349.523125	28.349523125	0.028349523125
1 apoth. or troy ounce	=	0.06857143	31,103.4768	31.1034768	0.0311034768
1 apoth. or troy pound	=	0.8228571	373,241.7216	373.2417216	0.3732417216
1 avdp. pound	=	1	453,592.37	453.59237	0.45359237
1 milligram	=	0.000002204623	1	0.001	0.000001
1 gram	=	0.002204623	1000	1	0.001
1 kilogram	=	2.204623	1,000,000	1000	1

5. TABLES OF EQUIVALENTS

In these tables it is necessary to differentiate between the "international foot" and the "survey foot"—the survey foot is underlined.

When the name of a unit is enclosed in brackets (thus, [1 hand] . . .), this indicates (1) that the unit is not in general current use in the United States, or (2) that the unit is believed to be based on "custom and usage" rather than on formal authoritative definition.

Equivalents involving decimals are, in most instances, rounded off to the third decimal place except where they are exact, in which cases these exact equivalents are so designated. The equivalents of the imprecise units "tablespoon" and "teaspoon" are rounded to the nearest milliliter.

Units of Length

angstrom (Å)[12]	0.1 nanometer (exactly). 0.0001 micrometer (exactly). 0.0000001 millimeter (exactly). 0.000000004 inch.
1 cable's length	120 fathoms (exactly). 720 <u>feet</u> (exactly). 219 meters.
1 centimeter (cm)	0.3937 inch.
1 chain (ch) (Gunter's or surveyor's)	66 <u>feet</u> (exactly). 20.1168 meters.
1 decimeter (dm)	3.937 inches.
1 dekameter (dam)	32.808 feet.
1 fathom	6 <u>feet</u> (exactly). 1.8288 meters.
1 foot (ft)	0.3048 meter (exactly).
1 furlong (fur)	10 chains (surveyor's) (exactly). 660 <u>feet</u> (exactly). 1/8 U.S. statute mile (exactly). 201.168 meters.
[1 hand]	4 inches.
1 inch (in)	2.54 centimeters (exactly).
1 kilometer (km)	0.621 mile.
1 league (land)	3 U.S. statute miles (exactly). 4.828 kilometers.
1 link (li) (Gunter's or surveyor's)	0.66 <u>foot</u> (exactly). 0.201168 meter.
1 meter (m)	39.37 inches. 1.094 yards.
1 micrometer	0.001 millimeter (exactly). 0.00003937 inch.
1 mil	0.001 inch (exactly). 0.0254 millimeter (exactly).
1 mile (mi) (U.S. statute)[13]	5280 <u>feet</u> survey (exactly). 1.609 kilometers.
1 mile (mi) (international)	5280 <u>feet</u> international (exactly).

---

[12] The angstrom is basically defined as 10^{-10} meter.

[13] The term "statute mile" originated with Queen Elizabeth I who changed the definition of the mile from the Roman mile of 5000 feet to the statute mile of 5280 feet. The international mile and the U.S. statute mile differ by about 3 millimeters although both are defined as being equal to 5280 feet. The international mile is based on the international foot (0.3048 meter) whereas the U.S. statute mile is based on the survey foot (1200/3937 meter).

1 mile (mi) (international nautical)[14]	1.852 kilometers (exactly). 1.151 survey miles.
1 millimeter (mm)	0.03937 inch.
1 nanometer (nm)	0.001 micrometer (exactly). 0.00000003937 inch.
1 Point (typography)	0.013837 inch (exactly). 1/72 inch (approximately). 0.351 millimeter.
1 rod (rd), pole, or perch	16-1/2 <u>feet</u> (exactly). 5.0292 meters.
1 yard (yd)	0.9144 meter (exactly).

Units of Area

1 acre[15]	43,560 square feet (exactly). 0.405 hectare.
1 are	119.599 square yards. 0.025 acre.
1 hectare	2.471 acres.
[1 square (building)]	100 square feet.
1 square centimeter (cm2)	0.155 square inch.
1 square decimeter (dm^2)	15.500 square inches.
1 square foot (ft^2)	929.030 square centimeters.
1 square inch (in^2)	6.4516 square centimeters (exactly).
1 square kilometer (km^2)	247.104 acres. 0.386 square mile.
1 square meter (m^2)	1.196 square yards. 10.764 square feet.
1 square mile (mi^2)	258.999 hectares.
1 square millimeter (mm^2)	0.002 square inch.
1 square rod (rd^2), sq pole, or sq perch	25.293 square meters.
1 square yard (yd^2)	0.836 square meter.

---

[14] The international nautical mile of 1852 meters (6076.11549 . . . feet) was adopted effective July 1, 1954, for use in the United States. The value formerly used in the United States was 6080.20 feet = 1 nautical (geographical or sea) mile.

[15] The question is often asked as to the length of a side of an acre of ground. An acre is a unit of area containing 43,560 square *feet*. It is not necessarily square, or even rectangular. But, if it is square, then the length of a side is equal to $\sqrt{43,560} = 208.710+$ *feet*.

Units of Capacity or Volume

1 barrel (bbl), liquid	31 to 42 gallons.[16]
1 barrel (bbl), standard for fruits, vegetables, and other dry commodities, except cranberries	7056 cubic inches. 105 dry quarts. 3.281 bushels, struck measure.
1 barrel (bbl), standard, cranberry	5826 cubic inches. 86-45/64 dry quarts. 2.709 bushels, struck measure.
1 bushel (bu) (U.S.) struck measure	2150.42 cubic inches (exactly). 35.239 liters.
[1 bushel, heaped (U.S.)]	2747.715 cubic inches. 1.278 bushels, struck measure.[17]
[1 bushel (bu) (British Imperial) 1.032 U.S. bushels, struck measure (struck measure)]	2219.36 cubic inches.
1 cord (cd) (firewood)	128 cubic feet (exactly).
1 cubic centimeter (cm³)	0.061 cubic inch.
1 cubic decimeter (dm³)	61.024 cubic inches.
1 cubic foot (ft³)	7.481 gallons. 28.316 cubic decimeters.
1 cubic inch (in³)	0.554 fluid ounce. 4.433 fluid drams. 16.387 cubic centimeters.
1 cubic meter (m³)	1.308 cubic yards.
1 cubic yard (yd³)	0.765 cubic meter.
1 cup, measuring	8 fluid ounces (exactly). 237 milliliters. 1/2 liquid pint (exactly).
1 dekaliter (daL)	2.642 gallons. 1.135 pecks.
1 dram, fluid (or liquid) (fl dr or ƒʒ) (U.S.)	1/8 fluid ounce (exactly). 0.226 cubic inch. 3.697 milliliters. 1.041 British fluid drachms.
[1 drachm, fluid (fl dr) (British)]	0.961 U.S. fluid dram. 0.217 cubic inch. 3.552 milliliters.

[16] There are a variety of "barrels" established by law or usage. For example, Federal taxes on fermented liquors are based on a barrel of 31 gallons; many State laws fix the "barrel for liquids" as 31-1/2 gallons; one State fixes a 36-gallon barrel for cistern measurement; Federal law recognizes a 40-gallon barrel for "proof spirits"; by custom, 42 gallons comprise a barrel of crude oil or petroleum products for statistical purposes, and this equivalent is recognized "for liquids" by four States.

[17] Frequently recognized as 1-1/4 bushels, struck measure.

1 gallon (gal) (U.S.)	231 cubic inches (exactly). 3.785 liters. 0.833 British gallon. 128 U.S. fluid ounces (exactly).
[1 gallon (gal) (British Imperial)]	277.42 cubic inches. 1.201 U.S. gallons. 4.546 liters. 160 British fluid ounces (exactly).
1 gill (gi)	7.219 cubic inches. 4 fluid ounces (exactly). 0.118 liter.
1 hectoliter (hL)	26.418 gallons. 2.838 bushels.
1 liter (1 cubic decimeter exactly)	1.057 liquid quarts. 0.908 dry quart. 61.025 cubic inches.
1 milliliter (mL)	0.271 fluid dram. 16.231 minims. 0.061 cubic inch.
1 ounce, fluid (or liquid) (fl oz or f℥)(U.S.)	1.805 cubic inches. 29.573 milliliters. 1.041 British fluid ounces.
[1 ounce, fluid (fl oz) (British)]	0.961 U.S. fluid ounce. 1.734 cubic inches. 28.412 milliliters.
1 peck (pk)	8.810 liters.
1 pint (pt), dry	33.600 cubic inches. 0.551 liter.
1 pint (pt), liquid	28.875 cubic inches (exactly). 0.473 liter.
1 quart (qt), dry (U.S.)	67.201 cubic inches. 1.101 liters. 0.969 British quart.
1 quart (qt), liquid (U.S.)	57.75 cubic inches (exactly). 0.946 liter. 0.833 British quart.
[1 quart (qt) (British)]	69.354 cubic inches. 1.032 U.S. dry quarts. 1.201 U.S. liquid quarts.
1 tablespoon, measuring	3 teaspoons (exactly). 15 milliliters. 4 fluid drams. 1/2 fluid ounce (exactly).
1 teaspoon, measuring	1/3 tablespoon (exactly). 5 milliliters. 1-1/3 fluid drams.[18]
1 water ton (English)	270.91 U.S. gallons. 224 British Imperial gallons (exactly).

[18] The equivalent "1 teaspoon = 1-1/3 fluid drams" has been found by the Bureau to correspond more closely with the actual capacities of "measuring" and silver teaspoons than the equivalent "1 teaspoon = 1 fluid dram," which is given by a number of dictionaries.

Units of Mass

1 assay ton[19] (AT)	29.167 grams.
1 carat (c)	200 milligrams (exactly). 3.086 grains.
1 dram apothecaries (dr ap or ʒ)	60 grains (exactly). 3.888 grams.
1 dram avoirdupois (dr avdp)	27-11/32 (= 27.344) grains. 1.777 grams.
1 gamma (γ)	1 microgram (exactly).
1 grain	64.79891 milligrams (exactly).
1 gram (g)	15.432 grains. 0.035 ounce, avoirdupois.
1 hundredweight, gross or long[20] (gross cwt)	112 pounds (exactly). 50.802 kilograms.
1 hundredweight, gross or short (cwt or net cwt)	100 pounds (exactly). 45.359 kilograms.
1 kilogram (kg)	2.205 pounds.
1 microgram (μg) [the Greek letter mu in combination with the letter g]	0.000001 gram (exactly).
1 milligram (mg)	0.015 grain.
1 ounce, avoirdupois (oz avdp)	437.5 grains (exactly). 0.911 troy or apothecaries ounce. 28.350 grams.
1 ounce, troy or apothecaries (oz t or oz ap or ℥)	480 grains (exactly). 1.097 avoirdupois ounces. 31.103 grams.
1 pennyweight (dwt)	1.555 grams.
1 point	0.01 carat. 2 milligrams.
1 pound, avoirdupois (lb avdp)	7000 grains (exactly). 1.215 troy or apothecaries pounds. 453.59237 grams (exactly).
1 pound, troy or apothecaries (lb t or lb ap)	5760 grains (exactly). 0.823 avoirdupois pound. 373.242 grams.
1 scruple (s ap or ℈)	20 grains (exactly). 1.296 grams.

[19] Used in assaying. The assay ton bears the same relation to the milligram that a ton of 2000 pounds avoirdupois bears to the ounce troy; hence the mass in milligrams of precious metal obtained from one assay ton of ore gives directly the number of troy ounces to the net ton.

[20] The gross or long ton and hundredweight are used commercially in the United States to only a very limited extent, usually in restricted industrial fields. The units are the same as the British "ton" and "hundredweight."

1 ton, gross or long[21]	2240 pounds (exactly).
	1.12 net tons (exactly).
	1.016 metric tons.
1 ton, metric (t)	2204.623 pounds.
	0.984 gross ton.
	1.102 net tons.
1 ton, net or short	2000 pounds (exactly).
	0.893 gross ton.
	0.907 metric ton.

---

[21] The gross or long ton and hundredweight are used commercially in the United States to a limited extent only, usually in restricted industrial fields. These units are the same as the British "ton" and "hundredweight."

Appendix D
Standard Normal Distribution

Tabulated values are $P(0 \le Z \le z)$ = shaded area under the standard normal curve.

z	.00	.01	.02	.03	.04	.05	.06	.07	.08	.09
0.0	.0000	.0040	.0080	.0120	.0160	.0199	.0239	.0279	.0319	.0359
0.1	.0398	.0438	.0478	.0517	.0557	.0596	.0636	.0675	.0714	.0753
0.2	.0793	.0832	.0871	.0910	.0948	.0987	.1026	.1064	.1103	.1141
0.3	.1179	.1217	.1255	.1293	.1331	.1368	.1406	.1443	.1480	.1517
0.4	.1554	.1591	.1628	.1664	.1700	.1736	.1772	.1808	.1844	.1879
0.5	.1915	.1950	.1985	.2019	.2054	.2088	.2123	.2157	.2190	.2224
0.6	.2257	.2291	.2324	.2357	.2389	.2422	.2454	.2486	.2517	.2549
0.7	.2580	.2611	.2642	.2673	.2704	.2734	.2764	.2794	.2823	.2852
0.8	.2881	.2910	.2939	.2967	.2995	.3023	.3051	.3078	.3106	.3133
0.9	.3159	.3186	.3212	.3238	.3264	.3289	.3315	.3340	.3365	.3389
1.0	.3413	.3438	.3461	.3485	.3508	.3531	.3554	.3577	.3599	.3621
1.1	.3643	.3665	.3686	.3708	.3729	.3749	.3770	.3790	.3810	.3830
1.2	.3849	.3869	.3888	.3907	.3925	.3944	.3962	.3980	.3997	.4015
1.3	.4032	.4049	.4066	.4082	.4099	.4115	.4131	.4147	.4162	.4177
1.4	.4192	.4207	.4222	.4236	.4251	.4265	.4279	.4292	.4306	.4319
1.5	.4332	.4345	.4357	.4370	.4382	.4394	.4406	.4418	.4429	.4441
1.6	.4452	.4463	.4474	.4484	.4495	.4505	.4515	.4525	.4535	.4545
1.7	.4554	.4564	.4573	.4582	.4591	.4599	.4608	.4616	.4625	.4633
1.8	.4641	.4649	.4656	.4664	.4671	.4678	.4686	.4693	.4699	.4706
1.9	.4713	.4719	.4726	.4732	.4738	.4744	.4750	.4756	.4761	.4767
2.0	.4772	.4778	.4783	.4788	.4793	.4798	.4803	.4808	.4812	.4817
2.1	.4821	.4826	.4830	.4834	.4838	.4842	.4846	.4850	.4854	.4857
2.2	.4861	.4864	.4868	.4871	.4875	.4878	.4881	.4884	.4887	.4890
2.3	.4893	.4896	.4898	.4901	.4904	.4906	.4909	.4911	.4913	.4916
2.4	.4918	.4920	.4922	.4925	.4927	.4929	.4931	.4932	.4934	.4936

Continued

Continued

z	.00	.01	.02	.03	.04	.05	.06	.07	.08	.09
2.5	.4938	.4940	.4941	.4943	.4945	.4946	.4948	.4949	.4951	.4952
2.6	.4953	.4955	.4956	.4957	.4959	.4960	.4961	.4962	.4963	.4964
2.7	.4965	.4966	.4967	.4968	.4969	.4970	.4971	.4972	.4973	.4974
2.8	.4974	.4975	.4976	.4977	.4977	.4978	.4979	.4979	.4980	.4981
2.9	.4981	.4982	.4982	.4983	.4984	.4984	.4985	.4985	.4986	.4986
3.0	.4987	.4987	.4987	.4988	.4988	.4989	.4989	.4989	.4990	.4990

For negative values of z, the probabilities are found by using the symmetric property.

Appendix E
Factors Helpful in Constructing Control Charts for Variables

n	A	A_2	A_3	C_4	$1/C_4$	B_3	B_4	B_5
2	2.12130	1.88060	2.65870	0.79788	1.25332	0.00000	3.26657	0.00000
3	1.73205	1.02307	1.95440	0.88623	1.12838	0.00000	2.56814	0.00000
4	1.50000	0.72851	1.62810	0.92132	1.08540	0.00000	2.26603	0.00000
5	1.34164	0.57680	1.42729	0.93999	1.06384	0.00000	2.08895	0.00000
6	1.22474	0.48332	1.28713	0.95153	1.05094	0.03033	1.96967	0.02886
7	1.13389	0.41934	1.18191	0.95937	1.04235	0.11770	1.88230	0.11292
8	1.06066	0.37255	1.09910	0.96503	1.03624	0.18508	1.81492	0.17861
9	1.00000	0.33670	1.03166	0.96931	1.03166	0.23912	1.76088	0.23179
10	0.94868	0.30821	0.97535	0.97266	1.02811	0.28372	1.71628	0.27596
11	0.90453	0.28507	0.92739	0.97535	1.02527	0.32128	1.67872	0.31336
12	0.86603	0.26582	0.88591	0.97756	1.02296	0.35352	1.64648	0.34559
13	0.83205	0.24942	0.84954	0.97941	1.02102	0.38162	1.61838	0.37377
14	0.80178	0.23533	0.81734	0.98097	1.01940	0.40622	1.59378	0.39849
15	0.77460	0.22310	0.78854	0.98232	1.01800	0.42826	1.57174	0.42069
16	0.75000	0.21234	0.76260	0.98348	1.01680	0.44783	1.55217	0.44043
17	0.72761	0.20279	0.73905	0.98451	1.01573	0.46574	1.53426	0.45852
18	0.70711	0.19426	0.71758	0.98541	1.01481	0.48185	1.51815	0.47482
19	0.68825	0.18657	0.69787	0.98621	1.01398	0.49656	1.50344	0.48971
20	0.67082	0.17960	0.67970	0.98693	1.01324	0.51015	1.48985	0.50348
21	0.65465	0.17328	0.66289	0.98758	1.01258	0.52272	1.47728	0.51623
22	0.63960	0.16748	0.64726	0.98817	1.01197	0.53440	1.46560	0.52808
23	0.62554	0.16214	0.63269	0.98870	1.01143	0.54514	1.45486	0.53898
24	0.61237	0.15869	0.61906	0.98919	1.01093	0.55527	1.44473	0.54927
25	0.60000	0.15263	0.60628	0.98964	1.01047	0.56478	1.43522	0.55893

Continued

Continued

n	B_6	d_2	$1/d_2$	d_3	D_1	D_2	D_3	D_4
2	2.60633	1.128	0.88652	0.853	0.000	3.687	0.0000	3.26862
3	2.27597	1.693	0.59067	0.888	0.000	4.357	0.0000	2.57354
4	2.08774	2.059	0.48567	0.880	0.000	4.699	0.0000	2.28218
5	1.96360	2.326	0.42992	0.864	0.000	4.918	0.0000	2.11436
6	1.87420	2.534	0.39463	0.848	0.000	5.078	0.0000	2.00395
7	1.80582	2.704	0.36982	0.833	0.205	5.203	0.0758	1.92419
8	1.75145	2.847	0.35125	0.820	0.387	5.307	0.1359	1.86407
9	1.70683	2.970	0.33670	0.808	0.546	5.394	0.1838	1.81616
10	1.66936	3.078	0.32489	0.797	0.687	5.469	0.2232	1.77680
11	1.63734	3.173	0.31516	0.787	0.812	5.534	0.2559	1.74409
12	1.60953	3.258	0.30694	0.778	0.924	5.592	0.2836	1.71639
13	1.58505	3.336	0.29976	0.770	1.026	5.646	0.3076	1.69245
14	1.56345	3.407	0.29351	0.763	1.118	5.696	0.3282	1.67185
15	1.54395	3.472	0.28802	0.756	1.204	5.740	0.3468	1.65323
16	1.52653	3.532	0.28313	0.750	1.282	5.782	0.3630	1.63703
17	1.51050	3.588	0.27871	0.744	1.356	5.820	0.3779	1.62207
18	1.49600	3.640	0.27473	0.739	1.423	5.857	0.3909	1.60907
19	1.48271	3.689	0.27108	0.734	1.487	5.891	0.4031	1.59691
20	1.47038	3.735	0.26774	0.729	1.548	5.922	0.4145	1.58554
21	1.45893	3.778	0.26469	0.724	1.606	5.950	0.4251	1.57491
22	1.44826	3.819	0.26185	0.720	1.659	5.979	0.4344	1.56559
23	1.43842	3.858	0.25920	0.716	1.710	6.006	0.4432	1.55677
24	1.42911	3.859	0.25913	0.712	1.723	5.995	0.4465	1.55351
25	1.42035	3.931	0.25439	0.708	1.807	6.055	0.4597	1.54032

Appendix F

Values of K_1 for Computing Repeatability Using the Range Method

	Number of trials						
n	2	3	4	5	6	7	8
1	3.65	2.70	2.30	2.08	1.93	1.82	1.74
2	4.02	2.85	2.40	2.15	1.98	1.86	1.77
3	4.19	2.91	2.43	2.16	2.00	1.87	1.78
4	4.26	2.94	2.44	2.17	2.00	1.88	1.79
5	4.33	2.96	2.45	2.18	2.01	1.89	1.79
6	4.36	2.98	2.46	2.19	2.01	1.89	1.79
7	4.40	2.98	2.46	2.19	2.02	1.89	1.79
8	4.44	2.99	2.48	2.19	2.02	1.89	1.79
9	4.44	2.99	2.48	2.20	2.02	1.89	1.80
10	4.44	2.99	2.48	2.20	2.02	1.89	1.80
11	4.44	3.01	2.48	2.20	2.02	1.89	1.80
12	4.48	3.01	2.49	2.20	2.02	1.89	1.81
13	4.48	3.01	2.49	2.20	2.02	1.90	1.81
14	4.48	3.01	2.49	2.20	2.03	1.90	1.81
15	4.48	3.01	2.49	2.20	2.03	1.90	1.81
$n \geq 16$	4.56	3.05	2.50	2.21	2.04	1.91	1.81

n = (# of parts [samples]) × (# of operators)

Continued

Continued

	Number of trials						
n	9	10	11	12	13	14	15
1	1.67	1.62	1.57	1.54	1.51	1.48	1.47
2	1.71	1.65	1.60	1.56	1.52	1.49	1.47
3	1.71	1.66	1.60	1.57	1.53	1.50	1.47
4	1.72	1.66	1.61	1.57	1.53	1.50	1.48
5	1.72	1.66	1.61	1.57	1.54	1.51	1.48
6	1.72	1.66	1.61	1.57	1.54	1.51	1.48
7	1.72	1.66	1.61	1.57	1.54	1.51	1.48
8	1.73	1.67	1.61	1.57	1.54	1.51	1.48
9	1.73	1.67	1.62	1.57	1.54	1.51	1.48
10	1.73	1.67	1.62	1.57	1.54	1.51	1.48
11	1.73	1.67	1.62	1.57	1.54	1.51	1.48
12	1.73	1.67	1.62	1.57	1.54	1.51	1.48
13	1.73	1.67	1.62	1.57	1.54	1.51	1.48
14	1.73	1.67	1.62	1.57	1.54	1.51	1.48
15	1.73	1.67	1.62	1.58	1.54	1.51	1.48
$n \geq 16$	1.73	1.67	1.62	1.58	1.54	1.51	1.48

n = (# of parts [samples]) × (# of operators)

Appendix G

Values of K_2 for Computing Reproducibility Using the Range Method

Number of operators												
3	4	5	6	7	8	9	10	11	12	13	14	15
2.70	2.30	2.08	1.93	1.82	1.74	1.67	1.62	1.57	1.54	1.51	1.48	1.47

Appendix H

Sample Tables of ANSI/ASQ Z1.4-2008 and ANSI/ASQ Z1.9-2008 Standards

AQL

Number of Sample Units from Last 10 Lots or Batches	0.010	0.015	0.025	0.040	0.065	0.10	0.15	0.25	0.40	0.65	1.0	1.5	2.5	4.0	6.5	10	15	25	40	65	100	150	250	400	650	1000
20–29	*	*	*	*	*	*	*	*	*	*	*	*	*	*	*	0	0	2	4	8	14	22	40	68	115	181
30–49	*	*	*	*	*	*	*	*	*	*	*	*	*	*	0	0	1	3	7	13	22	36	63	105	178	277
50–79	*	*	*	*	*	*	*	*	*	*	*	*	*	0	0	2	3	7	14	25	40	63	110	181	301	
80–129	*	*	*	*	*	*	*	*	*	*	*	*	0	0	2	4	7	14	24	42	68	105	181	297		
130–199	*	*	*	*	*	*	*	*	*	*	*	0	0	2	4	7	13	25	42	72	115	177	301	490		
200–319	*	*	*	*	*	*	*	*	*	*	0	0	2	4	8	14	22	40	68	115	181	277	471			
320–499	*	*	*	*	*	*	*	*	*	0	0	1	4	8	14	24	39	68	113	189						
500–799	*	*	*	*	*	*	*	*	0	0	2	3	7	14	25	40	63	110	181							
800–1249	*	*	*	*	*	*	*	0	0	2	4	7	14	24	42	68	105	181								
1250–1999	*	*	*	*	*	*	0	0	2	4	7	13	24	49	69	110	169									
2000–3149	*	*	*	*	*	0	0	2	4	8	14	22	40	68	115	181										
3150–4999	*	*	*	*	0	0	1	4	8	14	24	38	67	111	186											
5000–7999	*	*	*	0	0	2	3	7	14	25	40	63	110	181												
8000–12,499	*	*	0	0	2	4	7	14	24	42	68	105	181													
12,500–19,999	*	0	0	2	4	7	13	24	40	69	110	169														
20,000–31,499	0	0	2	4	8	14	22	40	68	115	181															
31,500 and over	0	1	4	8	14	24	38	67	111	186																

* = Denotes that the number of sample units from the last 10 lots or batches is not sufficient for reduced inspection for this AQL. In this instance, more than 10 lots or batches may be used for the calculation, provided that the lots or batches used are the most recent ones in sequence, that they have all been on normal inspection, and that none have been rejected while on original inspection.

Figure H.1   ANSI/ASQ Z1.4–2008 Table VIII: Limit numbers for reduced inspection.

Lot or Batch Size			Special Inspection Levels				General Inspection Levels		
			S-1	S-2	S-3	S-4	I	II	III
2	to	8	A	A	A	A	A	A	B
9	to	15	A	A	A	A	A	B	C
16	to	25	A	A	B	B	B	C	D
26	to	50	B	B	B	C	C	D	E
51	to	90	B	B	C	C	C	E	F
91	to	150	B	B	C	D	D	F	G
151	to	280	B	C	D	E	E	G	H
281	to	500	B	C	D	E	F	H	J
501	to	1200	C	C	E	F	G	J	K
1201	to	3200	C	D	E	G	H	K	L
3201	to	10,000	C	D	F	G	J	L	M
10,001	to	35,000	C	D	F	H	K	M	N
35,001	to	150,000	D	E	G	J	L	N	P
150,001	to	500,000	D	E	G	J	M	P	Q
500,001	and	over	D	E	H	K	N	Q	R

Figure H.2   ANSI/ASQ Z1.4-2008 Table I: Sample size code letters.

AQLs in Percent Nonconforming Items and Nonconformities per 100 Items (normal inspection)

Each AQL cell shows **Ac Re** (Ac = Acceptance number, Re = Rejection number). ↓ = use first sampling plan below arrow; ↑ = use first sampling plan above arrow.

Sample Size Code Letter	Sample Size	0.010	0.015	0.025	0.040	0.065	0.10	0.15	0.25	0.40	0.65	1.0	1.5	2.5	4.0	6.5	10	15	25	40	65	100	150	250	400	650	1000
A	2	↓	↓	↓	↓	↓	↓	↓	↓	↓	↓	↓	↓	↓	↓	↓	↓	0 1	1 2	2 3	3 4	5 6	7 8	10 11	14 15	21 22	30 31
B	3	↓	↓	↓	↓	↓	↓	↓	↓	↓	↓	↓	↓	↓	↓	↓	0 1	1 2	2 3	3 4	5 6	7 8	10 11	14 15	21 22	30 31	44 45
C	5	↓	↓	↓	↓	↓	↓	↓	↓	↓	↓	↓	↓	↓	↓	0 1	1 2	2 3	3 4	5 6	7 8	10 11	14 15	21 22	30 31	44 45	↑
D	8	↓	↓	↓	↓	↓	↓	↓	↓	↓	↓	↓	↓	↓	0 1	1 2	2 3	3 4	5 6	7 8	10 11	14 15	21 22	30 31	44 45	↑	↑
E	13	↓	↓	↓	↓	↓	↓	↓	↓	↓	↓	↓	↓	0 1	1 2	2 3	3 4	5 6	7 8	10 11	14 15	21 22	30 31	44 45	↑	↑	↑
F	20	↓	↓	↓	↓	↓	↓	↓	↓	↓	↓	↓	0 1	1 2	2 3	3 4	5 6	7 8	10 11	14 15	21 22	30 31	44 45	↑	↑	↑	↑
G	32	↓	↓	↓	↓	↓	↓	↓	↓	↓	↓	0 1	1 2	2 3	3 4	5 6	7 8	10 11	14 15	21 22	30 31	44 45	↑	↑	↑	↑	↑
H	50	↓	↓	↓	↓	↓	↓	↓	↓	↓	0 1	1 2	2 3	3 4	5 6	7 8	10 11	14 15	21 22	30 31	44 45	↑	↑	↑	↑	↑	↑
J	80	↓	↓	↓	↓	↓	↓	↓	↓	0 1	1 2	2 3	3 4	5 6	7 8	10 11	14 15	21 22	30 31	44 45	↑	↑	↑	↑	↑	↑	↑
K	125	↓	↓	↓	↓	↓	↓	↓	0 1	1 2	2 3	3 4	5 6	7 8	10 11	14 15	21 22	30 31	44 45	↑	↑	↑	↑	↑	↑	↑	↑
L	200	↓	↓	↓	↓	↓	↓	0 1	1 2	2 3	3 4	5 6	7 8	10 11	14 15	21 22	30 31	44 45	↑	↑	↑	↑	↑	↑	↑	↑	↑
M	315	↓	↓	↓	↓	↓	0 1	1 2	2 3	3 4	5 6	7 8	10 11	14 15	21 22	30 31	44 45	↑	↑	↑	↑	↑	↑	↑	↑	↑	↑
N	500	↓	↓	↓	↓	0 1	1 2	2 3	3 4	5 6	7 8	10 11	14 15	21 22	30 31	44 45	↑	↑	↑	↑	↑	↑	↑	↑	↑	↑	↑
P	800	↓	↓	↓	0 1	1 2	2 3	3 4	5 6	7 8	10 11	14 15	21 22	30 31	44 45	↑	↑	↑	↑	↑	↑	↑	↑	↑	↑	↑	↑
Q	1250	↓	↓	0 1	1 2	2 3	3 4	5 6	7 8	10 11	14 15	21 22	30 31	44 45	↑	↑	↑	↑	↑	↑	↑	↑	↑	↑	↑	↑	↑
R	2000	↓	0 1	1 2	2 3	3 4	5 6	7 8	10 11	14 15	21 22	30 31	44 45	↑	↑	↑	↑	↑	↑	↑	↑	↑	↑	↑	↑	↑	↑

↓ = Use first sampling plan below arrow. If sample size equals or exceeds lot size, carry out 100 percent inspection.

↑ = Use first sampling plan above arrow.

Ac = Acceptance number.

Re = Rejection number.

Figure H.3   ANSI/ASQ Z1.4-2008 Table II-A: Single sampling plans for normal inspection.

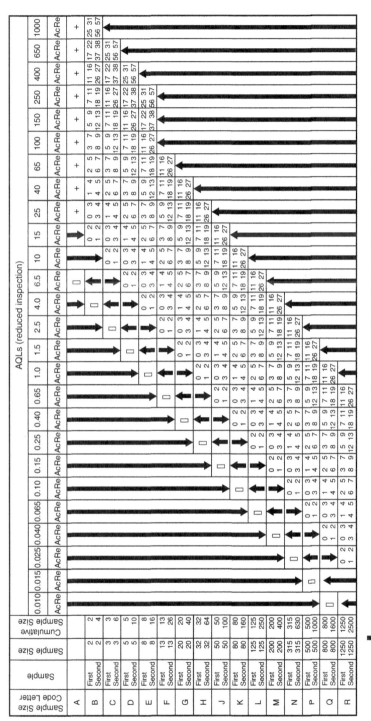

Figure H.4   ANSI/ASQ Z1.4–2008 Table III–A: Double sampling plans for normal inspection.

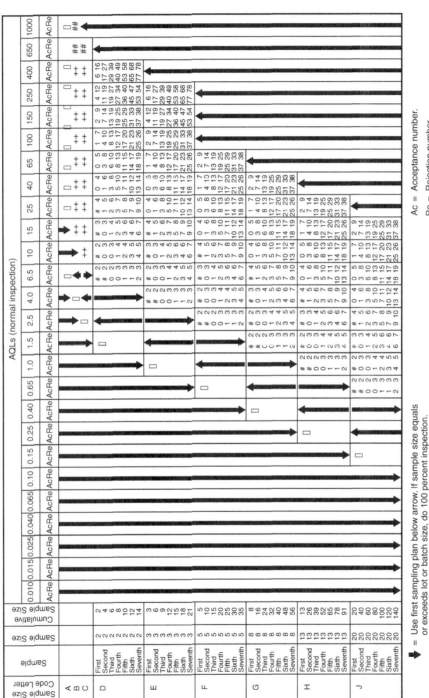

Figure H.5   ANSI/ASQ Z1.4-2008 Table IV-A: Multiple sampling plans for normal inspection.   *Continued*

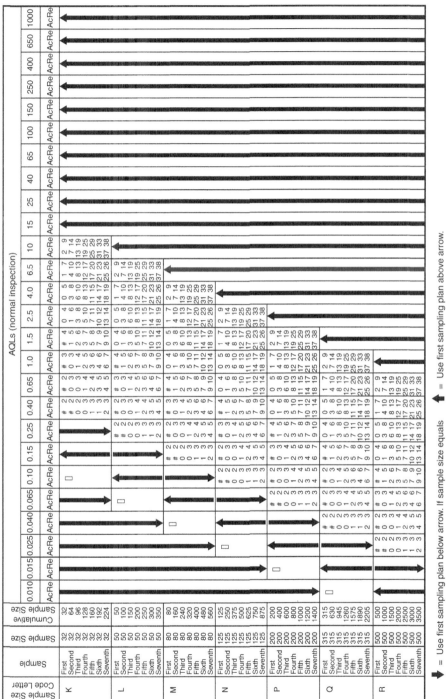

Figure H.5   *Continued.*

Lot Size			Inspection Levels				
			Special		General		
			S3	S4	I	II	III
2	to	8	B	B	B	B	C
9	to	15	B	B	B	B	D
16	to	25	B	B	B	C	E
26	to	50	B	B	C	D	F
51	to	90	B	B	D	E	G
91	to	150	B	C	E	F	H
151	to	280	B	D	F	G	I
281	to	400	C	E	G	H	J
401	to	500	C	E	G	I	J
501	to	1200	D	F	H	J	K
1201	to	3200	E	G	I	K	L
3201	to	10,000	F	H	J	L	M
10,001	to	35,000	G	I	K	M	N
35,001	to	150,000	H	J	L	N	P
150,001	to	500,000	H	K	M	P	P
500,001	and	over	H	K	N	P	P

Figure H.6　4.20 ANSI/ASQ Z1.9-2008 Table A-2*: Sample size code letters.**

* The theory governing inspection by variables depends on the properties of the normal distribution; therefore, this method of inspection is applicable only when there is reason to believe that the frequency distribution is normal.

** Sample size code letters given in body of table are applicable when the indicated inspection levels are to be used.

Sample Size Code Letter	Sample Size	AQLs (normal inspection)											
		T	.10	.15	.25	.40	.65	1.00	1.50	2.50	4.00	6.50	10.00
		k	k	k	k	k	k	k	k	k	k	k	k
B	3	↓	↓	↓	↓	↓	↓	↓	↓	.587	.502	.401	.296
C	4							↓	.651	.598	.525	.450	.364	.276
D	5				↓	↓	↓	.663	.614	.565	.498	.431	.352	.272
E	7			↓	.702	.659	.613	.569	.525	.465	.405	.336	.266
F	10	↓	↓	.916	.863	.811	.755	.703	.650	.579	.507	.424	.341
G	15	1.04	.999	.958	.903	.850	.792	.738	.684	.610	.536	.452	.368
H	25	1.10	1.05	1.01	.951	.896	.835	.779	.723	.647	.571	.484	.398
I	30	1.10	1.06	1.02	.959	.904	.843	.787	.730	.654	.577	.490	.403
J	40	1.13	1.08	1.04	.978	.921	.860	.803	.746	.668	.591	.503	.415
K	60	1.16	1.11	1.06	1.00	.948	.885	.826	.768	.689	.610	.521	.432
L	85	1.17	1.13	1.08	1.02	.962	.899	.839	.780	.701	.621	.530	.441
M	115	1.19	1.14	1.09	1.03	.975	.911	.851	.791	.711	.631	.539	.449
N	175	1.21	1.16	1.11	1.05	.994	.929	.868	.807	.726	.644	.552	.460
P	230	1.21	1.16	1.12	1.06	.996	.931	.870	.809	.728	.646	.553	.462
		.10	.15	.25	.40	.65	1.00	1.50	2.50	4.00	6.50	10.00	
		AQLs (tightened inspection)											

All AQL values are in percent nonconforming. T denotes plan used exclusively on tightened inspection and provides symbol for identification of appropriate OC curve.

↓ = Use first sampling plan below arrow, that is, both sample size and k value. When sample size equals or exceeds lot size, every item in the lot must be inspected.

Figure H.7   ANSI/ASQ Z1.9-2008 Table C-1: Master table for normal and tightened inspection for plans based on variability unknown (single specification limit–Form 1).

Q_U or Q_L	Sample size														
	3	4	5	7	10	15	20	25	30	35	50	75	100	150	200
0	50.00	50.00	50.00	50.00	50.00	50.00	50.00	50.00	50.00	50.00	50.00	50.00	50.00	50.00	50.00
.1	47.24	46.67	46.44	46.26	46.16	46.10	46.08	46.06	46.05	46.05	46.04	46.03	46.03	46.02	46.02
.2	44.46	43.33	42.90	42.54	42.35	42.24	42.19	42.16	42.15	42.13	42.11	42.10	42.09	42.09	42.08
.3	41.63	40.00	39.37	38.87	38.60	38.44	38.37	38.33	38.31	38.29	38.27	38.25	38.24	38.23	38.22
.31	41.35	39.67	39.02	38.50	38.23	38.06	37.99	37.95	37.93	37.91	37.89	37.87	37.86	37.85	37.84
.32	41.06	39.33	38.67	38.14	37.86	37.69	37.62	37.58	37.55	37.54	37.51	37.49	37.48	37.47	37.46
.33	40.77	39.00	38.32	37.78	37.49	37.31	37.24	37.20	37.18	37.16	37.13	37.11	37.10	37.09	37.08
.34	40.49	38.67	37.97	37.42	37.12	36.94	36.87	36.83	36.80	36.78	36.75	36.73	36.72	36.71	36.71
.35	40.20	38.33	37.62	37.06	36.75	36.57	36.49	36.45	36.43	36.41	36.38	36.36	36.35	36.34	36.33
.36	39.91	38.00	37.28	36.69	36.38	36.20	36.12	36.08	36.05	36.04	36.01	35.98	35.97	35.96	35.96
.37	39.62	37.67	36.93	36.33	36.02	35.83	35.75	35.71	35.68	35.66	35.63	35.61	35.60	35.59	35.58
.38	39.33	37.33	36.58	35.98	35.65	35.46	35.38	35.34	35.31	35.29	35.26	35.24	35.23	35.22	35.21
.39	39.03	37.00	36.23	35.62	35.29	35.10	35.02	34.97	34.94	34.93	34.89	34.87	34.86	34.85	34.84
.40	38.74	36.67	35.88	35.26	34.93	34.73	34.65	34.60	34.58	34.56	34.53	34.50	34.49	34.48	34.47
.41	38.45	36.33	35.54	34.90	34.57	34.37	34.28	34.24	34.21	34.19	34.16	34.13	34.12	34.11	34.11
.42	38.15	36.00	35.19	34.55	34.21	34.00	33.92	33.87	33.85	33.83	33.79	33.77	33.76	33.75	33.74
.43	37.85	35.67	34.85	34.19	33.85	33.64	33.56	33.51	33.48	33.46	33.43	33.40	33.39	33.38	33.38
.44	37.56	35.33	34.50	33.84	33.49	33.28	33.20	33.15	33.12	33.10	33.07	33.04	33.03	33.02	33.01
.45	37.26	35.00	34.16	33.49	33.13	32.92	32.84	32.79	32.76	32.74	32.71	32.68	32.67	32.66	32.65
.46	36.96	34.67	33.81	33.13	32.78	32.57	32.48	32.43	32.40	32.38	32.35	32.32	32.31	32.30	32.29
.47	36.66	34.33	33.47	32.78	32.42	32.21	32.12	32.07	32.04	32.02	31.99	31.96	31.95	31.94	31.93
.48	36.35	34.00	33.12	32.43	32.07	31.85	31.77	31.72	31.69	31.67	31.63	31.61	31.60	31.58	31.58
.49	36.05	33.67	32.78	32.08	31.72	31.50	31.41	31.36	31.33	31.31	31.28	31.25	31.24	31.23	31.22
.50	35.75	33.33	32.44	31.74	31.37	31.15	31.06	31.01	30.98	30.96	30.93	30.90	30.89	30.88	30.87
.51	35.44	33.00	32.10	31.39	31.02	30.80	30.71	30.66	30.63	30.61	30.57	30.55	30.54	30.53	30.52
.52	35.13	32.67	31.76	31.04	30.67	30.45	30.36	30.31	30.28	30.26	30.23	30.20	30.19	30.18	30.17
.53	34.82	32.33	31.42	30.70	30.32	30.10	30.01	29.96	29.93	29.91	29.88	29.85	29.84	29.83	29.82
.54	34.51	32.00	31.08	30.36	29.98	29.76	29.67	29.62	29.59	29.57	29.53	29.51	29.49	29.48	29.48
.55	34.20	31.67	30.74	30.01	29.64	29.41	29.32	29.27	29.24	29.22	29.19	29.16	29.15	29.14	29.13
.56	33.88	31.33	30.40	29.67	29.29	29.07	28.98	28.93	28.90	28.88	28.85	28.82	28.81	28.80	28.79
.57	33.57	31.00	30.06	29.33	28.95	28.73	28.64	28.59	28.56	28.54	28.51	28.48	28.47	28.46	28.45
.58	33.25	30.67	29.73	28.99	28.61	28.39	28.30	28.25	28.22	28.20	28.17	28.14	28.13	28.12	28.11
.59	32.93	30.33	29.39	28.66	28.28	28.05	27.96	27.92	27.89	27.87	27.83	27.81	27.79	27.78	27.78
.60	32.61	30.00	29.05	28.32	27.94	27.72	27.63	27.58	27.55	27.53	27.50	27.47	27.46	27.45	27.44
.61	32.28	29.67	28.72	27.98	27.60	27.39	27.30	27.25	27.22	27.20	27.16	27.14	27.13	27.11	27.11
.62	31.96	29.33	28.39	27.65	27.27	27.05	26.96	26.92	26.89	26.87	26.83	26.81	26.80	26.78	26.78
.63	31.63	29.00	28.05	27.32	26.94	26.72	26.63	26.59	26.56	26.54	26.50	26.48	26.47	26.46	26.45
.64	31.30	28.67	27.72	26.99	26.61	26.39	26.31	26.26	26.23	26.21	26.18	26.15	26.14	26.13	26.12
.65	30.97	28.33	27.39	26.66	26.28	26.07	25.98	25.93	25.90	25.88	25.85	25.83	25.82	25.81	25.80
.66	30.63	28.00	27.06	26.33	25.96	25.74	25.66	25.61	25.58	25.56	25.53	25.51	25.49	25.48	25.48
.67	30.30	27.67	26.73	26.00	25.63	25.42	25.33	25.29	25.26	25.24	25.21	25.19	25.17	25.16	25.16
.68	29.96	27.33	26.40	25.68	25.31	25.10	25.01	24.97	24.94	24.92	24.89	24.87	24.86	24.85	24.84
.69	29.61	27.00	26.07	25.35	24.99	24.78	24.70	24.65	24.62	24.60	24.57	24.55	24.54	24.53	24.52

Figure H.8 ANSI/ASQ Z1.9-2008 Table B-5: Table for estimating the lot percent nonconforming using standard deviation method. Values tabulated are read as percentages.

Continued

Q_U or Q_L	Sample size														
	3	4	5	7	10	15	20	25	30	35	50	75	100	150	200
.70	29.27	26.67	25.74	25.03	24.67	24.46	24.38	24.33	24.31	24.29	24.26	24.24	24.23	24.22	24.21
.71	28.92	26.33	25.41	24.71	24.35	24.15	24.06	24.02	23.99	23.98	23.95	23.92	23.91	23.90	23.90
.72	28.57	26.00	25.09	24.39	24.03	23.83	23.75	23.71	23.68	23.67	23.64	23.61	23.60	23.59	23.59
.73	28.22	25.67	24.76	24.07	23.72	23.52	23.44	23.40	23.37	23.36	23.33	23.31	23.30	23.29	23.28
.74	27.86	25.33	24.44	23.75	23.41	23.21	23.13	23.09	23.07	23.05	23.02	23.00	22.99	22.98	22.98
.75	27.50	25.00	24.11	23.44	23.10	22.90	22.83	22.79	22.76	22.75	22.72	22.70	22.69	22.68	22.68
.76	27.13	24.67	23.79	23.12	22.79	22.60	22.52	22.48	22.46	22.44	22.42	22.40	22.39	22.38	22.38
.77	26.76	24.33	23.47	22.81	22.48	22.30	22.22	22.18	22.16	22.14	22.12	22.10	22.09	22.08	22.08
.78	26.39	24.00	23.15	22.50	22.18	21.99	21.92	21.89	21.86	21.85	21.82	21.80	21.78	21.79	21.78
.79	26.02	23.67	22.83	22.19	21.87	21.70	21.63	21.59	21.57	21.55	21.53	21.51	21.50	21.49	21.49
.80	25.64	23.33	22.51	21.88	21.57	21.40	21.33	21.29	21.27	21.26	21.23	21.22	21.21	21.20	21.20
.81	25.25	23.00	22.19	21.58	21.27	21.10	21.04	21.00	20.98	20.97	20.94	20.93	20.92	20.91	20.91
.82	24.86	22.67	21.87	21.27	20.98	20.81	20.75	20.71	20.69	20.68	20.65	20.64	20.63	20.62	20.62
.83	24.47	22.33	21.56	29.97	29.68	20.52	20.46	20.42	20.40	20.39	20.37	20.35	20.35	20.34	20.34
.84	24.07	22.00	21.24	20.67	20.39	20.23	20.17	20.14	20.12	20.11	20.09	20.07	20.06	20.06	20.05
.85	23.67	21.67	20.93	20.37	20.10	19.94	19.89	19.86	19.84	19.82	19.80	19.79	19.78	19.78	19.77
.86	23.26	21.33	20.62	20.07	19.81	19.66	19.60	19.57	19.56	19.54	19.53	19.51	19.51	19.50	19.50
.87	22.84	21.00	20.31	19.78	19.52	19.38	19.32	19.30	19.28	19.27	19.25	19.24	19.23	19.23	19.22
.88	22.42	20.67	20.00	19.48	19.23	19.10	19.05	19.02	19.00	18.99	18.98	18.96	18.96	18.95	18.95
.89	21.99	20.33	19.69	19.19	18.95	18.82	18.77	18.74	18.73	18.72	18.70	18.69	18.69	18.68	18.68
.90	21.55	20.00	19.38	18.90	18.67	18.54	18.50	18.47	18.46	18.45	18.43	18.42	18.42	18.41	18.41
.91	21.11	19.67	19.07	18.61	18.39	18.27	18.23	18.20	18.19	18.18	18.17	18.16	18.15	18.15	18.15
.92	20.66	19.33	18.77	18.33	18.11	18.00	17.96	17.94	17.92	17.92	17.90	17.89	17.89	17.89	17.88
.93	20.19	19.00	18.46	18.04	17.84	17.73	17.69	17.67	17.66	17.65	17.64	17.63	17.63	17.62	17.62
.94	19.73	18.67	18.16	17.76	17.56	17.46	17.43	17.41	17.40	17.39	17.38	17.37	17.37	17.37	17.36
.95	19.25	18.33	17.86	17.48	17.29	17.20	17.17	17.16	17.14	17.13	17.12	17.12	17.11	17.11	17.11
.96	18.75	18.00	17.55	17.20	17.03	16.94	16.90	16.89	16.88	16.88	16.87	16.86	16.86	16.86	16.86
.97	18.25	17.67	17.25	16.92	16.76	16.68	16.65	16.63	16.62	16.62	16.61	16.61	16.61	16.61	16.60
.98	17.74	17.33	16.96	16.65	16.49	16.42	16.39	16.38	16.37	16.37	16.36	16.36	16.36	16.36	16.36
.99	17.21	17.00	16.66	16.37	16.23	16.16	16.14	16.13	16.12	16.12	16.12	16.11	16.11	16.11	16.11
1.00	16.67	16.67	16.36	16.10	15.97	15.91	15.89	15.88	15.88	15.87	15.87	15.87	15.87	15.87	15.87
1.01	16.11	16.33	16.07	15.83	15.72	15.66	15.64	15.63	15.63	15.63	15.63	15.62	15.62	15.62	15.62
1.02	15.53	16.00	15.78	15.56	15.46	15.41	15.40	15.39	15.39	15.38	15.38	15.38	15.38	15.39	15.39
1.03	14.93	15.67	15.48	15.30	15.21	15.17	15.15	15.15	15.15	15.15	15.15	15.15	15.15	15.15	15.15
1.04	14.31	15.33	15.19	15.03	14.96	14.92	14.91	14.91	14.91	14.91	14.91	14.91	14.91	14.91	14.91
1.05	13.66	15.00	14.91	14.77	14.71	14.68	14.67	14.67	14.67	14.67	14.68	14.68	14.68	14.68	14.68
1.06	12.98	14.67	14.62	14.51	14.46	14.44	14.44	14.44	14.44	14.44	14.45	14.45	14.45	14.45	14.45
1.07	12.27	14.33	14.33	14.26	14.22	14.20	14.20	14.21	14.21	14.21	14.22	14.22	14.22	14.23	14.22
1.08	11.51	14.00	14.05	14.00	13.97	13.97	13.97	13.98	13.98	13.98	13.99	13.99	14.00	14.00	14.00
1.09	10.71	13.67	13.76	13.75	13.73	13.74	13.74	13.75	13.75	13.76	13.77	13.77	13.77	13.78	13.78

Figure H.8   *Continued.*

Q_U or Q_L	Sample size														
	3	4	5	7	10	15	20	25	30	35	50	75	100	150	200
1.10	9.84	13.33	13.48	13.49	13.50	13.51	13.52	13.52	13.53	13.54	13.54	13.55	13.55	13.56	13.56
1.11	8.89	13.00	13.20	13.25	13.26	13.28	13.29	13.30	13.31	13.31	13.32	13.33	13.34	13.34	13.34
1.12	7.82	12.67	12.93	13.00	13.03	13.05	13.07	13.08	13.09	13.10	13.11	13.12	13.12	13.13	13.13
1.13	6.60	12.33	12.65	12.75	12.80	12.83	12.85	12.86	12.87	12.88	12.89	12.90	12.91	12.91	12.92
1.14	5.08	12.00	12.37	12.51	12.57	12.61	12.63	12.65	12.66	12.67	12.68	12.69	12.70	12.70	12.71
1.15	2.87	11.67	12.10	12.27	12.34	12.39	12.42	12.44	12.45	12.46	12.47	12.48	12.49	12.49	12.50
1.16	0.00	11.33	11.83	12.03	12.12	12.18	12.21	12.22	12.24	12.25	12.26	12.28	12.28	12.29	12.29
1.17	0.00	11.00	11.56	11.79	11.90	11.96	12.00	12.02	12.03	12.04	12.06	12.07	12.08	12.09	12.09
1.18	0.00	10.67	11.29	11.56	11.68	11.75	11.79	11.81	11.82	11.84	11.85	11.87	11.88	11.88	11.89
1.19	0.00	10.33	11.02	11.33	11.46	11.54	11.58	11.61	11.62	11.63	11.65	11.67	11.68	11.69	11.69
1.20	0.00	10.00	10.76	11.10	11.24	11.34	11.38	11.41	11.42	11.43	11.46	11.47	11.48	11.49	11.49
1.21	0.00	9.67	10.50	10.87	11.03	11.13	11.18	11.21	11.22	11.24	11.26	11.28	11.29	11.30	11.30
1.22	0.00	9.33	10.23	10.65	10.82	10.93	10.98	11.01	11.03	11.04	11.07	11.09	11.09	11.10	11.11
1.23	0.00	9.00	9.97	10.42	10.61	10.73	10.78	10.81	10.84	10.85	10.88	10.90	10.91	10.92	10.92
1.24	0.00	8.67	9.72	10.20	10.41	10.53	10.59	10.62	10.64	10.66	10.69	10.71	10.72	10.73	10.73
1.25	0.00	8.33	9.46	9.98	10.21	10.34	10.40	10.43	10.46	10.47	10.50	10.52	10.53	10.54	10.55
1.26	0.00	8.00	9.21	9.77	10.00	10.15	10.21	10.25	10.27	10.29	10.32	10.34	10.35	10.36	10.37
1.27	0.00	7.67	8.96	9.55	9.81	9.96	10.02	10.06	10.09	10.10	10.13	10.16	10.17	10.18	10.19
1.28	0.00	7.33	8.71	9.34	9.61	9.77	9.84	9.88	9.90	9.92	9.95	9.98	9.99	10.00	10.01
1.29	0.00	7.00	8.46	9.13	9.42	9.58	9.66	9.70	9.72	9.74	9.78	9.80	9.82	9.83	9.83
1.30	0.00	6.67	8.21	8.93	9.22	9.40	9.48	9.52	9.55	9.57	9.60	9.63	9.64	9.65	9.66
1.31	0.00	6.33	7.97	8.72	9.03	9.22	9.30	9.34	9.37	9.39	9.43	9.46	9.47	9.48	9.49
1.32	0.00	6.00	7.73	8.52	8.85	9.04	9.12	9.17	9.20	9.22	9.26	9.29	9.30	9.31	9.32
1.33	0.00	5.67	7.49	8.32	8.66	8.86	8.95	9.00	9.03	9.05	9.09	9.12	9.13	9.15	9.15
1.34	0.00	5.33	7.25	8.12	8.48	8.69	8.78	8.83	8.86	8.88	8.92	8.95	8.97	8.98	8.99
1.35	0.00	5.00	7.02	7.92	8.30	8.52	8.61	8.66	8.69	8.72	8.76	8.79	8.81	8.82	8.83
1.36	0.00	4.67	6.79	7.73	8.12	8.35	8.44	8.50	8.53	8.55	8.60	8.63	8.65	8.66	8.67
1.37	0.00	4.33	6.56	7.54	7.95	8.18	8.28	8.33	8.37	8.39	8.44	8.47	8.49	8.50	8.51
1.38	0.00	4.00	6.33	7.35	7.77	8.01	8.12	8.17	8.21	8.24	8.28	8.31	8.33	8.35	8.36
1.39	0.00	3.67	6.10	7.17	7.60	7.85	7.96	8.01	8.05	8.08	8.12	8.16	8.18	8.19	8.20
1.40	0.00	3.33	5.88	6.98	7.44	7.69	7.80	7.86	7.90	7.92	7.97	8.01	8.02	8.04	8.05
1.41	0.00	3.00	5.66	6.80	7.27	7.53	7.64	7.70	7.74	7.77	7.82	7.86	7.87	7.89	7.90
1.42	0.00	2.67	5.44	6.62	7.10	7.37	7.49	7.55	7.59	7.62	7.67	7.71	7.73	7.74	7.75
1.43	0.00	2.33	5.23	6.45	6.94	7.22	7.34	7.40	7.44	7.47	7.52	7.56	7.58	7.60	7.61
1.44	0.00	2.00	5.02	6.27	6.78	7.07	7.19	7.26	7.30	7.33	7.38	7.42	7.44	7.46	7.47
1.45	0.00	1.67	4.81	6.10	6.63	6.92	7.04	7.11	7.15	7.18	7.24	7.28	7.30	7.32	7.32
1.46	0.00	1.33	4.60	5.93	6.47	6.77	6.90	6.97	7.01	7.04	7.10	7.14	7.16	7.18	7.19
1.47	0.00	1.00	4,39	5.77	6.32	6.63	6.75	6.83	6.87	6.90	6.96	7.00	7.02	7.04	7.05
1.48	0.00	.67	4.19	5.60	6.17	6.48	6.61	6.69	6.73	6.77	6.82	6.86	6.88	6.90	6.91
1.49	0.00	.33	3.99	5.44	6.02	6.34	6.48	6.55	6.60	6.63	6.69	6.73	6.75	6.77	6.78

Figure H.8   *Continued.*

Q_U or Q_L	Sample size														
	3	4	5	7	10	15	20	25	30	35	50	75	100	150	200
1.50	0.00	0.00	3.80	5.28	5.87	6.20	6.34	6.41	6.46	6.50	6.55	6.60	6.62	6.64	6.65
1.51	0.00	0.00	3.61	5.13	5.73	6.06	6.20	6.28	6.33	6.36	6.42	6.47	6.49	6.51	6.52
1.52	0.00	0.00	3.42	4.97	5.59	5.93	6.07	6.15	6.20	6.23	6.29	6.34	6.36	6.38	6.39
1.53	0.00	0.00	3.23	4.82	5.45	5.80	5.94	6.02	6.07	6.11	6.17	6.21	6.24	6.26	6.27
1.54	0.00	0.00	3.05	4.67	5.31	5.67	5.81	5.89	5.95	5.98	6.04	6.09	6.11	6.13	6.15
1.55	0.00	0.00	2.87	4.52	5.18	5.54	5.69	5.77	5.82	5.86	5.92	5.97	5.99	6.01	6.02
1.56	0.00	0.00	2.69	4.38	5.05	5.41	5.56	5.65	5.70	5.74	5.80	5.85	5.87	5.89	5.90
1.57	0.00	0.00	2.52	4.24	4.92	5.29	5.44	5.53	5.58	5.62	5.68	5.73	5.75	5.78	5.79
1.58	0.00	0.00	2.35	4.10	4.79	5.16	5.32	5.41	5.46	5.50	5.56	5.61	5.64	5.66	5.67
1.59	0.00	0.00	2.19	3.96	4.66	5.04	5.20	5.29	5.34	5.38	5.45	5.50	5.52	5.55	5.56
1.60	0.00	0.00	2.03	3.83	4.54	4.92	5.08	5.17	5.23	5.27	5.33	5.38	5.41	5.43	5.44
1.61	0.00	0.00	1.87	3.69	4.41	4.81	4.97	5.06	5.12	5.16	5.22	5.27	5.30	5.32	5.33
1.62	0.00	0.00	1.72	3.57	4.30	4.69	4.86	4.95	5.01	5.04	5.11	5.16	5.19	5.21	5.23
1.63	0.00	0.00	1.57	3.44	4.18	4.58	4.75	4.84	4.90	4.94	5.01	5.06	5.08	5.11	5.12
1.64	0.00	0.00	1.42	3.31	4.06	4.47	4.64	4.73	4.79	4.83	4.90	4.95	4.98	5.00	5.01
1.65	0.00	0.00	1.28	3.19	3.95	4.36	4.53	4.62	4.68	4.72	4.79	4.85	4.87	4.90	4.91
1.66	0.00	0.00	1.15	3.07	3.84	4.25	4.43	4.52	4.58	4.62	4.69	4.74	4.77	4.80	4.81
1.67	0.00	0.00	1.02	2.95	3.73	4.15	4.32	4.42	4.48	4.52	4.59	4.64	4.67	4.70	4.71
1.68	0.00	0.00	0.89	2.84	3.62	4.05	4.22	4.32	4.38	4.42	4.49	4.55	4.57	4.60	4.61
1.69	0.00	0.00	0.77	2.73	3.52	3.94	4.12	4.22	4.28	4.32	4.39	4.45	4.47	4.50	4.51
1.70	0.00	0.00	0.66	2.62	3.41	3.84	4.02	4.12	4.18	4.22	4.30	4.35	4.38	4.41	4.42
1.71	0.00	0.00	0.55	2.51	3.31	3.75	3.93	4.02	4.09	4.13	4.20	4.26	4.29	4.31	4.32
1.72	0.00	0.00	0.45	2.41	3.21	3.65	3.83	3.93	3.99	4.04	4.11	4.17	4.19	4.22	4.23
1.73	0.00	0.00	0.36	2.30	3.11	3.56	3.74	3.84	3.90	3.94	4.02	4.08	4.10	4.13	4.14
1.74	0.00	0.00	0.27	2.20	3.02	3.46	3.65	3.75	3.81	3.85	3.93	3.99	4.01	4.04	4.05
1.75	0.00	0.00	0.19	2.11	2.93	3.37	3.56	3.66	3.72	3.77	3.84	3.90	3.93	3.95	3.97
1.76	0.00	0.00	0.12	2.01	2.83	3.28	3.47	3.57	3.63	3.68	3.76	3.81	3.84	3.87	3.88
1.77	0.00	0.00	0.06	1.92	2.74	3.20	3.38	3.48	3.55	3.59	3.67	3.73	3.76	3.78	3.80
1.78	0.00	0.00	0.02	1.83	2.66	3.11	3.30	3.40	3.47	3.51	3.59	3.64	3.67	3.70	3.71
1.79	0.00	0.00	0.00	1.74	2.57	3.03	3.21	3.32	3.38	3.43	3.51	3.56	3.59	3.62	3.63
1.80	0.00	0.00	0.00	1.65	2.49	2.94	3.13	3.24	3.30	3.35	3.43	3.48	3.51	3.54	3.55
1.81	0.00	0.00	0.00	1.57	2.40	2.86	3.05	31.6	3.22	3.27	3.35	3.40	3.43	3.46	3.47
1.82	0.00	0.00	0.00	1.49	2.32	2.79	2.98	3.08	3.15	3.19	3.27	3.33	3.36	3.38	3.40
1.83	0.00	0.00	0.00	1.41	2.25	2.71	2.90	3.00	3.07	3.11	3.19	3.25	3.28	3.31	3.32
1.84	0.00	0.00	0.00	1.34	2.17	2.63	2.82	2.93	2.99	3.04	3.12	3.18	3.21	3.23	3.25
1.85	0.00	0.00	0.00	1.26	2.09	2.56	2.75	2.85	2.92	2.97	3.05	3.10	3.13	3.16	3.17
1.86	0.00	0.00	0.00	1.19	2.02	2.48	2.68	2.78	2.85	2.89	2.97	3.03	3.06	3.09	3.10
1.87	0.00	0.00	0.00	1.12	1.95	2.41	2.61	2.71	2.78	2.82	2.90	2.96	2.99	3.02	3.03
1.88	0.00	0.00	0.00	1.06	1.88	2.34	2.54	2.64	2.71	2.75	2.83	2.89	2.92	2.95	2.96
1.89	0.00	0.00	0.00	0.99	1.81	2.28	2.47	2.57	2.64	2.69	2.77	2.83	2.85	2.88	2.90

Figure H.8   *Continued.*

Q_U or Q_L	Sample size														
	3	4	5	7	10	15	20	25	30	35	50	75	100	150	200
1.90	0.00	0.00	0.00	0.93	1.75	2.21	2.40	2.51	2.57	2.62	2.70	2.76	2.79	2.82	2.83
1.91	0.00	0.00	0.00	0.87	1.68	2.14	2.34	2.44	2.51	2.56	2.63	2.69	2.72	2.75	2.77
1.92	0.00	0.00	0.00	0.81	1.62	2.08	2.27	2.38	2.45	2.49	2.57	2.63	2.66	2.69	2.70
1.93	0.00	0.00	0.00	0.76	1.56	2.02	2.21	2.32	2.38	2.43	2.51	2.57	2.60	2.63	2.64
1.94	0.00	0.00	0.00	0.70	1.50	1.96	2.15	2.25	2.32	2.37	2.45	2.51	2.54	2.56	2.58
1.95	0.00	0.00	0.00	0.65	1.44	1.90	2.09	2.19	2.26	2.31	2.39	2.45	2.48	2.50	2.52
1.96	0.00	0.00	0.00	0.60	1.38	1.84	2.03	2.14	2.20	2.25	2.33	2.39	2.42	2.44	2.46
1.97	0.00	0.00	0.00	0.56	1.33	1.78	1.97	2.08	2.14	2.19	2.27	2.33	2.36	2.39	2.40
1.98	0.00	0.00	0.00	0.51	1.27	1.73	1.92	2.02	2.09	2.13	2.21	2.27	2.30	2.33	2.34
1.99	0.00	0.00	0.00	0.47	1.22	1.67	1.86	1.97	2.03	2.08	2.16	2.22	2.25	2.27	2.29
2.00	0.00	0.00	0.00	0.43	1.17	1.62	1.81	1.91	1.98	2.03	2.10	2.16	2.19	2.22	2.23
2.01	0.00	0.00	0.00	0.39	1.12	1.57	1.76	1.86	1.93	1.97	2.05	2.11	2.14	2.17	2.18
2.02	0.00	0.00	0.00	0.36	1.07	1.52	1.71	1.81	1.87	1.92	2.00	2.06	2.09	2.11	2.13
2.03	0.00	0.00	0.00	0.32	1.03	1.47	1.66	1.76	1.82	1.87	1.95	2.01	2.04	2.06	2.08
2.04	0.00	0.00	0.00	0.29	0.98	1.42	1.61	1.71	1.77	1.82	1.90	1.96	1.99	2.01	2.03
2.05	0.00	0.00	0.00	0.26	0.94	1.37	1.56	1.66	1.73	1.77	1.85	1.91	1.94	1.96	1.98
2.06	0.00	0.00	0.00	0.23	0.90	1.33	1.51	1.61	1.68	1.72	1.80	1.86	1.89	1.92	1.93
2.07	0.00	0.00	0.00	0.21	0.86	1.28	1.47	1.57	1.63	1.68	1.76	1.81	1.84	1.87	1.88
2.08	0.00	0.00	0.00	0.18	0.82	1.24	1.42	1.52	1.59	1.63	1.71	1.77	1.79	1.82	1.84
2.09	0.00	0.00	0.00	0.16	0.78	1.20	1.38	1.48	1.54	1.59	1.66	1.72	1.75	1.78	1.79
2.10	0.00	0.00	0.00	0.14	0.74	1.16	1.34	1.44	1.50	1.54	1.62	1.68	1.71	1.73	1.75
2.11	0.00	0.00	0.00	0.12	0.71	1.12	1.30	1.39	1.46	1.50	1.58	1.63	1.66	1.69	1.70
2.12	0.00	0.00	0.00	0.10	0.67	1.08	1.26	1.35	1.42	1.46	1.54	1.59	1.62	1.65	1.66
2.13	0.00	0.00	0.00	0.08	0.64	1.04	1.22	1.31	1.38	1.42	1.50	1.55	1.58	1.61	1.62
2.14	0.00	0.00	0.00	0.07	0.61	1.00	1.18	1.28	1.34	1.38	1.46	1.51	1.54	1.57	1.58
2.15	0.00	0.00	0.00	0.06	0.58	0.97	1.14	1.24	1.30	1.34	1.42	1.47	1.50	1.53	1.54
2.16	0.00	0.00	0.00	0.05	0.55	0.93	1.10	1.20	1.26	1.30	1.38	1.43	1.46	1.49	1.50
2.17	0.00	0.00	0.00	0.04	0.52	0.90	1.07	1.16	1.22	1.27	1.34	1.40	1.42	1.45	1.46
2.18	0.00	0.00	0.00	0.03	0.49	0.87	1.03	1.13	1.19	1.23	1.30	1.36	1.39	1.41	1.42
2.19	0.00	0.00	0.00	0.02	0.46	0.83	1.00	1.09	1.15	1.20	1.27	1.32	1.35	1.38	1.39
2.20	0.000	0.000	0.000	0.015	0.437	0.803	0.968	1.160	1.120	1.160	1.233	1.287	1.314	1.340	1.352
2.21	0.000	0.000	0.000	0.010	0.413	0.772	0.936	1.028	1.087	1.128	1.199	1.253	1.279	1.305	1.318
2.22	0.000	0.000	0.000	0.006	0.389	0.734	0.905	0.996	1.054	1.095	1.166	1.219	1.245	1.271	1.284
2.23	0.000	0.000	0.000	0.003	0.366	0.715	0.874	0.965	1.023	1.063	1.134	1.186	1.212	1.238	1.250
2.24	0.000	0.000	0.000	0.002	0.345	0.687	0.845	0.935	0.992	1.032	1.102	1.154	1.180	1.205	1.218
2.25	0.000	0.000	0.000	0.001	0.324	0.660	0.816	0.905	0.962	1.002	1.071	1.123	1.148	1.173	1.186
2.26	0.000	0.000	0.000	0.000	0.304	0.634	0.789	0.876	0.933	0.972	1.041	1.092	1.117	1.142	1.155
2.27	0.000	0.000	0.000	0.000	0.285	0.609	0.762	0.848	0.904	0.943	1.011	1.062	1.087	1.112	1.124
2.28	0.000	0.000	0.000	0.000	0.267	0.585	0.735	0.821	0.876	0.915	0.982	1.033	1.058	1.082	1.095
2.29	0.000	0.000	0.000	0.000	0.250	0.561	0.710	0.794	0.849	0.887	0.954	1.004	1.029	1.053	1.065

Figure H.8   *Continued.*

Q_U or Q_L	Sample size														
	3	4	5	7	10	15	20	25	30	35	50	75	100	150	200
2.30	0.000	0.000	0.000	0.000	0.233	0.538	0.685	0.769	0.823	0.861	0.927	0.977	1.001	1.025	1.037
2.31	0.000	0.000	0.000	0.000	0.218	0.516	0.661	0.743	0.797	0.834	0.900	0.949	0.974	0.998	1.009
2.32	0.000	0.000	0.000	0.000	0.203	0.495	0.637	0.719	0.772	0.809	0.874	0.923	0.947	0.971	0.982
2.33	0.000	0.000	0.000	0.000	0.189	0.474	0.614	0.695	0.748	0.784	0.848	0.897	0.921	0.944	0.956
2.34	0.000	0.000	0.000	0.000	0.175	0.454	0.592	0.672	0.724	0.760	0.824	0.872	0.895	0.919	0.930
2.35	0.000	0.000	0.000	0.000	0.163	0.435	0.571	0.650	0.701	0.736	0.799	0.847	0.870	0.893	0.905
2.36	0.000	0.000	0.000	0.000	0.151	0.416	0.550	0.628	0.678	0.714	0.776	0.823	0.846	0.869	0.880
2.37	0.000	0.000	0.000	0.000	0.139	0.398	0.530	0.606	0.656	0.691	0.753	0.799	0.822	0.845	0.856
2.38	0.000	0.000	0.000	0.000	0.128	0.381	0.510	0.586	0.635	0.670	0.730	0.777	0.799	0.822	0.833
2.39	0.000	0.000	0.000	0.000	0.118	0.364	0.491	0.566	0.614	0.648	0.709	0.754	0.777	0.799	0.810
2.40	0.000	0.000	0.000	0.000	0.109	0.348	0.473	0.546	0.594	0.628	0.687	0.732	0.755	0.777	0.787
2.41	0.000	0.000	0.000	0.000	0.100	0.332	0.455	0.527	0.575	0.608	0.667	0.711	0.733	0.755	0.766
2.42	0.000	0.000	0.000	0.000	0.091	0.317	0.437	0.509	0.555	0.588	0.646	0.691	0.712	0.734	0.744
2.43	0.000	0.000	0.000	0.000	0.083	0.302	0.421	0.491	0.537	0.569	0.627	0.670	0.692	0.713	0.724
2.44	0.000	0.000	0.000	0.000	0.076	0.288	0.404	0.474	0.519	0.551	0.608	0.651	0.672	0.693	0.703
2.45	0.000	0.000	0.000	0.000	0.069	0.275	0.389	0.457	0.501	0.533	0.589	0.632	0.653	0.673	0.684
2.46	0.000	0.000	0.000	0.000	0.063	0.262	0.373	0.440	0.484	0.516	0.571	0.613	0.634	0.654	0.664
2.47	0.000	0.000	0.000	0.000	0.057	0.249	0.359	0.425	0.468	0.499	0.553	0.595	0.615	0.636	0.646
2.48	0.000	0.000	0.000	0.000	0.051	0.237	0.345	0.409	0.452	0.482	0.536	0.577	0.597	0.617	0.627
2.49	0.000	0.000	0.000	0.000	0.046	0.226	0.331	0.394	0.436	0.466	0.519	0.560	0.580	0.600	0.609
2.50	0.000	0.000	0.000	0.000	0.041	0.214	0.317	0.380	0.421	0.451	0.503	0.543	0.563	0.582	0.592
2.51	0.000	0.000	0.000	0.000	0.037	0.204	0.305	0.366	0.407	0.436	0.487	0.527	0.546	0.565	0.575
2.52	0.000	0.000	0.000	0.000	0.033	0.193	0.292	0.352	0.392	0.421	0.472	0.511	0.530	0.549	0.559
2.53	0.000	0.000	0.000	0.000	0.029	0.184	0.280	0.339	0.379	0.407	0.457	0.495	0.514	0.533	0.542
2.54	0.000	0.000	0.000	0.000	0.026	0.174	0.268	0.326	0.365	0.393	0.442	0.480	0.499	0.517	0.527
2.55	0.000	0.000	0.000	0.000	0.023	0.165	0.257	0.314	0.352	0.379	0.428	0.465	0.484	0.502	0.511
2.56	0.000	0.000	0.000	0.000	0.020	0.156	0.246	0.302	0.340	0.366	0.414	0.451	0.469	0.487	0.496
2.57	0.000	0.000	0.000	0.000	0.017	0.148	0.236	0.291	0.327	0.354	0.401	0.437	0.455	0.473	0.482
2.58	0.000	0.000	0.000	0.000	0.015	0.140	0.226	0.279	0.316	0.341	0.388	0.424	0.441	0.459	0.468
2.59	0.000	0.000	0.000	0.000	0.013	0.133	0.216	0.269	0.304	0.330	0.375	0.410	0.428	0.445	0.454
2.60	0.000	0.000	0.000	0.000	0.011	0.125	0.207	0.258	0.293	0.318	0.363	0.398	0.415	0.432	0.441
2.61	0.000	0.000	0.000	0.000	0.009	0.118	0.198	0.248	0.282	0.307	0.351	0.385	0.402	0.419	0.428
2.62	0.000	0.000	0.000	0.000	0.008	0.112	0.189	0.238	0.272	0.296	0.339	0.373	0.390	0.406	0.415
2.63	0.000	0.000	0.000	0.000	0.007	0.105	0.181	0.229	0.262	0.285	0.328	0.361	0.378	0.394	0.402
2.64	0.000	0.000	0.000	0.000	0.006	0.099	0.172	0.220	0.252	0.275	0.317	0.350	0.366	0.382	0.390
2.65	0.000	0.000	0.000	0.000	0.005	0.094	0.165	0.211	0.242	0.265	0.307	0.339	0.355	0.371	0.379
2.66	0.000	0.000	0.000	0.000	0.004	0.088	0.157	0.202	0.233	0.256	0.296	0.328	0.344	0.359	0.367
2.67	0.000	0.000	0.000	0.000	0.003	0.083	0.150	0.194	0.224	0.246	0.286	0.317	0.333	0.348	0.356
2.68	0.000	0.000	0.000	0.000	0.002	0.078	0.143	0.186	0.216	0.237	0.277	0.307	0.322	0.338	0.345
2.69	0.000	0.000	0.000	0.000	0.002	0.073	0.136	0.179	0.208	0.229	0.267	0.297	0.312	0.327	0.335

Figure H.8   *Continued.*

Q_U or Q_L	Sample size														
	3	4	5	7	10	15	20	25	30	35	50	75	100	150	200
2.70	0.000	0.000	0.000	0.000	0.001	0.069	0.130	0.171	0.200	0.220	0.258	0.288	0.302	0.317	0.325
2.71	0.000	0.000	0.000	0.000	0.001	0.064	0.124	0.164	0.192	0.212	0.249	0.278	0.293	0.307	0.315
2.72	0.000	0.000	0.000	0.000	0.001	0.060	0.118	0.157	0.184	0.204	0.241	0.269	0.283	0.298	0.305
2.73	0.000	0.000	0.000	0.000	0.001	0.057	0.112	0.151	0.177	0.197	0.232	0.260	0.274	0.288	0.296
2.74	0.000	0.000	0.000	0.000	0.000	0.053	0.107	0.144	0.170	0.189	0.224	0.252	0.266	0.279	0.286
2.75	0.000	0.000	0.000	0.000	0.000	0.049	0.102	0.138	0.163	0.182	0.216	0.243	0.257	0.271	0.277
2.76	0.000	0.000	0.000	0.000	0.000	0.046	0.097	0.132	0.157	0.175	0.209	0.235	0.249	0.262	0.269
2.77	0.000	0.000	0.000	0.000	0.000	0.043	0.092	0.126	0.151	0.168	0.201	0.227	0.241	0.254	0.260
2.78	0.000	0.000	0.000	0.000	0.000	0.040	0.087	0.121	0.145	0.162	0.194	0.220	0.223	0.246	0.252
2.79	0.000	0.000	0.000	0.000	0.000	0.037	0.083	0.115	0.139	0.156	0.187	0.212	0.220	0.238	0.244
2.80	0.000	0.000	0.000	0.000	0.000	0.035	0.079	0.110	0.133	0.150	0.181	0.205	0.218	0.230	0.237
2.81	0.000	0.000	0.000	0.000	0.000	0.032	0.075	0.105	0.128	0.144	0.174	0.198	0.211	0.223	0.229
2.82	0.000	0.000	0.000	0.000	0.000	0.030	0.071	0.101	0.122	0.138	0.168	0.192	0.204	0.216	0.222
2.83	0.000	0.000	0.000	0.000	0.000	0.028	0.067	0.096	0.117	0.133	0.162	0.185	0.197	0.209	0.215
2.84	0.000	0.000	0.000	0.000	0.000	0.026	0.064	0.092	0.112	0.128	0.156	0.179	0.190	0.202	0.208
2.85	0.000	0.000	0.000	0.000	0.000	0.024	0.060	0.088	0.108	0.122	0.150	0.173	0.184	0.195	0.201
2.86	0.000	0.000	0.000	0.000	0.000	0.022	0.057	0.084	0.103	0.118	0.145	0.167	0.178	0.189	0.195
2.87	0.000	0.000	0.000	0.000	0.000	0.020	0.054	0.080	0.099	0.113	0.139	0.161	0.172	0.183	0.188
2.88	0.000	0.000	0.000	0.000	0.000	0.019	0.051	0.076	0.094	0.108	0.134	0.155	0.166	0.177	0.182
2.89	0.000	0.000	0.000	0.000	0.000	0.017	0.048	0.073	0.090	0.104	0.129	0.150	0.160	0.171	0.176
2.90	0.000	0.000	0.000	0.000	0.000	0.016	0.046	0.069	0.087	0.100	0.125	0.145	0.155	0.165	0.171
2.91	0.000	0.000	0.000	0.000	0.000	0.015	0.043	0.066	0.083	0.096	0.120	0.140	0.150	0.160	0.165
2.92	0.000	0.000	0.000	0.000	0.000	0.013	0.041	0.063	0.079	0.092	0.115	0.135	0.145	0.155	0.160
2.93	0.000	0.000	0.000	0.000	0.000	0.012	0.038	0.060	0.076	0.088	0.111	0.130	0.140	0.149	0.154
2.94	0.000	0.000	0.000	0.000	0.000	0.011	0.036	0.057	0.072	0.084	0.107	0.125	0.135	0.144	0.149
2.95	0.000	0.000	0.000	0.000	0.000	0.010	0.034	0.054	0.069	0.081	0.103	0.121	0.130	0.140	0.144
2.96	0.000	0.000	0.000	0.000	0.000	0.009	0.032	0.051	0.066	0.077	0.099	0.117	0.126	0.135	0.140
2.97	0.000	0.000	0.000	0.000	0.000	0.009	0.030	0.049	0.063	0.074	0.095	0.112	0.121	0.130	0.135
2.98	0.000	0.000	0.000	0.000	0.000	0.008	0.028	0.046	0.060	0.071	0.091	0.108	0.117	0.126	0.130
2.99	0.000	0.000	0.000	0.000	0.000	0.007	0.027	0.044	0.057	0.068	0.088	0.104	0.113	0.122	0.126
3.00	0.000	0.000	0.000	0.000	0.000	0.006	0.025	0.042	0.055	0.065	0.084	0.101	0.109	0.118	0.122
3.01	0.000	0.000	0.000	0.000	0.000	0.006	0.024	0.040	0.052	0.062	0.081	0.097	0.105	0.113	0.118
3.02	0.000	0.000	0.000	0.000	0.000	0.005	0.022	0.038	0.050	0.059	0.078	0.093	0.101	0.110	0.114
3.03	0.000	0.000	0.000	0.000	0.000	0.005	0.021	0.036	0.048	0.057	0.075	0.090	0.098	0.106	0.110
3.04	0.000	0.000	0.000	0.000	0.000	0.004	0.019	0.034	0.045	0.054	0.072	0.087	0.094	0.102	0.106
3.05	0.000	0.000	0.000	0.000	0.000	0.004	0.018	0.032	0.043	0.052	0.069	0.083	0.091	0.099	0.103
3.06	0.000	0.000	0.000	0.000	0.000	0.003	0.017	0.030	0.041	0.050	0.066	0.080	0.088	0.095	0.099
3.07	0.000	0.000	0.000	0.000	0.000	0.003	0.016	0.029	0.039	0.047	0.064	0.077	0.085	0.092	0.096
3.08	0.000	0.000	0.000	0.000	0.000	0.003	0.015	0.027	0.037	0.045	0.061	0.074	0.081	0.089	0.092
3.09	0.000	0.000	0.000	0.000	0.000	0.002	0.014	0.026	0.036	0.043	0.059	0.072	0.079	0.086	0.089

Figure H.8 *Continued.*

Q_U or Q_L	Sample size														
	3	4	5	7	10	15	20	25	30	35	50	75	100	150	200
3.10	0.000	0.000	0.000	0.000	0.000	0.002	0.013	0.024	0.034	0.041	0.056	0.069	0.076	0.083	0.086
3.11	0.000	0.000	0.000	0.000	0.000	0.002	0.012	0.023	0.032	0.039	0.054	0.066	0.073	0.080	0.083
3.12	0.000	0.000	0.000	0.000	0.000	0.002	0.011	0.022	0.031	0.038	0.052	0.064	0.070	0.077	0.080
3.13	0.000	0.000	0.000	0.000	0.000	0.002	0.011	0.021	0.029	0.036	0.050	0.061	0.068	0.074	0.077
3.14	0.000	0.000	0.000	0.000	0.000	0.001	0.010	0.019	0.028	0.034	0.048	0.059	0.065	0.071	0.075
3.15	0.000	0.000	0.000	0.000	0.000	0.001	0.009	0.018	0.026	0.033	0.046	0.057	0.063	0.069	0.072
3.16	0.000	0.000	0.000	0.000	0.000	0.001	0.009	0.017	0.025	0.031	0.044	0.055	0.060	0.066	0.069
3.17	0.000	0.000	0.000	0.000	0.000	0.001	0.008	0.016	0.024	0.030	0.042	0.053	0.058	0.064	0.067
3.18	0.000	0.000	0.000	0.000	0.000	0.001	0.007	0.015	0.022	0.028	0.040	0.050	0.056	0.062	0.065
3.19	0.000	0.000	0.000	0.000	0.000	0.001	0.007	0.015	0.021	0.027	0.038	0.049	0.054	0.059	0.062
3.20	0.000	0.000	0.000	0.000	0.000	0.001	0.006	0.014	0.020	0.026	0.037	0.047	0.052	0.057	0.060
3.21	0.000	0.000	0.000	0.000	0.000	0.000	0.006	0.013	0.019	0.024	0.035	0.045	0.050	0.055	0.058
3.22	0.000	0.000	0.000	0.000	0.000	0.000	0.005	0.012	0.018	0.023	0.034	0.043	0.048	0.053	0.056
3.23	0.000	0.000	0.000	0.000	0.000	0.000	0.005	0.011	0.017	0.022	0.032	0.041	0.046	0.051	0.054
3.24	0.000	0.000	0.000	0.000	0.000	0.000	0.005	0.011	0.016	0.021	0.031	0.040	0.044	0.049	0.052
3.25	0.000	0.000	0.000	0.000	0.000	0.000	0.004	0.010	0.015	0.020	0.030	0.038	0.043	0.048	0.050
3.26	0.000	0.000	0.000	0.000	0.000	0.000	0.004	0.009	0.015	0.019	0.028	0.037	0.042	0.046	0.048
3.27	0.000	0.000	0.000	0.000	0.000	0.000	0.004	0.009	0.014	0.018	0.027	0.035	0.040	0.044	0.046
3.28	0.000	0.000	0.000	0.000	0.000	0.000	0.003	0.008	0.013	0.017	0.026	0.034	0.038	0.042	0.045
3.29	0.000	0.000	0.000	0.000	0.000	0.000	0.003	0.008	0.012	0.016	0.025	0.032	0.037	0.041	0.043
3.30	0.000	0.000	0.000	0.000	0.000	0.000	0.003	0.007	0.012	0.015	0.024	0.031	0.035	0.039	0.042
3.31	0.000	0.000	0.000	0.000	0.000	0.000	0.003	0.007	0.011	0.015	0.023	0.030	0.034	0.038	0.040
3.32	0.000	0.000	0.000	0.000	0.000	0.000	0.002	0.006	0.010	0.014	0.022	0.029	0.032	0.036	0.038
3.33	0.000	0.000	0.000	0.000	0.000	0.000	0.002	0.006	0.010	0.013	0.021	0.027	0.031	0.035	0.037
3.34	0.000	0.000	0.000	0.000	0.000	0.000	0.002	0.006	0.009	0.013	0.020	0.026	0.030	0.034	0.036
3.35	0.000	0.000	0.000	0.000	0.000	0.000	0.002	0.005	0.009	0.012	0.019	0.025	0.029	0.032	0.034
3.36	0.000	0.000	0.000	0.000	0.000	0.000	0.002	0.005	0.008	0.011	0.018	0.024	0.028	0.031	0.033
3.37	0.000	0.000	0.000	0.000	0.000	0.000	0.002	0.005	0.008	0.011	0.017	0.023	0.026	0.030	0.032
3.38	0.000	0.000	0.000	0.000	0.000	0.000	0.001	0.004	0.007	0.010	0.016	0.022	0.025	0.029	0.031
3.39	0.000	0.000	0.000	0.000	0.000	0.000	0.001	0.004	0.007	0.010	0.016	0.021	0.024	0.028	0.029
3.40	0.000	0.000	0.000	0.000	0.000	0.000	0.001	0.004	0.007	0.009	0.015	0.020	0.023	0.027	0.028
3.41	0.000	0.000	0.000	0.000	0.000	0.000	0.001	0.003	0.006	0.009	0.014	0.020	0.022	0.026	0.027
3.42	0.000	0.000	0.000	0.000	0.000	0.000	0.001	0.003	0.006	0.008	0.014	0.019	0.022	0.025	0.026
3.43	0.000	0.000	0.000	0.000	0.000	0.000	0.001	0.003	0.005	0.008	0.013	0.018	0.021	0.024	0.025
3.44	0.000	0.000	0.000	0.000	0.000	0.000	0.001	0.003	0.005	0.007	0.012	0.017	0.020	0.023	0.024
3.45	0.000	0.000	0.000	0.000	0.000	0.000	0.001	0.003	0.005	0.007	0.012	0.016	0.019	0.022	0.023
3.46	0.000	0.000	0.000	0.000	0.000	0.000	0.001	0.002	0.005	0.007	0.011	0.016	0.018	0.021	0.022
3.47	0.000	0.000	0.000	0.000	0.000	0.000	0.001	0.002	0.004	0.006	0.011	0.015	0.018	0.020	0.022
3.48	0.000	0.000	0.000	0.000	0.000	0.000	0.001	0.002	0.004	0.006	0.010	0.014	0.017	0.019	0.021
3.49	0.000	0.000	0.000	0.000	0.000	0.000	0.000	0.002	0.004	0.005	0.010	0.014	0.016	0.019	0.020

Figure H.8   *Continued.*

Q_U or Q_L	Sample size														
	3	4	5	7	10	15	20	25	30	35	50	75	100	150	200
3.50	0.000	0.000	0.000	0.000	0.000	0.000	0.000	0.002	0.003	0.005	0.009	0.013	0.015	0.018	0.019
3.51	0.000	0.000	0.000	0.000	0.000	0.000	0.000	0.002	0.003	0.005	0.009	0.013	0.015	0.017	0.018
3.52	0.000	0.000	0.000	0.000	0.000	0.000	0.000	0.002	0.003	0.005	0.008	0.012	0.014	0.016	0.018
3.53	0.000	0.000	0.000	0.000	0.000	0.000	0.000	0.001	0.003	0.004	0.008	0.011	0.014	0.016	0.017
3.54	0.000	0.000	0.000	0.000	0.000	0.000	0.000	0.001	0.003	0.004	0.008	0.011	0.013	0.015	0.016
3.55	0.000	0.000	0.000	0.000	0.000	0.000	0.000	0.001	0.003	0.004	0.007	0.011	0.012	0.015	0.016
3.56	0.000	0.000	0.000	0.000	0.000	0.000	0.000	0.001	0.002	0.004	0.007	0.010	0.012	0.014	0.015
3.57	0.000	0.000	0.000	0.000	0.000	0.000	0.000	0.001	0.002	0.003	0.006	0.010	0.011	0.013	0.014
3.58	0.000	0.000	0.000	0.000	0.000	0.000	0.000	0.001	0.002	0.003	0.006	0.009	0.011	0.013	0.014
3.59	0.000	0.000	0.000	0.000	0.000	0.000	0.000	0.001	0.002	0.003	0.006	0.009	0.010	0.012	0.013
3.60	0.000	0.000	0.000	0.000	0.000	0.000	0.000	0.001	0.002	0.003	0.006	0.008	0.010	0.012	0.013
3.61	0.000	0.000	0.000	0.000	0.000	0.000	0.000	0.001	0.002	0.003	0.005	0.008	0.010	0.011	0.012
3.62	0.000	0.000	0.000	0.000	0.000	0.000	0.000	0.001	0.002	0.003	0.005	0.008	0.009	0.011	0.012
3.63	0.000	0.000	0.000	0.000	0.000	0.000	0.000	0.001	0.001	0.002	0.005	0.007	0.009	0.010	0.011
3.64	0.000	0.000	0.000	0.000	0.000	0.000	0.000	0.001	0.001	0.002	0.004	0.007	0.008	0.010	0.011
3.65	0.000	0.000	0.000	0.000	0.000	0.000	0.000	0.001	0.001	0.002	0.004	0.007	0.008	0.010	0.010
3.66	0.000	0.000	0.000	0.000	0.000	0.000	0.000	0.000	0.001	0.002	0.004	0.006	0.008	0.009	0.010
3.67	0.000	0.000	0.000	0.000	0.000	0.000	0.000	0.000	0.001	0.002	0.004	0.006	0.007	0.009	0.010
3.68	0.000	0.000	0.000	0.000	0.000	0.000	0.000	0.000	0.001	0.002	0.004	0.006	0.007	0.008	0.009
3.69	0.000	0.000	0.000	0.000	0.000	0.000	0.000	0.000	0.001	0.002	0.003	0.005	0.007	0.008	0.009
3.70	0.000	0.000	0.000	0.000	0.000	0.000	0.000	0.000	0.001	0.002	0.003	0.005	0.006	0.008	0.008
3.71	0.000	0.000	0.000	0.000	0.000	0.000	0.000	0.000	0.001	0.001	0.003	0.005	0.006	0.007	0.008
3.72	0.000	0.000	0.000	0.000	0.000	0.000	0.000	0.000	0.001	0.001	0.003	0.005	0.006	0.007	0.008
3.73	0.000	0.000	0.000	0.000	0.000	0.000	0.000	0.000	0.001	0.001	0.003	0.005	0.006	0.007	0.007
3.74	0.000	0.000	0.000	0.000	0.000	0.000	0.000	0.000	0.001	0.001	0.003	0.004	0.005	0.006	0.007
3.75	0.000	0.000	0.000	0.000	0.000	0.000	0.000	0.000	0.001	0.001	0.002	0.004	0.005	0.006	0.007
3.76	0.000	0.000	0.000	0.000	0.000	0.000	0.000	0.000	0.001	0.001	0.002	0.004	0.005	0.006	0.007
3.77	0.000	0.000	0.000	0.000	0.000	0.000	0.000	0.000	0.001	0.001	0.002	0.004	0.005	0.006	0.006
3.78	0.000	0.000	0.000	0.000	0.000	0.000	0.000	0.000	0.000	0.001	0.002	0.004	0.004	0.005	0.006
3.79	0.000	0.000	0.000	0.000	0.000	0.000	0.000	0.000	0.000	0.001	0.002	0.003	0.004	0.005	0.006
3.80	0.000	0.000	0.000	0.000	0.000	0.000	0.000	0.000	0.000	0.001	0.002	0.003	0.004	0.005	0.006
3.81	0.000	0.000	0.000	0.000	0.000	0.000	0.000	0.000	0.000	0.001	0.002	0.003	0.004	0.005	0.005
3.82	0.000	0.000	0.000	0.000	0.000	0.000	0.000	0.000	0.000	0.001	0.002	0.003	0.004	0.005	0.005
3.83	0.000	0.000	0.000	0.000	0.000	0.000	0.000	0.000	0.000	0.001	0.002	0.003	0.004	0.004	0.005
3.84	0.000	0.000	0.000	0.000	0.000	0.000	0.000	0.000	0.000	0.001	0.001	0.003	0.003	0.004	0.005
3.85	0.000	0.000	0.000	0.000	0.000	0.000	0.000	0.000	0.000	0.001	0.001	0.002	0.003	0.004	0.004
3.86	0.000	0.000	0.000	0.000	0.000	0.000	0.000	0.000	0.000	0.000	0.001	0.002	0.003	0.004	0.004
3.87	0.000	0.000	0.000	0.000	0.000	0.000	0.000	0.000	0.000	0.000	0.001	0.002	0.003	0.004	0.004
3.88	0.000	0.000	0.000	0.000	0.000	0.000	0.000	0.000	0.000	0.000	0.001	0.002	0.003	0.003	0.004
3.89	0.000	0.000	0.000	0.000	0.000	0.000	0.000	0.000	0.000	0.000	0.001	0.002	0.003	0.003	0.004
3.90	0.000	0.000	0.000	0.000	0.000	0.000	0.000	0.000	0.000	0.000	0.001	0.002	0.003	0.003	0.004

Figure H.8   *Continued.*

Sample Size Code Letter	Sample Size	AQLs (normal inspection)											
		T	.10	.15	.25	.40	.65	1.00	1.50	2.50	4.00	6.50	10.00
		M	M	M	M	M	M	M	M	M	M	M	M
B	3	↓	↓	↓	↓	↓	↓	↓	↓	7.59	18.86	26.94	33.69
C	4					↓	↓	1.49	5.46	10.88	16.41	22.84	29.43
D	5		↓	↓	↓	0.041	1.34	3.33	5.82	9.80	14.37	20.19	26.55
E	7	↓	0.005	0.087	0.421	1.05	2.13	3.54	5.34	8.40	12.19	17.34	23.30
F	10	0.077	0.179	0.349	0.714	1.27	2.14	3.27	4.72	7.26	10.53	15.17	20.73
G	15	0.186	0.311	0.491	0.839	1.33	2.09	3.06	4.32	6.55	9.48	13.74	18.97
H	20	0.228	0.356	0.531	0.864	1.33	2.03	2.93	4.10	6.18	8.95	13.01	18.07
I	25	0.250	0.378	0.551	0.874	1.32	2.00	2.86	3.97	5.98	8.65	12.60	17.55
J	35	0.253	0.373	0.534	0.833	1.24	1.87	2.66	3.70	5.58	8.11	11.89	16.67
K	50	0.243	0.355	0.503	0.778	1.16	1.73	2.47	3.44	5.21	7.61	11.23	15.87
L	75	0.225	0.326	0.461	0.711	1.06	1.59	2.27	3.17	4.83	7.10	10.58	15.07
M	100	0.218	0.315	0.444	0.684	1.02	1.52	2.18	3.06	4.67	6.88	10.29	14.71
N	150	0.202	0.292	0.412	0.636	0.946	1.42	2.05	2.88	4.42	6.56	9.86	14.18
P	200	0.204	0.294	0.414	0.637	0.945	1.42	2.04	2.86	4.39	6.52	9.80	14.11
		.10	.15	.25	.40	.65	1.00	1.50	2.50	4.00	6.50	10.00	
		AQLs (tightened inspection)											

All AQL values are in percent nonconforming. *T* denotes plan used exclusively on tightened inspection and provides symbol for identification of appropriate OC curve.

↓ = Use first sampling plan below arrow; that is, both sample size and *M* value. When sample size equals or exceeds lot size, every item in the lot must be inspected.

Figure H.9   ANSI/ASQ Z1.9-2008 Table B-3: Master table for normal and tightened inspection for plans based on variability unknown (double specification limit and Form 2– single specification limit).

Glossary of Inspection Terms

corrective action—Action taken to eliminate the root cause(s) and symptom(s) of an existing deviation or nonconformity to prevent recurrence.

critical defect—A defect that judgment and experience indicate is likely to result in hazardous or unsafe conditions for the individuals using, maintaining, or depending on the product; or a defect that judgment and experience indicate is likely to prevent performance of the unit.

defect—A departure of a quality characteristic from its intended level or state that occurs with a severity sufficient to cause an associated product or service not to satisfy intended normal or reasonably foreseeable usage requirements.

design review—Documented, comprehensive, and systematic examination of a design to evaluate its capability to fulfill the requirements for quality.

error—1. Error in measurement is the difference between the indicated value and the true value of a measured quantity. 2. A fault resulting from defective judgment, deficient knowledge, or carelessness. It is not to be confused with measurement error, which is the difference between a computed or measured value and the true or theoretical value.

flowchart—A graphical representation of the steps in a process. Flowcharts are drawn to better understand processes. The flowchart is one of the seven tools of quality.

inspection—The process of measuring, examining, testing, gauging, or otherwise comparing the unit with the applicable requirements.

major defect—A defect that will interfere with normal or reasonable foreseeable use, but will not cause a risk of damage or injury.

material control—A broad collection of tools for managing the items and lots in a production process.

material review board—A quality control committee or team, usually employed in manufacturing or other materials-processing installations, that has the responsibility and authority to deal with items or materials that do not conform to fitness-for-use specifications.

minor defect—A defect that may cause difficulty in assembly or use of the product but will not prevent the product from being properly used and does not pose any hazard to users.

mistake—Similar to an error but with the implication that it could be prevented by better training or attention.

nonconformity—A departure of a quality characteristic from its intended level or state that occurs with a severity sufficient to cause an associated product or service not to meet a specification requirement.

precision—The closeness of agreement between randomly selected individual measurements or test results.

product identification—A means of marking parts with a label, etching, engraving, ink, or other means so that different part numbers and other key attributes can be identified.

quality assurance—All the planned or systematic actions necessary to provide adequate confidence that a product or service will satisfy given needs.

quality audit—A systematic, independent examination and review to determine whether quality activities and related results comply with planned arrangements and whether these arrangements are implemented effectively and are suitable to achieve the objectives.

repeatability How close the measurements of an instrument are to each other if such measurements are repeated on a part under the same measuring conditions.

reproducibility—How close the measurements of an instrument are to each other if such measurements are repeated by different operators.

sample—A group of units, portions of material, or observations taken from a larger collection of units, quantity of material, or observations that serves to provide information that may be used as a basis for making a decision concerning the larger quantity.

standard—A statement, specification, or quantity of material against which measured outputs from a process may be judged as acceptable or unacceptable.

statistical process control (SPC)—The application of statistical techniques to control a process.

testing—A means of determining the capability of an item to meet specified requirements by subjecting the item to a set of physical, chemical, environmental, or operating actions and conditions.

traceability—The ability to trace the history, application, or location of an item or activity and like items or activities by means of recorded identification.

Index

A

acceptance number, 166
acceptance quality limit (AQL), 164
acceptance sampling, 161–62
  by attributes, 164
accuracy, 92, 132
action on output, 282–83
action on the process, 282
actions on the system, 284
acute angles, 27
air gauges, 59
air match gauging, 87
algebra, basic, 13–18
algebraic equations, solving, 13–18
American National Standards Institute
  (ANSI), 107, 374
American Society for Nondestructive Testing
  (ASNT), 195
American Society for Testing and Materials
  (ASTM), 106–7, 375
AND gates, 368
angle blocks, 102
angle measurement instruments, 100–102
ANOVA method, of measurement system
  analysis, 137–43
ANSI/ASQ Z1.4-2008 standard, 164, 166–67
  sample tables (Appendix H), 457–75
ANSI/ASQ Z1.9-2008 standard, 169–70
  sample tables (Appendix H), 457–75
appraisal costs, 327
appraiser variation (AV), 131
area, of basic geometric shapes, 19–21
arithmetic mean, 242, 246
AS9100 standards, 374
ASQ/ANSI/ISO 19011:2018 standard, 329, 331
assignable causes. *See* special causes
attribute, definition, 295–96
attribute gauges, 71–77
attribute sampling plans, types, 166
attributes charts, 295–310
audit, terms and definitions, 330
audits, quality. *See* quality audits
authentication, in security testing, 220
authorization, in security testing, 220

autocollimation, in optical tooling, 112–13
automated software testing, 215
automated testing tools, 215
automatic gauging, 81–85
Automotive Industry Action Group (AIAG),
  129, 321, 389
autoreflection, in optical tooling, 113
availability, in security testing, 220
average outgoing quality (AOQ), 165
average outgoing quality limit (AOQL), 165
average run length (ARL), 279–80, 81

B

back-pressure gauge, 87
balances, and scales, 106–7
bar chart, 229–30, 231–32
  creating in Minitab, 416, 417
basis path testing, 215
basis test set, 215
bebugging, 215
Bell Laboratories, 368
benchmark testing, 215–16
bevel protractor, 102
bias, 132
bivariate data, 233–34
Bloom's Taxonomy, 402
blueprints, 148–53
Body of Knowledge, Quality Inspector
  Certification (Appendix A), 395–402
bonus tolerances, 154
borescope, 67
box plot, 256–60
box-and-whisker plot, 256–60
  creating in Minitab, 412–14
  how to use, 259–60
brainstorming, 273–74, 378
Brinell hardness test, 207, 208, 209

C

c chart, 306–9
calibration, 121–28

documentation and history, 124
   procedures, 124
   standards, 121, 124–26
   systems, 121–24
calibration environment, 126–27
   specifications, 124
calibration equipment, 124
calibration interval, 122–23
caliper
   digital-reading, 61
   micrometer, 63–64, 64–65
   vernier, 60–63
   vernier micrometer, 64
cameras, in machine vision systems, 117–18
cause-and-effect diagram, 272–74
Celsius temperature units, conversions, 49–50
central tendency, measures of, 242–48
centrality, measures of, 242–48
Certified Quality Inspector, Body of Knowledge (Appendix A), 395–402
champion, team, 376
check sheet, 272
checklists, in quality audit, 333
circumference, of basic geometric shapes, 21–23
combination set, protractor, 102
common causes, 283
   versus special causes, 282–84
communication tools and techniques, in quality audit, 334
comparators, 111
   optical, 112, 114–16
compatibility testing, 216
complementary angles, 26
composite gauges, 74
compression testing, 206–7
computer resources (Appendix B), 403–30
concurrent engineering, 328
confidentiality, in security testing, 219
confined spaces, 373
conflict resolution, in teams, 378
consensus, in teams, 378
consumer's risk (β), 164–65
contact instruments, measuring, 60
continuous improvement techniques, 339–70
continuous sampling plans, 171
control charts, 276–79
   for attributes, 295–310
   benefits of, 279
   preparations for use of, 277–78
   rational subgroups for, 279
   for variables, 285–94
      factors helpful in constructing (Appendix E), 451–52
control limits

calculation of for $\bar{X}$ and R chart, 285–88
calculation of for $\bar{X}$ and S chart, 293–94
for np chart, 304–5
for p chart, 297–99
versus specification limits, 284
conversions, numeric (Appendix C), 51–55, 431–48
coordinate measuring machine (CMM), 67–71
   classification, 60–70
corrective action, 189–90
   prioritizing based on RPN, 362–63
corrective action requests (CARs), in quality audit, 334, 335
correlation coefficient, 235
cosines, law of, 34, 35–36
cost of (poor) quality, 327
C_p, process capability index, 315–19
C_{pk}, process capability index, 319–21
crash test, 204
critical defect, 187
   under ANSI/ASQ Z1.4-2008, 167
criticality, assessing, in FMEA, 363–64
crossed designs, in measurement system analysis, 137
customer satisfaction, importance of, 326

D

data set, skew of, 248
datum structure, 158–59
debugging, 217
decimals, 8–10
   adding and subtracting, 10
   converting to fractions, 55
   converting to percentages, 9
   and fraction equivalents, 8
   multiplying and dividing, 10
defect(s)
   under ANSI/ASQ Z1.4-2008, 167
   levels of severity, 187–88
   versus nonconformity, 187
defect concentration diagram, 274–75
Deming, W. Edwards, 269, 270, 340
descriptive statistics, calculating, in Minitab, 406–8
design FMEA, 354, 355–61, 364
design-based testing, 217
desk checking, 217
destructive testing, 201–5
   applications and objectives, 202
   methods, 202–5
detection, versus prevention, in quality improvement, 325–26
dial indicators, 66, 99–100

diascopic projection, 114
differential gauge, 87
digital cameras, 117–18
digital inspection systems, miscellaneous, 117–18
digital-reading caliper, 61
dispersion, measures of, 248–52
DMAIC (define–measure–analyze–improve–control) methodology, 347
dot plot, 228
    creating in Minitab, 410, 411
double sampling plans, 166, 168
double-end gauge, 71
drift, of instrument, 92
dynamic testing, 217

E

eddy current, method of nondestructive testing, 198
8D methodology, 364–67
electric limit gauges, 79
electron beam, as gauging standard, 60
electronic gauges, 59, 79–81
empirical rule, 250, 252
employee involvement, 375–76
employees, as resources, 375–79
empowerment, employee, 375
engineering drawings, 148–53
    line types and styles, 154
    parts of, 149–53
English measurement system, 39–43
    conversion to SI/metric system, 45–50
environment, gauge calibration, 126–27
environmental instrumentation, 88
environmental resources, 372–73
episcopic projection, 114
equations, solving
    by collecting terms, 15–16
    with parentheses, 16–17
    using one inverse operation, 14
    using two or more inverse operations, 15
equipment, out-of-calibration, effects of use, 127
equipment traceability, 126
equipment variation (EV), 131
equivalent fractions, 5
ergonomics, 373
error, sources of, 180–82
error-proofing, 343–44
errors, inspection, 180–83
exponents, 10–11, 51–52
external failure costs, 327
external measuring snap gauge, 72
external quality audit, 330

extreme values, 243–44, 256

F

facilitator, team, 376–77
factorials, 11
Fahrenheit temperature units, conversions, 49–50
fail-safing, 343
failure mode and effects analysis (FMEA), 348–64
    basic steps in, 351–52
    inputs to, 350
    outputs from, 351
    planning for, 348–49
    quality tools used in, 350–51
    quantifying risk in, 352–54
    responsibility for, 349
    selecting a standard for, 348
    summary, 364
    team members, 349–50
    types of, 354–55
fault tree analysis (FTA), 368
final inspection, 179–80, 331
first article inspection report (FAI), 381–82, 389
first-piece inspection, 179
fishbone diagram, 272–74
five hows methodology, 368
five whys methodology, 367–68
5S methodology, 342–43
fixed gauge, 71
flaws, in surfaces, 107–8
flinching, 182
flow, in lean, 345
flow gauge, 87
flowchart, 270
    in inspection, 177
    in traceability, 185
flush pin gauge, 77
force gauging, 87
force testing, 203–4
fractions, 4–8
    converting to decimals, 8, 54–55
    decimal equivalents, 8
    with like denominators, adding and subtracting, 5–6
    multiplying and dividing, 7–8
    with unequal denominators, adding and subtracting, 6–7
frame grabbers, 117
free-bend test, 203
frequency distribution curves, 239
frequency distribution table, 223, 224
    interpretation of, 224–28

for quantitative data, 224
frequency histogram, 236, 237–38
frequency polygon, 236, 239
functional decomposition, 217
functional requirements, 217
functional testing, in software development, 214–15
functionality testing, 205–7
  definition, 205
  methods, 206–7
  objectives, 205

G

gauge blocks, 65–66
gauge calibration environment, 126–27
gauge correlation, 94–95
gauge handling, preservation, and storage, 92–94
gauge maker's rule, in gauge selection, 91
gauge repeatability and reproducibility (GR&R), 129–30
  versus measurement system analysis, 129–30
gauge repeatability and reproducibility study (GR&R study), 131
  ANOVA method, 137–40
  graphical representation of, 140–43
gauge selection, handling, and use, 91–95
gauges
  attribute, 71–77
  automatic, 81–85
  common, 59–78
  electronic, 59, 79–81
  handling, 92–94
  pneumatic, 59, 85–87
  preservation, 92–94
  special, 77, 79–90
  storage, 92–94
  surface finish, 110
  transfer, 77
  variable, 60–71
gauges, special, and applications, 79–90
gauging components, automatic, 81–85
geometric dimensioning and tolerancing (GD&T), 147
  terminology and symbols, 153–54
geometric shapes
  areas of, 19–21
  circumference of, 21–23
  perimeter of, 21–23
  surface area of, 24–26
  volume of, 23
geometric tolerances, 151–53
geometry, basic, 19–26
Gilbreth, Frank, 270

Gilbreth, Lillian, 270
Godfrey, A. Blanton, 327
go/no-go gauge, 71
graphical methods, in descriptive statistics, 223–42
graphical summary, creating in Minitab, 415–16
graphs, creating in Minitab, 408–14
greatest common factor (GCF), 5
guided-bend test, 203

H

hardness testing, 204, 207–10
hearing conservation, 373
hierarchical designs, in measurement system analysis, 137
histograms, 234–40
  creating in Minitab, 409–10
hygrometer, 88

I

identification
  in calibration, methods, 123
  mechanics of, 186 87
  principles of, 186
imaginary numbers, 10
impact test, 203–4
improper fractions, 5
inclination, measuring, 118
inclinometer, 118
incoming material inspection, 177–78
indicating micrometer, 65
inductance-bridge transducer, 79
inequalities, solving, 17–18
  with negatively signed values, 18
initial sample inspection report (ISIR), 382–89
in-process inspection, 179
inspection
  definition, 175
  levels of, under ANSI/ASQ Z1.4-2008, 167
  planning and processes, 175–93
  purposes of, 177–78
  tasks, 175–76
  and testing, 145–220
  versus testing, 214
  types of, 177–80
inspection equipment
  optical, 112–16
  specialized, 105–19
inspection errors, 180–83
inspection gauges, 71
inspection microscopes, 112

inspection plan, items, 179–80
inspection planning, 176–77
inspection stations, location, 176–77
inspector qualifications, 182
inspector training, 183, 188
integrity, in security testing, 219
interferometry, 82–84
internal failure costs, 327
internal quality audit, 330
International Organization for
    Standardization (ISO), 107, 374
International Organization of Legal
    Metrology (OIML), 107
international standards, 125
interquartile range, 252, 256
inverse operations, 13
    solving equations using, 14–15
inverse trigonometric functions, 32
irrational numbers, 8–9
Ishikawa diagram, 272–74
ISO 9001 standard, 380–81
    requirements for traceability, 184
ISO/IEC 17025 standard, 94, 95

J

Juran, Joseph M., 327

K

K_1, values of for computing repeatability
    (Appendix F), 453–54
K_2, values of for computing reproducibility
    (Appendix G), 455
kaizen, 345
Kelvin temperature units, 49–50

L

laser inspection instruments, 112, 114
laser tracker, 117
lasers, 60, 84
law of cosines, 34, 35–36
law of sines, 33, 37–38
lay, of surface, 108
lean concepts, 345
lean production, 342
lean tools, 342–45
least common denominator, 6–7
least material condition (LMC), 154
Lennox Industries, 173
leveling, in optical tooling, 114
levels of inspection, under ANSI/ASQ Z1.4-
    2008, 167

levels of severity, of defects, 187–88
light waves, as gauging standard, 59
limit gauge, 71
linear variable displacement transformer
    (LVDT) transducer, 79
linearity, 92, 132
liquid penetrant, method of nondestructive
    testing, 201
local actions, 283–84
lock-out/tag-out, electrical, 373
log sheets, in quality audit, 333
lot size, 166
lot tolerance percent defective (LTPD), 164

M

machine tooling, interferometry applications
    in, 84
machine vision, 84–85
    systems, 116–17
magnetic, method of nondestructive testing,
    200
magnification, 92
major defect, 187
    under ANSI/ASQ Z1.4-2008, 167
manual testing, 217–18
mass, and weight, 105
    measuring, 105–9
master gauges, 71
material, nonconforming, identification of,
    186–87
material inspection, incoming, 177–78
material review board (MRB), 191–92
material safety data sheets (MSDSs), 372
material segregation, 191
mathematics
    basic shop, 3–12
    technical, 1–55
maximum material condition (MMC), 151,
    152, 154
mean, 242, 243–44, 246
measurement, definition under AIAG, 129
measurement capability index (MCI), 131–32,
    143–44
    as percentage of process specification, 144
    as percentage of process variation, 143–44
measurement conversions, 431–48 (Appendix
    C)
measurement instruments, 59–78
measurement process, variability in, 130
measurement scales, in gauges, 77
measurement system analysis (MSA), 129–44
    versus GR&R, 129–30
measurement system performance,
    evaluating, 131
measurement systems, 39–50

English, 39–43
metric, 43–45
SI, 43–45
software-based, 116–18
measurements, adding and subtracting, 12
measures of centrality, 242–48
measures of dispersion, 242, 248–52
measures of percentages, 242, 252–56
mechanical drawing, 147
mechanical gauges, 59
median, 244–46
meetings, management of, 379
metallography, 205
metric (measurement), 218
metric measurement system, 43–45
    conversion to English system, 45–50
metrology, 57–144
    surface, 107–9
microhardness testing, 210
micrometer, screw-thread, 75–76
micrometer caliper, 63–64, 64–65
    digital, 64
    vernier, 64
MIL-SPEC military specifications, 374
MIL-STD military standards, 374
MIL-STD-1235B standard, 171, 172–73
Minitab, 403–30
minor defect, 187
    under ANSI/ASQ Z1.4-2008, 167
mixed numbers, adding or subtracting, 7
mode, 246, 247
model based definition (MBD), 153
modified condition/decision coverage, 218
modified condition/decision testing, 218
Mohs scale, 204
monkey testing, 219
muda, 342
multidimension gauge, 87
multimeters, 81
multiple sampling plans, 166, 168–69

N

National Institute for Standards and
    Technology (NIST), 106, 122, 123, 124–
    25, 126
National Materials Advisory Board (NMAB),
    196
national standards, 125
natural tolerance limits, 315
negative exponents, 52
negative numbers, 3–4
negative testing, 219
negatively signed values, solving inequalities
    with, 18

nested designs, in measurement system
    analysis, 137
nick-break test, 203
noise, workplace, 373
nonconforming material
    control of, 188–90
    disposition of, 191–92
    identification of, 186–87
nonconforming product, control of, 188–89
nonconforming unit, versus nonconformity,
    306–9
nonconformity
    versus defect, 187
    versus nonconforming unit, 306–9
noncontact instruments, measuring, 60
nondestructive evaluation (NDE). *See*
    nondestructive testing
nondestructive testing (NDT), 195–201
    applications and objectives, 195–96
    definition, 195
    methods, 196–201
nonlimit gauge, 71
non-repudiation, in security testing, 220
normal distribution, 260–66
normal probability function, characteristics
    of, 260
np chart, 304-5
numbers
    mixed, adding or subtracting, 7
    negative, 3–4
    positive, 3–4
    real, properties of, 3, 13
numeric conversions, 51–55
numerical methods, in descriptive statistics,
    242–60

O

oblique triangles, 32–38
obtuse angles, 27
occupational safety and health, regulations,
    372
Occupational Safety and Health
    Administration (OSHA), 372, 373
100 percent inspection, 161
operating characteristic (OC) curve, 163–64,
    280–82
operator fallibility, 181
operator variation, 131
optical comparators, 111, 112, 114–16
optical edge finder, 112
optical flats, 82, 84
optical inspection equipment, 112–16
optical noncontact instruments, measuring,
    60

optical projecting comparator, 114
optical projector, 111
optical tooling, 112–16
OR gates, 368
order of operations, 11
ordered stem-and-leaf diagram, 240–42
orthographic views, 153–54
oscilloscopes, 81
OSHA Code of Federal Regulations (CFR)
    Title 29, 372–73
outliers, 256
out-of-calibration equipment, effects of
    using, 127
output, action on, 282–83

P

p chart
    for fraction nonconforming, 296–301
        interpreting, 299–301
    for fraction nonconforming with variable
        samples, 302–3
parameters, versus statistics, 242
Pareto, Vilfredo, 230
Pareto chart, 230–33
part alignment, 158–59
Pearson correlation coefficient, 235
PEMDAS acronym, 11, 16
percentage(s)
    converting decimals to, 9
    measures of, 252–56
percentiles, 252–54
perimeter, of basic geometric shapes, 21–23
personal protective equipment (PPE), 372–73
pie chart, 228–29
    creating in Minitab, 416, 418
plan–do–check–act (PDCA) cycle, 339–41
plan–do–study–act (PDSA) cycle, 339–41
planizing, in optical tooling, 113
plug gauges, 72
plumbing, in optical tooling, 114
pneumatic gauges, 59, 85–87
poka-yoke, 343–44
population mean, 243, 244
population standard deviation, 250, 420, 422
population variance, 249
portability testing, 219
position control, tolerance of, 154
position tolerances, 154, 157–58
positive exponents, 51
positive numbers, 3–4
positive testing, 219
powers of 10, 52
P_p, process capability index, 321–22
P_{pk}, process capability index, 321–22

precision, 132
prevention, versus detection, in quality
    improvement, 325–26
prevention costs, 327
preventive action, 190
primary standards, 125
prime factorization, 6
prime number, 6
probability distributions, creating in Minitab,
    416–22
problem-solving tools, 339–70
process
    action on, 282
    definition, 270–72
    evaluation, 282
    versus product, 327–28
    variation, 131, 283
process audit, 331
process capability analysis, 310–22
    in Minitab, 422–30
process capability index (PCI), 143, 310–22
    definition, 313
process equipment, 121
process evaluation, 282
process FMEA, 354, 355–61, 364
process map. *See* flowchart
process variability, 130
producer's risk (α), 164
product, versus process, 327–28
product identification, mechanics of, 186–87
product/service audit, 331
product traceability, 184–85
production part approval process (PPAP),
    389–90
profile, 107
    measuring, 111
profiling gauge, 110
progressive (plug) gauge, 71, 72
proper fractions, 5
protractors, 102
pull system, 345
push system, 345
pyrometer, 81
Pythagorean theorem, 27–28, 30, 31

Q

QS-9000 standards, 374
qualitative data, 224
quality
    basic concepts and benefits, 269–70
    definition, 327
    poor, cost of, 327
quality assurance, 221–392
quality audits, 329–36

outcomes, 334–36
process, 332–33
reporting and follow-up, 335–36
roles and responsibilities in, 331–32
terms and definitions, 330
tools, 333–34
types of, 330–31
quality control tools, seven basic, 337–38
quality costs, four categories, 327
quality documentation, 379–89
basic, 390–91
quality improvement, 325–28
terms and concepts, 325–27
quality inspector, characteristics of, 183
Quality Systems (QS), 374
quality techniques, and tools, 337–38
quality tools, and techniques, 337–38
quantitative data, 224–28
quartiles, 252, 255

R

radiation, method of nondestructive testing,
196–98
random causes. *See* common causes
random errors, 180
random sampling, 163
range, 248–49
range-based method, of measurement system
analysis, 131–36
Rankin temperature units, 49
rational numbers, 8
rational subgroups, for control charts, 279
real numbers, properties of, 3, 13
recovery testing, 219
rectifying sampling, 162
reference documents, 374–75
reference gauges, 71
reference standard, 126
relative frequency histogram, 236, 237–38
relative frequency polygon, 236, 239
repeatability, 92, 131, 132, 133–34
reproducibility, 131, 132, 133–34
resolution, 92
resources, 371–92
computer (Appendix B), 403–30
employees as, 375–79
environmental and safety, 372–73
RFID (radio-frequency identification), 123
right triangle, 27–28
solving for unknown sides and angles of,
30–32
ring gauges, 72
risk, components of, 352

risk priority number (RPN), taking action
based on, 352–53, 359, 361
Rockwell hardness test, 208, 209
root cause analysis, 347–48
5 whys, 367–68
roughness, 107, 108–9
average (Ra), 108–11
measuring, 107–9
rounding, number, 11
roundness, measurement of, 111
rule of ten, in gauge selection, 91
run chart, 275–76

S

safety resources, 372–73
sample mean, 243
sample size, 166
sample standard deviation, 250, 292, 316
sample statistics, calculation of, 285
sample variance, 250
sampling, 161–73
advantages of, 162–63
concepts, 163–66
types of, under ANSI/ASQ Z1.4-2008,
168–69
sampling plans, 166–69, 334
sampling standards, 166–69
Sauer Danfoss Company, 186
scales, and balances, 106–7
scatter plot, 233–34
creating in Minitab, 412, 413
scientific method, 346
scientific notation, 52–54
converting back to original form, 54
screening, 161, 162, 178
screw pitch gauges, 76–77
screw-thread micrometer, 75–76
secondary standards, 126
sector gauges, 74
security testing, 219–20
sequential sampling plans, 171
serious defect, 187
service delivery FMEA, 354
service/product audit, 331
shape, measuring, 111
Shewhart, Walter, 340
Shewhart ($\bar{X}$ and R) control chart. *See* $\bar{X}$ and
R control chart
Shewhart ($\bar{X}$ and S) control chart. *See* $\bar{X}$ and
S control chart
shop math, basic, 3–12
SI measurement system, 43–45
conversion to English system, 45–50

significant digits, 12
 multiplying and dividing using, 12
simple protractor, 102
simplified fractions, 5
sine bar, 101–2
sine table, 102
sines, law of, 33, 37–38
single sampling plans, 166, 168
Six Sigma phases, 346–48
skew, of data set, 248
smart cameras, 117
snap gauges, 72—73
software
 for test equipment, 213–20
 verification testing, 213–24
software development, functional testing in,
    214–15
software testing, terminology, 215–20
software-based measurement systems,
    116–18
sorting, 161
spaces, confined, 373
special causes, 283
 versus common causes, 282–84
specification limits, versus control limits, 284
spline gauges, 74
square, of a number, 10–11
square root, 10
stability, 132
standard deviation, 250–52
standard normal distribution, 260–62
standard normal distribution table, 262–68,
    449–50 (Appendix D)
standard normal random variable, 262
standard repair, 191–92
standardized random variable, 262
standards, reference, 374–75
 in calibration, 121
Starlink seed corn, contamination incident,
    186–87
statistical control, 277
statistical process control (SPC), 269–323
statistics
 basic, and applications, 223–68
 versus parameters, 242
steel rule, 60
stem-and-leaf diagram, 240–42
Sturgis's formula, 224, 228
supplementary angles, 26
surface area, of basic geometric shapes, 24–26
surface characteristics, 107–8
surface finish
 gauges, 110–11
 measuring, 109–11
surface metrology, 107–9

surface plate, 97
 angle measurement instruments, 100–102
 equipment, 97–100
 tools and techniques, 97–103
surface quality specifications, 108–9
switching procedures, in sampling, 167
symmetry, of data set, 248
system audit, 330–31
system FMEA, 354
systematic errors, 181

T

teams
 roles and responsibilities, 376–77
 stages of development, 377–78
technical drawings, parts of, 149–53
technical mathematics, 1–55
telescope gauge, 77
temperature probe, 67
templates, 76
tensile testing, 202–3
tension test, 202–3, 206
10:1 rule, 91
test equipment, verification of software for,
    213–24
testing
 and inspection, 145–220
 versus inspection, 214
 methods, 195–211
thermometer, 67
thread plug gauges, 75–76
thread snap gauges, 72–73
tickler file, in calibration, 123
tilt sensor, 118
tolerance(s), 150–53
tolerance of position control, 154
torque testing, 206
traceability
 definition, 220
 equipment, 126
 product, 184–85
tracking methods, in calibration, 123
training, inspector, 183, 188
transfer gauges, 77
transfer standard, 126
transit, 113
triangle
 oblique, 32–38
 right, 27–28
trigonometric functions, 28–30
 inverse, 32
 values of, for some common angles, 28
trigonometric identities, 28–30

trigonometry, basic, 27–38
truncating, number, 11
two-way ANOVA table with interaction,
    interpretation, 137
two-way ANOVA table without interaction,
    interpretation, 137–38

U

u chart, 309–13
ultrasonic, method of nondestructive testing,
    198–200
uncertainty, in calibration, 123
United States Department of Defense (DoD),
    374
units of measurement, general tables of
    (Appendix C), 431–48

V

validation testing, 220
value stream mapping, 344–45
variability
    in measurement process, 130
    process, 130
variable gauges, 60–71
variable inductance transducer, 79
variable transformer transducer, 79
variables charts, 285–94
    factors helpful in constructing
        (Appendix E), 451–52
variables sampling plans, 169–70
variance, 249–50, 251
variation, process, 283
vendor certification, 162
vendor qualification, 162
venturi gauge, 87

vernier caliper, 60–63
vernier height gauge, 61–63, 100
vernier micrometer caliper, 64
vernier scales, 64
Vickers hardness test, 208–9, 210
Vickers pyramid number, 208
video inspection systems, 112, 196
visual, method of nondestructive testing, 196
volume, of basic geometric shapes, 23

W

waste, lean tools for eliminating, 342–45
waviness, 107
    measuring, 109–10
weight, and mass, 105
    measuring, 106
working gauges, 71
working papers, in quality audit, 334–35
working standard, 126

X

$\bar{X}$ and R control chart, 285–92
    interpretation of, 288–91
    when process mean μ and process
        standard deviation σ are known,
        291–92
$\bar{X}$ and S control chart, 292–94
X-ray inspection, 85
    method of nondestructive testing, 196–98

Y

Y14.3-2003 *Multiview and Sectional View
    Drawings* standard, 153

WHY ASQ?

ASQ is a global community of people passionate about quality, who use the tools, their ideas and expertise to make our world work better. ASQ: The Global Voice of Quality.

FOR INDIVIDUALS

Advance your career to the next level of excellence.

ASQ offers you access to the tools, techniques and insights that can help distinguish an ordinary career from an extraordinary one.

FOR ORGANIZATIONS

Your culture of quality begins here.

ASQ organizational membership provides the invaluable resources you need to concentrate on product, service and experiential quality and continuous improvement for powerful top-line and bottom-line results.

www.asq.org/why-asq

ASQ
The Global Voice of Quality

TRAINING   CERTIFICATION   CONFERENCES   MEMBERSHIP   PUBLICATIONS

BELONG TO THE QUALITY COMMUNITY

JOINING THE ASQ GLOBAL QUALITY COMMUNITY
GIVES YOU A STRONG COMPETITIVE ADVANTAGE.

For people passionate about improvement, ASQ is the global knowledge
network that links the best ideas, tools, and experts — because ASQ has the
reputation and reach to bring together the diverse quality and continuous
improvement champions who are transforming our world.

- 75,000 individual and organizational members in 150 countries
- 250 sections and local member communities
- 25 forums and divisions covering industries and topics
- 30,000+ Quality Resources items, including articles, case studies, research
  and more
- 19 certifications
- 200+ training courses

ASQ
The Global Voice of Quality

For more information, **visit asq.org/communities-networking.**

ASK A LIBRARIAN

Have questions? Looking for answers?
In need of information? Ask a librarian!

Customized research assistance from ASQ's research librarian
is one of the many benefits of membership. ASQ's research
librarian is available to answer your research requests using
the everexpanding library of current and credible resources,
including journals, conference proceedings, case studies, and
Quality Press publications.

You can also contact the librarian to request permission
to reuse or reprint ASQ copyrighted material, such as
ASQ journal articles and Quality Press book excerpts.

**For more information or to submit a question,
visit asq.org/quality-resources/ask-a-librarian.**

ASQ
The Global Voice of Quality

TRAINING   CERTIFICATION   CONFERENCES   MEMBERSHIP   PUBLICATIONS